electrical and mechanical networks

an introduction to their analysis

McGRAW-HILL ELECTRICAL AND ELECTRONIC ENGINEERING SERIES

Frederick Emmons Terman, *Consulting Editor*
W. W. Harman and J. G. Truxal, *Associate Consulting Editors*

Electrical and M

WILLIS W. HARMAN
Professor of Electrical Engineering
Stanford University

DEAN W. LYTLE
Associate Professor of Electrical Engineering
University of Washington

echanical

etworks

AN INTRODUCTION TO
THEIR ANALYSIS

McGRAW-HILL BOOK COMPANY, INC.

New York San Francisco Toronto London

1962

ELECTRICAL AND MECHANICAL NETWORKS

Library of Congress Catalog Card Number 61-17340

26590

THE MAPLE PRESS COMPANY, YORK, PA.

To Charlene and Marilyn

preface

When the notes on which the first half of this book is based were first used to teach sophomores at Stanford University in 1953, the approach was quite radical; now, as this material reaches publication stage, it may seem "old hat" to some. So rapidly do fashions change in our field. There are those among us who can recall when new texts were proudly advertised as "classroom-tested for fifteen years before publication." Today, however, when publishing contracts are often granted while the embryonic book is still little more than a tentative collection of chapter headings and when the time span between rough notes and published book is sometimes only a matter of months, the distinction of having been used in note form for eight years may seem to some a dubious one for this text to have. It makes the book seem almost by definition out of date. Nevertheless, it does mean that the material presented here, when supplemented by classroom aid and encouragement, has been found to be comprehensible to students at the sophomore-junior level.

The approach to the analysis of linear systems represented by the first five chapters is one which was introduced to the engineering profession by A. E. Kennelly and Vannevar Bush before World War I† and then lost sight of for over twenty years. This is the conceptually simple, but potentially rigorous and powerful, method of describing the linear network by finding the ratio of excitation to response when the excitation is of the form e^{st}. This ratio (impedance in the case of a one-port electrical network in which the voltage is excitation and the current is response) is used to find the complete transient response. The forced term is obtained by writing the excitation as the sum (or integral) of terms of the form e^{st} and dividing each term by the excitation-response ratio with the appropriate value of s inserted. The

† A. E. Kennelly, The Impedances, Angular Velocities and Frequencies of Oscillating-current Circuits, *Proc. IRE*, 4:47–48 (1916); V. Bush, Oscillating-current Circuits by the Method of Generalized Angular Velocities, *Trans. AIEE*, 36:207–221 (1917).

natural behavior is obtained as a sum of terms of the form $A_i e^{s_i t}$, where the A_i are constants determined by initial conditions and the s_i are the values of s which make the excitation-response function equal to zero.

This approach is developed through a carefully chosen, graded series of examples in which the student is led to consider how the analysis methods he is to learn might have been originally devised. In later chapters, the methods are presented in a more systematic context, but initially the student is repeatedly invited to go through the experience of facing a new problem and inventing the analysis technique which will yield the solution. In Chapter 2, for example, he "discovers" the use of the impedance function for finding the natural behavior of simple two-element networks. In Chapter 3, faced with the new situation of the sinusoidal steady state, he finds that a simple extension allows him to handle this as well. Chapter 4 leads him to complete transient solutions, and Chapter 5 to resonance phenomena and the complex-frequency plane. In this modified case method of presentation, each advance in analytical technique is "invented" in response to a new challenge. (This approach is in contrast to the logically attractive, but psychologically less effective, method of first laying a solid foundation of topology, matrix algebra, and network theorems, after which the weary student is ready to solve an RC transient problem.)

Chapter 6 constitutes an interlude on the subject of electric power and related topics. It can be omitted without incurring serious interruption of the main discussion.

Chapter 7 extends the usefulness of the discovered methods through the table of unit-impulse responses (the Laplace transform table). The power of the tools now available is demonstrated by application to several practical examples. (The relationship of this approach to the Fourier-Laplace approach is discussed in Chapter 13, which can be taken up any time after Chapter 7.)

Chapters 8 and 9 deal with systematic methods of writing and solving network equations for more complex situations. Chapter 10 is another interlude primarily on electrical topics—this time on mutual inductance.

Chapters 11 and 12 apply the analysis methods previously developed for electrical and mechanical networks to electromechanical energy-conversion and control systems, serving as introductions to more advanced work in these areas. Chapter 14, too, points to the future, with brief discussions of approaches to be used when networks are nonlumped (distributed), non-time-invariant, or nonlinear.

To ponder on the task of listing acknowledgments is to realize how many persons, contemporary and historical, have contributed to the writing of this text by their own writings, by discussions with the authors, and by words of encouragement. Since it seems futile to attempt to list them, perhaps they will forgive omission of all names except that of Marilyn Marguerite Lytle, whose forbearance during the many hours her husband was at the writing desk and whose typing of hundreds of pages of manuscript went far beyond the wifely duties agreed to in the marriage contract.

Willis W. Harman
Dean W. Lytle

contents

list of tables

simple electrical and mechanical systems

Engineers are, for the most part, concerned with the design, construction, and operation of complex systems for accomplishing certain physical tasks. Some of these complexes deal primarily with material—highway systems for transportation of goods and persons, industrial systems for quantity production of refrigerators and television sets, apparatus for large-scale chemical and metallurgical processing, water-supply and sewage-removal systems, and food-processing plants, to name a few. Others have to do with energy—electric power systems for transforming chemical energy in coal to electrical energy in the home, power plants for transportation equipment of all types, servomechanisms for the accurate control of energy, refrigeration and air-conditioning systems. A third group, including communication systems and computing machines, deal with the transmission and the processing of information or data.

In all phases of this work the need continually arises for answers to such questions as the following:

How should a particular portion of one of these complexes be designed so as to accomplish its task most effectively and economically?

What is the best method of operation from the standpoints of economy, reliability, and effectiveness?

How will operation be affected by the failure of a certain component, and how can the seriousness of the consequences be minimized?

Very few such questions can be answered directly. Most often the answers must be obtained by choosing a tentative solution or design, testing it by experiment or analysis, devising a new solution on the basis of what has been learned, testing this, and so on. Because testing by mathematical analysis is usually cheaper than testing by experiment, and also because the results are usually in more general form and give more insight into the relative effects of the various elements of the problem, analysis plays an increasingly important role in engineering.

ANALYSIS OF COMPONENT SYSTEMS Because of the complexity of the over-all systems it is ordinarily most practicable to subdivide them into smaller component systems and to deal with these individually.

The essential steps in analyzing these component systems are the following:

1. The physical system to be analyzed is represented by a mathematical model. This always involves approximations and assumptions which limit the application of the results of the analysis. It is most important, therefore, that the approximations involved be clearly stated and kept in mind.
2. Solutions are found for the mathematical equations which represent (although imperfectly) the physical system. This step is mathematics, whereas the first and third are engineering.
3. The mathematical solutions are interpreted physically. They are examined to evaluate the effects of assumptions and approximations and to make certain that they are physically reasonable. Finally, the information is presented in the most useful form (design formulas, tables, curves, etc.).

We propose, in this book, to study methods of analyzing mechanical and electrical systems. That is to say, we wish to examine physical systems such as those pictured in Fig. 1-1 with the ultimate aim of predicting their behavior when they are subjected to certain forces or conditions.

The universe is so constructed that the same mathematical equations often describe a number of different physical situations. In this case the various physical systems are called *analogues*. It is profitable to study such systems side by side, since the methods of analysis which are developed for one will apply equally well to the others. Furthermore, systems in which electrical and mechanical elements are combined are common—the entire field of servomechanisms is of this nature. Thus, there are compelling reasons for developing analysis methods which will be generally applicable.

1-1 MECHANICAL NETWORK ELEMENTS

Let us begin by considering the spring-mounted refrigerator motor and compressor of Fig. 1-1a. The first step to take in the study

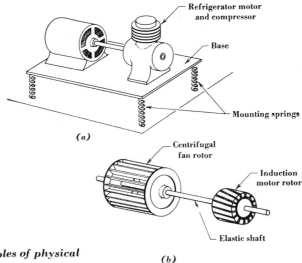

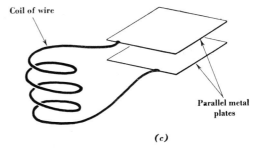

Fig. 1-1. Examples of physical systems.

(a)

(b)

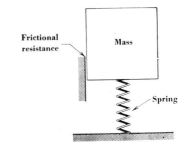

(c)

of this system is to reduce it to an approximate model which is simpler than the actual system and yet adequate for the purpose at hand. For example, if only vertical oscillations are of interest, the combined effect of the four mounting springs may be approximated by a single equivalent spring. The combined mass of the motor, compressor, and base may be considered to be at a point, and the over-all frictional power

Fig. 1-2. Approximate model for Fig. 1-1a.

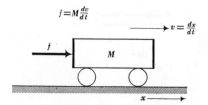

$f = M\frac{dv}{dt}$

$\longrightarrow v = \frac{dx}{dt}$

f

M

$x \longrightarrow$

Fig. 1-3. The relation among mass, force, and acceleration.

loss may be concentrated in a small region. This gives the approximate model (mechanical *network*) of Fig. 1-2.†

In studying quantitatively the three mechanical system components which appear in this model, it will be advantageous to start from the concept of energy, since energy has the quality of universality. The principle of conservation of energy states that energy may be converted from one to another of various forms but that it is always the same energy. It may appear as mechanical, electrical, thermal, or chemical energy; it may diffuse as electromagnetic radiation, or it may be wrapped up in a particularly compact form as mass, as in an unexploded atomic bomb; but it is always a quantity which can be accounted for and measured.

MASS The kinetic energy (energy of motion) possessed by a moving body (Fig. 1-3) is found experimentally to be proportional to the square of its velocity v. The constant of proportionality is taken to be $M/2$, where M is the *mass* of the body. Thus, the kinetic energy is written

$$W_k = \tfrac{1}{2}Mv^2 \tag{1-1}$$

From this equation the mass of a body may be defined as a measure of its ability to store kinetic energy.

An alternative definition of mass is deduced by taking the derivative of both sides of Eq. (1-1). The time rate of change of energy is power p; hence

$$\frac{dW_k}{dt} = p = Mv\,\frac{dv}{dt} \tag{1-2}$$

† *System, device, model, network,* and *circuit* are all used more or less interchangeably in the literature of mechanical and electrical analysis. The unfortunate result is that none of these words retains a precise meaning. In this text, we shall use *network* when we are referring to the mathematical models of mechanical or electrical systems or devices. *System* is such a broad term that no effort will be made to restrict it to either models or actual physical devices. Thus, a term such as *system elements* can occur when either a device or its model is being discussed. *Circuit* will be used interchangeably with *system* in discussing electrical devices.

Another term which can cause confusion is *equivalent*. This word is often used in compounds like *equivalent system, equivalent circuit,* and *equivalent model.* In combinations of this sort the term invariably means equivalent in some restricted sense, such as equivalent over a certain range or with regard to some specified property.

But the instantaneous power delivered by a force is the product of force and velocity, fv. Inserting this in Eq. (1-2), we find

$$f = M\frac{dv}{dt} \tag{1-3}$$

Thus the mass may also be defined as the factor of proportionality between applied force and the acceleration it produces.

UNITS   Two systems of units are in common use in engineering work, the *meter-kilogram-second* (mks) and the *English*.

The mks unit of distance is the meter; the unit of mass is the kilogram. Thus a mass of one kilogram, moving with a velocity of one meter per second, has a kinetic energy of one-half kilogram-meter^2 per second^2. Kilogram-meter^2 per second^2 is a rather clumsy expression to have to speak or write, and this unit of energy is termed a *joule*, in honor of the British physicist who made important contributions toward the formulation of the conservation-of-energy principle. Power is measured in joules per second, or *watts*.

The mks unit of force is, from Eq. (1-3) (since only quantities expressible in the same units can be equated), a kilogram-meter per second^2. Again, a shorter term is desirable, and that chosen is the *newton*. A newton is equal to 0.225 pound, about the force required to lift your morning cup of coffee.

In the English unit system the unit of length is the *foot*, and the unit of force is the *pound*. The pound is also the measure of weight, the force due to gravitational attraction. From Eq. (1-3) the mass of a body is seen to be equal to its weight divided by the acceleration produced by gravitational force g, approximately 32.2 feet per second^2. The unit of mass is called a *slug*:

$$M \text{ (slugs)} = \frac{w \text{ (pounds)}}{g} \tag{1-4}$$

(The mass of four gallons of water is approximately one slug.)

Energy in the English system is measured in foot-pounds and power in foot-pounds per second. The two unit systems are compared in Table 1-1.

COMPLIANCE   A second mechanical network element is also defined from an experimental energy relation, namely, that the energy stored in a spring is approximately proportional to the square of the distance it is compressed or extended. The factor of proportionality is commonly taken to be $1/2K$, where K is termed the *compliance* of the

TABLE 1-1   *Comparison of English and MKS Units*

Quantity	English	MKS
Mass	Slug	Kilogram
Length	Foot	Meter
Time	Second	Second
Force	Pound	Newton
Weight	Pound	Newton
Energy	Foot-pound	Joule = newton-meter
Power	Foot-pound/second	Watt = joule/second

Weight = mass $\times$ g

g = acceleration due to gravity

    = 32.2 ft/sec² = 9.8 m/sec²

spring. Thus the potential energy stored in a spring compressed from its normal length by a distance x (Fig. 1-4) is

$$W_p = \frac{1}{2K} x^2 \tag{1-5}$$

Differentiating both sides of this equation with respect to time to find the power, we obtain

$$p = \frac{dW_p}{dt} = \frac{1}{K} x \frac{dx}{dt} = \frac{xv}{K} \tag{1-6}$$

Since power is the product of force and velocity, the relation between the force required to stretch or compress a spring and the displacement is

$$f = \frac{x}{K} \tag{1-7}$$

Compliance may be defined either from the energy expression (1-5) or from Eq. (1-7), in which it is seen to be the displacement per unit force. The term stems from the second definition, since compliance is here a measure of the amount the spring yields to the force. It may be measured in meters per newton in mks units or in feet per pound in English units. (The spring constant, or stiffness, the reciprocal of the compliance, is also often used to describe a spring.)

    The proportionality between force and displacement expressed in Eq. (1-7) is found only over a limited range of displacements (Fig.

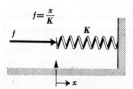

$f = \dfrac{x}{K}$

Fig. 1-4. The relation among force, displacement, and spring compliance.

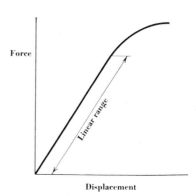

Force

Linear range

Displacement

Fig. 1-5. Force vs. displacement for a spring, showing the limited range over which a linear relationship holds.

1-5). If the applied force is too large, so that this proportionality does not hold, the network element is termed a *nonlinear* one. Nonlinear systems are relatively difficult to treat, and we shall henceforth assume that, unless otherwise specified, the network elements with which we deal are linear—that is, that they are described to a reasonable degree of accuracy by such relations as Eqs. (1-3) and (1-7). The term *linear* arises from the fact that the relationships between the variables f, x, and dv/dt in these equations are the same as the relationships in an equation of a straight line. The subject of nonlinear elements will receive attention again in later discussions.

FRICTIONAL RESISTANCE A third type of mechanical network element is *frictional resistance*, exemplified by the dashpot of Fig. 1-6. This dashpot (similar to the shock absorber of an automobile) consists of a piston which moves in a loosely fitted, fluid-filled cylinder. As it moves, kinetic energy is imparted to the fluid and is ultimately converted to energy in the form of heat. Thus, this third element differs from the first two in that energy is lost from a system in its frictional resistance, whereas it is stored in a moving mass or a compressed spring. Mass and compliance are *energy-storing* elements, and frictional resistance is an *energy-dissipating* element.

We shall assume that the instantaneous power loss due to frictional resistance is proportional to the square of the velocity of the moving part—the piston in the case of the dashpot. Thus,

$$p = fv = Dv^2 \qquad (1\text{-}8)$$

where D is the constant of proportionality, termed the frictional resistance. Dividing both sides of the equation by the velocity, we see

Fig. 1-6. Dashpot and the relation among force, velocity, and frictional resistance.

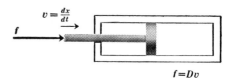

$v = \dfrac{dx}{dt}$

f

$f = Dv$

that D may also be defined as the ratio of instantaneous force to instantaneous velocity:

$$f = Dv \tag{1-9}$$

The parameter D is seen to have the dimensions of force over velocity or (since force itself has the dimensions of mass times acceleration) mass over time. Thus the unit of D is a kilogram per second in the mks system or a slug per second in the English system.

The proportionality between applied force and resulting velocity expressed in Eq. (1-9) is approximately true for the dashpot under discussion; it is a much less accurate statement for the familiar dry friction (of a sliding block, for example), where the force is nearly independent of the velocity. There is, however, a compelling reason for assuming this proportionality, namely, that of simplicity in analysis. As will be seen presently, this assumption leads to equations which are quite easy to solve, whereas any other assumption provokes serious mathematical difficulty. When the relation of Eq. (1-9) holds, we say that the frictional resistance is a linear network element. A discussion of nonlinear frictional resistance can be found in some books on nonlinear mechanics.†

PROBLEMS

Problem solving is a valuable aid, not only in acquiring knowledge, but also in forming orderly and precise thought habits. To obtain the maximum benefits from the problems in this text, the following should be done wherever applicable:

1. State clearly the assumptions and approximations which are found necessary in order to proceed with the problem solution.
2. Check the final result for physical reasonableness, and evaluate the effect of the assumptions and approximations on the validity of the solution.

Some of the problem statements will include superfluous data; this is the realistic situation, in which it is necessary to select the data which will be useful. On the other hand, some of the problem statements will be deficient in data, and needed information will have to be assumed or obtained from other sources.

1-1   The force of gravity on the surface of the moon is approximately one-sixth of its value on the surface of the earth. A body weighs 32.2 lb

† See, for example, J. J. Stoker, "Nonlinear Vibrations," Interscience Publishers, Inc., New York, 1950.

on the earth. How much would it weigh on the moon? What would be its mass on the moon?

What would be its apparent weight as measured by a counterpoise type of balance which had been calibrated on the earth? As measured by a spring balance?

1-2 (a) A weight of 10 lb is gradually lowered onto a helical spring, and the spring is found to be compressed 2 in. What is the compliance of the spring?

(b) A mass of 2 kg is gradually lowered onto a helical spring, and the spring is found to be compressed 0.02 m. What is the compliance of the spring?

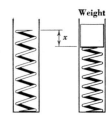

Fig. P 1-2

1-3 The figure shows a bumper designed to bring a coasting railroad car to a stop. The car weighs 3,220 lb and is traveling with a velocity of 10 ft/sec when it strikes the spring. If the

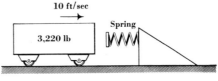

Fig. P 1-3

spring is not to compress more than 6 in., what must be its compliance?

What will be the maximum force exerted on the car by the spring?

1-4 Consider the weight in Prob. 1-2a to be held in contact with the *uncompressed* spring and then suddenly released. Compute, from energy considerations, the maximum amount by which the spring is compressed. Can you suggest a graphical solution for this problem in which the various energies involved would be plotted against the displacement of the upper end of the spring?

1-5 Consider the weight in Prob. 1-2a to be held 3 in. above the upper end of the uncompressed spring and then released. Compute, from energy considerations, the maximum amount by which the spring is compressed.

1-6 A mass M is released from a distance h above the end of an uncompressed helical spring, as in Prob. 1-5. The compliance of the spring is K. Show that the maximum compression of the spring is given by

$$x_{\max} = MgK + \sqrt{(MgK)^2 + 2MghK}$$

This is obtained from a quadratic equation. Justify the neglect of the second solution of the equation.

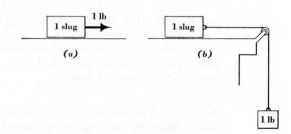

(a)   *(b)*

Fig. P 1-7

1-7 (a) A mass of 1 slug starts from rest and moves on a frictionless, level platform subject to a force of 1 lb. Obtain expressions for the acceleration, velocity, and distance as functions of time, using the relations $v = \int a\, dt$ and $x = \int v\, dt$.

(b) A mass of 1 slug starts from rest and moves on a frictionless, level table, being pulled by a string which is attached to a 1-lb weight (passing over a pulley at the edge of the table). Find the velocity as a function of time.

How long will it take the weight to drop, and the block to move, a distance of 1 ft? What is the velocity of the block at this time? What is the total kinetic energy of the system at this time? How does this compare with the potential energy lost by the weight in dropping 1 ft?

1-8 (a) It is desired to impart to a mass of 2 slugs a velocity given by the expression $v = t - t^2/4$ ft/sec during the time interval from $t = 0$ to $t = 4$ sec and a velocity of zero at all other times. Find an expression for the force which must be applied. Plot the velocity and force as functions of time.

(b) It is desired to impart to the end of a spring of compliance 0.5 ft/lb (the other end of the spring being fixed) the velocity specified in part a. Find and plot the force required. (Note that displacement is the integral of velocity.)

1-9 (a) It is desired to impart to a mass of 2 slugs a velocity as plotted in the figure. Plot the required force.

(b) It is desired to impart to the end of a spring of compliance 0.5 ft/lb and negligible mass a velocity as

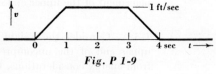

Fig. P 1-9

plotted in the figure. Plot the force required to produce this velocity.

1-2 ELECTRICAL NETWORK ELEMENTS

Before proceeding to analyze a simple mechanical system—that is, to predict from the known characteristics of network elements what will happen under certain conditions—let us examine the types of elements which appear in electrical systems.

In discussing the components of mechanical systems, we found that all the quantities involved can be measured in units which are combinations of the basic dimensions of mass, length, and time— kilograms, meters, and seconds in the mks system. To treat electrical circuit elements, it is necessary to add a fourth basic unit, which is purely electrical. It is convenient to take this to be the coulomb, which is the amount of negative electric charge on 6.24×10^{18} electrons.

The velocity, or rate of change of displacement, turns out to be a useful quantity in working with mechanical systems. In somewhat similar fashion, it is convenient in electrical circuit theory to deal with the time rate of change or rate of transfer of electric charge. This rate of change of charge is the electric current i, measured in coulombs per second, or *amperes*. The unit is named after the French physicist Ampère, who, together with the Scottish mathematician J. C. Maxwell, laid the foundation for the mathematical analysis of electric- and magnetic-field problems.†

ELECTRIC AND MAGNETIC FIELDS We must say a brief word about these electric and magnetic fields. A mass experiences a force due to the presence of another nearby mass, and we speak of this force in terms of the *gravitational field*. Thus the gravitational field at the surface of the earth is about 9.80 newtons/kg, or 32.2 lb/slug.

In similar manner, an electric charge experiences a force when it is near another charge accumulation; this force is described in terms of an *electric field*.

The magnitude of the electric field at a point in space is equal to the force on an electric charge placed at that point divided by the amount of the charge. Thus electric field intensity is measured in newtons per coulomb. For many purposes it is more convenient to speak of electric field strength in terms of *volts per meter*. (The *volt* is named for the Italian physicist Volta, who touched off the electrical nineteenth century with his invention of the electric battery.) The intensity in volts per meter is numerically the same as the intensity in newtons per coulomb (Fig. 1-7). Thus a volt is a newton-meter per coulomb.

> † Some historical references will be found in the Selected Bibliography, which follows the Appendix.

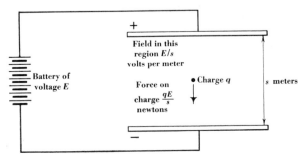

Fig. 1-7. The relation between the electric field strength between two parallel plates and the force on a charged particle.

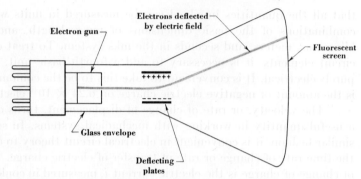

Fig. 1-8. Cathode-ray tube, indicating the manner in which an electron beam is deflected by an electric field.

But observe that the newton-meter, or joule, is a unit of energy. Thus the volt has dimensions of joules per coulomb. Indeed, the physical significance of a one-volt difference of potential between two points is that energy in the amount of one joule will be required to transfer one coulomb of charge from one point to the other. Thus, in Fig. 1-7, to move the charge q from the lower to the upper plate will require Eq joules.

The effect of the force on a charge in an electric field is most easily observed in the familiar cathode-ray tube (Fig. 1-8). In this device a beam of electrons, emitted from an electron gun, passes between two metal electrodes called deflecting plates. When these plates are electrically connected to a source of voltage, charges accumulate on the plates, and an electric field is set up between them. The force exerted on the electrons by this field causes them to acquire a transverse component of velocity. The result is that the spot on the fluorescent screen produced by the impinging of electrons is moved a distance propor-

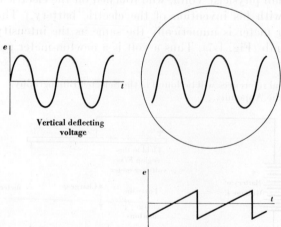

Fig. 1-9. Cathode-ray-screen pattern, showing the vertical and horizontal deflecting voltages used to produce it.

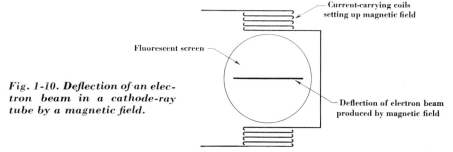

Fluorescent screen

Current-carrying coils
setting up magnetic field

Deflection of electron beam
produced by magnetic field

Fig. 1-10. Deflection of an electron beam in a cathode-ray tube by a magnetic field.

tional to the deflecting voltage. In one mode of cathode-ray-tube operation, a horizontally deflecting voltage is used to cause the beam to move from left to right at a constant rate. Then, with a signal voltage applied to the vertical deflecting plates, the spot traces out a plot of this signal voltage as a function of time (Fig. 1-9).

Another type of field, a *magnetic field*, is produced by charges in motion or electric currents.† The presence of a magnetic field is disclosed by the force observed on moving charges or electric currents (on the current-carrying conductors in a motor, for example). The electron beam in a cathode-ray tube consists of charges in motion and may be deflected by a magnetic field (Fig. 1-10)—in fact, this is the usual means employed to make the luminous spot in a television picture tube trace out the scanning raster.

Energy is required to separate charge accumulations and to set up an electric field. This energy is spoken of as being stored in the electric field. Energy is also required to set up current flow with the accompanying magnetic field, and this energy is said to be stored in the magnetic field.

RESISTANCE Electrical energy may be stored in electric and magnetic fields; it may also be converted to other forms of energy—mechanical energy in a motor, radiant energy in an electric light, sound energy in a loudspeaker, thermal energy in a hot plate. The portion of an electrical circuit in which electrical energy is converted to heat is called a *resistor*. The power or rate of conversion of energy is found in most cases to be proportional to the square of the current:

$$p_R = Ri^2 \qquad (1\text{-}10)$$

The *resistance R*, the constant of proportionality, is measured in watts per ampere², or *ohms*, a unit named after the German physicist Georg Ohm.

Note the similarity between this equation and Eq. (1-8) for the thermal power loss due to friction in a mechanical system. The current

---

† Permanent magnets also produce magnetic fields. However, this effect can be attributed to the motion of the electrons within the molecular structure of the magnet itself (see Chap. 11).

and electrical resistance of an electrical network may be considered analogous, respectively, to the velocity and frictional resistance of a mechanical network.

When a physical structure capable of converting electric power to heat is represented by an idealized resistance, a number of approximations are involved. In the first place, power is not always exactly proportional to the square of the current, and in some cases there are important deviations from this law. In particular, the factor R is dependent upon temperature. The resistance of a 120-volt 100-watt incandescent lamp is about 1 ohm when it is operating at rated voltage and only a fraction of this when the filament is at room temperature.

Even if the resistance is relatively constant, electric and magnetic fields are certainly present whenever current is flowing; in many instances the energy stored therein can be neglected. The power dissipation is distributed throughout the volume of the resistor, and this distribution is influenced by various factors. A change in this distribution may result in a change of resistance. The phenomenon of *skin effect*, a crowding of high-frequency currents to the surface of a conductor, is a case in point. The difference in current distribution may cause the resistance of a conductor to be considerably greater for high-frequency alternating current than for unidirectional current flow.

Again we see an example of the general truth that, in order to set up a tractable mathematical model, various assumptions and approximations must be made. Every physical situation to be analyzed must be carefully examined to determine whether the approximations are reasonable ones. The results of the analysis must be similarly examined to see how these assumptions and approximations affect their validity and applicability.

Now let us return to Eq. (1-10) and look at this relation in the light of Fig. 1-11. Here a constant current of i amp flows through a resistance of R ohms. Appearing across the resistor is a potential difference of e_R volts, a necessary consequence of the fact that electrical energy is being dissipated. From the definition of a volt, it follows that in the process of passing a charge of q coulombs through the resistor, electrical energy is given up in the amount $e_R q$ joules. The current i is the rate at which charge passes through the resistor; hence $e_R i$ is the rate at which electrical energy is converted to heat in the resistor:

$$p_R \text{ (watts)} = e_R \text{ (volts)} \, i \text{ (amperes)} \qquad (1\text{-}11)$$

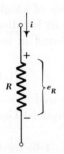

Fig. 1-11. Current flow through a resistor, illustrating directional and polarity markings.

Comparison of this with Eq. (1-10) yields the familiar Ohm's law:

$$e_R \text{ (volts)} = R \text{ (ohms)} \, i \text{ (amperes)} \qquad (1\text{-}12)$$

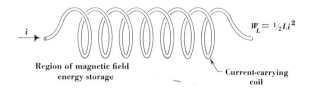

Fig. 1-12. An inductor, a region in which magnetic field energy may be stored.

Region of magnetic field energy storage

Current-carrying coil

INDUCTANCE The region around a current-carrying coil of wire is a region of fairly dense storage of magnetic field energy. The measure of the ability of such a coil (Fig. 1-12) to store energy is termed its *inductance*, L, and the coil is called an *inductor*. The stored energy is found to be proportional to the square of the value of electric current. The unit of inductance is defined in such a way that the expression for the stored energy W_L is similar in form to the formula for mechanical kinetic energy:

$$W_L = \tfrac{1}{2}Li^2 \tag{1-13}$$

Inductance is thus measured in units which have the dimensions of energy over current squared. The unit of inductance may be considered to be defined by the above equation when W_L is in joules and i in amperes. This unit is named the *henry*, after Joseph Henry, the first Secretary of the Smithsonian Institution, in recognition of the importance of his early experimental work in electromagnetic induction. Inductances of the order of microhenrys or millihenrys for inductors with nonmagnetic cores and of many henrys for iron-core inductors are typical.†

Comparing the expression for the kinetic energy of a moving mass, $W_k = \tfrac{1}{2}Mv^2$, with Eq. (1-13), we see that mass and inductance can be considered analogous quantities. Inductance is commonly defined from a standpoint other than that of stored energy. The strength of the magnetic field about an inductor is found to be proportional to the inductance and also to the current. A field quantity called *magnetic flux* is so defined that the total flux linking the inductor current flow is numerically equal to the product Li. In terms of the field concept, then, inductance is defined as flux linkages per ampere. This is analogous to defining mass as momentum per unit velocity— a perfectly acceptable, if not very common, definition.

The instantaneous power flow into an inductor is the rate of change of stored energy:

$$p_L = \frac{dW_L}{dt} = Li\frac{di}{dt} \tag{1-14}$$

But power is, in general, the product of voltage and current:

† The following metric prefixes are very commonly found with electrical units: mega- (one million), kilo- (one thousand), milli- (one-thousandth), micro- (one-millionth).

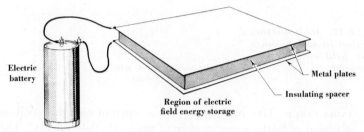

Fig. 1-13. A capacitor, a region in which electric field energy may be stored.

$$p \text{ (joules/second)} = e \text{ (joules/coulomb)} \, i \text{ (coulombs/second)} \quad (1\text{-}15)$$

Thus $L \, di/dt$ is a voltage, the so-called voltage of self-induction:

$$e_L = L \frac{di}{dt} \quad (1\text{-}16)$$

CAPACITANCE   A region in which the primary storage of energy is in the electric field is lumped into a circuit element called a *capacitor*. The name *capacitance* and the symbol C are given to the measure of the ability of such a circuit element to store electric charge. The stored charge is found to be proportional to the voltage across the capacitor:

$$q = Ce_C \quad (1\text{-}17)$$

The constant of proportionality, C, is measured in coulombs per volt, or *farads*. This unit is named after the preeminent electrical experimenter Michael Faraday. If the plates in the capacitor of Fig. 1-13 were spaced 1 mm apart, the area, in order to have a capacitance of 1 farad, would have to be nearly 50 miles^2. Thus, typical capacitances are measured in microfarads or micromicrofarads. (*Pico* is sometimes substituted for *micromicro*.)

An alternative way of defining the unit of capacitance is from the stored-energy relation

$$W_C = \frac{1}{2}Ce_C{}^2 = \frac{1}{2}\frac{1}{C}q^2 \quad (1\text{-}18)$$

This is reminiscent of our discussion of the spring, where we found that compliance can be defined from either a force relation or an energy relation. Here again we have consistency between the two definitions, since the instantaneous power is

$$p = \frac{dW_C}{dt} = \frac{1}{C}q\frac{dq}{dt} = e_C i \quad (1\text{-}19)$$

1-3 SUMMARY

The definitions of the mechanical and electrical network elements are in terms of relations *based on experimental observations*. A certain amount of freedom is allowable in regard to which relations are con-

TABLE 1-2   *Energy-Power and Force-Velocity or Voltage-Current Relations*

Energy-Power Relations		Force-Velocity or Voltage-Current Relations
Mechanical:		
$p = Dv^2$		$f_D = Dv$
$W_k = \frac{1}{2}Mv^2$	$p = \dfrac{dW}{dt} = fv$	$f_M = M\dfrac{dv}{dt}$
$W_p = \dfrac{1}{2K}x^2$		$f_K = \dfrac{x}{K}$
Electrical:		
$p = Ri^2$		$e_R = Ri$
$W_L = \frac{1}{2}Li^2$	$p = \dfrac{dW}{dt} = ei$	$e_L = L\dfrac{di}{dt}$
$W_c = \dfrac{1}{2C}q^2$		$e_C = \dfrac{q}{C}$

sidered basic and which derived. This is emphasized in the arrangement of Table 1-2. Here the energy-power relations are grouped in the left-hand column, and the force-velocity and voltage-current relations are collected on the right. Either group may be considered basic, with the other derived by means of the connecting relations in the center. Thus the two sets are consistent and interrelated.

Note that the relations which can be verified by experiment are primarily proportionality relations. The sizes of the various units are so chosen that as many as possible of the proportionality constants will be unity.

It is not necessary to know how to compute values of resistance, inductance, and capacitance from physical dimensions in order to proceed with a study of electrical network analysis, any more than it is necessary to be able to compute the spring constant of a helical spring to understand the oscillations in a mechanical system. We shall have little to say here on the subject of the computation of spring compliances. Likewise, the study of electric and magnetic field theory, by means of which inductance and capacitance are computed, will be left for other texts to discuss.

The behavior of the mechanical and electrical network elements is summarized in Fig. 1-14. For the mechanical elements the relations between the velocity and the force which would have to be applied to produce that velocity are indicated; for the electrical elements the current and the voltage necessary to maintain that current are related. The similarity between the mathematical relations involved indicates that various electrical quantities can be considered analogues of quantities in the mechanical domain. These analogies are pointed out in Table 1-3.

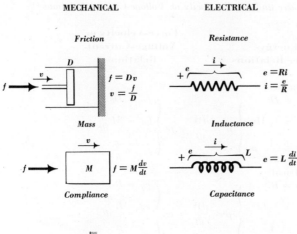

Fig. 1-14. Summary of mechanical and electrical network elements.

TABLE 1-3   *Analogous Quantities in Mechanical and Electrical Systems (MKS Units)*

Mechanical			Electrical		
Force	f	Newtons	Voltage	e	Volts
Displacement	x	Meters	Charge	q	Coulombs
Velocity	v	Meters/second	Current	i	Amperes
Mass	M	Kilograms	Inductance	L	Henrys
Compliance	K	Meters/newton	Capacitance	C	Farads
Frictional resistance	D	Newton-seconds/meter	Resistance	R	Ohms

Kinetic energy, $\frac{1}{2}Mv^2$

Potential energy, $\frac{1}{2}Kf^2 = \frac{x^2}{2K}$

Frictional power loss, Dv^2

Instantaneous power, fv

Momentum, Mv

Compliance—displacement per unit force

Mass—momentum per unit velocity

Reaction forces:
  Friction, Dv

  Inertia, $M\dfrac{dv}{dt}$

  Spring, $\dfrac{x}{K} = \dfrac{1}{K}\int v\,dt$

Magnetic energy, $\frac{1}{2}Li^2$

Electrical energy, $\frac{1}{2}Ce^2 = \dfrac{q^2}{2C}$

Resistance power loss, Ri^2

Instantaneous power, ei

Flux linkages, Li

Capacitance—charge per unit voltage

Inductance—flux linkages per unit current

Voltage drops:
  Resistance, Ri

  Inductance, $L\dfrac{di}{dt}$

  Capacitance, $\dfrac{q}{C} = \dfrac{1}{C}\int i\,dt$

The concept of analogous systems is an important and powerful one. Its importance, first of all, lies in the fact that the analysis methods developed for one system are applicable to other, analogous systems. It points the way to the analysis of mixed systems, containing, for example, both electrical and mechanical elements. Furthermore, it has extensive application in experimental studies in which, for one reason or another, measurements are more conveniently made on an analogue than on the actual system whose behavior is desired.

We shall assume in the discussions to follow that the network elements with which we deal are idealized ones—in other words, that they are (1) *lumped* (the energy storage or power dissipation is localized), (2) *linear* (the linear relations of Fig. 1-14 hold), and (3) *constant* (the values do not vary with time). None of these three properties can be strictly true of physical system elements, but they may be approximately true within limited ranges of force, voltage, velocity, or current. The degree to which they fail to describe faithfully the behavior of the physical system elements limits the validity of the analysis results.

P R O B L E M S

1-10   Assume that a method is available for measuring thermal energy (such as measuring the change in temperature in a container of water) and electric charge (such as measuring the amount of silver deposited electrolytically from a silver nitrate solution). Devise experimental methods by means of which the electrical circuit elements R, L, and C might be measured.

    If in these procedures you plan to use electric meters whose readings are proportional to voltage or current, explain how the measurements of thermal energy and charge might be used to calibrate these meters. (In other words, how might the manufacturer of the voltmeter determine how to mark off the scale?)

1-11   A capacitor of capacitance C farads is charged to a voltage E and discharged through a coil of L henrys and negligible resistance. The maximum current occurs when all the energy initially stored in the capacitor has been transferred to the magnetic field of the inductor. Show that this maximum current is $E \sqrt{C/L}$ amp.

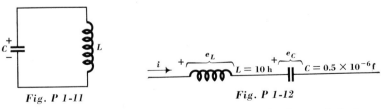

Fig. P 1-11   Fig. P 1-12

1-12   A current is caused to flow in an inductor of 10 henrys inductance and a capacitor of 0.5×10^{-6} farad capacitance. During the interval from $t = 0$ to $t = 4 \times 10^{-3}$ sec it is described by the expression $i = t - 250t^2$; at all other times it is zero. Find and plot the voltage across the inductor and across the capacitor.

1-13   A current with instantaneous value as plotted in the figure flows in a 10-henry inductor and a 0.5×10^{-6} farad capacitor. Plot the voltage across the inductor and across the capacitor.

Fig. P 1-13

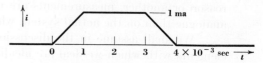

1-14   The voltage applied to the circuit shown varies with time as indicated in the figure. At $t = 2$ sec find:

    (*a*) The current through the capacitor.
    (*b*) The energy stored in the capacitor.
    (*c*) The instantaneous power flow into the capacitor.
    (*d*) The current through the inductor.
    (*e*) The energy stored in the inductor.
    (*f*) The instantaneous power flow into the inductor.

Fig. P 1-14

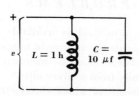 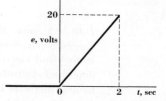

1-4   INTRODUCTORY PROBLEM

The form of the analysis which we are about to study is, in a sense, an invention.† Though it was originally devised to solve electrical-circuit problems, it is equally applicable to various types of mechanical, thermal, and acoustic systems.

It is our aim to become accustomed to thinking of these circuits and systems in terms of certain compact descriptions, which will be called by various names—impedance, transfer function, and others. These descriptions will be exploited to yield results which can be obtained by other means only with considerably greater difficulty.

To accomplish this aim, we shall attempt, as far as possible, to reexperience the discovery of the analysis methods we are to use. Thus we shall not find our knowledge and procedures neatly formulated, cookbook-style, ready for application. Rather, we shall face a selection of problems of gradually increasing difficulty and shall develop the methods of solving them as they are needed. An attempt will be made

† Historical references for these analysis methods will be found in the Selected Bibliography.

to present each step in the growing body of experience as the sort of thing we might think of doing if we faced the particular problem for the first time in history. We shall strive in this way to make this type of analysis one of our natural and accustomed modes of thought, operating on the principle that we remember best what we ourselves discover.

This approach will, of necessity, yield knowledge in a somewhat disorderly fashion. From time to time, therefore, we shall have to review and summarize the accumulating experience and put it into convenient form for later reference.

THE *M-D* NETWORK   In the light of these explanatory remarks on method of procedure, let us consider an introductory problem in which the center of attraction is an automobile traveling on a level road (Fig. 1-15a). We are required to find how the velocity varies with time when the automobile is coasting (no applied force).

Because of air resistance and other forms of friction, there is a frictional power loss which is more or less proportional to the square of the velocity. These various distributed losses we may lump together into an equivalent frictional resistance D. The distributed mass of the automobile we lump into an equivalent mass M at its center of gravity. In this manner we arrive at the approximate model of Fig. 1-15b. It is this idealized model of the actual physical situation which we shall analyze with our yet-to-be-discovered mathematical tools.

The next step is to express in mathematical form the governing physical laws as applied to the particular system. Let us denote the position of the body by the coordinate x, the distance to the right of some arbitrary reference point. Thus a negative x simply indicates a position to the left of the reference. The rate of change of x, dx/dt, is the velocity v. When so defined, a positive v signifies motion to the right; a negative v, motion to the left.

We shall assume that the force necessary to overcome the effect of friction is Dv, as was discussed earlier. This force is positive when v is positive; that is, the required force is to the right if the body is moving toward the right.

The force necessary to cause a change in velocity is $M\,dv/dt$. This is positive (to the right) if dv/dt is positive, that is, if the velocity

(a)   *(b)*

Fig. 1-15. (a) An automobile traveling on a level road and (b) its approximate model.

to the right is increasing in magnitude or if the velocity to the left is decreasing.

The applied force, if any, must be equal to the sum of the friction force and the inertial force. (This is an application of *D'Alembert's principle*, which states that the applied force is equal to the sum of the reaction forces.) In equation form this statement becomes

$$\text{Applied force} = M\frac{dv}{dt} + Dv = 0 \tag{1-20}$$

We should pause to note that any equation which is written with the aid of D'Alembert's principle, or the summing of forces, may also be written from the standpoint of conservation of energy. If there is no external source of power in the system under consideration, the power dissipated in frictional resistance must come from the stored energy represented by the motion of the mass. Thus the sum of the time rate of change of stored energy and the power dissipation must be zero:

$$\frac{d}{dt}\left(\tfrac{1}{2}Mv^2\right) + Dv^2 = 0 \tag{1-21}$$

Performing the indicated differentiation and factoring out the common v gives Eq. (1-20).

DIFFERENTIAL EQUATIONS Equation (1-20) is a *differential equation*. It differs from an algebraic equation in that not only the unknown function v but also its derivative appears. This equation is the governing equation of our system, and our job is to solve it—that is, to find some expression for v which, when differentiated with respect to time and substituted in the differential equation, will satisfy the relation expressed in the equation.

Examination of Eq. (1-20) discloses some information about the form of v. First of all, it is apparent (since both M and D are positive quantities) that v and dv/dt have opposite signs. Physically, this means that, in whichever direction the body is moving, the magnitude of its velocity is decreasing. Rearrangement of Eq. (1-20) yields

$$\frac{dv}{dt} = -\frac{D}{M}v \tag{1-22}$$

It is quite possible to use this form to obtain graphically a plot of the velocity as a function of time. This is demonstrated in Fig. 1-16, and a study of the process is an aid to understanding the nature of a differential equation and the sort of information it contains.

Suppose we know that v has a value v_0 at some time, say $t = 0$. Its rate of change is, from Eq. (1-22), $-Dv_0/M$. This, then, is the slope of the curve of v versus t at $t = 0$. Assuming v to change at this rate for a time Δt, we find a new value $v_1 = v_0 - Dv_0\,\Delta t/M$ at $t = \Delta t$. This

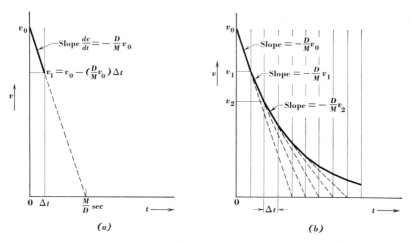

Fig. 1-16. Graphical method of obtaining a solution for Eq. (1-22).

yields a new slope for the curve of v versus t, which may be assumed to hold for a second time interval, and so on until the final curve is obtained, as in Fig. 1-16b.

The graphical solution of a differential equation often involves considerable labor if accurate results are required. When it can be carried out, an analytical method of solution is ordinarily to be preferred over graphical or automatic-computer methods, both because it may be less laborious and because the result is usually in a more generally applicable form.

There is more than one approach to an analytical solution of Eq. (1-20). We could, for example, put all the terms containing v on one side and all the terms containing t on the other (thus separating the two differentials dv and dt) and then integrate both sides. This method will work only with very simple equations, and we shall choose an attack which will turn out to be of much more general use.

We note that if this equation is to be true for all values of t, then v and dv/dt must vary in the same way with time. One must, in fact, be simply a constant times the other. Thus we are led to search for a mathematical function of t whose derivative has the same form as the function itself.

THE EXPONENTIAL FUNCTION Let us see whether we can find the function we seek in the form of a sum of terms of successively higher powers of t,

$$f(t) = a_0 + a_1 t + a_2 t^2 + a_3 t^3 + \cdots \tag{1-23}$$

where the a's are constants yet to be determined.

Not all functions can be expanded in such a simple power series, of course, but many can. When this series is differentiated, one term at a time, we find

$$\frac{df}{dt} = a_1 + 2a_2t + 3a_3t^2 + \cdots \tag{1-24}$$

Now we note that these two series are equal if

$$a_1 = a_0 \qquad a_2 = \frac{a_1}{2} = \frac{a_0}{2} \qquad \text{etc.}$$

In other words, the function

$$f(t) = 1 + t + \frac{t^2}{2!} + \frac{t^3}{3!} + \frac{t^4}{4!} + \cdots \tag{1-25}$$

has the desired property. Its derivative is the same function back again.

The function defined by this series is a most remarkable one. Its remarkable properties will appear as we go along, but we should stop to note one of these properties at the present time. Consider the series for $f(t)$ for two values of t:

$$f(t_1) = 1 + t_1 + \frac{t_1^2}{2!} + \frac{t_1^3}{3!} + \cdots$$

and $\qquad f(t_2) = 1 + t_2 + \frac{t_2^2}{2!} + \frac{t_2^3}{3!} + \cdots \tag{1-26}$

Now note that if these two series are multiplied together, we obtain

$$f(t_1)f(t_2) = 1 + (t_1 + t_2) + \frac{(t_1 + t_2)^2}{2!} + \frac{(t_1 + t_2)^3}{3!} + \cdots$$

$$= f(t_1 + t_2) \tag{1-27}$$

This suggests that $f(t)$ is of the form (constant)^t, for the law regarding exponents in multiplication is fulfilled. So it is, and the constant is the well-known

$$e \triangleq f(1) = 1 + 1 + \frac{1}{2!} + \frac{1}{3!} + \frac{1}{4!} + \cdots = 2.718 \tag{1-28}$$

The following are some of the rules for manipulation of the exponential function e^t (Fig. 1-17):

$$\frac{d}{dt} e^t = e^t \qquad \int e^t \, dt = e^t + \text{constant} \tag{1-29}$$

$$e^{bt}e^{ct} = e^{(b+c)t} \tag{1-30}$$

$$\frac{d}{dt}(ae^{bt}) = abe^{bt} \tag{1-31}$$

$$\int ae^{bt} \, dt = \frac{a}{b} e^{bt} + \text{constant} \tag{1-32}$$

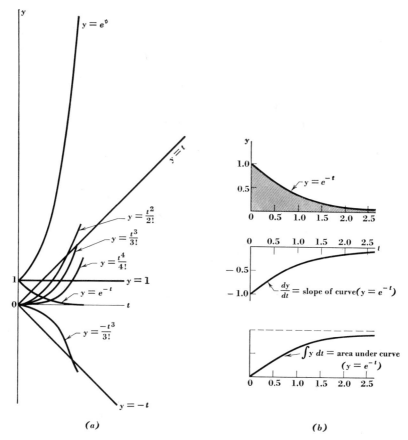

Fig. 1-17. Properties of the functions e^t and e^{-t}, showing (a) how the terms in the series add to form the functions and (b) the form of the derivative and integral of e^{-t}.

SOLUTION OF THE EQUATION   Now, to continue with the solving of our differential equation, it appears that a solution of the form†

$$v = Ve^{st} \qquad \frac{dv}{dt} = sVe^{st} \qquad (1\text{-}33)$$

has the proper characteristics to satisfy Eq. (1-20). When this solution is inserted, the equation takes the form

$$(sM + D)Ve^{st} = 0 \qquad (1\text{-}34)$$

† We shall follow the practice of using lower-case letters (v, f, e, i, etc.) for the instantaneous values of time-varying quantities and capitals (V, F, E, I, etc.) for the amplitude constants appearing in the mathematical expressions for these quantities.

Apparently either V or $sM + D$ must equal zero. The first alternative is a rather uninteresting one, so we choose the second:

$$sM + D = 0 \qquad s = \frac{-D}{M} \tag{1-35}$$

Thus,
$$v = Ve^{-Dt/M} \tag{1-36}$$

is the solution to Eq. (1-20).

Note that the constant V is the value of the velocity at time $t = 0$ (that is, at the time the velocity is known) since e^0 is seen from the series definition to be equal to 1.

PROBLEMS

1-15 A mass M moves along a level surface, restrained, as indicated in the figure, by a spring of compliance K. The frictional resistance is D. There is no externally applied force.

Fig. P 1-15

(a) Suggest a convenient reference point to use as $x = 0$.

(b) Write an equation which expresses mathematically the statement that the rate of decrease of the total energy stored in the moving mass and the spring must equal the power dissipation in the frictional resistance.

(c) Write a differential equation, using the displacement x as the dependent variable (the upper variable in the derivative form), expressing mathematically the statement that the sum of the spring, inertial, and friction forces equals zero (D'Alembert's principle).

(d) Show that the equation obtained in part c can be derived by differentiation of the equation written in part b.

1-16 A mass of 1 slug starts from rest and moves on a level surface subject to a force of 1 lb. The frictional resistance is known from previous measurement to be 1 slug/sec. Equating the applied force to the sum of the inertial and friction forces, solve for the acceleration dv/dt in terms of D, M, v, and f.

Find the initial acceleration from the condition that $v = 0$ at $t = 0$. Assume that this value of acceleration prevails for, say, $\frac{1}{5}$ sec. At the end of this time find the new velocity and the new acceleration; assume that this value of acceleration holds for a second time interval. Find the velocity and acceleration after the second time interval, and proceed in this fashion to plot a curve of velocity vs. time. (The acceleration, being the slope of the velocity curve, can be evaluated graphically.)

1-17   In the analysis of a system, the following differential equation is obtained, involving the displacement x as a function of time:

$$\frac{d^2x}{dt^2} + x = 0$$

In addition, it is known that at time $t = 0$ the velocity dx/dt is 0 and the displacement x is 1.

Assume a solution in the form of a power series with undetermined coefficients. Substitute this into the equation and evaluate the coefficients. Sketch the sum of the first four terms of the series as a function of time up to time $t = 4$.

1-5   SOLUTION OF AN INTRODUCTORY PROBLEM

To return to the mechanical system of Fig. 1-15, let us assume that at some instant (say $t = 0$) the automobile passes a certain point with velocity V ft/sec. The velocity at any later time is then given by Eq. (1-36).

The acceleration is the rate of change, or the derivative, of the velocity,

$$\frac{dv}{dt} = -\frac{DV}{M} e^{-Dt/M} \tag{1-37}$$

It is seen to be negative, indicating that the velocity decreases with increasing time.

In a short interval of time of length Δt, the automobile travels a differential distance $v \, \Delta t$, where v is the average velocity during that time interval. Thus the distance traveled at a time t is the sum of these differential distances. This sum takes the form of an integral if the lengths of the time intervals are made very small:

$$x = \Sigma v \, \Delta t = \int Ve^{-Dt/M} \, dt$$
$$= -\frac{M}{D} Ve^{-Dt/M} + \text{constant} \tag{1-38}$$

The value of this constant depends upon the reference point which has been chosen for distance measurement. At time $t = 0$ the distance which has been traveled from the starting point is, of course, zero. If this starting point is taken as the reference $x = 0$, we find, by substituting $x = 0$ and $t = 0$ in Eq. (1-38), that the constant has

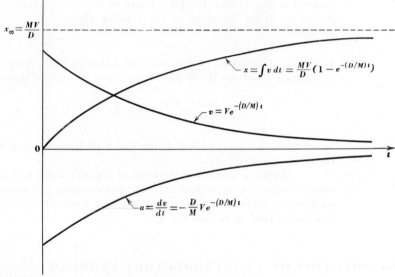

Fig. 1-18. Velocity, acceleration, and distance expressions plotted as functions of time for the mechanical system of Fig. 1-15.

the value MV/D. The distance expression thus becomes

$$x = \frac{MV}{D}(1 - e^{-Dt/M}) \qquad (1\text{-}39)$$

These expressions are shown plotted in Fig. 1-18.

A numerical example will help us visualize what the mathematical expressions tell us about the behavior of this particular system. Suppose we have an automobile with a mass of 50 slugs and we wish to measure the frictional resistance D. The car is driven on a level road at a velocity of 30 mph (44 ft/sec). At the instant it passes a reference point the clutch is disengaged. It then coasts to a stop 880 ft from the reference point.

The distance as a function of time is expressed in Eq. (1-39). The final distance x_∞ at which the velocity decreases to zero (never quite becoming zero in the ideal case) is seen to be MV/D. From this the frictional resistance is calculated to be

$$D = \frac{MV}{x_\infty} = \frac{(50)(44)}{880} = 2.5 \text{ slugs/sec} \qquad (1\text{-}40)$$

MOTIONAL IMPEDANCE Let us look at this introductory problem once more from a slightly different viewpoint. Note that if an exponential form is assumed for the velocity ($v = Ve^{st}$), the applied force required to produce this velocity is

$$\text{Applied force} = (sM + D)Ve^{st} \qquad (1\text{-}41)$$

The quantity $sM + D$ is the ratio of applied force to velocity *if* the velocity varies exponentially with time. This quantity is a measure of the amount the system elements conspire to impede the motion; it is often called the mechanical or motional *impedance*.

If it was desired, for example, to have the velocity increase as

$$v = Ve^{\alpha t} \qquad (1\text{-}42)$$

the necessary applied force could be obtained by multiplying this velocity by the impedance. The appropriate value for s would have to be used, of course—in this case, the constant α. Thus (see Fig. 1-19)

$$\text{Applied force} = (\alpha M + D)Ve^{\alpha t} \qquad (1\text{-}43)$$

Now, under what conditions can we have motion without the application of external force? Apparently only if the impedance—the ratio of required force to velocity—is zero. That is, we find out what values of s permit motion without applied force by setting the impedance $sM + D$ equal to zero.

The exponential form obtained as a solution to the system equation (1-20) is termed the *natural behavior* of the system—the behavior in the absence of external forces. This might also be called the *free* or *force-free* behavior or mode of behavior.

The type of solution exemplified by Eq. (1-43), on the other hand, is termed *forced behavior*—behavior in response to externally applied forces. Both types of behavior may be present simultaneously, as we shall see later.

The natural behavior of linear circuits and systems is exponential in character; we shall enlarge upon this statement as we go along. The natural, or *characteristic*, values for s ($-D/M$ in this first example) are determined from an algebraic equation in s. In this introductory example we have seen that this *characteristic equation* may be obtained in

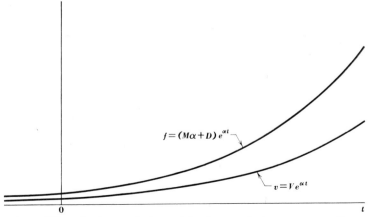

Fig. 1-19. A possible velocity variation with time and the corresponding applied force for the mechanical system of Fig. 1-15.

three ways, expressing, in a sense, three levels of sophistication regarding linear system analysis:

1. The law of conservation of energy may be applied, yielding Eq. (1-21).
2. D'Alembert's principle may be invoked, giving Eq. (1-20).
3. The motional-impedance concept may be utilized, by setting the impedance equal to zero in the absence of an applied force, to write Eq. (1-35) directly.

The motional impedance as used here is a particular example of a powerful conceptual tool in dealing with linear and nearly linear systems—the *system function*. This is a general term which we shall take to indicate the ratio of one system variable to another when both are varying as e^{st}. As stated above, the motional impedance utilized in this exercise is one example; electrical impedance as introduced in the next section is another, as is the transfer function defined in Sec. 7-1. Most of our efforts in succeeding chapters will be devoted to developing and exploiting this system-function concept.

PROBLEM

1-18   A current-carrying inductor may store a considerable amount of energy. When it is desired to disconnect such an inductor, it is necessary to take precautions to ensure that dangerously high voltages will not occur at the moment of disconnecting, when the rate of change of current is highest.

Consider an inductance L carrying a current I_0. At time $t = 0$ a switch is closed so that a resistance R is connected across the inductance, and immediately thereafter the connection to the source is opened. Thus the initial condition in the RL circuit is $i = I_0$ at $t = 0$.

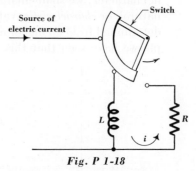

Fig. P 1-18

(a) Write the differential equation governing the behavior of a circuit consisting of a resistance R and an inductance L in series. Solve for the current as a function of time by assuming a solution in exponential form and applying the known initial condition.

(b) Assume a value for L of 1 henry. What value of resistance R will be required so that the voltage across the inductor will never exceed 1,000 volts? The initial current I_0 is 10 amp.

For this value of resistance, plot the voltage across the inductor as a function of time.

natural behavior
of networks

Following the approach specified earlier, let us now undertake a group of analyses of increasing complexity. Some of these will be discussed here; others will be left as problems. Each of the analyses undertaken will lead to an extension of the methods used, and the power to solve new problems will grow out of these experiences. Every so often we shall stop to sum up these experiences and to formulate our knowledge.

2-1 NATURAL BEHAVIOR OF A SIMPLE ELECTRICAL CIRCUIT

The first system we shall study is a possible application of the electrical network of Fig. 2-1.

In the most common type of radar a burst of high-frequency energy lasting for a very short time—about a millionth of a second—is emitted at periodic intervals. A fraction of this energy is reflected from the object being detected and received back at the radar. A measurement is made of the time it takes the signal to travel to the target and return, and this provides a determination of the distance to the target. In order for the transmitter vacuum tube to provide the required burst of radio-frequency energy, a very high voltage must be applied to it for a very short time.

Figure 2-1 shows a capacitor connected, through a switch, to a resistor (the resistor in this case representing the transmitting tube of the radar). If the capacitor is charged to a high voltage and the switch is then closed, a very high current will flow through the resistor for a short period of time, until the capacitor is discharged. Hence the voltage across the resistance (which is simply R times the current) will be high for a short time interval. Let us suppose it is desired to investigate the suitability of this circuit for the radar application mentioned.

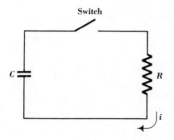

Switch

C R i

Fig. 2-1. Resistance-capacitance circuit for producing a voltage pulse.

THE NETWORK EQUATION   The first step is to write the governing differential equation for the network. From this we can learn how the system behaves and determine whether it will be suitable for the application specified.

Let us assume a positive flow of current to be in the direction indicated in Fig. 2-1. It must be emphasized that this has nothing whatever to do with the way the current actually flows. The direction of current flow is by definition the direction in which positive charge is transferred. Electrical conduction in metals is due to electron flow (or, more accurately, to a very slow average drift velocity superimposed upon relatively high random velocities), and electrons have a negative charge. Thus, the direction of current flow is in the opposite direction to the drift velocity of the electrons.† The actual direction of current flow is usually unknown at the outset; furthermore, the current flow may reverse direction any number of times. The direction of positive current flow is assumed only for the purpose of writing the network equations. The ultimate physical significance is that a positive value of current at any instant implies instantaneous current flow in the direction indicated; a negative value implies current in the opposite direction.

We wish to be able to write $i = dq/dt$, or

$$q = \int dq = \int i \, dt \tag{2-1}$$

Thus, by arbitrarily selecting the direction of current flow which we shall call positive, we determine the signs corresponding to a positive charge on the capacitor. Since a positive current flow will tend to build up a positive-charge accumulation on the lower capacitor plate and a

---

† This drift velocity is typically a minute fraction of an inch per second, compared with velocities of thousands of miles per second for electrons in typical vacuum tubes. Electrical conduction in gases or liquids may be due in part to the motion of positively charged particles which move in the opposite direction to the electron flow.

    Since most electrical conduction is electronic, it would have been slightly more convenient had the electronic charge been taken as positive. However, the terms *positive* charge and *negative* charge had been settled upon for well over a century before the existence of the electron and its role in conduction were demonstrated.

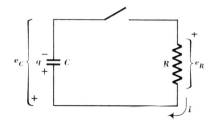

Fig. 2-2. Circuit of Fig. 2-1, showing as-
sumed positive directions of currents
and voltages.

negative-charge accumulation on the upper capacitor plate, this
capacitor charge must be taken to be positive. The directions of positive voltage drops due to positive current flow are thus determined as
indicated in Fig. 2-2.

To write the differential equation, we invoke *Kirchhoff's law*, the
electrical analogue of D'Alembert's principle. Kirchhoff's law states
that the applied voltage is equal to the sum of the voltage drops about
a closed loop.† This gives the desired equation:

$$e_R + e_C = Ri + \frac{1}{C} \int i \, dt = 0 \qquad (2\text{-}2)$$

For the mechanical system studied in Sec. 1-4 we found that the
network equation could be written either by summing forces or by
using an energy relation. A similar situation exists here—Eq. (2-2)
can be obtained by equating the sum of the resistor power loss and the
time rate of change of stored energy to zero (by conservation of energy):

$$Ri^2 + \frac{d}{dt}\left(\frac{1}{2}\frac{q^2}{C}\right) = 0 \qquad (2\text{-}3)$$

Performing the indicated differentiation and factoring out the common
term $i = dq/dt$ yield Eq. (2-2).

THE SOLUTION   We wish to find for the current a mathematical solution
which will satisfy Eq. (2-2) for all instants of time. Inspection of this
equation reveals that its solution must be in the form of a function
whose integral also has this form. Again the suitability of the exponential function is indicated. Hence we assume

$$i = Ie^{st} \qquad (2\text{-}4)$$

where I and s are constants to be determined.

Substitution of this assumed solution into Eq. (2-2) results in

$$\left(R + \frac{1}{sC}\right)Ie^{st} = 0 \qquad (2\text{-}5)$$

† This statement assumes that there is no time-varying magnetic
flux threading the loop other than that accounted for by the lumped
inductances of the coils in the loop.

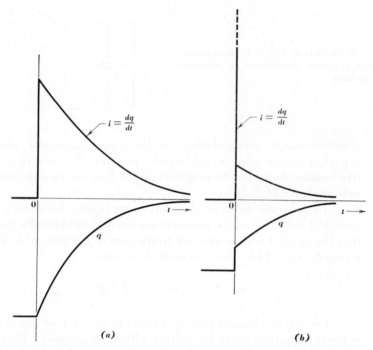

Fig. 2-3. *The charge on a capacitor may vary as in part a but not as in part b, since an infinite current through the resistor would require infinite power and is physically impossible.*

Setting the quantity $R + 1/sC$ equal to zero yields

$$s = \frac{-1}{RC} \tag{2-6}$$

Notice that the characteristic number s depends only upon the network. On the other hand, the constant I can be determined only after we specify the *initial conditions.*

Let us assume that the capacitor C was initially charged to a voltage $-E_0$, corresponding to an initial charge $Q_0 = -CE_0$. (From Fig. 2-2 we can see that a negative charge will cause the current to flow initially in a positive direction.) Let the switch be closed at a time $t = 0$. The instant the switch is closed, a current begins to flow, and this current is the time rate of change of the capacitor charge. It is apparent that the charge cannot change instantaneously, since this would require infinite current flow (Fig. 2-3), and thus *just after* the switch is closed (let us call this time $t = 0_+$), the charge must still be the value Q_0, and the capacitor voltage must be $Q_0/C = -E_0$.

The sum of the capacitor and resistor voltages must be zero, as previously noted. Thus

$$(e_C + e_R)_{t=0_+} = -E_0 + Ri_{t=0_+} = 0 \tag{2-7}$$

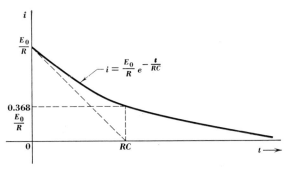

Fig. 2-4. Current flow in the circuit of Fig. 2-2.

This may be solved for the current $i_{t=0_+}$ [$= I$, from Eq. (2-4)], and thus the final solution becomes (see Fig. 2-4)

$$i = \frac{E_0}{R} e^{-t/RC} \qquad (2\text{-}8)$$

The voltage across the resistor is

$$e_R = iR = E_0 e^{-t/RC} \qquad (2\text{-}9)$$

After the switch is closed, the capacitor voltage e_C is equal to the negative of the resistor voltage e_R, as is apparent from Eq. (2-2). To check our results, we might find the capacitor voltage and verify this:

$$e_C = \frac{1}{C} \int i \, dt = \frac{1}{C} \int \frac{E_0}{R} e^{-t/RC} \, dt$$
$$= -E_0 e^{-t/RC} \qquad (2\text{-}10)$$

These results are plotted in Fig. 2-5.

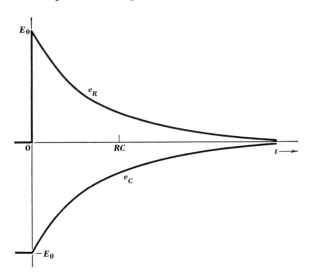

Fig. 2-5. Resistor and capacitor voltage drops in the circuit of Fig. 2-2.

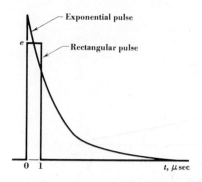

Fig. 2-6. Comparison of exponential pulse with an idealized rectangular pulse.

Note that at $t = RC$ sec the resistor voltage has already dropped to $e^{-1} = 0.368$ of its initial value. This is a convenient measure of the length of time the voltage pulse lasts (some such arbitrary measure is needed, since theoretically the voltage is different from zero for an infinite length of time). This time measure, RC sec, is customarily called the *time constant* of the circuit.

We are now in a position partially to answer the question of the suitability of this circuit for the radar application originally discussed. A voltage pulse might be desired which would be constant for, say, 1 μsec and which would be zero thereafter (Fig. 2-6). The pulse resulting from our simple circuit departs from this idealized rectangular shape rather seriously. Other circuits can be devised which give output pulses approaching the rectangular form much more closely.

If it should be decided, however, that the exponential pulse shape is satisfactory, we can easily design the network. Suppose the initial voltage is to be 10,000 volts and the resistor representing the transmitting tube is 100 ohms. Then, from Eq. (2-8), the initial current is 100 amp. If the time constant is to be 1 μsec, the capacitor must have the value 0.01 μf. The initial stored energy is $\frac{1}{2}CE_0^2 = \frac{1}{2}$ joule. The initial rate at which power flows into the resistor is $I^2R = 10^6$ watts (1,000 kw). If the entire cycle is repeated 1,000 times a second (a typical value), the average power is $\frac{1}{2}$ joule/msec, or 500 watts.

ELECTRICAL IMPEDANCE Before leaving this problem, let us reexamine it from a slightly different standpoint. Note that if an exponential

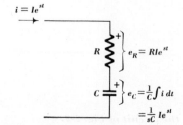

Fig. 2-7. RC circuit with assumed exponential form for the current flow.

form $i = Ie^{st}$ is assumed for the current through a resistance R and a capacitance C in series, then the total voltage across the RC combination, and hence the voltage required to produce this current, is

$$e = \left(R + \frac{1}{sC} \right) Ie^{st} \tag{2-11}$$

(see Fig. 2-7).†

The quantity $R + 1/sC$ in Eq. (2-11) is the ratio of total voltage to current *if* the current varies exponentially with time. This quantity is a measure of the amount that the circuit elements conspire to impede the current flow, and we call it the electrical *impedance*.

Under what conditions can we have current flow without any applied voltage? Only if the impedance—the ratio of required voltage to current—is zero. We determine the values of s that will permit natural behavior—current flow without any applied voltage—by setting the impedance equal to zero. In the present example this results in Eq. (2-6).

The electrical impedance **Z** of an electrical network element is defined as the ratio of applied voltage to current *if* the current varies as e^{st}. For the three types of electrical network elements, the impedances are

Resistance	R
Inductance	sL
Capacitance	$\dfrac{1}{sC}$

In Fig. 2-2 the resistance and capacitance are so connected (in series) that the total voltage drop across the two elements is the sum of the individual voltage drops. Thus the impedance of the two elements in series is the sum of the two individual impedances.

The concepts of electrical and mechanical impedance functions will be elaborated and extended as succeeding examples are taken up.

P R O B L E M S

2-1   (a) Consider the exponential current pulse of Fig. 2-4. Obtain an expression for the charge on the capacitor by integrating the current expression. (Note that the constant of integration must be adjusted to give the proper value of charge at $t = 0$.) What fraction of the initial

---

† More precisely, since the indefinite integral in Eq. (2-2) is understood to mean $q = q_0 + \int_0^t i\, dt$, Eq. (2-11) contains the implicit assumption that $q_0 = I/s$. Application of the voltage of Eq. (2-11) at $t = 0$ will result in the current Ie^{st} if the initial charge on the capacitor is I/s; if not, an additional term will be present as well.

charge remains at time $t = RC$ sec? What fraction of the original energy remains stored in the capacitor at $t = RC$?

(b) Obtain an expression for the instantaneous power flow into the resistor. Integrate this to obtain an expression for the total energy dissipated in the resistor at any time. (Note that the constant of integration must be adjusted to give zero energy dissipated at $t = 0$.) What fraction of the initial stored energy has been dissipated in the resistor by time $t = RC$ sec? Check this result with the result of part a.

(c) Plot the current as a function of time, as in Fig. 2-4. On the same time scale, sketch curves showing the fraction of the original energy which remains stored in the capacitor and the fraction converted to thermal energy in the resistor.

2-2   Consider a system consisting of a spring of compliance K connected to a dashpot of frictional resistance D. The spring is initially compressed an amount X_0 and released at time $t = 0$.

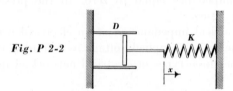

Fig. P 2-2

Write a differential equation expressing the fact that the sum of the spring and friction forces is equal to zero. Solve it by assuming an exponential solution. Sketch a plot of the spring displacement as a function of time.

2-3   The mechanical system of Fig. 1-15 has a motional impedance $sM + D$. Let $M = 50$ slugs and $D = 2.5$ slugs/sec.

(a) Suppose that it is desired to have the automobile move after time $t = 0$ with a velocity given by the expression

$$v = 50e^{-0.1t} - 50e^{-0.5t} \qquad \text{ft/sec}$$

Sketch a plot of this velocity vs. time. What will be the total distance traveled after a very long time?

(b) Find the force required to produce the first term in the velocity expression by multiplying this term by the appropriate value of motional impedance. Similarly, find the force corresponding to the second term. The force required to produce the given velocity is the sum of these two components. Sketch a plot of this force as a function of time.

(c) Check by comparing this result with the force obtained by substituting the expression for v in the differential equation

$$f = M\frac{dv}{dt} + Dv$$

2-4   An electrical circuit consisting of a resistance R and an inductance L in series has an impedance $sL + R$. Let $R = 10$ ohms and $L = 0.1$ henry. Suppose that it is desired to produce a current pulse, starting at $t = 0$, described by the expression

$$i = 5e^{-100t} - 5e^{-500t} \qquad \text{amp}$$

Making use of the concept of electrical impedance, find the voltage corresponding to each of the two current terms and compute the required applied voltage, which is the sum of these two components.

Plot the current and voltage as functions of time.

2-2   NATURAL OSCILLATIONS IN A MECHANICAL SYSTEM

The study of a vibrating system such as the mass and spring in Fig. 2-8 should prove to be most interesting. This two-element network might represent any of a multitude of devices, ranging from a vibration damper to a pogo stick.

The physical behavior is well known. If the mass is displaced from its rest position, resulting in energy storage due to compression or extension of the spring, and then released, the system will oscillate at its natural resonant frequency. That is, the mass will move back and forth through its rest (zero-stored-energy) position, the initial energy being stored alternately as potential energy in the spring and as kinetic energy in the moving mass.

THE SYSTEM EQUATION   In order to emphasize that we are learning successively more sophisticated methods of procedure, let us study this system from three approaches, which we may designate by the three words *energy, force,* and *impedance.* As we shall see, they are all equivalent.

First, we may write an equation expressing the fact that if no energy is added to the network after the initial energy storage and if no energy is lost through friction, the total energy in the network remains constant. Thus the time rate of change of the sum of kinetic

Fig. 2-8. Mass-and-spring oscillating mechanical system.

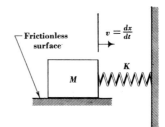

and potential energies is zero:

$$\frac{d}{dt}\left(\frac{1}{2}Mv^2 + \frac{1}{2}\frac{1}{K}x^2\right) = 0 \tag{2-12}$$

Performing the indicated differentiation yields

$$Mv\frac{dv}{dt} + \frac{1}{K}x\frac{dx}{dt} = 0 \tag{2-13}$$

Now $x = \int v\, dt$, and $v = dx/dt$ is seen to be a factor common to both terms. Thus Eq. (2-13) may be rewritten

$$M\frac{dv}{dt} + \frac{1}{K}\int v\, dt = 0 \tag{2-14}$$

Referring to Fig. 1-14, we see that this equation could have been written directly by making use of the second approach, that is, by applying D'Alembert's principle that the sum of the reaction forces is equal to the applied force.

To solve Eq. (2-14), we assume an exponential solution $v = Ve^{st}$, thus obtaining

$$\left(sM + \frac{1}{sK}\right)Ve^{st} = 0 \tag{2-15}$$

Setting the first factor equal to zero results in

$$sM + \frac{1}{sK} = 0 \tag{2-16}$$

But now we see that this equation could have been written directly by a third approach employing the impedance concept. The motional impedance of an element is the ratio of force to velocity, assuming both quantities to vary exponentially (as e^{st}) with time. Thus for the three types of mechanical system elements the impedances are

Frictional resistance	D
Mass	sM
Compliance	$\dfrac{1}{sK}$

For the system of Fig. 2-8 the impedance is

$$Z_m = sM + \frac{1}{sK} \tag{2-17}$$

If motion is to be present without applied force, the motional impedance must be zero—hence Eq. (2-16).

Thus the natural behavior of the system results when the characteristic number s satisfies Eq. (2-16):

$$s = \pm\sqrt{-\frac{1}{MK}} \tag{2-18}$$

We are brought to a sudden halt by the appearance of a square root of a negative number. This result can be written, alternatively, as

$$s = \pm j \sqrt{\frac{1}{MK}} \tag{2-19}$$

where j indicates $\sqrt{-1}$. However, this is not a very satisfying sort of quantity to have appearing in a result which presumably represents some sort of physical behavior. Numbers preceded by j are the so-called "imaginary" numbers, and the physical things we are dealing with are very real indeed.

EXPONENTIAL AND TRIGONOMETRIC FUNCTIONS   Since this exponential with an imaginary exponent has forced itself to our attention, we had better find out what sort of function it is. Rewriting the series definition for the exponential function, Eq. (1-25), for the case of an imaginary exponent, we find

$$e^{j\theta} = 1 + j\theta + \frac{(j\theta)^2}{2!} + \frac{(j\theta)^3}{3!} + \frac{(j\theta)^4}{4!} + \cdots \tag{2-20}$$

One of the best ways to become familiar with a new function is to represent it graphically in some fashion. It is conventional to plot imaginary numbers as ordinates and real, or ordinary, numbers as abscissas. Note that, since $j = \sqrt{-1}$,

$$\begin{array}{ll} j^2 = -1 & j^3 = (-1) \times j = -j \\ j^4 = (-1)^2 = 1 & j^5 = j \times j^4 = j \end{array} \tag{2-21}$$

and so on. Thus

$$e^{j\theta} = 1 + j\theta - \frac{\theta^2}{2!} - j\frac{\theta^3}{3!} + \frac{\theta^4}{4!} + \cdots \tag{2-22}$$

This series representation tells us to go a distance 1 to the east, then turn and go a distance θ to the north, $\theta^2/2!$ to the west, $\theta^3/3!$ south, and so on (Fig. 2-9). If this is done carefully, we find that $e^{j\theta}$ is

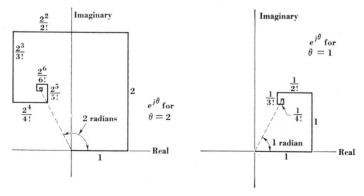

Fig. 2-9. *Graphical representation of the series for $e^{j\theta}$ for two values of θ.*

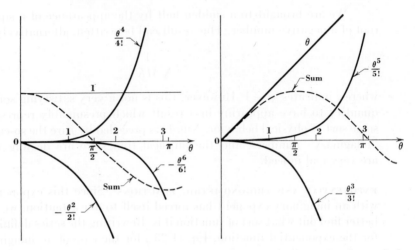

Fig. 2-10. Graphical representation of the real and imaginary portions of the series for $e^{j\theta}$.

equivalent to directions to proceed a distance 1 in a direction making an angle of θ radians with the real axis. (Curiouser and curiouser, as Alice would say!)

Taking another look at Eq. (2-22), we see that we can group the terms in the following way:

$$e^{j\theta} = \left(1 - \frac{\theta^2}{2!} + \frac{\theta^4}{4!} - \frac{\theta^6}{6!} + \cdots\right) + j\left(\theta - \frac{\theta^3}{3!} + \frac{\theta^5}{5!} - \frac{\theta^7}{7!} + \cdots\right)$$
(2-23)

The real and imaginary parts of Eq. (2-23) are plotted against θ in Fig. 2-10 and are seen to look surprisingly like the cos θ and sin θ functions. Indeed, if we reflect that $e^{j\theta}$ is (or, more accurately, may be represented by) a line of unit length rotated from the real axis by an angle of θ radians, we see by a simple geometrical consideration (Fig. 2-11) that the real and imaginary parts are cos θ and sin θ, respectively.

Thus we have the following mathematical identities:†

$$\cos \theta = 1 - \frac{\theta^2}{2!} + \frac{\theta^4}{4!} - \frac{\theta^6}{6!} \cdots$$
(2-24)

$$\sin \theta = \theta - \frac{\theta^3}{3!} + \frac{\theta^5}{5!} - \frac{\theta^7}{7!} \cdots$$
(2-25)

$$e^{j\theta} = \cos \theta + j \sin \theta$$
(2-26)

† Equations (2-24) and (2-25) can be derived, alternatively, by assuming a power-series representation such as Eq. (1-23) for the functions sin θ and cos θ. The values for the unknown coefficients in the series can be obtained by successively differentiating these series (noting that the derivative of cos θ is − sin θ and that the derivative of sin θ is cos θ) and setting $\theta = 0$ in each of the derivative expressions.

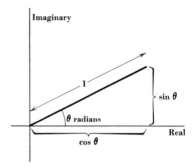

Fig. 2-11. Relation between $e^{j\theta}$ and the trigonometric functions.

Equation (2-26) is known as Euler's identity. The following additional identities are easily obtained:

$$e^{-j\theta} = \cos\theta - j\sin\theta \qquad (2\text{-}27)$$
$$e^{j\theta} + e^{-j\theta} = 2\cos\theta \qquad (2\text{-}28)$$
$$e^{j\theta} - e^{-j\theta} = 2j\sin\theta \qquad (2\text{-}29)$$

BACK TO THE PHYSICAL SYSTEM Returning to the physical system under discussion, let us, for the sake of brevity, introduce the symbol

$$\omega \text{ (omega) } = \sqrt{\frac{1}{MK}} \qquad (2\text{-}30)$$

The two values of s which give the natural behavior of the system are, then, $j\omega$ and $-j\omega$. Both $e^{j\omega t}$ and $e^{-j\omega t}$ satisfy the system differential equation (2-14).

Equations of the sort we have encountered here, in which the derivatives or integrals appear only to the first power [there are no terms like $(dx/dt)^2$ or $\sqrt{dx/dt}$], are called *linear differential* or *integro-differential* equations. Linear equations have the general property that if f_1 and f_2 are individually solutions of the equation, $Af_1 + Bf_2$ is also a solution, where A and B are any constants. This follows from the rule for differentiating a sum,

$$\frac{d}{dt}(f_1 + f_2) = \frac{df_1}{dt} + \frac{df_2}{dt} \qquad (2\text{-}31)$$

and this property is termed the *superposition* property.

We want the most general solution to Eq. (2-14), so we shall take a sum or superposition of the two possible solutions, each multiplied by a constant, which is, as yet, unknown:

$$\begin{aligned}
v &= A'e^{j\omega t} + B'e^{-j\omega t} \\
&= A'(\cos\omega t + j\sin\omega t) + B'(\cos\omega t - j\sin\omega t) \\
&= (A' + B')\cos\omega t + j(A' - B')\sin\omega t \\
&= A\cos\omega t + B\sin\omega t \qquad (2\text{-}32)
\end{aligned}$$

This last form is the most convenient for our use.

Observing that ωt apparently is in units of radians, we may conclude that ω is in units of radians per second. Thus, if $M = 1$ slug and $K = 1$ ft/lb, ω will be 1 radian/sec. Since a complete revolution of the line in Fig. 2-11 amounts to an increase in angle of 2π radians and since this corresponds to a complete alternation of $\cos \omega t$ from 1 to -1 and back again, we see that the frequency of alternation in this case is $1/2\pi$ alternations, or cycles, per second. In general, the frequency of oscillation is $\omega/2\pi$ cps.

In order to evaluate the constants A and B, we need some knowledge of the starting conditions. Suppose, for example, that the spring is compressed by a displacement x_0 and that the system is released from a stationary condition at time $t = 0$. If the velocity of the mass is zero just before it is released, it must still be zero the instant *after* release, since an instantaneous change in velocity would imply instantaneously infinite acceleration and, hence, infinite force. This is a little more than we usually have available.

Thus the initial conditions at time $t = 0_+$ are

$$x = x_0 \quad \text{and} \quad v = \frac{dx}{dt} = 0 \qquad (2\text{-}33)$$

Substituting $v = 0$ and $t = 0$ into Eq. (2-32) immediately yields the information that the constant A equals zero. Thus

$$v = B \sin \omega t \qquad (2\text{-}34)$$

Distance is the integral of velocity:

$$x = \int v\, dt + \text{constant} = -\frac{B}{\omega} \cos \omega t + \text{constant} \qquad (2\text{-}35)$$

If $x = 0$ is chosen as the average position, the constant is made zero. Now, substituting $t = 0$ and $x = x_0$, we find

$$B = -\omega x_0 \qquad (2\text{-}36)$$

Thus the final solutions are

$$x = x_0 \cos \omega t \qquad (2\text{-}37)$$
$$v = -\omega x_0 \sin \omega t \qquad (2\text{-}38)$$

These are plotted in Fig. 2-12.

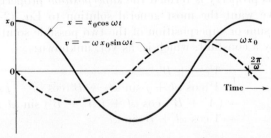

Fig. 2-12. *Instantaneous displacement and velocity of the mass in Fig. 2-8.*

In the process of obtaining these solutions, various *complex* quantities (having both real and imaginary parts) appeared. It is reassuring to see that the final solutions, representing physically real quantities, are wholly real mathematically (and, furthermore, agree qualitatively with the expected physical behavior of the system). That this would be so was to be expected, for we should have been at a loss to know what physical significance to attach to an imaginary quantity if one had shown up in the final solution.

PROBLEMS

2-5 An electrical circuit consists of an inductance L and a capacitance C connected together through a switch. The capacitor is charged to a voltage E_0 and the switch is closed at time $t = 0$.

(*a*) What is the impedance of the closed loop? Find the allowed values of the characteristic number s corresponding to the natural behavior of the system.

Fig. P 2-5

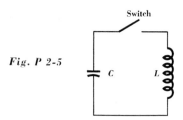

(*b*) Write an expression for the current as a function of time. [The general expression will contain two arbitrary constants. These constants can be evaluated from the initial conditions at $t = 0$, namely, the known capacitor voltage and the fact that the current remains zero the instant after the switch is closed. (Why?)]

(*c*) For the values $L = 1$ henry, $C = 1$ μf (10^{-6} farad), and $E_0 = 100$ volts, plot with suitable scales the instantaneous current flow as a function of time.

2-6 (*a*) A mass of 2 kg is suspended from a helical spring and found to extend it 6 cm. Compute the natural period of oscillation of the system consisting of the mass and spring. Attempt to do this without making use of the information about the numerical value of the mass. (The gravitational force exerted upon a mass M kg is Mg newtons, where g is the gravitational acceleration, approximately 9.8 m/sec².)

(*b*) Assume that the mass is released from the level at which the spring is unextended and that it is allowed to oscillate vertically. Sketch a plot of the position of the mass and its velocity as functions of time. At what position does the maximum velocity occur, and what is its value? How does this compare with the value that the velocity would have at this position if the mass had been allowed to fall freely instead of being attached to the spring?

2-3 PRELIMINARY SUMMARY OF NATURAL BEHAVIOR

Thus far we have examined some simple systems, both mechanical and electrical—so simple, in fact, that each contained but two network elements. As a further limitation, the investigation of these networks has been restricted to the phenomena which occur when there are no externally applied forces or sources of energy; in other words, we have been concerned only with the so-called "natural behavior" of the system.

In each of the networks studied, a quantity has been defined which is termed the impedance. The impedances of the three linear electrical network elements R, L, and C, *defined as the ratio of voltage to current when both are varying as* e^{st}, are R, sL, and $1/sC$, respectively. When two (or more) of these elements are connected in series so that the same electric current is common to all, the voltage across the combination is the sum of the element voltages (Fig. 2-13). Hence the impedance of the series combination is the sum of the element impedances.

The natural behavior of an electrical circuit consisting of two (or more) elements connected in a closed loop can be found by setting the total impedance of the loop equal to zero. (This follows from the fact that current flow cannot occur in the absence of a driving voltage unless the loop impedance is zero.) From the resulting equation we can obtain the characteristic numbers s which characterize the natural behavior of the system.

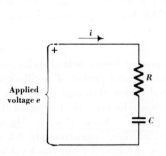

Step 1. The differential equation is

$$e = Ri + \frac{1}{C} \int i \, dt$$

Step 2. If $e = E e^{st}$ and $i = I e^{st}$,

$$\mathbf{Z} \triangleq \frac{e}{i} = \frac{E e^{st}}{I e^{st}} = R + \frac{1}{sC}$$

Step 3. For natural behavior ($e = 0$)

$$\mathbf{Z} = 0 \qquad s = -\frac{1}{RC}$$

Step 4. Thus

$$i = A e^{-(1/RC)t}$$

Fig. 2-13. *Summary of the investigation of natural behavior of a simple electrical network.*

Step 1. The differential equation is

$$f = M\frac{dv}{dt} + \frac{1}{K}\int v\, dt$$

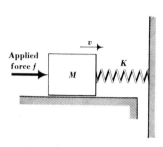

Step 2. If $f = Fe^{st}$ and $v = Ve^{st}$,

$$\mathbf{Z}_m \triangleq \frac{f}{v} = \frac{Fe^{st}}{Ve^{st}} = sM + \frac{1}{sK}$$

Step 3. For natural behavior $(f = 0)$

$$\mathbf{Z}_m = 0 \qquad s = \pm j\,\frac{1}{\sqrt{MK}} = \pm j\omega$$

Step 4. Thus

$$v = A'e^{j\omega t} + B'e^{-j\omega t}$$

Fig. 2-14. Summary of the investigation of natural behavior of a simple mechanical network.

The impedance of a mechanical network element is defined as *the ratio of force to velocity when both quantities vary with time as* e^{st}. The impedances of the three mechanical network elements D, M, and K are D, sM, and $1/sK$, respectively. If two (or more) of these elements are combined into a one-dimensional translational system in such a way that the velocity associated with each element is the same while the applied force is equal to the sum of the element forces (Fig. 2-14), then the impedance of the over-all network is the sum of the element impedances. The natural behavior, the behavior when the applied force is zero, is found by setting this impedance equal to zero. The characteristic values of s so obtained indicate the nature of the motion of the system in the absence of any applied force.

The characteristic numbers s have dimensions of seconds^{-1} and completely characterize the natural behavior of the system. Thus, as we have found, the natural behavior of a system in which s is real (and negative) is a current or velocity which decays exponentially with time. Imaginary values of s indicate sinusoidal oscillations.

Table 2-1 summarizes the information we have obtained thus far. As with any complex numbers, the values of these characteristic numbers (the *zeros* of the impedance) can be conveniently represented graphically by plotting the real part of s (σ) as abscissa and the imaginary part $(j\omega)$ as ordinate. They are so indicated by small circles in Table 2-1. For completeness, the values of s at which the impedance is infinite (called *poles*) are indicated by small crosses. These graphical representations will take on more meaning, and their use will become more apparent, as we proceed.

In later chapters we shall apply these methods to more complicated and interesting networks than the two-element combinations studied thus far. First, however, we shall investigate in the next chapter how these methods can be extended to take care of the case of externally applied forces and voltages.

TABLE 2-1 Summary of Natural Behavior of Two-element Systems

System	Schematic Drawing	System Differential Equation	Characteristic Equation (for Determining s)	Characteristic Numbers (and Plot on Complex-number Plane)	Natural Modes of Behavior
LR electric circuit		$L\dfrac{di}{dt} + Ri = 0$	$Z = sL + R = 0$	$s = -\dfrac{R}{L}$	$Ae^{-\frac{R}{L}t}$
M-D mechanical system		$M\dfrac{dv}{dt} + Dv = 0$	$Z_m = sM + D = 0$	$s = -\dfrac{D}{M}$	$Ae^{-\frac{D}{M}t}$
RC electric circuit		$Ri + \dfrac{1}{C}\displaystyle\int i\,dt = 0$	$Z = R + \dfrac{1}{sC} = 0$	$s = -\dfrac{1}{RC}$	$Ae^{-\frac{1}{RC}t}$
D-K mechanical system		$Dv + \dfrac{1}{K}\displaystyle\int v\,dt = 0$	$Z_m = D + \dfrac{1}{sK} = 0$	$s = -\dfrac{1}{DK}$	$Ae^{-\frac{1}{DK}t}$
LC electric circuit		$L\dfrac{di}{dt} + \dfrac{1}{C}\displaystyle\int i\,dt = 0$	$Z = sL + \dfrac{1}{sC} = 0$	$s = \pm j\dfrac{1}{\sqrt{LC}} = \pm j\omega_0$	$A\cos\omega_0 t + D\sin\omega_0 t$
M-K mechanical system		$M\dfrac{dv}{dt} + \dfrac{1}{K}\displaystyle\int v\,dt = 0$	$Z_m = sM + \dfrac{1}{sK} = 0$	$s = \pm j\dfrac{1}{\sqrt{MK}} = \pm j\omega_0$	$A\cos\omega_0 t + D\sin\omega_0 t$

2-4 DIMENSIONS AND CHECKING

In the discussion of units in Sec. 1-1, use was made of the principle that in any meaningful equation the terms equated must be the same sorts of things; they must have the same *dimensions*. Volts cannot be equated to amperes, nor feet to pounds. (Feet may be equated to centimeters, however, by inclusion of the proper conversion factor.) Following this principle, in the discussion of Eq. (2-10) we deduced that the product RC has the dimensions of time. Somewhat later, in Sec. 2-2, the quantity $1/\sqrt{MK}$ was interpreted as radians per second. The time has come to link these various statements with a more systematic summary of units and dimensions.[†]

UNITS AND DIMENSIONS   By *dimension* is meant an observable physical property, such as mass, length, time, or electric current. Measurement of a physical quantity consists in comparing it with some standard, or *unit*, of the same dimensions. Various systems of units are in use, but, as mentioned earlier, we shall discuss only two of these—the English and the mks. Thus, length is measured in feet or meters, mass in slugs or kilograms, etc.

In dealing with mechanical systems it is convenient to consider mass, length, and time to be fundamental dimensions.[‡] The dimensions of other quantities are then derived from basic relations interrelating these quantities. Force, for example, as is manifest from the relation $f = M \, dv/dt$, has dimensions of (mass)(length)(time)$^{-2}$. The units of force are slug-feet per second^2 in the English system or kilogram-meters per second^2 in the mks system.

Electrical quantities can be expressed in terms of the units of mass, length, time, and charge. For many purposes, however, it is slightly more convenient to take the fundamental units to be those of charge, time, and energy. (Of course, energy is, in turn, expressible in terms of mass, length, and time.) For example, the energy-storage expression for an inductance $\frac{1}{2}Li^2$ indicates that inductance has dimensions of (energy)(time)^2(charge)$^{-2}$. The dimensions of the mechanical and electrical quantities we have met so far are summarized in Table 2-2.

Consider now the quantity $1/\sqrt{MK}$. In the mks system, compliance K is expressed in meters per newton. Since a newton is a kilogram-meter per second^2, the unit of compliance may alternatively

---

† References that may be consulted for further investigation of this topic are mentioned in the Selected Bibliography.

‡ There is considerable arbitrariness in this choice of the three fundamental dimensions. Force, length, and time are sometimes used, and other choices are allowable though not so convenient in certain respects.

TABLE 2-2   *Units of Electrical and Mechanical Parameters*

Units of Mechanical System Quantities

	English System	MKS System	Dimensions
Distance	ft	m	L
Velocity	ft/sec	m/sec	LT^{-1}
Acceleration	ft/sec²	m/sec²	LT^{-2}
Mass	slugs	kg	M
Force	slug-ft/sec² (lb)	kg-m/sec² (newtons)	MLT^{-2}
Frictional resistance	slugs/sec	kg/sec	MT^{-1}
Compliance	ft/lb	m/newton	$M^{-1}T^2$
Energy	ft-lb	newton-m (joules)	ML^2T^{-2}

Units of Electrical Circuit Quantities

	MKS System	Dimensions
Charge	coulombs	Q
Current	coulombs/sec (amp)	QT^{-1}
Resistance	joule-sec/coulomb² (ohms)	$ML^2T^{-1}Q^{-2}$
Inductance	joule-sec²/coulomb² (henrys)	ML^2Q^{-2}
Capacitance	coulombs²/joule (farads)	$M^{-1}L^{-2}T^2Q^2$
Voltage	joules/coulomb (volts)	$ML^2T^{-2}Q^{-1}$

$$M = \text{mass}$$
$$L = \text{length}$$
$$T = \text{time}$$
$$Q = \text{charge}$$

be taken to be seconds² per kilogram. Mass M, of course, is measured in kilograms; the product MK thus is expressible in units of seconds² and $1/\sqrt{MK}$ in units of seconds⁻¹. (A radian is defined as the ratio of two lengths—an arc to a radius—and hence is dimensionless. Thus this result is compatible with the interpretation of $1/\sqrt{MK}$ as radians per second.)

Again, take the product RC. The dimensions of R, from the expression for power i^2R, are watts per ampere² or joule-seconds per coulomb². From the energy-storage expression for a capacitor $(q^2/2C)$, C is seen to be expressible in coulombs² per joule. Thus the product RC is, indeed, measurable in seconds.

DIMENSIONAL CHECKING These considerations lead to one of the most valuable methods for checking an analysis to detect possible errors. Since every equation in an analysis should be dimensionally homogeneous, constant checking of this point can disclose many types of errors and locate the point at which they occurred.

Suppose, for example, that we wish to find from the current expression Eq. (2-8) the energy which has been converted to heat in the resistor at any time. The power dissipation is i^2R, and an erroneous calculation yields the following expression for the total energy dissipation:

$$W = \int_0^t i^2R \, dt = \frac{E_0^2}{R} \int_0^t e^{-2t/RC} \, dt = \frac{E_0^2C}{2R} (1 - e^{-2t/RC}) \qquad (2\text{-}39)$$

Note, first of all, that the exponent $-2t/RC$ is dimensionless. Exponentials, trigonometric functions, logarithms, and similar mathematical functions are pure, dimensionless numbers. Likewise, their arguments are dimensionless. (Such an expression as $\log R_1 - \log R_2$ appears at first glance to be a violation of this. However, if the logarithmic terms are first gathered together as $\log (R_1/R_2)$, the statement holds.)

To continue the check, we find the units of the term E_0^2C/R to be

$$\frac{\text{volts}^2 \times \text{farads}}{\text{ohms}} = \frac{\text{joules}^2}{\text{coulombs}^2} \frac{\text{coulombs}^2}{\text{joules}} \frac{\text{coulombs}^2}{\text{joule-seconds}} \neq \text{joules}$$

Something is obviously wrong, and reexamination discloses an error in the integration; the result should be

$$W = \frac{E_0^2C}{2} (1 - e^{-2t/RC}) \qquad (2\text{-}40)$$

A second example will further emphasize the point. The equivalent resistance of two resistors R_1 and R_2 connected in *parallel* (so that they are subjected to the same voltage as in Fig. 2-15) is $R_1R_2/(R_1 + R_2)$. Fallacious reasoning extends this formula to give the equivalent resistance of three resistors in parallel as $R_1R_2R_3/(R_1 + R_2 + R_3)$. Dimensional checking shows this result to be absurd.

LIMITING-CASE CHECKING Too much emphasis cannot be placed on the necessity for checking results. Decimal points are misplaced, terms are mislaid, errors occur—occasionally even with automatic computing machines and frequently in operations involving the human brain. To err is human—to check and recheck is the mark of a good engineer. Reliability of results is essential in any engineering work, either analytical or experimental.

Experimental verification of the results of analysis is, of course, the most comprehensive and effective check of all. But since experi-

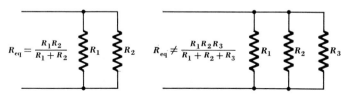

Fig. 2-15. Parallel connection of resistors—an example of dimensional checking.

ments are both costly and time-consuming, other means must be relied upon to a major extent. Among these is repetition of the analysis by an alternative method or by another person.

One of the most important of all checks is that of general reasonableness. Does the result make physical sense? Is it consistent with previous experience and knowledge? Results of a microsecond for the period of a pendulum or of a farad for the capacitance of an electrical circuit element should be viewed with suspicion. In retrospect, do the assumptions made in setting up the problem and the approximations made along the way seem justified? How do they limit the accuracy or applicability of the results?

A particularly valuable check of this sort is that of examining limiting cases of parameter values for which the correct result is known or can be easily found. For example, in Eq. (2-40), if either E_0 or C is set equal to zero, W becomes zero, which is reasonable, since in these limiting cases there is no stored energy to be dissipated. As t approaches infinity, the dissipated energy approaches $\frac{1}{2}CE_0^2$, which was the original stored energy; again this is what we expect. If R is made infinite (an open circuit) as a limiting case, the exponential becomes $e^0 = 1$, and the dissipated energy remains zero, as it should, since the capacitor now does not discharge.

Finally, if R is allowed to approach zero, we find that the final dissipated energy (as $t \rightarrow \infty$) does not approach zero, as we might have been tempted rashly to assume (since the power dissipation is i^2R). But this, too, can be reconciled with the physical situation, since reference to Eq. (2-8) indicates that the current approaches infinity as R approaches zero.

DIMENSIONLESS-RATIO PLOTTING   The result of an analysis will typically be a mathematical expression like Eq. (2-40). In the very conciseness of such an expression—embodying, as it does, a rather complete description of a physical phenomenon—lie both its value and its limitation. So much information may be contained in a brief mathematical formula that considerable interpretation may be necessary in order to comprehend its significance. For this reason the mathematical expression is usually not the terminus of the investigation. Rather, a graphical representation is often the most suitable means for presenting the results for interpretation and use.

Given values of the parameters E_0, C, and R, a plot of W versus t could certainly be made from Eq. (2-40). However, a change in any one of these quantities would necessitate replotting. Furthermore, it would not be apparent from these plots just how the magnitudes of the parameters affect the variation of W with time.

A much more useful plot can be obtained by forming dimensionless ratios involving the quantities of interest and plotting the equation

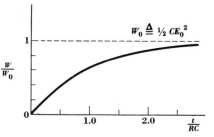

Fig. 2-16. Dimensionless-ratio plot of Eq. (2-40).

in terms of these. One way to do this is indicated in Fig. 2-16. Here the variable t is divided by a *normalizing*, or standardizing, quantity with the dimensions of time to form a dimensionless ratio. Similarly, the dissipated energy is *normalized* with respect to a quantity having the dimensions of energy; in this case an obvious choice is the original stored energy $W_0 = \frac{1}{2}CE_0^2$. The plot is made in terms of these dimensionless ratios.

This simple and compact representation has several advantages. In the first place, the results are presented in the most general form, applicable to any set of parameter values. The influence of the various parameters on the nature of the phenomenon is made apparent. (For example, making R very small results in an extremely high power flow, so that the stored energy is almost completely dissipated in a very short time interval.) Finally, it will usually be found that the numerical quantities encountered, when relations are put in a form involving dimensionless ratios, are of a convenient size—neither very large nor very small compared with unity.

The concepts discussed in this section will become clearer as they are applied to additional examples in succeeding chapters.

PROBLEMS

2-7   The following differential equation is obtained for the electrical circuit shown:

$$RL\frac{d^2i}{dt^2} + \frac{L}{C}\frac{di}{dt} + \frac{R}{C}i = L\frac{d^2e}{dt^2} + R\frac{de}{dt}$$

Check this equation to see that it is dimensionally correct. Indicate errors, if any.

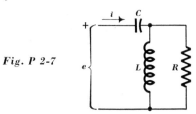

Fig. P 2-7

2-8   A two-conductor transmission line has a velocity of propagation of electromagnetic energy of $1/\sqrt{lc}$ m/sec, where l and c are the inductance and capacitance per meter length of line. Check this statement dimensionally.

2-9   Two bodies weighing W_1 and W_2 lb are interconnected by a spring and a dashpot, as shown. The two slide on a frictionless surface. A force f is applied to W_1, and as a result W_2 moves with a velocity $v(t)$; analysis shows that the two are related by the following differential equation:

$$\frac{W_1 W_2}{g^2}\frac{d^3v}{dt^3} + \frac{W_1 + W_2}{g}D\frac{d^2v}{dt^2} + \frac{W_1 + W_2}{gK}\frac{dv}{dt} = D\frac{df}{dt} + \frac{f}{K}$$

where g is the gravitational acceleration. Check this equation to see that it is dimensionally correct. Indicate errors, if any.

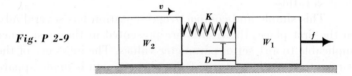

Fig. P 2-9

2-10   Check the differential equation of Prob. 2-9 by the limiting-case method and indicate any errors.

2-11   The following expression is derived for the impedance of the circuit shown:

$$\mathbf{Z} = \frac{s^2 RLC + s(CR^2 + L) + R}{s^2 LC + sRC + 1}$$

(a) Check this dimensionally and indicate any errors.
(b) Check by the limiting-case method and indicate any errors.

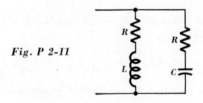

Fig. P 2-11

forced behavior of
simple networks

In every physical system there is some dissipation of energy, or conversion of energy to the thermal form. Thus, in any electrical or mechanical system the natural behavior (which may be initiated by release of a spring, insertion or removal of a battery or generator, etc.) eventually dies away. The stored electrical or mechanical energy responsible for the natural behavior is ultimately transformed into heat. This will be true even in systems like the mass-spring combination studied in Sec. 2-2, where the friction was assumed negligibly small.

On the other hand, sustained oscillations may be maintained through the action of an externally applied source of power. This source may be the periodic force which causes a mechanical system to vibrate or the alternating voltage from an electric generator applied to an electrical circuit. If the periodic driving force has been applied for a sufficiently long time, any natural-behavior terms which may have been initiated by its application will long since have disappeared. Thus we may study the *forced* or *steady-state*† behavior quite independently of the natural behavior.

During the time interval immediately after application of a power source, the system is in a state of combined natural and forced behavior. This situation may be easily handled when the techniques of finding the natural behavior and steady-state behavior have been mastered separately.

---

† These two terms are not completely interchangeable, although both are commonly used in referring to the behavior of a system that is subjected to a sinusoidally varying driving force. The term *forced* behavior is in contradistinction to *natural* behavior and indicates an externally applied driving force. *Steady-state* is the antithesis of *transient* and implies periodicity in contrast to nonrecurrence. Thus the response of a system to the periodic driving force of Fig. 3-1 could be termed either forced or steady-state behavior; the response to a single, nonrecurring pulse would be forced but transient.

3-1   SINUSOIDS AND COMPLEX NUMBERS

Forced oscillations or steady-state behavior occurs when a system is subjected to a driving force or voltage which varies periodically in time—perhaps something like that indicated in Fig. 3-1a. Our first move will be to restrict the present discussion to a particular kind of periodic driving force, namely, one whose amplitude varies like a sine or cosine function.

This is not really a restriction at all, for any periodic waveform can be expressed as the sum of a number of sinusoidal functions, as is indicated in Fig. 3-2. We cannot stop here to investigate how to determine the proper amounts of sine and cosine waves to add together to produce a given waveform. Suffice it to say that this can be done and will be discussed at length in Chap. 13.

As long as the network elements behave as we have postulated thus far, so that the differential equations contain derivatives to the first power only (are linear) and the derivatives in these equations have constant coefficients—as long as these things hold true, the network response to a periodic driving force is simply the sum of the responses to the individual sinusoidal components. Thus, restricting the initial study to sinusoidal driving forces or voltages is not merely treating a special case, as it might appear to be at first glance.

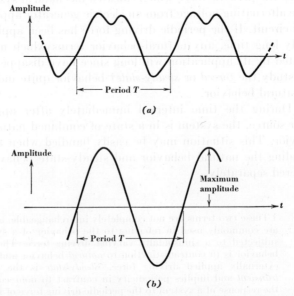

Fig. 3-1. Distinction between a periodic function and a sinusoidal function. (a) Periodic driving force; (b) harmonic, or sinusoidal, driving force.

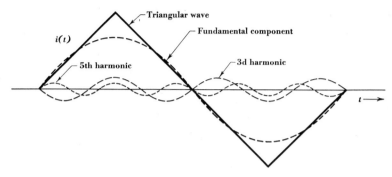

Fig. 3-2. Triangular waveform and some of the sinusoidal components which add together to form it.

AN ELEMENTARY EXAMPLE   An elementary problem will aid in pointing the way toward the general method of solution which we seek. Suppose we have a resistance R and an inductance L in series, connected across a generator. The impedance of this circuit is, as we have seen, $R + sL$; that is, this is the ratio of applied voltage to current when the current is varying as e^{st}. To find the natural behavior of the circuit, we should set this impedance equal to zero.

But now we wish to consider the case in which there is a driving voltage. Let us assume that the current is to be $I \cos \omega t$ (where ω is 2π times the frequency of alternation). We desire to know the voltage which must be applied to produce this current.

The key to the answer lies in expressing the current in terms of exponential functions, which we can do with the aid of Euler's relation. Thus,

$$I \cos \omega t = \frac{I}{2} e^{j\omega t} + \frac{I}{2} e^{-j\omega t} \tag{3-1}$$

The graphical representation of this equation will be important to us. Recall that $e^{j\theta}$ may be represented as a line of length 1 making an angle of θ radians with the real axis (see Fig. 2-11). Thus, $e^{j\omega t}$ may be represented as a line of length 1 making an angle ωt with the real axis—in other words, rotating in a counterclockwise direction with the angular velocity ω radians/sec. Its horizontal projection is $\cos \omega t$, and its vertical projection is $\sin \omega t$. Hence it is easy to see how a combination of $e^{j\omega t}$ (represented by a line rotating in a counterclockwise direction) and $e^{-j\omega t}$ (represented by a line rotating in a clockwise direction) can form the cosine function, which is always real but which varies in magnitude. The horizontal projections of the two components add, and the vertical projections cancel (Fig. 3-3).

Thus, although the current expression is not in the form of a constant times e^{st}, it can be broken into two components each of which is in this form—one with $s = j\omega$ and the other with $s = -j\omega$. Now we

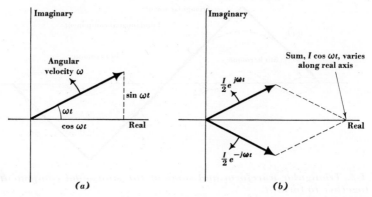

Fig. 3-3. (*a*) *Graphical representation of* $e^{j\omega t}$; (*b*) *graphical representation of* $I \cos \omega t$.

shall utilize a very important technique based upon the linearity of the network. The current as given by Eq. (3-1) is a sum of two terms. We can consider the effect of each term on the network separately and then add the separate effects to yield the total effect. The network impedance applicable to the first term is $R + sL$ with $s = j\omega$, that is, $R + j\omega L$. The network impedance applicable to the second term is $R + sL$ with $s = -j\omega$. For each current component of Eq. (3-1), the corresponding voltage component is obtained by multiplying by the appropriate impedance (since impedance is by definition the ratio of voltage to current when both are varying as e^{st}).

These two voltage components can be added, by the superposition principle, to give the total applied voltage:

$$e = (R + j\omega L)\frac{I}{2} e^{j\omega t} + (R - j\omega L)\frac{I}{2} e^{-j\omega t}$$

$$= \frac{I}{2}[(R + j\omega L)(\cos \omega t + j \sin \omega t) + (R - j\omega L)(\cos \omega t - j \sin \omega t)]$$

$$= RI \cos \omega t - \omega LI \sin \omega t \tag{3-2}$$

These two terms represent the voltages across the resistance and inductance, respectively, since the first vanishes if $R = 0$ and the second if $L = 0$. They are, of course, simply $e_R = Ri$ and $e_L = L \, di/dt$, which have been arrived at in a somewhat roundabout fashion.

The final expression for the voltage is entirely real; all the imaginary terms have canceled out. We should hardly know how to interpret an imaginary value for the instantaneous voltage were we to obtain such a result.

SUM OF TWO SINUSOIDAL FUNCTIONS The current and the two voltage terms of Eq. (3-2) are plotted in Fig. 3-4. The two plots of e_R and e_L are added to obtain the over-all voltage e. We see that this voltage,

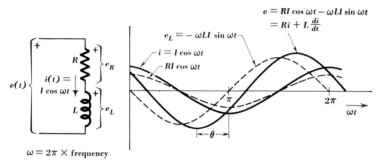

Fig. 3-4. Voltage and current in an RL circuit.

consisting of the sum of two sinusoidal terms, is also sinusoidal. This is no accident; it is generally true that the sum or difference of any two sinusoidal functions of the same frequency is a third sinusoidal function.

This statement follows from some trigonometric identities which are easily derived from Euler's relations. Note that

$$
\begin{aligned}
\cos{(x+y)} &= \tfrac{1}{2}(e^{j(x+y)} + e^{-j(x+y)}) \\
&= \tfrac{1}{2}(e^{jx}e^{jy} + e^{-jx}e^{-jy}) \\
&= \tfrac{1}{2}[(\cos x + j \sin x)(\cos y + j \sin y) \\
&\qquad\qquad + (\cos x - j \sin x)(\cos y - j \sin y)] \\
&= \cos x \cos y - \sin x \sin y \qquad\qquad (3\text{-}3)
\end{aligned}
$$

In similar fashion, it is easy to prove the following identities, which are listed here for reference:

$$
\begin{aligned}
\cos{(x-y)} &= \cos x \cos y + \sin x \sin y & (3\text{-}4) \\
\sin{(x+y)} &= \sin x \cos y + \cos x \sin y & (3\text{-}5) \\
\sin{(x-y)} &= \sin x \cos y - \cos x \sin y & (3\text{-}6)
\end{aligned}
$$

Equation (3-3) may be used to change the form of Eq. (3-2) to indicate more clearly the fact that the voltage varies sinusoidally with time, reaching its maximum value slightly before the current maximum occurs. Rewriting Eq. (3-2) so that it appears in the form of Eq. (3-3), we find

$$
\begin{aligned}
e &= I(R \cos \omega t - \omega L \sin \omega t) \\
&= \sqrt{R^2 + \omega^2 L^2}\, I \left(\frac{R}{\sqrt{R^2 + \omega^2 L^2}} \cos \omega t - \frac{\omega L}{\sqrt{R^2 + \omega^2 L^2}} \sin \omega t \right) \\
&= ZI(\cos \theta \cos \omega t - \sin \theta \sin \omega t) \\
&= ZI \cos{(\omega t + \theta)} \qquad\qquad (3\text{-}7)
\end{aligned}
$$

where the significance of the symbols Z and θ is indicated in Fig. 3-5. Note that Z is the magnitude of the impedance $\mathbf{Z}$ with s equal to either $j\omega$ or $-j\omega$. The magnitude of a complex number is the square

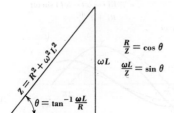

$$\frac{R}{Z} = \cos \theta$$

$$\frac{\omega L}{Z} = \sin \theta$$

Fig. 3-5. Trigonometric relations involved in writing Eq. (3-7).

root of the sum of the squares of the real and imaginary parts of that number.

ANOTHER APPROACH We have seen that the voltage required to produce the current $I \cos \omega t$ through a series combination of R and L is given by Eq. (3-2) or its equivalent, Eq. (3-7). This result was obtained by expressing the current in the form of a sum of exponential functions and making use of the impedance concept. (In this simple example the result can also be obtained by direct substitution of $i = I \cos \omega t$ into the differential equation

$$e = Ri + L\frac{di}{dt} \tag{3-8}$$

but this method is useful only in certain elementary cases.)

A slight modification of the procedure used in obtaining Eq. (3-2) is even more convenient and forms the basis for an extremely powerful method of analysis. This approach can be developed from inspection of Eqs. (3-1) and (3-2).

Note that the two voltage components in Eq. (3-2) resulting from the two current terms in Eq. (3-1) are exactly the same except that the j's which appear in the first and second components are opposite in sign. Thus the two components have equal real parts, and their imaginary parts are negatives of each other. When the two components are added, the imaginary parts cancel, and the result is just twice the real part of one component alone.

Thus (letting the symbol Re indicate "the real part of")

$$e = \mathrm{Re}\,[(R + j\omega L)Ie^{j\omega t}]$$
$$= \mathrm{Re}\,[I(R + j\omega L)(\cos \omega t + j \sin \omega t)]$$
$$= RI \cos \omega t - LI \sin \omega t \tag{3-9}$$

Summarizing,

$$i = I \cos \omega t = \mathrm{Re}\,(Ie^{j\omega t}) \tag{3-10}$$
$$e = \mathrm{Re}\,(\mathbf{Z}Ie^{j\omega t}) \tag{3-11}$$

Concentrated in the last two equations is the essential concept we are to use for obtaining forced or steady-state responses to sinusoidal inputs.

A comparison of Eqs. (3-9) and (3-10) indicates that the impedance $\mathbf{Z}$ is $R + j\omega L$, that is, $R + sL$ with $s = j\omega$. The substitution of $+j\omega$ rather than $-j\omega$ for s occurs because we have chosen to work with the positive exponential part of the current expression. We shall continue this practice throughout our study of networks with sinusoidal driving functions; that is, the impedance $\mathbf{Z}$ will be computed by substituting $+j\omega$ for s.

PROBLEMS

3-1   A 1-ohm resistor, a 1-mh inductor, and a 1,000-μf capacitor carry a current

$$i = \cos 1,000t - \cos 3,000t$$

(*a*) Sketch plots of the voltages e_R, e_L, and e_C as functions of time.

(*b*) Attempt to make a general statement regarding the relative amplitudes of the sinusoidal components of nonsinusoidal periodic waveforms as affected by differentiation and integration.

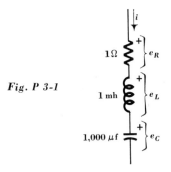

Fig. P 3-1

3-2   Derive Eq. (3-6). With the aid of this identity, express Eq. (3-2) in the form

$$e = -ZI \sin (\omega t - \phi)$$

and explain the relation of the angle ϕ to the angle θ in Eq. (3-7).

3-2 ALGEBRA OF COMPLEX NUMBERS

It is becoming increasingly evident that we shall need facility in the manipulation of these complex numbers we keep running across. First, however, let us investigate how complex numbers may be used to represent the sinusoidally varying quantities—currents and voltages, velocities and forces—with which we wish to deal.

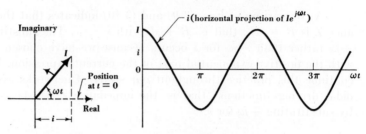

Fig. 3-6. Graphical representation of the equation $i = \mathrm{Re}\ (I\ {}^{j\omega t})$.

REPRESENTATION OF SINUSOIDS Figure 3-6 shows a graphical representation of Eq. (3-10). The complex quantity $Ie^{j\omega t}$ is represented by a line of length I rotating in a counterclockwise direction with angular velocity $\omega = 2\pi f$ radians/sec, or $360f$ deg/sec. The horizontal projection, or real part, of this rotating line is the instantaneous current.

In Fig. 3-7 this concept is extended to show graphical representations of

$$I \cos\left(\omega t + \frac{\pi}{4}\right) = \mathrm{Re}\ (Ie^{j(\omega t + \pi/4)})$$

$$= \mathrm{Re}\left[I\left(\cos\frac{\pi}{4} + j\sin\frac{\pi}{4}\right)e^{j\omega t}\right]$$

$$= \mathrm{Re}\ [(0.707I + j0.707I)e^{j\omega t}] \qquad (3\text{-}12)$$

and

$$I \sin \omega t = I \cos\left(\omega t - \frac{\pi}{2}\right) = \mathrm{Re}\ (Ie^{-j\pi/2}e^{j\omega t})$$

$$= \mathrm{Re}\left\{I\left[\cos\left(-\frac{\pi}{2}\right) + j\sin\left(-\frac{\pi}{2}\right)\right]e^{j\omega t}\right\}$$

$$= \mathrm{Re}\ (-jIe^{j\omega t}) \qquad (3\text{-}13)$$

Now, if we are going to use this representation repeatedly, we shall soon tire of writing "real part of" and "times $e^{j\omega t}$." The repeated instructions to "rotate with angular velocity ω radians/sec and take the horizontal projection" will also become tedious. Let us therefore agree among ourselves that these operations are understood even though not written out.

In other words, to represent an electric current, we shall write only that quantity (a complex number) which when multiplied by $e^{j\omega t}$ will have a real part equal to the instantaneous current. This complex quantity will be indicated by a boldface symbol **I** (or **E** in the case of voltage, **V** in the case of velocity, etc.). Quantities such as **I**, **E**, and **V** are termed *phasors*. Thus, the expression **I** = 10, for example, is a symbolic representation of the instantaneous current. It is to be interpreted as meaning that, to find the current, we are to multiply 10 by $e^{j\omega t}$ and take the real part of the product, which is 10 cos ωt.†

† In the case of electrical quantities, if "effective values" are being used, the statements of this paragraph must be modified slightly. This will be discussed in Sec. 3-7.

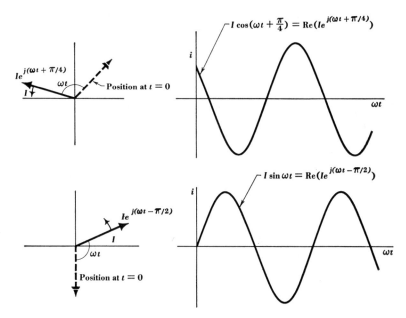

Fig. 3-7. Graphical representations of Eqs. (3-12) and (3-13).

The phasor notation outlined above lends itself nicely to graphical representation in the form of *phasor diagrams*. Any phasor, since it is simply a complex number, can be represented as a line in the complex plane from the origin to the point specified by the complex number. This line can also be thought of as the $t = 0$ position of the rotating line whose horizontal projection is the instantaneous value of the quantity denoted by the phasor.

For example, let us find the phasor representing the instantaneous current

$$i = 10 \cos (\omega t - 60°) \tag{3-14}$$

which is plotted in Fig. 3-8a. The phasor $\mathbf{I}$ could be found through some trigonometric manipulation as a complex number which multi-

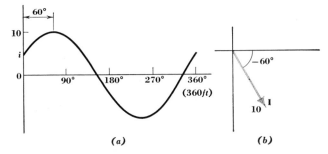

Fig. 3-8. (a) Plot of the current $i = 10 \cos (\omega t - 60°)$; (b) phasor representation.

plies $e^{j\omega t}$ and yields Eq. (3-14) as its real part. However, a somewhat simpler method is available. The current given in Eq. (3-14) has an instantaneous value given by the horizontal projection of the line $\mathbf{I}e^{j\omega t}$, where $\mathbf{I}$ is the phasor representation of the current. The current i of Eq. (3-14) reaches a maximum of 10 when $\omega t = 60°$. Equivalently, i reaches a maximum when the rotating line $\mathbf{I}e^{j\omega t}$ passes through the horizontal. Consequently, the length of $\mathbf{I}e^{j\omega t}$ must be 10, and its position at $t = 0$ must be at an angle of $-60°$. Thus the phasor we seek is

$$\mathbf{I} = 10 \cos 60° - j10 \sin 60° = 10\underline{/-60°} \qquad (3\text{-}15)$$

This phasor is represented graphically in Fig. 3-8b.

We have seen that $e^{j\theta}$ is an operator which rotates a complex number by θ radians. Thus the four symbolic representations of the current,

$$\begin{aligned}
\mathbf{I} &= 10\underline{/-60°} & &\text{polar form} \\
&= 10 \cos 60° - j10 \sin 60° \\
&= 5.00 - j8.66 & &\text{rectangular form} \\
&= 10e^{-j\pi/3} & &\text{exponential form} \qquad (3\text{-}16)
\end{aligned}$$

and the graphical representation of Fig. 3-8b are completely equivalent and are simply different ways of expressing the same knowledge. The instantaneous current as a function of time is obtained by taking the real part of $\mathbf{I}e^{j\omega t}$ or, in the case of the graphical representation, the horizontal projection of the rotating line $\mathbf{I}e^{j\omega t}$ which rotates in a counterclockwise direction with the angular velocity of ω radians/sec.

ADDITION AND SUBTRACTION OF PHASORS Now that we see how complex numbers or phasors can be used, both symbolically and graphically, to represent sinusoidally varying quantities, it is time to learn how to perform certain elementary manipulations with them. Let us consider the two phasors

$$\begin{aligned}
\mathbf{A} &= Ae^{j\theta} = A_r + jA_i = A \cos \theta + jA \sin \theta \\
\mathbf{B} &= Be^{j\phi} = B_r + jB_i = B \cos \phi + jB \sin \phi
\end{aligned} \qquad (3\text{-}17)$$

The basic rule of the algebra of complex numbers is that *real and imaginary components must be added separately*. Thus the rules for addition and subtraction of complex numbers are similar to the corresponding rules for force vectors in mechanics.

It is most convenient to have the quantities in rectangular form for addition or subtraction. Addition is then simply a matter of adding the real and imaginary parts separately (Fig. 3-9):

$$(A_r + jA_i) + (B_r + jB_i) = (A_r + B_r) + j(A_i + B_i) \qquad (3\text{-}18)$$

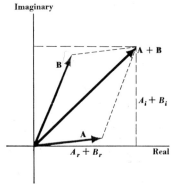

Fig. 3-9. Graphical representation of the operation of addition of two complex quantities.

Subtraction of a complex quantity is equivalent to adding its negative (Fig. 3-10). It is performed by subtracting the real and imaginary parts separately:

$$(A_r + jA_i) - (B_r + jB_i) = (A_r - B_r) + j(A_i - B_i) \quad (3\text{-}19)$$

MULTIPLICATION Complex quantities are multiplied symbolically in exactly the same way as any other algebraic quantities:

$$(A_r + jA_i)(B_r + jB_i) = (A_rB_r - A_iB_i) + j(A_rB_i + A_iB_r) \quad (3\text{-}20)$$

This operation assumes a somewhat neater form in the polar or exponential representations. If we write, instead of A_r, $A \cos \theta$, and so on, Eq. (3-20) becomes

$$A\underline{/\theta}\, B\underline{/\phi} = (A \cos \theta\, B \cos \phi - A \sin \theta\, B \sin \phi)$$
$$+ j(A \cos \theta\, B \sin \phi + A \sin \theta\, B \cos \phi) \quad (3\text{-}21)$$

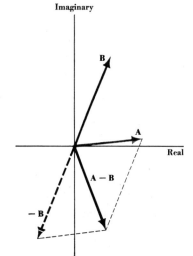

Fig. 3-10. Graphical representation of the subtraction of one complex quantity from another.

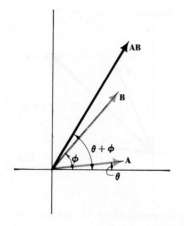

Fig. 3-11. Multiplication of $A\underline{/\theta}$ **by** $B\underline{/\phi}$.

Making use of the trigonometric identities of Eqs. (3-4) to (3-6), we can write the expression of Eq. (3-21) as

$$A\underline{/\theta}\,B\underline{/\phi} = AB\cos(\theta + \phi) + jAB\sin(\theta + \phi) = AB\underline{/\theta + \phi} \quad (3\text{-}22)$$

This result could have been written immediately from the rule of multiplication of exponentials:

$$(Ae^{j\theta})(Be^{j\phi}) = ABe^{j(\theta+\phi)} \quad (3\text{-}23)$$

Thus the product of two complex quantities has a magnitude equal to the *product of the component magnitudes* and an angle equal to the sum of the component angles (Fig. 3-11).

For example,

$$(1 + j)(-1 + j) = (\sqrt{2}\,\underline{/45°})(\sqrt{2}\,\underline{/135°}) = 2\underline{/180°} = -2$$

as can be verified by performing the multiplication in rectangular form, as in Eq. (3-20).

DIVISION Division is the inverse process of multiplication. It follows that (see Fig. 3-12)

$$\frac{Ae^{j\theta}}{Be^{j\phi}} = \frac{A}{B}\,e^{j(\theta-\phi)} \quad (3\text{-}24)$$

or

$$\frac{A\underline{/\theta}}{B\underline{/\phi}} = \frac{A}{B}\,\underline{/\theta - \phi} \quad (3\text{-}25)$$

Division may also be performed in the rectangular form. Suppose, for example, that we want the quotient $(1 + j2)/(2 + j1)$. The real and imaginary parts of this can be separated by multiplying both numerator and denominator by such a factor as to make the denominator purely real.

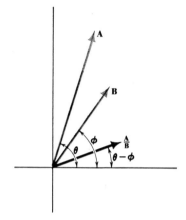

Fig. 3-12. Division of $A\underline{/\theta}$ *by* $B\underline{/\phi}$.

The appropriate factor is one which has the same magnitude but the negative angle, since $B\underline{/\phi}$ times $B\underline{/-\phi}$ is $B^2\underline{/0°}$. (Actually, any quantity with the negative angle would do, but the one with the same magnitude is usually the handiest.) The complex quantity $B\underline{/-\phi}$ is called the *conjugate* of $B\underline{/\phi}$. It has the same magnitude but the negative angle, or the same real part but the negative imaginary part.

Multiplying, in our example, both numerator and denominator by the conjugate of the denominator, then, gives

$$\frac{1 + j2}{2 + j1} = \frac{(1 + j2)(2 - j1)}{(2 + j1)(2 - j1)} = \frac{4}{5} + j\frac{3}{5} \tag{3-26}$$

Summarizing, the quotient of two complex quantities has a magnitude equal to the *quotient of the component magnitudes* and an angle equal to the *difference between the component angles*. The operation may be performed in rectangular form by *multiplying numerator and denominator by the conjugate of the denominator*.

POWERS AND ROOTS Powers and roots of complex quantities are most conveniently obtained from the polar or exponential forms. From the rule for multiplication, it follows that

$$(A\underline{/\theta})^n = A^n\underline{/n\theta} \tag{3-27}$$

or

$$(Ae^{j\theta})^n = A^n e^{jn\theta} \tag{3-28}$$

Root taking is the inverse process:

$$\sqrt[n]{Ae^{j\theta}} = \sqrt[n]{A}\, e^{j\theta/n} \tag{3-29}$$

since this is the quantity which, when raised to the nth power, gives $Ae^{j\theta}$. Note that $Ae^{j\theta}$, $Ae^{j(\theta+2\pi)}$, $Ae^{j(\theta+4\pi)}$, $Ae^{j(\theta+6\pi)}$, . . . are all exactly the same quantities. However, the nth root of each of these equal quantities, obtained by Eq. (3-29), will be different. The conclusion is that there are n distinct nth roots of any number $Ae^{j\theta}$. This agrees with our experiences with real numbers—the square root of 4 is -2 as well as $+2$. The n numbers which are the nth roots of $Ae^{j\theta}$ are $\sqrt[n]{A}\ e^{j\theta/n},\ \sqrt[n]{A}\ e^{j(\theta+2\pi)/n},\ \ldots,\ \sqrt[n]{A}\ e^{j[\theta+2(n-1)\pi]/n}$.

PROBLEMS

3-3   Find the phasor representations of the following sinusoidally varying quantities:

$$e = 20 \cos (\omega t + 30°)$$
$$v = 10 \sin (\omega t - 60°)$$
$$f = 5 \cos \omega t - 5 \sin \omega t$$

3-4   Show that

$$3\underline{/22°} + 4\underline{/112°} = 5\underline{/75.1°}$$
$$(2 + j2)(3e^{j\pi/6}) = 8.48\underline{/75°}$$
$$(1 + j1)^4 = -4 + j0$$
$$\sqrt[3]{-1} = -1 \qquad 0.5 + j0.866 \qquad 0.5 - j0.866$$
$$\frac{3 - j2}{1 + j3} = -0.3 - j1.1$$

3-5   Express $(8.66 + j5.0)e^{j\pi/5}$ in rectangular form.

3-6   The impedance of the circuit shown is given by

$$\mathbf{Z} = \frac{(R + jX)(-2jX)}{R + jX - j2X}$$

Compute the magnitude and angle of $\mathbf{Z} = Z\underline{/\theta}$ for $R = 0$, $R = X/2$, $R = X$, $R = 2X$, $R = 5X$, $R = 10X$, $R = \infty$. Sketch plots of Z and θ versus R.

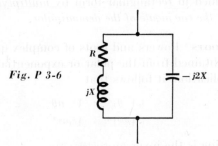

Fig. P 3-6

3-3 THE PHASOR METHOD OF SOLUTION

Let us now consolidate our gains by applying the phasor method to work out the electrical example of Fig. 3-13.

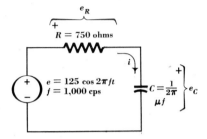

Fig. 3-13. Electrical circuit to be solved by the phasor method.

A voltage $e = 125 \cos 2\pi ft$ at a frequency $f = 1,000$ cps is supplied to a circuit consisting of a 750-ohm resistance in series with a capacitance of $1/2\pi$ μf. It is desired to find the current.

VOLTAGE AND CURRENT PHASORS Our first step is to find the phasor representing the voltage. Since

$$e = 125 \cos 2\pi ft = \text{Re } (125e^{j2\pi ft}) = \text{Re } (125e^{j\omega t}) \qquad (3\text{-}30)$$

the phasor we seek is $\mathbf{E} = 125\underline{/0°}$.† This is the quantity which yields the instantaneous voltage when the operations "multiply by $e^{j\omega t}$" and "take the real part of" are performed. Alternatively, in the graphical representation, $125\underline{/0°}$ is the $t = 0$ magnitude and position of the line segment rotating with angular velocity ω and having a horizontal projection equal to the instantaneous voltage (Fig. 3-14). With what may be wearisome repetition, we again point out that $\mathbf{E}$ is *not* the voltage; it is a *representation* of the voltage (although for brevity we may call it the voltage).

Next, we find the impedance of the circuit. This is $R + 1/sC$ or, for $s = j\omega$,

$$\mathbf{Z} = R + \frac{1}{j\omega C} = 750 - j1,000 = 1,250\underline{/-53.1°} \qquad (3\text{-}31)$$

represented graphically in Fig. 3-15a.

> † In this representation the magnitude of the phasor represents the *peak* value of the voltage. Sometimes *effective* values, lower than peak values by the factor $1/\sqrt{2}$, are used. This is discussed later, in Sec. 3-7. It makes absolutely no difference whether phasor magnitudes are taken to represent peak or effective values, as long as the same choice is consistently made throughout a given problem.

Fig. 3-14. Rotating phasor whose horizontal projection gives the instantaneous voltage $125 \cos \omega t$.

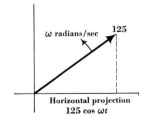

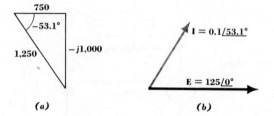

Fig. 3-15. (a) Impedance triangle for the circuit of Fig.
3-13; (b) phasor diagram
for the circuit of Fig. 3-13.

(a)   (b)

This value of impedance is, by definition, the ratio of voltage
to current *if* the voltage and current are varying as $e^{j\omega t}$. That is,

$$Z = \frac{Ee^{j\omega t}}{Ie^{j\omega t}} = \frac{E}{I} \tag{3-32}$$

Thus, to find **I**, the phasor representation of the current, we divide
the voltage by the impedance:

$$I = \frac{E}{Z} = \frac{125\underline{/0°}}{1{,}250\underline{/-53.1°}} = 0.1\underline{/53.1°} = 0.06 + j0.08 \tag{3-33}$$

On the phasor diagram (Fig. 3-15b) the current phasor has a magnitude
equal to the quotient of the voltage and impedance magnitudes and
a phase angle equal to the difference between the phase angle of the
voltage and the angle of the impedance.

The significance of the phasor diagram is indicated in Fig. 3-16,
where the instantaneous values of voltage and current are plotted.
The peak amplitude of the current is seen to be 0.1 amp, occurring
53.1° before the voltage peak. The mathematical expression for the
instantaneous current is

$$\begin{aligned}
i &= \mathrm{Re}\ (Ie^{j\omega t}) \\
&= \mathrm{Re}\ [(0.06 + j0.08)(\cos \omega t + j \sin \omega t)] \\
&= 0.06 \cos \omega t - 0.08 \sin \omega t \\
&= 0.1 \cos (\omega t + 53.1°) \tag{3-34}
\end{aligned}$$

This is the result originally sought. It can be checked by substitution

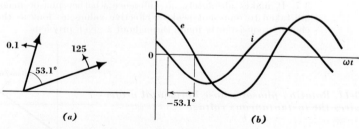

Fig. 3-16. (a) *Rotating phasors representing current and voltage for the circuit
of Fig. 3-13; (b) instantaneous current and voltage.*

into the integrodifferential equation for the circuit:

$$e = Ri + \frac{1}{C} \int i \, dt \tag{3-35}$$

Often in steady-state analysis the expression for the instantaneous value of a quantity (such as electric current) is not of so much interest as a statement of its peak amplitude and its phase angle with respect to some other quantity (in the present case the applied voltage). Thus in this example the current representation $\mathbf{I} = 0.1\underline{/53.1°}$, containing this information, might be considered the solution. The phasor representation is more concise than the expression for the instantaneous value and, properly interpreted, contains the same information.

JUSTIFICATION OF THE METHOD Let us run over this again, in reverse order this time, to see why what we did was justifiable. Using the exponential forms for voltage and current, we can rewrite Eq. (3-35) as

$$\text{Re } (\mathbf{E}e^{j\omega t}) = R \text{ Re } (\mathbf{I}e^{j\omega t}) + \frac{1}{C} \int \text{Re } (\mathbf{I}e^{j\omega t}) \, dt \tag{3-36}$$

Now, the operations of "taking the real part of" and of differentiating or integrating are interchangeable in order of performance. This is apparent from the following demonstrations. Let x and y be two real functions of t; then

$$\text{Re}\left[\frac{d}{dt}(x + jy)\right] = \text{Re}\left(\frac{dx}{dt} + j\frac{dy}{dt}\right) = \frac{dx}{dt} = \frac{d}{dt}[\text{Re }(x + jy)]$$

$$\text{Re }[\int(x + jy) \, dt] = \text{Re }(\int x \, dt + j\int y \, dt) = \int x \, dt = \int \text{Re }(x + jy) \, dt$$

Thus Eq. (3-36) may be rewritten

$$\text{Re } (\mathbf{E}e^{j\omega t}) = \text{Re}\left[\mathbf{I}\left(R + \frac{1}{j\omega C}\right)e^{j\omega t}\right] \tag{3-37}$$

Hence we conclude that

$$\mathbf{E} = \mathbf{IZ} \tag{3-38}$$

which is Ohm's law of steady-state circuit analysis.

VOLTAGE-CURRENT RELATIONS IN SINGLE ELEMENTS It will be instructive to study the relations between the current and the voltages appearing across the individual circuit elements.

The resistor-voltage phasor is simply the product of the current phasor and the impedance of the resistor:

$$\mathbf{E}_R = \mathbf{I}\mathbf{Z}_R = (0.1\underline{/53.1°})(750) = 75\underline{/53.1°} \tag{3-39}$$

Similarly, the capacitor voltage is

$$\mathbf{E}_C = \mathbf{I}\mathbf{Z}_C = (0.1\underline{/53.1°})(-j1,000) = 100\underline{/-36.9°} \tag{3-40}$$

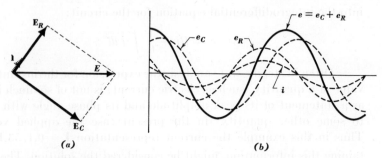

Fig. 3-17. (a) *Phasor diagram and* (b) *plot of instantaneous values of voltages in the circuit of Fig. 3-13.*

The sum of these two voltages is the applied voltage **E**. This is shown on the phasor diagram of Fig. 3-17a and in the instantaneous plots of Fig. 3-17b.

Note that the current reaches its maximum value when the capacitor voltage is zero and that the capacitor voltage is maximum a quarter of a cycle later at the time the current is zero. Physically, this results from the proportionality between the capacitor voltage and the charge. Current must flow into the capacitor *before* the charge and voltage can build up. Thus the current into a capacitor *leads* the voltage across the capacitor by 90°.

On the other hand, the current in the inductive circuit of Fig. 3-4 was found to *lag* the voltage across the inductor by 90°. This is a manifestation of the physical fact that the voltage is proportional to the rate of change of flux and of current. The voltage must build up before the current will start to increase. The voltage has its peak value when the current is changing most rapidly, a quarter-cycle before the peak value of current is reached.

In summary, the current and voltage associated with a resistance are in phase. For an inductance the current lags the voltage by 90°, and for a capacitance the current leads the voltage by 90°. The current through a series combination of resistance and inductance lags the applied voltage by an angle less than 90°. The current through a series combination of resistance and capacitance leads the applied voltage by a similar angle.

PROBLEMS

3-7   An electrical circuit consists of a 200-ohm resistor and a 1-henry inductor connected in series with a voltage $e = 100 \cos \omega t$. The frequency is 60 cps.

Find the phasor representation of the current and construct a phasor diagram showing **E**, $\mathbf{E}_R$, $\mathbf{E}_L$, and **I**.

Sketch the waveforms of the various currents and voltages.

3-8   An electrical circuit consists of a 1-henry inductance and a 1-μf capacitance connected in series with a voltage $100 \cos 2\pi ft$. Find the current, and sketch phasor diagrams and waveforms for frequencies of 60 and 400 cps.

3-9   A voltage $100 \cos \omega t$ is applied to the circuit shown. Find the current in each branch and the total current. Sketch a phasor diagram showing the voltage and all three currents.

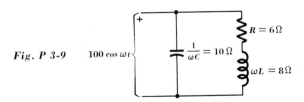

Fig. P 3-9 $100 \cos \omega t$

3-10   A voltage $e = 141 \cos 500t$ is impressed across an impedance $\mathbf{Z}$; the resulting current is found to be $i = 3.52 \sin (500t + 60°)$.

     (*a*) Make a rough sketch of the voltage and current waveforms. How long does it take the voltage to go through one complete cycle?

     (*b*) What is the phasor representation of the current?

     (*c*) What is the impedance $\mathbf{Z}$?

     (*d*) If the impedance consists of either a resistance and an inductance in series or a resistance and a capacitance in series, what are the values of R and of L or C?

     (*e*) If the impedance consists of either a resistance and an inductance in parallel or a resistance and a capacitance in parallel, what are the values of R and of L or C?

     (*f*) What is the time average of the product of e and i (power)?

3-4   VIBRATION-ISOLATION EXAMPLE

     The phasor method is equally applicable to mechanical systems. Consider the problem of mounting a machine such as an air compressor or an automobile engine to minimize the vibration force transmitted to the supporting structure.

     Any unbalance in the rotor of such a machine will result in the application of a periodic force to the machine. To see how this comes about, imagine an air compressor with a vertically moving piston of mass m (Fig. 3-18). Assume that when the compressor is operating, the piston moves with a displacement given by the expression

$$x_p = X_p \cos \omega t \tag{3-41}$$

where X_p is the peak displacement and ω is the angular velocity of the flywheel in radians per second.

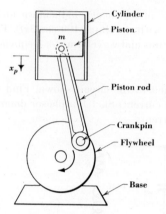

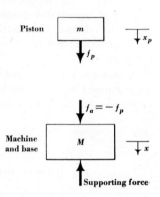

Fig. 3-18. Air-compressor assembly.

Fig. 3-19. Equivalent system for Fig. 3-18.

The force required to produce this motion is

$$f_p = m \frac{d^2 x_p}{dt^2} = -\omega^2 m X_p \cos \omega t \qquad (3\text{-}42)$$

If the piston rod is assumed to have negligible mass, it must push as hard on the crankpin at the one end as it does on the piston at the other. Thus the force exerted on the compressor through the piston rod is (Fig. 3-19)

$$f = -f_p = F \cos \omega t \qquad (3\text{-}43)$$

where $F = \omega^2 m X_p$.

To reduce the amount of force transmitted to the structure which supports the machine, some kind of spring mounting is universally used (Fig. 3-20a). If steel springs are used, the damping or friction is negligible.

We wish to analyze such a system to obtain some information on how large the spring compliance should be made to provide the most effective vibration isolation.

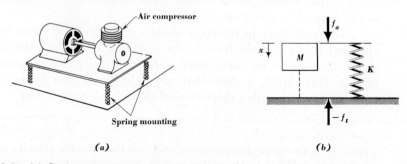

(a)

(b)

Fig. 3-20. (a) Spring-mounted air compressor; (b) approximate model.

APPLICATION OF PHASOR METHODS First of all, it is necessary to set up a simplified approximate model from which to write the system equations. Let us restrict the present investigation to vertical oscillations in which the motor, compressor, and base move as a unit and are constrained to move in the vertical direction only (no twisting, rocking, etc.). Thus the combined effect of the four identical mounting springs may be lumped into the equivalent compliance K. (You can easily establish that K is just one-fourth of the compliance of one of the springs individually.)

To eliminate certain complications that we have no desire to go into at the moment, let us assume that the piston mass m is small compared with the total mass M and that the piston displacement is large compared with the amplitude of vertical oscillations of the machine. Again, to simplify the problem, we shall neglect the force on the piston due to air pressure in the cylinder. (This force is balanced by an equal and opposite force on the cylinder head.)

Making these various approximations and assumptions, we arrive at the mechanical network of Fig. 3-20b.† Our problem is now reduced to the study of this system.

Assume that a periodic force

$$f_a = F \cos \omega t \tag{3-44}$$

is applied, where F is the peak amplitude of the force. Following the approach of the last section, we represent this applied force by a phasor

$$\mathbf{F}_a = F\underline{/0°} \tag{3-45}$$

Note that, by assuming the time $t = 0$ to be the instant at which this applied force reaches its peak value, we have selected the applied force phasor as a reference phasor. All other phasors will have phase angles measuring their positions with respect to this reference phasor.

The motional impedance of this system has already been discussed in Sec. 2-2 and found to be

$$\mathbf{Z}_m = sM + \frac{1}{sK} \tag{2-17}$$

The impedance to a sinusoidal force at the radian frequency ω is

$$\mathbf{Z}_m = j\omega M + \frac{1}{j\omega K} \tag{3-46}$$

---

† Note particularly the dashed line joining the equivalent mass to "ground," that is, to the inertial reference frame. This serves to remind us that inertial forces depend upon the state of motion with respect to this reference frame. It will be particularly helpful when we study more elaborate interconnections of mechanical elements.

Now, by exactly the same logic as in the preceding section, the phasor representing the velocity is found from

$$\mathbf{V} = \frac{\mathbf{F}_a}{\mathbf{Z}_m} = \frac{F/0°}{j(\omega M - 1/\omega K)} \tag{3-47}$$

The object of the spring mounting is to make the ratio of the transmitted force to the applied force as small as practicable. Whereas the applied force is the sum of the mass and spring forces, the transmitted force is the spring force alone. The phasor representing the transmitted force is found by multiplying the velocity phasor by the spring impedance:

$$\mathbf{F}_t = \mathbf{V}\mathbf{Z}_K = \mathbf{V}\left(-j\frac{1}{\omega K}\right) \tag{3-48}$$

From Eq. (3-48) we could find the instantaneous transmitted force if we desired. However, we are primarily interested in the ratio of the magnitudes of the peak values of transmitted and applied force. This we can obtain from the ratio of the phasors which represent the two forces:

$$\frac{\mathbf{F}_t}{\mathbf{F}_a} = \frac{-1/\omega K}{\omega M - 1/\omega K} \tag{3-49}$$

This ratio will generally be a complex number whose magnitude is the ratio of the peak amplitudes of transmitted and applied forces and whose phase angle is the angle by which the transmitted-force variation leads the applied-force variation. This angle is presumably not of interest in the present investigation, although we can easily see that it is always either 0° or 180°.

INTERPRETATION OF RESULTS The result (3-49) will be put in slightly more convenient form if both numerator and denominator are multiplied by ωK. When this is done, we note the occurrence of the combination MK. This can be expressed in terms of the characteristic radian frequency of the system $\omega_0 = 1/\sqrt{MK}$ [Table 2-1 or Eq. (2-19)], resulting finally in

$$\frac{\mathbf{F}_t}{\mathbf{F}_a} = \frac{-1}{\omega^2/\omega_0^2 - 1} \tag{3-50}$$

The magnitude of the expression F_t/F_a is of most interest, since it is the numerical ratio of the peak transmitted force to the peak applied force. It is plotted in Fig. 3-21.

In one respect Fig. 3-21 shows that the result of our investigation is perhaps somewhat unexpected. Unless the springs are designed to give a large equivalent compliance K (that is, unless they are very flexible), we may be better off if we mount the compressor directly

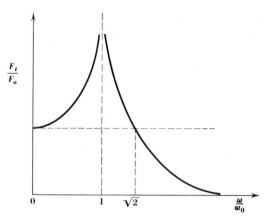

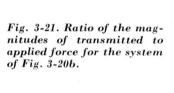

Fig. 3-21. Ratio of the magnitudes of transmitted to applied force for the system of Fig. 3-20b.

on the floor. If the natural oscillation frequency $1/2\pi \sqrt{MK}$ cps is greater than $1/\sqrt{2}$ times the applied frequency, the springs actually make matters worse; *the transmitted force is greater than the applied force!* (This is similar to the effect of repeated application of a small force to the pendulum of a clock, causing it to swing to an amplitude where the restoring force is much greater than the applied force.) On the other hand, by making the natural resonant frequency very low, the transmitted force can be made quite small.

The significance of the phase angle of Eq. (3-50) is very simply explained. For applied frequencies less than the natural resonant frequency ($\omega < \omega_0$, that is, low applied frequency or stiff springs), the angle of the force ratio is zero; the two forces are in phase. When the instantaneous applied force is in a downward direction, so also is the instantaneous transmitted force.

On the other hand, if the applied frequency is greater than the natural resonant frequency ($\omega > \omega_0$, that is, high applied frequency or flexible springs), the relative phase angle is 180°. Thus, at an instant when the applied force is downward, the force transmitted to the floor is upward.

Note that the most convenient representation of the results of this example, in Fig. 3-21, involves plotting, not the transmitted force and the applied frequency, but dimensionless ratios involving these quantities. Thus, the ratio of transmitted force to applied force is plotted against the ratio of applied frequency to the natural resonant frequency of the system. The advantage of this scheme, as discussed in Sec. 2-4, is that the curve applies, not to one specific system for which calculations have been made, but rather to all M-K systems with any values of the system elements M and K.

This representation of results in the form of *normalized* engineering design curves is both common and convenient, and we shall frequently present results in this way. The appropriate normalizing quantities to use (F_a and ω_0 in this example) are not always so obvious, and often there are several equally suitable choices. Future examples will shed still more illumination on this matter.

PROBLEMS

3-11   Note, from Eq. (3-43), that the applied force in the vibration-isolation example of this section depends upon the radian frequency of piston oscillation ω as well as upon the peak displacement X_p. If the compressor is to be operated at variable speed (and, we may assume, constant piston displacement X_p), it may be of interest to know how the transmitted force can be expected to vary with speed (that is, with ω). Thus, we may wish to investigate the variation of the ratio F_t/X_p with ω.

Find and plot an expression for the dimensionless ratio $F_t/\omega_0{}^2mX_p$ as a function of ω/ω_0; interpret the results. (What are the allowable ranges of operating speeds? In what range of speeds is operation probable? Are any precautions suggested to be observed during the period of acceleration just after the compressor is started? What is the transmitted force at very high speeds, and how does it depend upon m and M?)

3-12   In the vibration-isolation example of this section the amplitude of vertical oscillation of the compressor is of interest, since the mounting springs must be high enough to prevent the compressor base from hitting the floor at the peaks of oscillation.

From Eqs. (3-43) and (3-47) find the phasor representation of the compressor displacement $\mathbf{X}$ (note that $\mathbf{V} = j\omega\mathbf{X}$). Study the ratio X/X_p; attempt to find a suitable way of representing it graphically as a function of ω/ω_0. Interpret the resulting curve in terms of the mounting-spring design and of operating instructions.

3-13   A force $f_a = F \cos \omega t$ is applied to the mass-dashpot system shown, resulting in a force f_t being transmitted to the supporting structure. Find expressions for the phasor representations of applied and transmitted forces F_a and F_t. Plot the magnitude ratio F_t/F_a versus ω/ω_1, where ω_1 is some suitably chosen normalizing frequency.

Fig. P 3-13

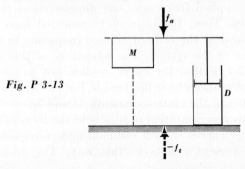

3-14 A force $f_a = F \cos \omega t$ is applied to the spring-dashpot combination shown. Find expressions for the phasor representations of the applied force $\mathbf{F}_a$, the spring force $\mathbf{F}_K$, and the dashpot force $\mathbf{F}_D$. Roughly sketch a phasor diagram showing the relation of these three phasors for a rather low frequency and for a high frequency.

  Sketch curves of the magnitude ratios F_K/F_a and F_D/F_a versus ω/ω_1, where ω_1 is some suitable normalizing frequency.

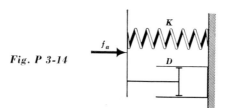

Fig. P 3-14

3-15 An electrical circuit consists of an inductance L and a resistance R in series; the impedance is $\mathbf{Z} = R + j\omega L = Z\underline{/\theta}$. The magnitude Z is the ratio of peak applied voltage to peak current; the angle θ is the phase angle by which the applied voltage leads the current.

  Plot, fairly accurately, curves of normalized impedance Z/R and θ as functions of normalized frequency ω/ω_1, where $\omega_1 \triangleq R/L$.

  Use these curves to find the current in Prob. 3-7.

3-16 A mechanical system similar to that of Prob. 1-15 is described by the differential equation

$$f = M\frac{dv}{dt} + Dv + \frac{1}{K}\int v\,dt$$

Assume that a force $f = F \cos (\omega t + \theta)$ has been applied for a sufficiently long time for the amplitudes of any natural-behavior terms to be negligible.

  Carefully explaining the justification for each step, demonstrate the truth of the following equation:

$$\mathbf{F} = \mathbf{Z}_m\mathbf{V}$$

where $\mathbf{F}$ and $\mathbf{V}$ are the phasor representations of the force and velocity and $\mathbf{Z}_m \triangleq D + j(\omega M - 1/\omega K)$.

3-17 An electrical circuit consisting of a resistance, an inductance, and a capacitance in series with a voltage source is described by the following differential equation:

$$e = L\frac{di}{dt} + Ri + \frac{1}{C}\int i\,dt$$

Assume that a voltage $e = E \cos (\omega t + \theta)$ has been applied for a sufficiently long time for the amplitudes of any natural-behavior terms to be negligible.

Carefully explaining the justification for each step, demonstrate the truth of the equation

$$E = ZI$$

where E and I are the phasor representations of the voltage and current and $Z \triangleq R + j(\omega L - 1/\omega C)$.

3-5 ELECTRICAL ELEMENTS IN PARALLEL

Before attempting to summarize the treatment of forced behavior, let us work out two additional examples.

For the first of these, consider the capacitor of Fig. 3-22a, consisting of two parallel capacitor plates separated by a nonideal dielectric. The best dielectric, or insulating, substances are expensive, and it is sometimes desirable to use a cheaper material. With a poor insulator between a pair of capacitor plates, an applied voltage produces not only storage of charge but also a small current flow through the insulator. The effect of this current flow on the impedance properties of the capacitor is of interest.

A suitable approximate network model is shown in Fig. 3-22b. The capacitance C is the value that would be obtained with a perfect dielectric between the plates. The resistance R represents the effect of the leakage current. (Its value could be determined approximately from a measurement of the d-c flow with a constant voltage across the capacitor.) These two elements are connected in *parallel;* that is, the same voltage appears across both of them. If a voltage represented by the phasor E is placed across this parallel combination, the resulting current through the resistance is $I_R = E/R$; that through the capacitance is $I_C = E/Z_C = j\omega CE$.

Now, barring the possibility of the piling up or the disappearance of electric charge (electrons) at a junction of conductors, at any instant the current leaving the junction must exactly equal the current entering. (This observation is sometimes called *Kirchhoff's current law;* the voltage law of Kirchhoff was introduced in Sec. 2-1.) Thus the

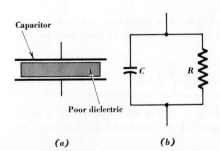

Capacitor

Poor dielectric

(a)   *(b)*

Fig. 3-22. (a) *Capacitor with a poor insulating material between the capacitor plates;* (b) *approximate network model.*

total current flowing to the parallel combination is the sum of the two element currents $\mathbf{I}_R$ and $\mathbf{I}_C$, or

$$\mathbf{I}_T = \mathbf{I}_R + \mathbf{I}_C \tag{3-51}$$

The impedance of the parallel combination is, by definition, $\mathbf{Z}_T = \mathbf{E}/\mathbf{I}_T$; so Eq. (3-51) may be written

$$\frac{\mathbf{E}}{\mathbf{Z}_T} = \frac{\mathbf{E}}{R} + \frac{\mathbf{E}}{\mathbf{Z}_C} \tag{3-52}$$

The $\mathbf{E}$ is common to all terms; hence

$$\frac{1}{\mathbf{Z}_T} = \frac{1}{R} + \frac{1}{\mathbf{Z}_C} \tag{3-53}$$

This relation between total and branch impedances is here derived for a specific circuit, but the argument is easily seen to apply to parallel combinations in general. Thus, if $\mathbf{Z}_1$, $\mathbf{Z}_2$, $\mathbf{Z}_3$, etc., are connected in parallel, the total impedance $\mathbf{Z}_T$ is related to the branch impedances by (Fig. 3-23)

$$\frac{1}{\mathbf{Z}_T} = \frac{1}{\mathbf{Z}_1} + \frac{1}{\mathbf{Z}_2} + \frac{1}{\mathbf{Z}_3} + \cdots \tag{3-54}$$

Solving Eq. (3-53) for $\mathbf{Z}_T$ yields, for the impedance of the RC combination of Fig. 3-22,

$$\mathbf{Z}_T = \frac{R}{1 + j\omega CR} \tag{3-55}$$

This can be separated into real and imaginary parts by multiplying numerator and denominator by the conjugate of the denominator, $1 - j\omega CR$:

$$\mathbf{Z}_T = \frac{R}{1 + (\omega CR)^2} - j\frac{\omega CR^2}{1 + (\omega CR)^2} \tag{3-56}$$

SUBSTITUTION OF A SERIES CONNECTION FOR A PARALLEL CONNECTION In the following chapters it will become evident that parallel connections of network elements are as common as series connections and are no more difficult to analyze. In some cases, however, a series connection of elements may be more convenient in visualizing the circuit's behavior than a parallel connection. The opposite will be true in other situations. Consequently, a technique which will allow us to represent

Fig. 3-23. Impedance in parallel. The equivalent impedance is given by Eq. (3-54).

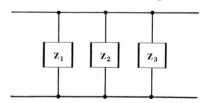

Fig. 3-24. Series form of an equivalent circuit for an imperfect capacitor.

a parallel connection of elements as a series connection will prove valuable. We shall devise such a technique for the imperfect-capacitor network just introduced. This technique is easily extendable to other networks.

Equation (3-56) has a real and a negative imaginary part, just as does the impedance of a series connection of a capacitance and resistance. Thus, Eq. (3-56) may be rewritten as

$$Z_T = R_{eq} - j\frac{1}{\omega C_{eq}} \tag{3-57}$$

where we define an equivalent resistance

$$R_{eq} \triangleq \frac{R}{1 + (\omega CR)^2} \tag{3-58}$$

and an equivalent capacitance

$$C_{eq} \triangleq C\frac{1 + (\omega CR)^2}{(\omega CR)^2} \tag{3-59}$$

Consequently, the combination of elements in Fig. 3-24 is equivalent (as far as the total impedance is concerned) to the network of Fig. 3-22b.

We have seen that the product CR has dimensions of time, so that we can define a normalizing frequency

$$\omega_1 = \frac{1}{CR} \tag{3-60}$$

Equations (3-58) and (3-59) may then be written

$$R_{eq} = R\frac{1}{1 + (\omega/\omega_1)^2} \tag{3-61}$$

$$C_{eq} = C\frac{1 + (\omega/\omega_1)^2}{(\omega/\omega_1)^2} \tag{3-62}$$

These are plotted in Fig. 3-25. Equations (3-61) and (3-62) make it quite obvious that no real resistor and capacitor may be connected in series as in Fig. 3-24 to yield the same impedance as given in Eq. (3-56). The equivalent resistance and capacitance are not constants but are functions of the frequency ω.

To take a specific numerical example, suppose $R = 1$ megohm (1 million ohms) and $C = 1$ μf. Then $\omega_1 = 1$, corresponding to a frequency of $1/2\pi$ cps. Thus at a frequency of 60 cps an equivalent circuit for this imperfect capacitor is a capacitance of 1 μf (C_{eq} differs from C by only about 1 part in 100,000) in series with a resistance

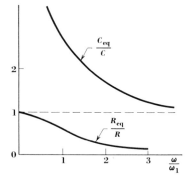

Fig. 3-25. Values of R_{eq} and C_{eq} in Fig. 3-24.

$R_{eq} = 7.0$ ohms. Since the impedance of a 1-μf capacitor at 60 cps is about 2,650 ohms, the effect of the leakage is not a very important one. At higher frequencies it is even less so. (On the other hand, a 1-megohm leakage in a 1-μμf† capacitor would cause it to behave quite unlike a perfect capacitor even at frequencies of hundreds of kilocycles.)

Using the above numerical values, we can easily find the current when a voltage of $100/0°$ is impressed across the capacitor. The impedance is

$$\mathbf{Z}_T = 7 - j2{,}650 = 2{,}650/{-}89.85° \tag{3-63}$$

and thus the current is (see Fig. 3-26)

$$\mathbf{I} = \frac{\mathbf{E}}{\mathbf{Z}_T} = \frac{100/0°}{2{,}650/{-}89.85°} = 0.0377/89.85° \tag{3-64}$$

† 1 μμf (micromicrofarad) = 10^{-12} farad.

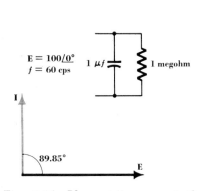

Fig. 3-26. Phasor diagram of the current and voltage in an imperfect capacitor.

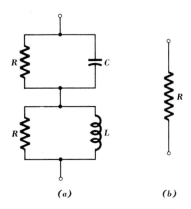

Fig. 3-27. Two networks which have the same impedance at all frequencies if the relation $R = \sqrt{L/C}$ is satisfied.

This may be checked by computing the currents through the two parallel elements separately and adding them.

Note that the equivalent series resistance of 7 ohms is valid only for the frequency 60 cps or for a frequency range near 60 cps; for other frequencies, R_{eq} and C_{eq} will have other values. Networks may have terminal equivalence in the sense that they have the same impedance at all frequencies. The network of Fig. 3-27 is one such example.

PROBLEMS

3-18   Find the total impedance of a parallel combination of a resistance R and an inductance L. Assuming that this can be represented as $\mathbf{Z}_T = R_{eq} + j\omega L_{eq}$, find expressions for R_{eq} and L_{eq} as functions of frequency. Plot curves (similar to Fig. 3-25) of R_{eq}/R and L_{eq}/L versus ω/ω_2, where ω_2 is a convenient normalizing frequency.

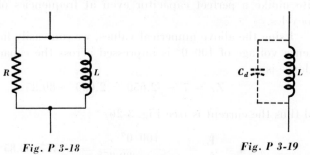

Fig. P 3-18   Fig. P 3-19

3-19   The apparent inductance of a coil of wire is found by measurement to be relatively independent of frequency at low frequencies but to increase with frequency at higher frequencies. It is suggested that this effect can be explained in terms of the equivalent circuit shown in the figure, where L indicates the "true" coil inductance and C_d represents the distributed capacitance due to the electric field between the turns of the coil.

(*a*) Investigate this suggestion by examining the impedance of the parallel combination shown as a function of frequency. Assume that this impedance can be represented as $j\omega L_{eq}$; sketch a plot of L_{eq}/L as a function of frequency (the frequency scale being in terms of an appropriate dimensionless quantity).

(*b*) Can you suggest a method for obtaining the values of L and C_d from a series of impedance measurements made on the coil at different excitation frequencies?

3-20   Verify that the networks of Fig. 3-27 have the same impedance at all frequencies if the condition $R = \sqrt{L/C}$ is satisfied. (The total impedance of Fig. 3-27a is the sum of the impedances of the two parallel combinations.)

3-6 MECHANICAL ELEMENTS IN TANDEM

Before pausing to summarize the treatment of forced behavior, let us consider as a final example the mechanical system of Fig. 3-28. This combination of a dashpot and spring is to be used in an application where it is desired to provide damping for low-frequency vibrations but to have the damping ineffective for high-frequency oscillations. To determine whether or not it will operate as advertised, let us investigate the motional impedance at the dashpot piston.

Suppose that a force represented by the phasor $\mathbf{F}$ is applied at the piston. Since the elements are connected in tandem, this force is also transmitted to the spring.

Let the relative velocity between dashpot cylinder and piston, dx_D/dt, be represented by the phasor $\mathbf{V}_D$. Similarly, let the velocity associated with the spring, dx_K/dt, be $\mathbf{V}_K$ $(= j\omega\mathbf{X}_K)$. The usual impedance relations yield

$$\mathbf{V}_D = \frac{\mathbf{F}}{D} \qquad \mathbf{V}_K = \frac{\mathbf{F}}{\mathbf{Z}_K} = j\omega K\mathbf{F} \qquad (3\text{-}65)$$

The piston displacement is the sum of x_D and x_K; thus the piston velocity is

$$\mathbf{V} = \mathbf{V}_D + \mathbf{V}_K \qquad (3\text{-}66)$$

The impedance at the piston is, by definition, $\mathbf{Z}_P = \mathbf{F}/\mathbf{V}$, so Eq. (3-66) may be written (factoring out the $\mathbf{F}$ which is common to each term)

$$\frac{1}{\mathbf{Z}_P} = \frac{1}{D} + \frac{1}{\mathbf{Z}_K} \qquad (3\text{-}67)$$

Rearranging gives

$$\mathbf{Z}_P = \frac{D}{1 + j\omega K D} \qquad (3\text{-}68)$$

Equation (3-68) is in exactly the same form as Eq. (3-55) and could be discussed along the same lines (see Sec. 3-5). We see that for low-frequency excitation the impedance of the combination is very nearly the frictional resistance D. On the other hand, for very high frequency excitation the impedance is nearly equal to the impedance of the spring alone, and damping is negligible.

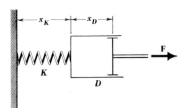

Fig. 3-28. Dashpot and spring connected in tandem.

The same logic which led to Eq. (3-67) could be used to give a general relation between the over-all impedance and the element impedance Z_1, Z_2, etc., when more mechanical elements are connected in tandem:

$$\frac{1}{Z_T} = \frac{1}{Z_1} + \frac{1}{Z_2} + \frac{1}{Z_3} + \cdots \qquad (3\text{-}69)$$

Table 3-1 provides a convenient summary of the manner in which impedances (or their reciprocals) combine to give the over-all impedance when elements (or groups of elements) are connected together.

TABLE 3-1   *Combinations of System Elements*

Type of Elements	Connected		Add Driving Point
Electrical	In series	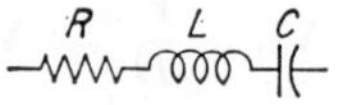	Voltage-current ratios (impedances)
Electrical	In parallel	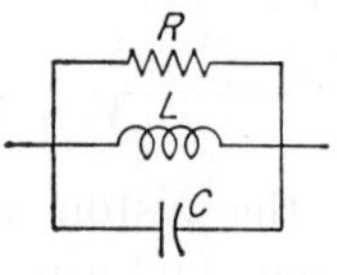	Current-voltage ratios (admittances)
Mechanical	Abreast	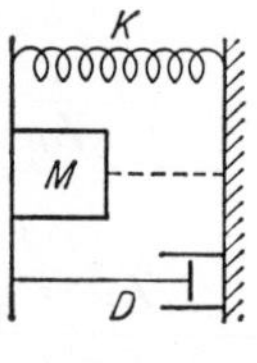	Force-velocity ratios (motional impedances)
Mechanical	In tandem	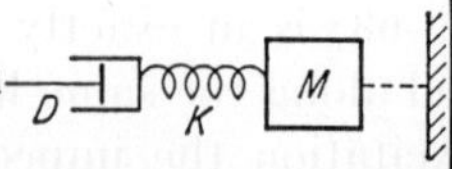	Velocity-force ratios

PROBLEMS

3-21   The dashpot piston in the figure is moved with a peak displacement X and a radian frequency of oscillation ω. Find an expression for the displacement (phasor representation) of the mass M, using the concept of motional impedances in tandem.

Choose suitable normalizing quantities and plot a curve of normalized displacement vs. normalized oscillation frequency.

Plot a curve of the phase angle between the motion of the piston and the motion of the mass, as a function of ω.

Fig. P 3-21

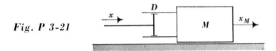

3-22   The mass M_1 represents a cutting head in a hand tool which must oscillate horizontally with a motion $x = X \cos \omega t$, where X is the peak displacement from center and ω is 2π times the frequency of oscillation. In order to reduce the force required to produce this motion (and thus reduce the objectionable force which will be transmitted back to the operator's hand), a vibration absorber is added which consists of a spring K and a mass M connected in tandem as shown. (Assume that M is considerably smaller than M_1.)

     (*a*) Let the motion of the cutting head M_1 be represented by the phasor $\mathbf{X}$. Write an expression for the impedance of the spring-mass combination K-M. Write an expression for the phasor representation of the force $\mathbf{F}_K$ transmitted by the spring.

     (*b*) Write an expression for the total applied force $\mathbf{F}$ that will be required.

     (*c*) What should be the value of the spring compliance K, in terms of M_1 and M, in order to make the magnitude of the applied force F as small as possible? What is this minimum value for F? Discuss.

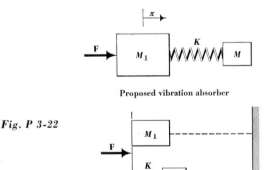

Proposed vibration absorber

Fig. P 3-22

Preferable diagrammatic representation

3-23   In Prob. 3-22, assume the following numerical values: $M_1 = 9$ g, $M = 1$ g, $X = 2$ mm.

     (*a*) Find the value of the spring compliance K for which the minimum applied force will occur at $\omega = 100$ radians/sec.

     (*b*) For this value of K, plot the peak value of applied force F versus ω for values of ω from 0 to 200. Plot also the required force for M_1 alone, with no vibration absorber.

(c) Discuss with the aid of this plot the range of speeds of operation over which the vibration absorber is effective. Can you suggest how the vibration absorber might be redesigned to increase this range? Discuss the use of this type of vibration absorber for variable-speed operation.

3-7 SUMMARY OF FORCED BEHAVIOR

To summarize, then, sinusoidally varying voltages, currents, forces, and velocities are representable as complex numbers or phasors. The significance of the phasor may be stated in either of two ways. The instantaneous value of the quantity represented is equal to the horizontal projection of a rotating line segment (with angular velocity ω radians/sec). This line segment at $t = 0$ is the phasor. Alternatively, when the phasor representation is multiplied by $e^{i\omega t}$, the real part of the product is the instantaneous value.

In many cases it is not necessary to know the instantaneous value at every instant of time. The maximum value, together with the frequency and the phase angle with respect to some other quantity (that is, the phasor representation), suffices for a description. Often one sees expressions such as "a current of 10 at an angle of $-30°$." What is meant is that this is the phasor *representation* of the current.

EFFECTIVE VALUES OF CURRENT AND VOLTAGE In the case of electrical quantities a further complication arises. To see why, consider a resistor R with a current $i = I_m \cos \omega t$ flowing through it. The instantaneous power is (see Fig. 3-29)

$$p = i^2 R = (I_m \cos \omega t)^2 R$$
$$= \frac{I_m^2}{2} R(1 + \cos 2\omega t) \tag{3-70}$$

Usually, however, it is the average power, rather than the instantaneous power, which is the quantity of interest. From Eq. (3-70) we see that the average power is $I_m^2 R/2$.

It is convenient to have alternating current measured in such a way that an alternating current has the same power-producing capability as the same number of amperes of direct current. If this is to be accomplished, the a-c measure, it is easily seen, must be $I_m/\sqrt{2}$. This measure is called the *effective* value. Electric meters are almost universally calibrated to record effective values, and so effective values are most commonly used in the field. Thus a current

$$i = 10 \cos (\omega t + 30°)$$

has a peak, or maximum, value of 10 amp and an effective value of 7.07 amp. Its phasor representation would usually be written $7.07\underline{/30°}$.

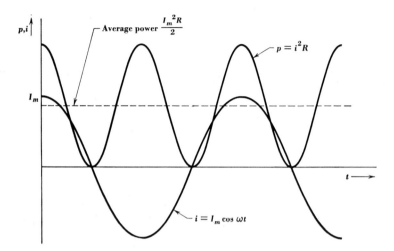

Fig. 3-29. Current through a resistor and the associated average power.

If the phasor representation is in terms of the effective value, it must be multiplied by $\sqrt{2}$ before it is converted to instantaneous current or voltage.

IMPEDANCE The electrical and mechanical driving-point impedances for the forced-behavior case may be defined, respectively, as the ratios of the phasor representations of voltage and current and of force and velocity, as follows:

$$\mathbf{Z}_{\text{elec}} = \frac{\mathbf{E}}{\mathbf{I}} \qquad (3\text{-}71)$$

$$\mathbf{Z}_{\text{mech}} = \frac{\mathbf{V}}{\mathbf{F}} \qquad (3\text{-}72)$$

where the quantities are related as indicated in Fig. 3-30. Note that the voltage and current, or force and velocity, directions are so defined that the impedance will be a positive number if a pure resistance or a frictional resistance is substituted for the impedance.

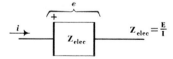

Fig. 3-30. Electrical and mechanical impedance relations.

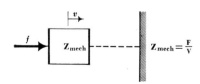

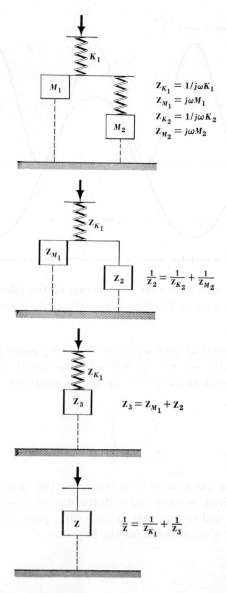

$$Z_{K_1} = 1/j\omega K_1$$
$$Z_{M_1} = j\omega M_1$$
$$Z_{K_2} = 1/j\omega K_2$$
$$Z_{M_2} = j\omega M_2$$

Fig. 3-31. Successive stages in the reduction of a mechanical network to a single impedance.

$$\frac{1}{Z_2} = \frac{1}{Z_{K_2}} + \frac{1}{Z_{M_2}}$$

$$Z_3 = Z_{M_1} + Z_2$$

$$\frac{1}{Z} = \frac{1}{Z_{K_1}} + \frac{1}{Z_3}$$

The impedance of the various system elements for forced behavior is given below:

Electrical		**Mechanical**	
Resistance	R	Frictional resistance	D
Inductance	$j\omega L$	Mass	$j\omega M$
Capacitance	$\dfrac{1}{j\omega C}$	Compliance	$\dfrac{1}{j\omega K}$

When electrical elements (or combinations of elements) are connected in series or when mechanical elements are connected abreast, their impedances add; when electrical elements are connected in parallel or when mechanical elements are connected in tandem, the reciprocals of their impedances add. These rules are summarized in Table 3-1.

Figures 3-31 and 3-32 illustrate the way in which the impedances of elements in more complicated configurations may be combined to give the over-all impedance of the combination. Successive reductions, following the rules of Table 3-1, finally result in a single expression for the total impedance.

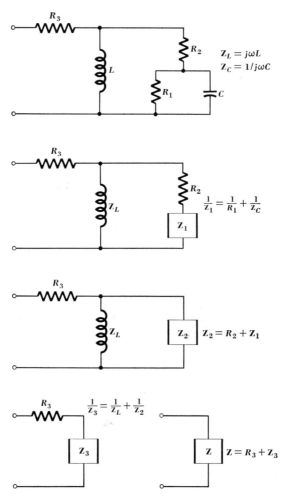

Fig. 3-32. Successive stages in the reduction of an electrical network to a single impedance.

P R O B L E M S

3-24   (*a*) A current $\sqrt{2}\,I_1 \cos \omega t$ (where I_1 is the effective value) flows through a resistance R. Simultaneously, a second current $\sqrt{2}\,I_2 \sin 3\omega t$ flows through the same resistor. Show that the total average power converted to heat is $R(I_1{}^2 + I_2{}^2)$ watts. (Note that power is not a linear function of current; so the superposition principle cannot be used directly.)

(*b*) A current $\sqrt{2}\,I_1 \cos \omega t$ flows through a resistance R; simultaneously, a second current $\sqrt{2}\,I_2 \cos \omega t$ flows through the same resistor. Find the total average power loss.

3-25   Find the impedances of the given electrical networks at the terminals shown. Use limiting-case and dimensional checking.

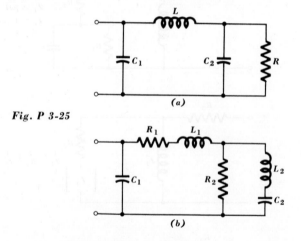

Fig. P 3-25

(*a*)

(*b*)

3-26   Find expressions for the mechanical impedances of the systems shown at the positions of the arrows. Check your results by limiting-case and dimensional methods.

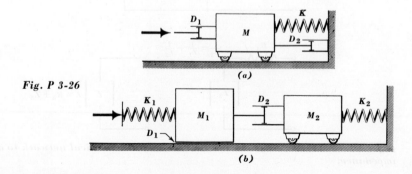

Fig. P 3-26

(*a*)

(*b*)

3-27   (*a*) Write an expression for the impedance of the circuit shown.
      (*b*) A generator supplying a voltage $E \cos \omega t$ is connected to the terminals. What is the value of ω for which the circuit is resonant, in the sense that the generator current is in phase with the voltage (impedance is purely resistive)?

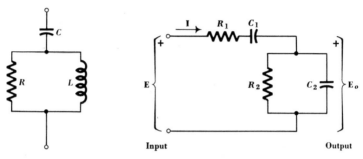

Fig. P 3-27   *Fig. P 3-28*

3-28   (*a*) In the circuit shown, **E** is a sinusoidally varying voltage of frequency f cps. Derive an expression for the current phasor **I** and, hence, for the ratio of output to input voltages E_o/E.
      (*b*) Obtain an expression, in terms of the circuit elements R_1, C_1, R_2, and C_2, for the frequency at which E_o and E are in phase. (Check both results, in so far as it appears practicable, by dimensional and limiting-case checking.)

3-29   A sinusoidal voltage of magnitude 100 volts (effective) is applied to the network shown. Find the total average power and the power into each resistor.

Fig. P 3-29

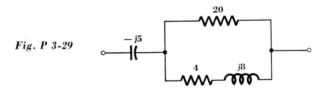

3-30   A sensitive instrument of mass M is supported on springs of total compliance K. The floor vibrates vertically with a motion $x_f = X_f \cos \omega t$.
      (*a*) Find the magnitude of the peak force transmitted to the instrument and plot as a function of (normalized) frequency.
      (*b*) Discuss the choice of the value of compliance in designing the spring mounting and the effectiveness of this mounting in reducing the applied force below what it would be if the instrument were mounted directly on the floor.

3-31   Find values of R_1, R_2, and C_1, in terms of R_a, R_b, and C_a in the figure, such that the impedance of the second network will be the same as the impedance of the first at all values of frequency.

Fig. P 3-31

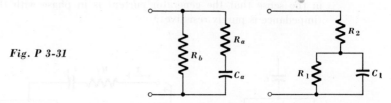

3-32   One common type of capacitor is constructed of two sheets of metal foil, placed between sheets of specially prepared paper and rolled into a cylinder, as indicated in the figure. The capacitor thus formed is imperfect, both because the paper is not a perfect insulator and because there is a certain amount of inductance associated with the leads and foil. Thus a reasonably accurate equivalent circuit is that shown in the figure.

In the design of a 1-μf capacitor the leakage resistance is computed to be 1 megohm (10^6 ohms) and the lead inductance is estimated at 10^{-5} henry.

(*a*) Find the steady-state impedance of this capacitor at frequencies of 10 cps, 1 kc, and 100 kc. Compare these with the impedance of an ideal 1-μf capacitor at the same frequencies.

(*b*) State the approximate frequency range over which you would say this capacitor is equivalent, to a reasonable degree of accuracy, to the ideal capacitor. Present reasoning to justify your answer.

Fig. P 3-32

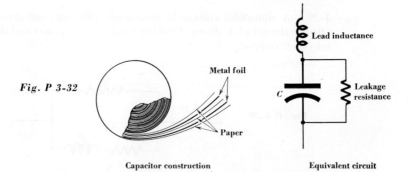

Capacitor construction   Equivalent circuit

3-33   The figure indicates the principle of an instrument which can be used for making vibration measurements.

Assume that the vibrating surface moves vertically with a displacement $x_2 = X_2 \cos \omega t$. The force transmitted through the spring of compliance K causes the mass M to vibrate with a displacement x_1 measured from its equilibrium position. The spring force is $(1/K)(x_1 - x_2)$. The relative displacement $x_1 - x_2$ is read on the scale.

(*a*) Write the differential equation for the system and solve it for x_1 or $v_1 = dx_1/dt$, making use of the phasor methods discussed in this chapter. Find and plot the ratio of the peak scale reading to the peak displacement X_2 as a function of ω.

(b) Under what conditions will the scale reading be a reliable indication of the vibration amplitude X_2?

(c) Under what conditions could this device be used to measure the peak acceleration of the surface $\omega^2 X_2$?

Fig. P 3-33

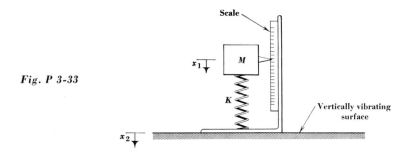

3-34 Part a of the drawing illustrates the structure of a four-arm bridge circuit. The element M is a sensitive meter or other indicating

Fig. P 3-34

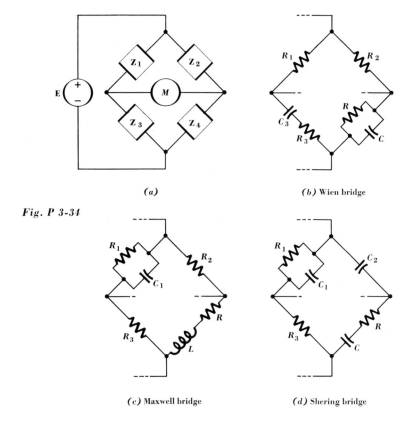

(a)   (b) Wien bridge

(c) Maxwell bridge   (d) Shering bridge

device. The bridge is said to be balanced if there is no current through M (that is, if the voltage across M is zero). If the applied voltage is sinusoidal with radian frequency ω, find the balance conditions relating Z_1, Z_2, Z_3, and Z_4 which must be met in order for the bridge to be balanced. Parts b, c, and d illustrate three particular bridge circuits. Assume that the parameters without subscripts are unknown and are to be measured by means of the bridge. Express the unknown parameters in terms of the others when the bridge is balanced.

transient behavior of simple networks

We shall mean by the term *transient behavior* the general case in which natural- and forced-behavior components may be present simultaneously. A simple example will help make the concept clear.

4-1 CURRENT BUILD-UP IN AN INDUCTANCE

When a direct voltage is suddenly impressed on an inductance, such as the field winding of a generator, the current does not rise instantaneously to its final value, which is limited by the circuit resistance. The manner in which the current approaches this final value we propose to investigate, using the concept of impedance.

The current with which we deal is that of Fig. 4-1. At time $t = 0$, the switch is closed, impressing a constant voltage E across the series combination of R and L. Desired is an expression for the current as a function of time.

First let us write the expression for the impedance of the circuit:

$$\mathbf{Z}(s) = R + sL \tag{4-1}$$

Forced behavior of the circuit will occur at zero frequency, $s = j\omega = 0$. For this value of s the impedance is $\mathbf{Z}(0) = R$, and the forced current is E/R (as expected).

But this is not the only current component which can flow. As we saw earlier, the natural behavior of the circuit may occur for

Fig. 4-1. RL circuit for transient analysis.

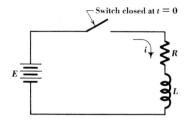

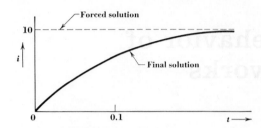

Fig. 4-2. Current in the circuit of Fig. 4-1.

such values of s as make the impedance zero—in this example, $\mathbf{Z}(s) = 0$ at $s = -R/L$. Thus the natural-behavior current component is $Ae^{-Rt/L}$, and the total solution is

$$i = \frac{E}{R} + Ae^{-Rt/L} \tag{4-2}$$

where A is an unknown constant to be determined from the initial conditions.

We assume that the inductor current was zero prior to the closing of the switch. It cannot change instantaneously, so $i = 0$ at $t = 0_+$. Setting $t = 0$ in Eq. (4-2) shows that the proper value of A is $-E/R$. Thus the final solution is

$$i = \frac{E}{R}\left(1 - e^{-Rt/L}\right) \tag{4-3}$$

This is plotted in Fig. 4-2 for $E = 100$ volts, $R = 10$ ohms, $L = 1$ henry.

We have seen that our results are often most valuable when plotted in the form of normalized design curves. A convenient normalizing current in the present case is $i_0 = E/R$, and a suitable normalizing time is $t_0 = L/R$ sec. (The latter is often called the time constant of the circuit.) Equation (4-3) then becomes

$$\frac{i}{i_0} = 1 - e^{-t/t_0} \tag{4-4}$$

which is plotted in Fig. 4-3. The curve of Fig. 4-2 is only a special case, points for which could be picked off Fig. 4-3 by making the substitutions $i_0 = 10$ and $t_0 = 0.1$.

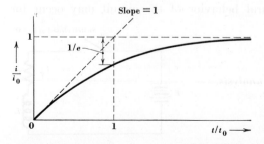

Fig. 4-3. Normalized current vs. time for the circuit of Fig. 4-1.

P R O B L E M S

4-1   At time $t = 0$ the mass in the figure is at rest, and its displacement is $x = 0$. A constant force F is suddenly applied.

(*a*) Write the impedance expression for the system. Find the value of the impedance at $s = 0$ and hence the forced-behavior velocity term.

(*b*) Under what conditions ($Z_m = 0$ or $Z_m \to \infty$) is it possible to have a velocity term which does not depend on the applied force, that is, a natural-behavior term? Find the value of s which satisfies this condition.

(*c*) Combine the results of (*a*) and (*b*) to form the expression for the velocity as a function of time. Sketch a plot.

(*d*) Find the expression for the displacement.

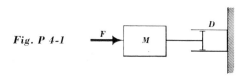

Fig. P 4-1

4-2   At time $t = 0$ a constant voltage E is suddenly impressed across a series combination of a resistance R and a capacitance C. Find the expression for the resulting current flow as a function of time; plot.

4-3   A box of mass M rests on a platform which is stationary until time $t = 0$ and which then starts to move with a constant velocity V. The frictional resistance between box and platform is D.

(*a*) Find the impedance of the M-D combination. (Note the equivalent system in the figure.) Find the forced-behavior term of the force f between the box and the platform.

(*b*) Under what conditions ($Z_m = 0$ or $Z_m \to \infty$) would it be possible to have a force acting between the box and platform with zero platform velocity (natural behavior)? Find the natural-behavior term of the force.

(*c*) Combine the results of parts *a* and *b* to obtain the force f as a function of time; plot.

(*d*) Find and plot the velocity of the mass, v_M, in response to the force found in part *c*.

Fig. P 4-3

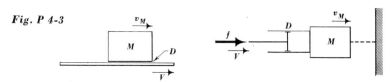

Box and moving platform   Equivalent system

4-4   High-vacuum pentodes characteristically supply to a load circuit a current which is very nearly independent of the load impedance
and which depends only upon the voltage applied to a control element
called a grid. Assume such a pentode to be connected to a parallel combination of a resistance R and a capacitance C as shown in the figure.
Prior to time $t = 0$ the control voltage is held at such a value that the
pentode supplies no current; at $t = 0$ it is suddenly changed to a value
such that the tube supplies a constant current I.

    (*a*) Write the expression for the load impedance. Find the
forced-behavior term of the voltage e.

    (*b*) For what value of load impedance could there be an output
voltage without any driving current? Determine the value of s which
yields this condition and find the corresponding natural-behavior term
of e.

    (*c*) Combine the terms of parts *a* and *b* to obtain the voltage
e as a function of time.

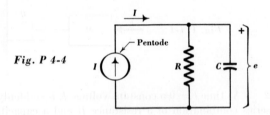

Fig. P 4-4

4-2 SWITCHING TRANSIENTS IN AN *RL* CIRCUIT

    Let us next investigate the same circuit with an a-c generator
substituted for the battery (Fig. 4-4). Let the applied voltage be 141
cos $(377 + \theta)$. (The effective value of the voltage is 100 volts at 60
cps.) The circuit impedance is

$$Z(s) = R + sL \tag{4-5}$$

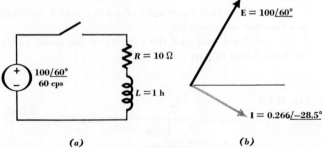

(*a*)   (*b*)

Fig. 4-4. (*a*) *RL circuit in which transient behavior is to be studied;* (*b*) *phasor
diagram for the forced solution.*

for the forced component $s = j\omega$, and the impedance is

$$\mathbf{Z}(j\omega) = R + j\omega L$$
$$= 10 + j377 = 377\underline{/88.5°} \qquad (4\text{-}6)$$

The phasor representation of the applied voltage is

$$\mathbf{E} = 100\underline{/\theta}$$

The transient solution will depend upon the instant the switch is closed. Suppose the switch is closed 60° after the voltage is maximum, so that $\theta = 60°$. Then the current phasor is

$$\mathbf{I} = \frac{\mathbf{E}}{\mathbf{Z}} = \frac{100\underline{/60°}}{377\underline{/88.5°}} = 0.266\underline{/-28.5°} \qquad (4\text{-}7)$$

The instantaneous magnitude of the forced solution is (see Fig. 4-5)

$$i = \sqrt{2}\,(0.266)\cos(\omega t - 28.5°) \qquad (4\text{-}8)$$

At $t = 0$ this has the value of 0.330.

But the instantaneous current at $t = 0$ must be zero. The difference between the forced value and the value prescribed by initial conditions must be made up by the natural-behavior component.

The natural-behavior component is again given by $Ae^{-Rt/L}$. The constant A is computed from the condition that $i = 0$ at $t = 0_+$. Thus, $A = -0.330$, and the transient current is

$$i = 0.376\cos(\omega t - 28.5°) - 0.330e^{-10t} \qquad (4\text{-}9)$$

which is plotted in Fig. 4-5.

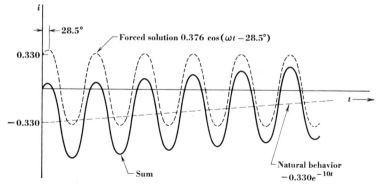

Fig. 4-5. Transient behavior (sum of forced and natural terms) of the circuit of Fig. 4-4.

PROBLEM

4-5   In the example of Sec. 4-2, is there a point on the impressed voltage waveform such that, if the switch is closed at that instant, the natural-behavior component of the current will be zero? If not, explain in physical terms why not. If so, find the value of θ.

4-3 SWITCHING TRANSIENTS IN AN *RC* CIRCUIT

A second example will help to clarify the procedure for finding the transient solution. Let us consider a series resistance-capacitance circuit connected at $t = 0$ to an alternating-voltage source (Fig. 4-6). Assume that the generator voltage is $\sqrt{2}\, E \cos{(\omega t + \theta)}$, where E is the effective value of the voltage. The circuit impedance is

$$\mathbf{Z}(s) = R + \frac{1}{sC} \tag{4-10}$$

FORCED BEHAVIOR   For the forced component, $s = j\omega$, and the impedance is

$$\mathbf{Z}(j\omega) = R + \frac{1}{j\omega C} \tag{4-11}$$

The voltage may be represented by the phasor $\mathbf{E} = E\underline{/\theta}$, and the current phasor is $\mathbf{I} = \mathbf{E}/\mathbf{Z}(j\omega)$.

We shall work out this example for a specific set of numerical values. Let $C = 1$ μf, $R = 1{,}000$ ohms, and $E = 1{,}000$ volts at a frequency of 60 cps. Then

$$\mathbf{Z} = 1{,}000 - j2{,}650 = 2{,}834\underline{/-69.3°} \tag{4-12}$$

Suppose the switch is closed at the instant the voltage is maximum, so that $\theta = 0$. Then

$$\mathbf{I} = \frac{1{,}000\underline{/0°}}{2{,}834\underline{/-69.3°}} = 0.353\underline{/69.3°} \tag{4-13}$$

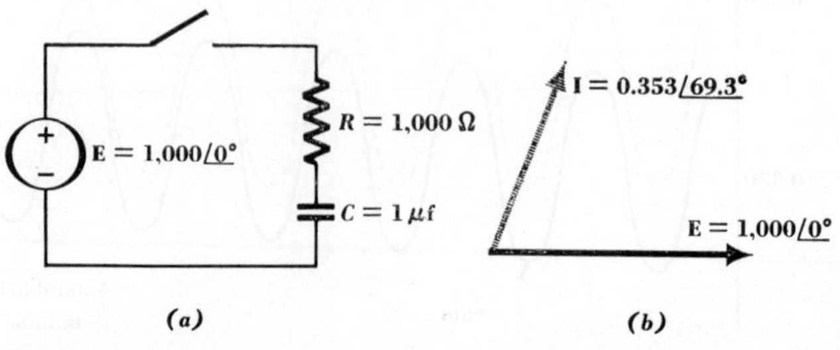

(a)   *(b)*

Fig. 4-6. *RC circuit for the analysis of transient behavior.* (a) *Circuit diagram;* (b) *phasor diagram for the forced solution.*

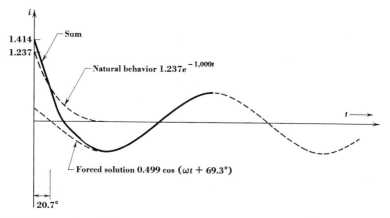

Fig. 4-7. The summing of forced and natural terms to give the transient be-havior of the circuit of Fig. 4-6.

Thus the instantaneous value of the forced solution is (see Fig. 4-7)

$$i_{\text{forced}} = \sqrt{2}\ (0.353)\ \cos\ (\omega t + 69.3°) \tag{4-14}$$

TRANSIENT SOLUTION The natural behavior of the circuit occurs in general for the values of s that make $\mathbf{Z} = 0$—in the present case, for $s = -1/RC$. Thus the natural behavior is

$$i_{\text{nb}} = Ae^{-t/RC} = Ae^{-1,000t} \tag{4-15}$$

The total current is the sum of the forced- and natural-behavior terms.

The constant A must have such a value that the initial conditions of the circuit are satisfied. We assume that just before the switch is closed, there is no charge on the capacitor. The capacitor charge, and hence its voltage, cannot change instantaneously since this would imply infinite current flow. Thus at $t = 0$ the capacitor voltage is zero, and Kirchhoff's law gives

$$i_{t=0} = \frac{e_{t=0}}{R} = \frac{\sqrt{2}\ (1,000)\ \cos\ 0°}{1,000} = 1.414\ \text{amp} \tag{4-16}$$

At $t = 0$ the instantaneous value of i_{forced} is

$$\sqrt{2}\ (0.353)\ \cos\ 69.3° = 0.177\ \text{amp}$$

Thus, to satisfy the initial conditions of Eq. (4-16),

$$A = 1.414 - 0.177 = 1.237 \tag{4-17}$$

The entire solution follows (see Fig. 4-7):

$$i = 0.499\ \cos\ (\omega t + 69.3°) + 1.237e^{-1,000t} \tag{4-18}$$

PROBLEMS

4-6   (*a*) In the example of Sec. 4-3 assume the switch to be closed at the instant the voltage is zero. Find and plot the instantaneous current during the first $\frac{1}{60}$ sec.

(*b*) Is there an instant at which the switch could be closed that would result in zero magnitude of the natural-behavior term? If so, specify the value or values of θ.

4-7   A mass is at rest at time $t = 0$, when an oscillating force $f = 10 \sin 10\pi t$ newtons is suddenly applied, as shown in the figure.

(*a*) Find the expression for the velocity of the mass after $t = 0$.

(*b*) Obtain an expression for the displacement of the mass. Sketch a rough plot of the displacement vs. time for the first 2 sec.

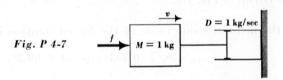

Fig. P 4-7

4-8   A level platform moves horizontally with an x-directed velocity $v_p = 5 \sin 2\pi t$. At time $t = 0$ a box of mass $M = 10$ kg is placed on the platform at point $x = 0$. The frictional resistance between the box and the platform is $D = 20$ kg/sec. Find the subsequent motion of the box.

4-9   Prior to the connection of the battery, the capacitor is uncharged, and there is no current through the inductor. The switch is closed at time $t = 0$. Find and sketch plots of:

(*a*) Current in the inductive branch.

(*b*) Current in the capacitive branch.

(*c*) Total current through the switch.

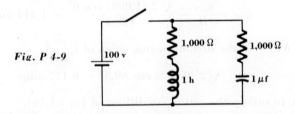

Fig. P 4-9

4-10   Consider the following statement: One cycle after an alternating voltage is applied to a series RC circuit the natural-behavior component of current will invariably be small compared with the maximum of the steady-state component. Is this true? If so, demonstrate.

4-4 TRANSIENT RESPONSE WITH AN EXPONENTIAL EXCITATION

Let us consider now a situation in which an excitation, or driving function, is applied to a system and yet no steady-state response is produced. This will occur whenever the excitation is not constant or periodic. This example will illustrate our earlier comment that a forced solution need not be a steady-state solution.

AN EXPONENTIALLY DECAYING FORCE APPLIED TO A MASS-FRICTION SYSTEM
Figure 4-8 illustrates a mechanical network and the force applied to it. The mechanical impedance of this network is

$$\mathbf{Z}_m = sM + D \tag{4-19}$$

Since the applied force is exponential (with $s = -\alpha$), the forced solution for the velocity is found by dividing the force by the impedance:

$$v_{\text{forced}} = \frac{f}{\mathbf{Z}_m} = \frac{Fe^{-\alpha t}}{D - \alpha M} \tag{4-20}$$

Once again, in order to satisfy the initial conditions, we must take into account the natural solution. The natural solution is

$$v_{\text{natural}} = Ae^{-at} \tag{4-21}$$

where

$$a = \frac{D}{M} \tag{4-22}$$

This solution was obtained in the usual manner, by finding the value of s which makes the impedance zero.

The complete solution for the velocity is the sum of the forced and natural solutions:

$$v = \frac{Fe^{-\alpha t}}{D - \alpha M} + Ae^{-at} \tag{4-23}$$

If the mass has no initial velocity at $t = 0$, the constant A is seen to be $-F/(D - \alpha M)$, and Eq. (4-23) becomes

$$v = \frac{F}{D - \alpha M} (e^{-\alpha t} - e^{-at}) \tag{4-24}$$

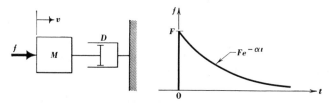

Fig. 4-8. A mechanical network and the force applied to it.

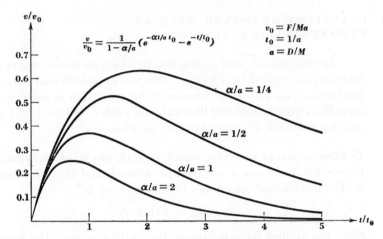

Fig. 4-9. The velocity of the mass in Fig. 4-8 for different exponent values in the exponential driving force.

The velocity as given by Eq. (4-24) is quite easy to plot for various values of α. A problem arises, however, when $\alpha = a$. At first glance, it appears that when this condition occurs, the velocity is identically zero for all values of t. A more careful inspection shows that when M is factored from the denominator and Eq. (4-22) applied, the velocity expression becomes

$$v = \frac{F}{M(a - \alpha)} (e^{-\alpha t} - e^{-at}) \qquad (4\text{-}25)$$

Now we see that when $\alpha = a$, the expression becomes $0/0$ and is indeterminate. By applying Lhopital's rule (let $\alpha = a + x$ and find the limit as $x \to 0$ by differentiating numerator and denominator with respect to x), we find that Eq. (4-25) becomes

$$v = \frac{F}{M} t e^{-at} \qquad \text{for } \alpha = a \qquad (4\text{-}26)$$

Under the conditions which yield the velocity of Eq. (4-26), the forced and natural parts of the network response cannot be distinguished.

Figure 4-9 illustrates the velocity of the mass in Fig. 4-8 for a number of values of the ratio α/a. Note that although the two expressions for the velocity, Eqs. (4-25) and (4-26), look considerably different in form, there is a smooth transition from curve to curve.

4-5 SUMMARY OF TRANSIENT-RESPONSE CALCULATIONS IN TERMS OF THE RESPONSE FUNCTION

We have examined a number of specific linear networks and found their responses to various (exponential) excitations. At this point it would seem advisable to consolidate our knowledge and to record it here, for future reference, in as general a form as possible. First, let us state the general form of the problems we have been solving. The network differential equations relating response to excitation have thus far always been of the following form:

$$a_1 \frac{dr(t)}{dt} + a_2 r(t) + a_3 \int r(t) \, dt = e(t) \qquad (4\text{-}27)$$

The excitation is $e(t)$ and the response $r(t)$. The constants a_1, a_2, and a_3 depend upon the network elements. So far, we have dealt only with network differential equations containing two of the three terms of Eq. (4-27). We include all three here as a generalization,† and in anticipation of the next chapter, where three-element networks are investigated.

The excitations with which we have dealt have been exponential in nature—a single exponential or a sum of exponentials. For the sake of illustration, let us assume that $e(t)$ in Eq. (4-27) is the sum of two exponentials:

$$e(t) = A e^{\alpha t} + B e^{\beta t} \qquad (4\text{-}28)$$

The exponents α and β may be real, imaginary, complex, or zero.

Because Eq. (4-27) is a linear equation, we may apply superposition and solve for the response due to one term of $e(t)$. Then we may find the response due to the second term and add these two responses together. We have seen that if the right-hand side of Eq. (4-27) is a single exponential, a solution can be found by assuming that the response is a single exponential with the same exponent. Thus, if

$$e(t) = A e^{\alpha t} \qquad (4\text{-}29)$$
then
$$r(t) = C_\alpha e^{\alpha t} \qquad (4\text{-}30)$$

where C_α is a constant that can be found by substituting Eqs. (4-29) and (4-30) into Eq. (4-27). Doing this, we obtain

$$\left(a_1 \alpha + a_2 + \frac{a_3}{\alpha} \right) C_\alpha e^{\alpha t} = A e^{\alpha t}$$

$$C_\alpha = \frac{A}{a_1 \alpha + a_2 + a_3/\alpha} \qquad (4\text{-}31)$$

The developments above may be restated in a different form as follows: *If the excitation of a system satisfying Eq. (4-27) is of the form e^{st}, then the response is of the same form, and the ratio of response to excitation (the response function) is*

$$\mathbf{R}(s) = \textit{response function} \triangleq \frac{r(t)}{e(t)} = \frac{1}{a_1 s + a_2 + a_3/s} \qquad (4\text{-}32)$$

† A two-term differential equation is derived from Eq. (4-27) by setting one of the a parameters equal to zero.

Making use of the definition above, we can say that a solution of Eq. (4-27), when the excitation is given by Eq. (4-28), is

$$r(t) = r_\alpha(t) + r_\beta(t) = \mathbf{R}(s = \alpha)Ae^{\alpha t} + \mathbf{R}(s = \beta)Be^{\beta t} \qquad (4\text{-}33)$$

We have been careful to state that Eq. (4-33) is *a* solution and not *the* solution. In general, we would find that the solution given by Eq. (4-33) cannot satisfy the initial conditions which may be applied to the particular network under study. The reason for this is that Eq. (4-33) gives only the forced response (the driven, particular solution). There is an additional possible response which is called the natural response (the homogeneous solution).

As indicated by Eq. (4-33), the forced response can be found with the aid of the response function. Let us turn to this function in order to find the natural solution. It should be clear from Eq. (4-32) that the response function becomes infinite for certain values of s (the values of s which make the denominator zero). What is the significance of the fact that the response function can become infinite? It means that there can be an exponential response term, with exponent containing the value of s which makes the response function infinite, even though the excitation is zero. In other words, the ratio of response to excitation is infinite.

The differential equation under investigation yields a response function which becomes infinite for two values of s (say s_1 and s_2). Consequently, the natural response is

$$r_n(t) = C_1 e^{s_1 t} + C_2 e^{s_2 t} \qquad (4\text{-}34)$$

where C_1 and C_2 are constants which depend upon initial conditions. Note that the result above is the solution to the homogeneous form of Eq. (4-27):

$$a_1 \frac{dr_n(t)}{dt} + a_2 r_n(t) + a_3 \int r_n(t)\, dt = 0 \qquad (4\text{-}35)$$

Combining the forced- and natural-behavior terms yields the total solution of Eq. (4-27):

$$\begin{aligned} r(t) &= r_\alpha(t) + r_\beta(t) + r_n(t) \\ &= \mathbf{R}(\alpha)Ae^{\alpha t} + \mathbf{R}(\beta)Be^{\beta t} + C_1 e^{s_1 t} + C_2 e^{s_2 t} \end{aligned} \qquad (4\text{-}36)$$

The response as given by Eq. (4-36) must satisfy the network initial conditions. The constants C_1 and C_2 are adjusted so that the initial conditions are met.

RÉSUMÉ The foregoing discussion can be generalized and condensed to yield the following statement: A network described by a linear ordinary integrodifferential equation with constant coefficients, of the form of Eq. (4-27) or more complex (that is, with higher derivatives or multiple integrals), has associated with it a response function $\mathbf{R}(s)$. The response function is found by specifying that the excitation $e(t)$ be equal to e^{st}. Then, by assuming that $r(t)$ is some constant times e^{st}, we can solve the differential equation to obtain the proper value of this constant. The ratio of the response to the excitation under these conditions is the response function:

$$\mathbf{R}(s) \triangleq \frac{r(t)}{e(t)} \qquad \text{when both } e(t) \text{ and } r(t) \text{ vary as } e^{st} \qquad (4\text{-}37)$$

Finally, if the actual excitation is

$$e(t) = \sum_{n=1}^{N} A_n e^{\alpha_n t} \qquad (4\text{-}38)$$

then the total response is

$$r(t) = \sum_{n=1}^{N} \mathbf{R}(\alpha_n) A_n e^{\alpha_n t} + \sum_{k=1}^{K} C_k e^{s_k t} \qquad (4\text{-}39)$$

where the s_k are the values of s which make $\mathbf{R}(s)$ infinite.

If one of the α_n exponents of Eq. (4-38) happens to have the same value as one of the s_k exponents, the forced response will have a term of the form $t e^{\alpha_n t}$. This was demonstrated in the previous section. The value of the constant coefficient which multiplies this term can be found by substitution into the differential equation.

THE RELATION OF THE TERM *response function* TO OTHER TERMS WITH SIMILAR MEANINGS   There are a number of "function" terms—*system function, response function, transfer function, driving-point function, impedance function, admittance function*—which are commonly used in network analysis. Not only do the meanings of these terms overlap considerably, but there are inconsistencies from user to user. This naturally leads to a certain amount of confusion. In order to minimize the confusion in this text, let us attempt to explain how these terms will be used here.

All these functions are ratios of one network variable to another when both are varying as e^{st}. Consequently, they are all functions of s. *System function* will be used as an all-inclusive term. That is to say, all the functions listed above are system functions. The *response function* has been defined above. The *transfer function* is a response function in which the excitation and response are at two different points, or terminals, in the network. A *driving-point function* is a response function (or its reciprocal) with excitation and response measured at the same point. When used without qualifying adjectives, the terms *impedance* and *admittance*, as defined previously, refer to driving-point functions. In Chap. 9, however, it will be convenient to define *transfer impedances* and *transfer admittances,* which are transfer functions.

PROBLEMS

4-11 The figure illustrates four networks and four excitations. Find the indicated response of each network to each excitation. None of the networks contains initial stored energy.

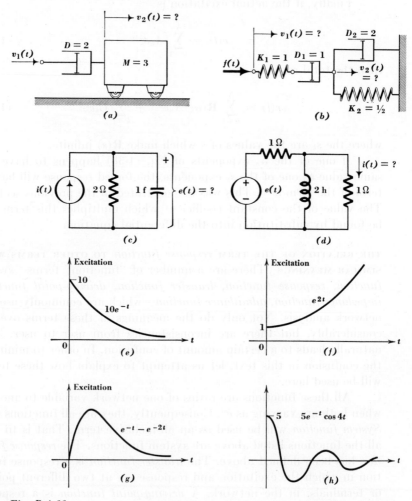

Fig. P 4-11

4-12 The current in the inductor at $t = 0$ is 2 amp, with direction as shown. Find the current if the applied voltage for $t > 0$ is $100e^{-100t}$.

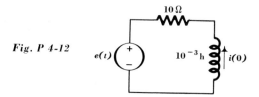

Fig. P 4-12

4-13 A mass of 10 kg is sliding along a plane with frictional constant $D = 1$ kg/sec. An exponential force $10e^{-\alpha t}$ newtons is applied at $t = 0$ in order to stop the motion of the mass. If the velocity of the mass is 10 m/sec at $t = 0$, find the expression for the velocity for $t > 0$. Plot this velocity for several values of α. What should α be in order to make the mass finally come to rest at the exact point where the stopping force was first applied?

4-14 For the circuit shown, find the following response functions: (a) $i(t)/e(t)$, (b) $e_C(t)/e(t)$, (c) $e_L(t)/e(t)$. Find the following system functions: (d) $e_C(t)/e_L(t)$, (e) $[e_C(t) + e_R(t)]/[(e_L(t) + e_R(t)]$.

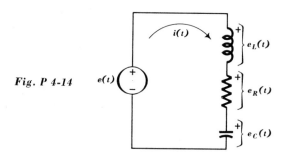

Fig. P 4-14

4-15 The forced response to an excitation $Ae^{\alpha t}$ is $\mathbf{R}(\alpha)Ae^{\alpha t}$, where $\mathbf{R}(s)$ is the response function. If α coincides with one of the values of s which makes $\mathbf{R}(s)$ infinite, the response is $Bte^{\alpha t}$. Prove that

$$B = \mathbf{Q}(\alpha)A \qquad \text{where } \mathbf{Q}(s) = \cfrac{1}{\dfrac{d}{ds}\left[\dfrac{1}{\mathbf{R}(s)}\right]}$$

4-16 It is desired to find out something about the response at a particular point in a given complex electrical network. Demonstrate that:

　　　(a) If there is no initial stored energy, the initial value of the response can be found by replacing all capacitors by short circuits and all inductors by open circuits and then solving for the initial response of the purely resistive network.

　　　(b) If the excitation is constant after $t = 0$, the final value of the response can be found by replacing all capacitors by open circuits and all inductors by short circuits and solving for the final response of the purely resistive network.

4-17   To illustrate the rules set down in the preceding problem, find the initial and final values of the responses indicated on the accompanying diagrams.

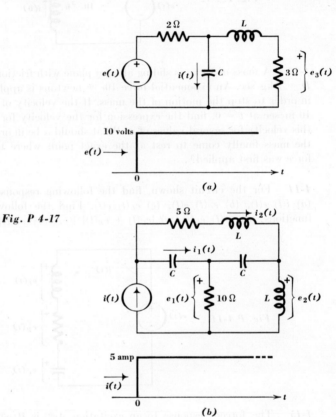

Fig. P 4-17

(a)

(b)

some three-element networks

Now that we have mastered the basic tools of circuit analysis, we shall certainly want to try our hand at some more complex systems. Again we shall select from both mechanical and electrical examples to emphasize the generality of the methods.

5-1 AUTOMOBILE SUSPENSION

Figure 5-1 shows a somewhat oversimplified mechanical network which is roughly equivalent to an automobile spring and shock-absorber suspension. A bump in the road will cause the springs to deflect, and without the shock absorbers the body would then undergo vertical oscillations. The purpose of the shock absorbers (represented in the equivalent network by the frictional resistance D) is to damp out these oscillations and reduce the "bounce." This action we shall now investigate.

The impedance of the network can be written immediately from Table 3-1:

$$\mathbf{Z}_m = sM + D + \frac{1}{sK} \tag{5-1}$$

We seek the natural behavior of the system (no applied force). Hence we solve for the values of s which make $\mathbf{Z}_m$ equal to zero. There are

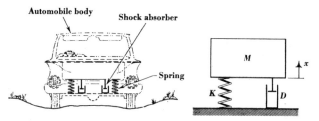

Fig. 5-1. Approximate equivalent network for automobile spring and shock-absorber suspension.

two such values:

$$s_1, s_2 = \frac{-D}{2M} \pm \sqrt{\left(\frac{D}{2M}\right)^2 - \frac{1}{MK}} \tag{5-2}$$

if $(D/2M)^2$ is larger than $1/MK$, or if the converse is true,

$$s_1, s_2 = \frac{-D}{2M} \pm j\sqrt{\frac{1}{MK} - \left(\frac{D}{2M}\right)^2} \tag{5-3}$$

In either case the solution is

$$v = Ae^{s_1 t} + Be^{s_2 t} \tag{5-4}$$

with A and B dependent upon initial conditions.

As we might suspect, the system behavior if s_1 and s_2 are complex is radically different from its character if s_1 and s_2 are real. For this reason it will be necessary to study these cases separately.

CASE I. $D > 2\sqrt{M/K}$ (s_1, s_2 **REAL**)   The two roots in this case are both real and negative:

$$s_1 = \frac{-D}{2M} + \sqrt{\left(\frac{D}{2M}\right)^2 - \frac{1}{MK}}$$

$$s_2 = \frac{-D}{2M} - \sqrt{\left(\frac{D}{2M}\right)^2 - \frac{1}{MK}} \tag{5-5}$$

They can be represented on the complex s plane in the manner we have already used in Table 2-1 (see Fig. 5-2). The velocity and displacement expressions have the form

$$v = Ae^{s_1 t} + Be^{s_2 t} \tag{5-6}$$

$$x = \int v \, dt = \frac{A}{s_1} e^{s_1 t} + \frac{B}{s_2} e^{s_2 t} \tag{5-7}$$

In the latter the constant of integration is set equal to zero by choosing $x = 0$ to be the equilibrium displacement which the system will assume after all natural behavior has died away ($t \to \infty$).

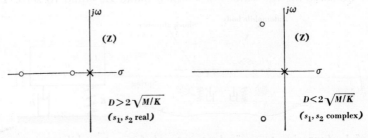

Fig. 5-2. Diagrammatic representation of roots of $Z_m = 0$ in the complex s plane.

The manner in which the velocity and displacement will vary with time depends upon the initial conditions. Let us assume that the spring is compressed a distance x_0 and released at $t = 0$. The initial conditions are, then, $v = 0$ and $x = -x_0$. Substituting these into Eqs. (5-6) and (5-7) yields

$$0 = A + B$$
$$-x_0 = \frac{A}{s_1} + \frac{B}{s_2} \tag{5-8}$$

These may be easily solved for A and B and the final solutions obtained:

$$v = \frac{s_1 s_2}{s_1 - s_2} x_0(e^{s_1 t} - e^{s_2 t}) \tag{5-9}$$

$$x = \frac{x_0}{s_1 - s_2} (s_2 e^{s_1 t} - s_1 e^{s_2 t}) \tag{5-10}$$

These values are plotted in Fig. 5-3 for the case $D = 4\sqrt{M/K}$. Notice that, in order to increase the generality of these curves, they are plotted in terms of dimensionless variables. Thus, instead of plotting the numerical value of x for a particular initial displacement, the ratio x/x_0 is plotted. Again, the ratio of v to a standardizing or normalizing velocity is plotted. Here the normalizing quantity $x_0/\sqrt{MK}$ has no particular physical significance but is merely a convenient collection of parameters which has the dimensions of velocity, as may be easily verified. Finally, the time is divided by the normalizing time $\sqrt{MK}$.

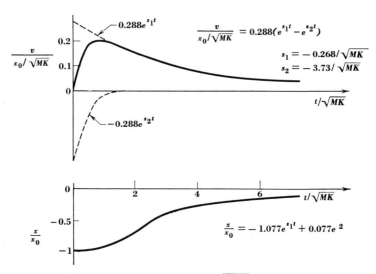

Fig. 5-3. Velocity and displacement for $D = 4\sqrt{M/K}$, with initial displacement $-x_0$, for the system of Fig. 5-1.

There is no necessity for choosing any particular groupings of parameters for normalizing quantities. For example, the quantity M/D also has the dimensions of time and would be equally suitable in the present example.

Let us investigate a simple numerical example to see the sort of information we may obtain from a dimensionless curve such as the one shown in Fig. 5-3. Suppose that the automobile weighs 1,610 lb. (Its mass is 50 slugs.) Two 150-lb men climb upon the front and rear bumpers, and as a result of the added weight, the springs are observed to compress 2 in. The men then jump off simultaneously, and the problem is to find the subsequent motion of the automobile body. It is assumed that shock-absorber equivalent resistance is such that $D = 4\sqrt{M/K}$.

First we may compute the spring compliance

$$K = \frac{\frac{2}{12} \text{ ft}}{300 \text{ lb}} = \frac{1}{1,800} \text{ ft/lb} \tag{5-11}$$

Thus the quantity $\sqrt{MK}$ equals $\frac{1}{6}$ sec, and $x_0/\sqrt{MK} = 1$ ft/sec. From Fig. 5-3 we see that the velocity rises rapidly to a value slightly over 0.2 ft/sec and then decreases slowly toward zero. The displacement decreases from $\frac{1}{6}$ ft toward zero, and after 1 sec $(t/\sqrt{MK} = 6)$ is only 20 per cent of its initial value.

CASE II. $D < 2\sqrt{M/K}$ (s_1, s_2 COMPLEX)   Now let us look into the case in which the shock absorbers have lost some fluid, so that D is less than $2\sqrt{M/K}$. Now the values of s_1 and s_2 are complex—let us write them as

$$s_1 = -\alpha + j\omega_1 \qquad s_2 = -\alpha - j\omega_1$$

where $\qquad \alpha \triangleq \dfrac{D}{2M} \qquad \omega_1 \triangleq \sqrt{\dfrac{1}{MK} - \left(\dfrac{D}{2M}\right)^2}$ $\tag{5-12}$

Again, the amplitudes with which the two components occur are unknown and must be determined from the initial conditions, which we shall assume to be the same as before, $v = 0$ and $x = -x_0$ at $t = 0$. Thus we can write

$$v = A'e^{(-\alpha+j\omega_1)t} + B'e^{(-\alpha-j\omega_1)t} \tag{5-13}$$

where A' and B' are to be determined.

We see that $e^{-\alpha t}$ is a factor of both terms. Making use of the Euler relation [Eqs. (2-26) and (2-27)] allows us to write the solution as

$$v = e^{-\alpha t}(A \cos \omega_1 t + B \sin \omega_1 t) \tag{5-14}$$

where A and B are new unknown constants, simply combinations of A' and B'. This is a more convenient form for evaluation of the constants A and B, for since all other quantities on both sides of this equation are real numbers, A and B must be real numbers also.

Before the initial conditions can be applied, an expression for the displacement is necessary. This is obtained again as the integral of v; integration by parts (or use of the integral tables) gives the formidable expression

$$x = \int v \, dt = \frac{e^{-\alpha t}}{\alpha^2 + \omega_1{}^2} [(\omega_1 A - \alpha B) \sin \omega_1 t$$
$$- (\alpha A + \omega_1 B) \cos \omega_1 t] \quad (5\text{-}15)$$

One initial condition is $v = 0$ when $t = 0$. Since $\sin 0 = 0$, this can be true only if $A = 0$. The second condition is that $x = -x_0$; from Eq. (5-15) it is easily established that this is fulfilled if

$$B = \frac{x_0}{\omega_1} (\alpha^2 + \omega_1{}^2) \quad (5\text{-}16)$$

The final form of the solutions is thus

$$v = \frac{x_0}{\omega_1} (\alpha^2 + \omega_1{}^2) e^{-\alpha t} \sin \omega_1 t \quad (5\text{-}17)$$

$$x = -x_0 e^{-\alpha t} \left(\cos \omega_1 t + \frac{\alpha}{\omega_1} \sin \omega_1 t \right) \quad (5\text{-}18)$$

which are plotted in Fig. 5-4 for $D = \sqrt{M/K}$.

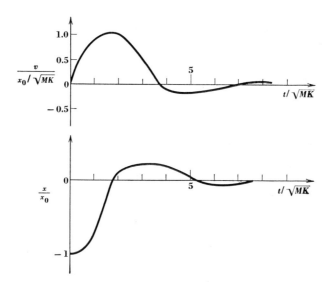

Fig. 5-4. Velocity and displacement for $D = \sqrt{M/K}$, with initial displacement $-x_0$, for the system of Fig. 5-1.

CASE III. $D = 2 \sqrt{M/K}$ (CRITICAL DAMPING) We come now to the intermediate case $D = 2 \sqrt{M/K}$. At first this looks very simple. The
quantity which we have defined as ω_1 in Eqs. (5-12) is zero, and there
is only one possible value for s, namely, $-\alpha = -D/2M$. Hence we
write

$$v = Ae^{-\alpha t} \tag{5-19}$$

But we are headed for trouble in a hurry. The velocity must be
zero at time $t = 0$, and there is no way that this can be arranged unless
$A = 0$. This is obviously not satisfactory—there must be something
wrong.

Let us go back to case I, where there were two values for s, and
take a closer look. There the velocity turned out to be of the following
form

$$v = \frac{s_1 s_2}{s_1 - s_2} x_0 (e^{s_1 t} - e^{s_2 t}) \tag{5-20}$$

where $\qquad s_1 = -\alpha + \delta \qquad s_2 = -\alpha - \delta \tag{5-21}$

with $\qquad \delta \triangleq \sqrt{\left(\frac{D}{2M}\right)^2 - \frac{1}{MK}} \tag{5-22}$

Suppose we write this as

$$v = \frac{(-\alpha + \delta)(-\alpha - \delta)}{2\delta} x_0 e^{-\alpha t}(e^{\delta t} - e^{-\delta t}) \tag{5-23}$$

Now, to get from case I to case III, we let δ get very small and dis-
appear.

Simply setting $\delta = 0$ will not do, for then we have 0 divided by
0, which is not very helpful. Since this is equivalent to dropping all
the terms in the exponential series except the first, which is the constant 1 (the others all get very small as $\delta \to 0$), let us try keeping the
first two. When δt is very small, $e^{\delta t} \approx 1 - \delta t$. The remainder of the
terms are very small indeed, since they contain even higher powers
of δt.

Making this substitution, and a similar one for $e^{-\delta t}$, we find that
the 2δ cancels out of the denominator and we are left with

$$v = \alpha^2 x_0 t e^{-\alpha t} \tag{5-24}$$

This, then, is the result we should obtain. Obviously we shall
never make it by starting from Eq. (5-19). But this assumed solution
looked suspiciously inadequate from the start. Having obtained solu-

tions with two unknown constants to be evaluated for both case I and case II, we rather expected the same for case III.

Consulting a mathematician friend, we find that our surmise was correct and that we should have started with

$$v = Ae^{-\alpha t} + Bte^{-\alpha t} \tag{5-25}$$

With the particular initial conditions chosen, the constant A is obviously zero, and performing integration by parts on the second term gives

$$x = \frac{-B}{\alpha^2}(1 + \alpha t)e^{-\alpha t} \tag{5-26}$$

Setting $x = -x_0$ when $t = 0$ gives the final solutions

$$\begin{aligned}v &= \alpha^2 x_0 t e^{-\alpha t} \\ x &= -x_0(1 + \alpha t)e^{-\alpha t}\end{aligned} \tag{5-27}$$

These are plotted in Fig. 5-5.

In summary, we have seen that the general character of the natural behavior depends upon whether the values of s which make the impedance zero are real, imaginary, or complex. Figure 5-6 attempts to indicate this in pictorial form.

The solution for velocity (or displacement, for that matter, or force, which we did not look into) consists of one term for each characteristic number, each in the form of an exponential times a constant. [Special treatment had to be applied to obtain Eq. (5-25).] The constants are evaluated from the initial conditions.

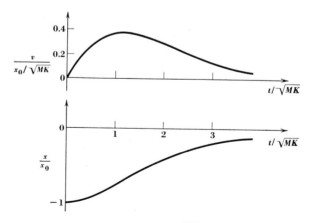

Fig. 5-5. Velocity and displacement for $D = 2\sqrt{M/K}$, with initial displacement $-x_0$, for the system of Fig. 5-1.

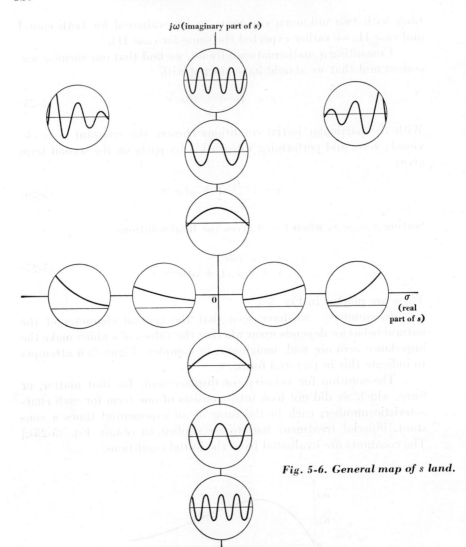

Fig. 5-6. General map of s land.

PROBLEMS

5-1   Compute and plot curves similar to those of Fig. 5-3 for the case $D = 2\sqrt{2}\sqrt{M/K}$.

5-2   The figure illustrates a device for smoothly bringing a coasting

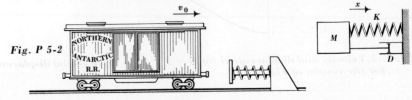

Fig. P 5-2

freight car to a stop. The approximate equivalent network is the same as that of Fig. 5-1, but the initial conditions are in terms of velocity rather than displacement. Assume that the car strikes the bumper at zero time; thus, at $t = 0$, $x = 0$ and $v = v_0$.

    (a) Solve for the resulting motion for the case $D > 2\sqrt{M/K}$.

    (b) Sketch a rough plot of the distance and velocity as functions of time if $D = 4\sqrt{M/K}$. Will the car remain in contact with the bumper plate, or will it bounce back with reversed velocity?

5-3   Find the motion of the freight car in Prob. 5-2 for the case $D = 2\sqrt{M/K}$; the initial conditions are $x = 0$ and $v = v_0$, as before. Plot velocity and displacement as functions of $t/\sqrt{MK}$.

5-4   Assume that the weight of the freight car in Prob. 5-2 is 12,990 lb and that the velocity with which it strikes the bumper is 7.5 mph. The spring compliance is 4×10^{-4} ft/lb, and the frictional resistance of the damping mechanism is 2,000 slugs/sec. Find the maximum distance the spring compresses after the car strikes it.

5-5   Assume that the automobile considered in Sec. 5-1 weighs 1,610 lb and that the initial displacement of the springs is 4 in. Using the curves of Figs. 5-3 to 5-5 (and, if available, Prob. 5-1), sketch a plot of the maximum vertical velocity achieved:

    (a) As a function of D if the spring compliance is $K = 1/1,800$ ft/lb.

    (b) As a function of K if the frictional resistance is $D = 600$ slugs/sec.

5-6   The capacitor in the figure is initially charged to a voltage of 100 volts, and the switch is closed at $t = 0$. Making use of the concept of analogues and of Figs. 5-3 to 5-5, sketch a plot of current in amperes vs. time in milliseconds.

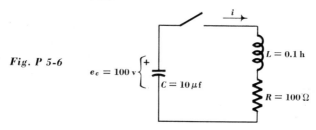

Fig. P 5-6 $e_c = 100$ v $C = 10\,\mu$f $L = 0.1$ h $R = 100\,\Omega$

5-2 ELECTRICAL SERIES RESONANCE

    Let us now proceed to a study of the electrical circuit of Fig. 5-7 and concern ourselves only with the forced solution. We shall learn something about the phenomenon of resonance and shall see that this circuit can be quite useful in certain applications.

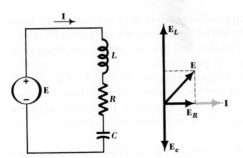

Fig. 5-7. Electrical circuit for the study of series resonance.

The impedance of the series combination of R, L, and C is easily obtainable from Table 3-1:

$$\mathbf{Z} = sL + R + \frac{1}{sC} \tag{5-28}$$

The first thing we notice is that this is very similar to Eq. (5-1) for the mechanical system of Fig. 5-1, which, indeed, is an analogue to the electrical system.

Thus we can predict almost immediately the sort of natural behavior we should expect. A study of the natural behavior of this system would follow exactly the same arguments as in Sec. 5-1 and would arrive at similar results.

However, let us instead look into the forced behavior. Assume that a sinusoidal voltage represented by the phasor $\mathbf{E}$ is applied to the series RLC circuit. The current phasor, then, is $\mathbf{I} = \mathbf{E}/\mathbf{Z}$, where

$$\mathbf{Z} = Z\underline{/\theta} = j\omega L + R + \frac{1}{j\omega C} = R + j\left(\omega L - \frac{1}{\omega C}\right) \tag{5-29}$$

and ω is the radian frequency of the applied voltage.

NORMALIZED RESONANCE CURVES For any given element values and voltage we could, of course, compute the current. However, if our objective is to study this circuit and learn as much as possible about its behavior, it will profit us to attempt to plot some dimensionless curves which will summarize the desired information. Of particular interest will be the current vs. frequency curves.

It is apparent from Eq. (5-29) that the magnitude of the impedance will be the lowest at the frequency $\omega_r = 1/\sqrt{LC}$, since at this frequency the *reactance*, or the imaginary part of the impedance, is zero (Fig. 5-8). Thus, if the applied voltage is held constant and the frequency is varied, the current will be maximum at the frequency ω_r, which is termed the resonant frequency.

It looks as though convenient normalizing values would be ω_r for frequency and the maximum current phasor $\mathbf{I}_m = \mathbf{E}/R$. With a

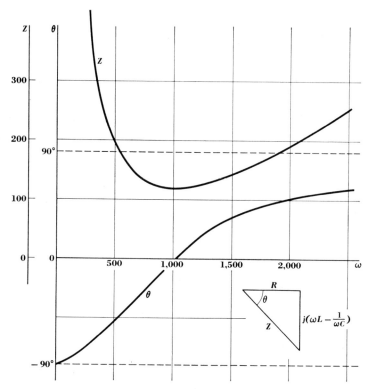

Fig. 5-8. Variation of the magnitude and phase angle of the impedance of the circuit of Fig. 5-7 with frequency (computed for R = 120 ohms, L = 0.1 henry, C = 10⁻⁵ farad).

little rearranging we obtain

$$\frac{\mathbf{I}}{\mathbf{I}_m} = \frac{1}{1 + j(\omega L/R - 1/\omega CR)} = \frac{1}{1 + j\left(\dfrac{\omega_r L}{R}\dfrac{\omega}{\omega_r} - \dfrac{1}{\omega_r CR}\dfrac{\omega_r}{\omega}\right)} \qquad (5\text{-}30)$$

In this last shuffle we have accomplished the end of having ω appear everywhere divided by ω_r. The dimensionless parameters $\omega_r L/R$ and $1/\omega_r CR$ both appear, but from the expression for ω_r we see that they are equal. Thus let us define, to reduce the number of symbols involved,

$$Q \triangleq \frac{\omega_r L}{R} = \frac{1}{\omega_r CR} \qquad (5\text{-}31)$$

The current expression becomes

$$\frac{\mathbf{I}}{\mathbf{I}_m} = \frac{1}{1 + jQ(\omega/\omega_r - \omega_r/\omega)} \qquad (5\text{-}32)$$

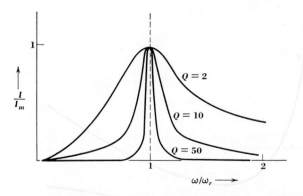

Fig. 5-9. *Normalized curves of current vs. frequency for the circuit of Fig. 5-7.*

If I and $I_m = E/R$ represent the magnitudes of current and maximum current, respectively,

$$\frac{I}{I_m} = \frac{1}{\sqrt{1 + Q^2(\omega/\omega_r - \omega_r/\omega)^2}} \tag{5-33}$$

If we were interested in phase-angle information, we could also obtain this from Eq. (5-32). For the present, however, let us be content with a study of the magnitude alone. Equation (5-33) is plotted in Fig. 5-9 for several values of Q.

The predominant characteristic of the series-resonant circuit is apparent in this figure. If Q is high, notice that a voltage produces significant current flow only if its frequency is within a very narrow range around ω_r. Thus the circuit is capable of acting as an electrical *filter*, in the sense that it can filter, or separate out, desired frequencies from undesired ones. Figure 5-10 illustrates the sort of circuit arrangement which might be used to separate a voltage of radian frequency near ω_r from a group of voltages of various frequencies. Similar circuits are common in radio and communication apparatus.

THE Q METER   The symbols that appear in a circuit diagram are merely approximations to physical elements. A physical coil or capacitor can never store energy without some loss, nor can a physical spring or

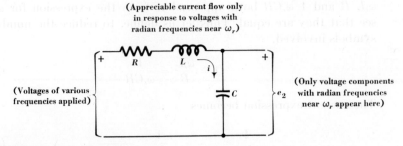

Fig. 5-10. *A simple electrical filter.*

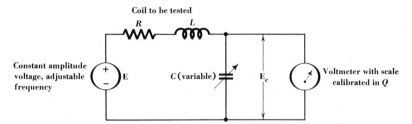

Fig. 5-11. A circuit for measuring the Q of a coil.

moving mass. Thus the circuit elements R and L in Fig. 5-7 might represent a physical inductor and its inherent resistance.

It is common practice to define a factor which gives a measure of the degree to which a physical element or resonant system approaches the ideal of lossless energy storage. This factor is given the symbol Q (for quality):

$$Q \triangleq \frac{\text{maximum energy stored}}{\text{energy loss per radian}} \qquad (5\text{-}34)$$

Let us compute the quality factor for a physical coil which is found to be reasonably well approximated by an inductance L in series with a resistance R. Assume a sinusoidal current flowing through the coil with radian frequency and rms† current I (maximum value of current $\sqrt{2}\,I$). The maximum energy stored in the inductance is $\frac{1}{2}L(\sqrt{2}\,I)^2 = LI^2$. The energy loss per second (power) in the resistor is I^2R, and the energy loss per radian is I^2R/ω. Thus the value of Q, computed by Eq. (5-34), is $\omega L/R$. Note that Q is a function of frequency, and its value at the resonant frequency of the circuit of Fig. 5-7 is exactly the dimensionless parameter Q used in Eq. (5-32). The Q of a high-quality coil is typically of the order of a few hundred.

The Q of a coil may be measured directly in the simple circuit of Fig. 5-11, which makes use of the properties of a series-resonant circuit. A known voltage E, of the frequency ω at which the value of Q is desired, is applied to the series-resonant circuit made up of the coil and a variable capacitor. The capacitor is adjusted to resonance, or until the current attains its maximum value E/R. (This is almost, but not quite, the same value that gives the maximum voltage across the capacitor.) The measured voltage across the capacitor is, then,

$$E_c = I_m Z_c = \frac{E}{R}\frac{1}{\omega_r C} = QE \qquad (5\text{-}35)$$

Thus Q is the ratio of E_c to E. If E is held constant, the voltmeter scale can be calibrated to read directly in Q.

† The abbreviation rms, signifying "root-mean-square," is synonymous with "effective"; the effective current is obtained by taking the square root of the average of the squared instantaneous value.

PROBLEMS

5-7 Assume that the capacitor in the figure is initially uncharged and that the switch has been in the position shown sufficiently long for all transients to have disappeared. At time $t = 0$ the switch is moved to the right, closing the circuit through the capacitor and disconnecting the battery. Thus at time $t = 0_+$ the capacitor current is $i = 0.05$, and the voltage is $e_c = 0$.

Find and plot an expression for the current i as a function of time.

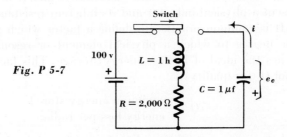

Fig. P 5-7

5-8 Find an expression for the ratio of the output to input voltages (magnitude only, E_2/E_1) for the filter of Fig. 5-10. Arrange it in a suitable form for plotting and sketch a rough plot similar to Fig. 5-9. (Establish points for $\omega = 0$ and $\omega = \omega_r$ and the trend as $\omega \to \infty$, and rough in the remainder of the plot.)

5-9 (a) The circuit diagram of an electrical filter is shown. If $C = 0.05 \ \mu f$, $L = 0.002$ henry, $R = 200$ ohms, and the applied voltage E_1 is $100\underline{/0°}$ at a frequency of 15 kc, find the current I and the voltage E_2 which appears across the output terminals. Construct a phasor diagram showing E_1, I, E_R, E_C, and E_2.

(b) Calculate and plot against frequency (for the range of frequencies 12 to 20 kc) the magnitude and phase angle of $I = I\underline{/\theta}$.

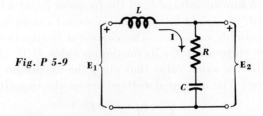

Fig. P 5-9

5-10 (a) Referring to the discussion of the Q meter (Fig. 5-11), find the value of capacitance C, in terms of R, L, and ω, which gives the condition of maximum current $I_{max} = E/R$.

(b) Find the value of C which gives the condition of maximum voltage across the capacitor. By approximately what percentage does this differ from the value in part a if the Q of the coil is 10?

5-3 ELECTRICAL PARALLEL RESONANCE

Figure 5-12 represents a tuned amplifier of the sort used in practically every radio and television set. A pentode is a type of vacuum tube which receives its name from the number of metallic structures (elements) inside the tube which affect its operation. It is represented schematically in Fig. 5-12 as a generator, or source, whose output is controlled by the input voltage.

This sort of control component is not unfamiliar. A gasoline engine with its throttle valve, a rheostat-controlled sewing-machine motor, an electric generator in which the output voltage is adjusted by changing the field current—all are examples of system components in which an input quantity controls an output quantity (usually at a much higher power level).

In the case of the pentode, the input quantity is a voltage, and the output quantity is a current. Under appropriate conditions the current is directly proportional to the input voltage, the constant of proportionality being termed the *mutual conductance* of the tube, g_m. Thus

$$I = g_m E_i \qquad (5\text{-}36)$$

where E_i is assumed to be sinusoidal with radian frequency ω. (Here we are speaking of the alternating components of the current and voltage. Various direct currents and voltages are required to make the tube function, but these we omit from our consideration.)

To formulate the system equation, the current I in Fig. 5-12 is set equal to the sum of the three currents $I_R = E_o/R$, $I_L = E_o/j\omega L$, and $I_C = E_o(j\omega C)$. (Note that we are now sufficiently sophisticated to use the shorthand term "current" instead of always meticulously writing out "the phasor representation of the current.") If we were to take a set of numerical values for the circuit elements, choose a value of E_o, and then compute the currents for a value of frequency below the resonant frequency, we might obtain a phasor diagram something like Fig. 5-13a. For the resonant frequency $\omega_r = 1/\sqrt{LC}$, $I_L = -I_C$, and the diagram would look like Fig. 5-13b. Notice that for the same voltage the current is much less in Fig. 5-13b than in Fig.

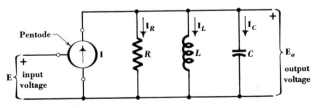

Fig. 5-12. Approximate model for the a-c (signal) behavior of a tuned vacuum-tube (pentode) amplifier.

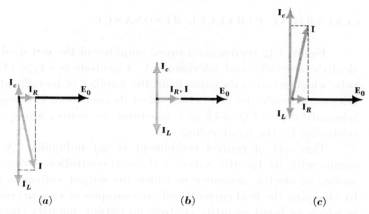

Fig. 5-13. Phasor diagrams showing currents and voltages in the circuit of Fig. 5-12 for (a) frequency below resonance, (b) resonant frequency, (c) frequency above resonance.

5-13a; consequently for the same current the voltage would be much greater at the resonant frequency than at the lower frequency. Figure 5-13c shows the diagram for a frequency above the resonant frequency. These diagrams illustrate that the impedance of the parallel combination $\mathbf{E}_o/\mathbf{I}$ is relatively large in the vicinity of the resonant frequency.

Writing the summation of currents in equation form and factoring out $\mathbf{E}_o$ from each of the component currents, we obtain

$$\mathbf{I} = \mathbf{E}_o \left(j\omega C + \frac{1}{R} + \frac{1}{j\omega L} \right) = \mathbf{E}_o \mathbf{Y} \qquad (5\text{-}37)$$

where $\mathbf{Y}$ is used to indicate the complex quantity

$$\mathbf{Y} \triangleq \left(j\omega C + \frac{1}{R} + \frac{1}{j\omega L} \right) \qquad (5\text{-}38)$$

When $\mathbf{E}_o$ is the quantity to be solved for, we may use

$$\mathbf{E}_o = \frac{\mathbf{I}}{\mathbf{Y}} \qquad (5\text{-}39)$$

It is apparent that $\mathbf{Y} = 1/\mathbf{Z}$, where $\mathbf{Z} = \mathbf{E}_o/\mathbf{I}$ is the complex impedance of the three elements R, L, and C in parallel. The reciprocal of an impedance has the dimensions of ohms^{-1}, or mhos, and is, in general, termed an *admittance*. The reciprocal of a resistance (a purely real admittance) is called a *conductance*.

DUALS AND ANALOGUES We may save ourselves some labor if we note that Eq. (5-38) is similar in form to Eq. (5-29), which we have studied in some detail. In fact, we find that Figs. 5-7 and 5-12 and their associated equations (5-29) and (5-38) can be converted from one to the other by making the changes indicated in Table 5-1.

TABLE 5-1   *Dual Quantities*

Voltage source	Current source
Series connection	Parallel connection
Impedance **Z**	Admittance **Y**
Voltage **E**	Current **I**
Inductance L	Capacitance C
Capacitance C	Inductance L
Resistance R	Conductance $G = \dfrac{1}{R}$

$$e = Ri$$

$$i = Ge$$

$$e = L\frac{di}{dt}$$

$$i = C\frac{de}{dt}$$

$$e = \frac{1}{C}\int i\,dt$$

$$i = \frac{1}{L}\int e\,dt$$

$$e = Ri + L\frac{di}{dt} + \frac{1}{C}\int i\,dt$$

$$i = Ge + C\frac{de}{dt} + \frac{1}{L}\int e\,dt$$

Thus the circuits of Figs. 5-7 and 5-12 are described by the same equation, although with different symbols. They are analogues, but of a particular type called *duals*. Since Eq. (5-29) has already been studied, the results can be utilized for the present example by simply exchanging all quantities for their duals.

In this fashion we obtain the curve of Fig. 5-14 for the ratio E_o/E_i (called the amplifier *gain*) in Fig. 5-12. Here $\omega_r = 1/\sqrt{LC}$ and $Q = \omega_r CR$. The action of the circuit of amplifying inputs with frequencies near the resonant frequency is apparent. This property is utilized in radio and television receivers to separate signals of desired and undesired frequencies.

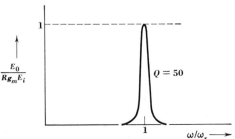

Fig. 5-14. Normalized amplifier gain vs. frequency for the circuit of Fig. 5-12.

$$\frac{E_0}{R g_m E_i}$$

$$Q = 50$$

$$\omega/\omega_r \longrightarrow$$

TABLE 5-2   *A Second System of Mechanical-Electrical Analogies*

Mechanical	Electrical
Force f	Current i
Displacement x	Flux linkages Li
Velocity $v = \dfrac{dx}{dt}$	Voltage $e = \dfrac{d(Li)}{dt}$
Frictional resistance D	Conductance G
Mass M	Capacitance C
Spring compliance K	Inductance L

It should be noted that, since the equations describing dual networks are the same except for the difference in symbols, a second form of analogy between mechanical and electrical systems can be set up (Table 5-2). In one respect the analogues obtained on this basis are superior to those derived from Table 1-3: the arrangements of elements in the mechanical and electrical analogues are similar, as well as the equations. This may be seen in the analogues illustrated in Fig. 5-15. Not all systems have analogues or duals, but many do, and the concepts are helpful ones.

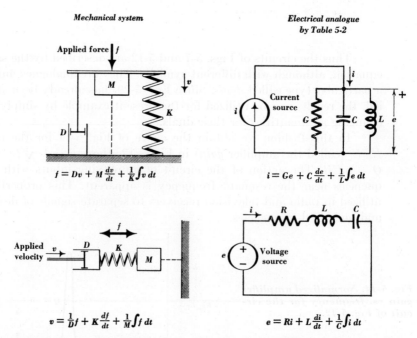

$$f = Dv + M\frac{dv}{dt} + \frac{1}{K}\textstyle\int v\,dt$$

$$i = Ge + C\frac{de}{dt} + \frac{1}{L}\textstyle\int e\,dt$$

$$v = \frac{1}{D}f + K\frac{df}{dt} + \frac{1}{M}\textstyle\int f\,dt$$

$$e = Ri + L\frac{di}{dt} + \frac{1}{C}\textstyle\int i\,dt$$

Fig. 5-15. *Mechanical and electrical analogues according to Table 5-2. (The two electrical circuits are duals, and the two mechanical networks are mechanical duals.)*

PROBLEMS

5-11   (a) Write an expression, similar to Eq. (5-33), for the normalized gain of the amplifier of Fig. 5-12. Substitute in this equation the new frequency variable δ by letting $\omega = \omega_r(1 + \delta)$. [That is, $\delta \triangleq (\omega - \omega_r)/\omega_r$ is the fractional deviation of frequency from the resonant frequency.] Show that when $\delta = \pm\frac{1}{2}Q$, the gain is approximately $1/\sqrt{2}$ of the gain at resonance.

   (b) Show that, for the case of high Q, the gain expression reduces to

$$\frac{\text{Gain}}{g_m R} = \frac{1}{\sqrt{1 + 4Q^2\delta^2}}$$

Plot normalized gain versus $2Q\delta$.

5-12   Assume the following numerical values for the vacuum-tube amplifier whose equivalent circuit is shown in Fig. 5-12:

   $g_m = 0.002$ mho (ohm^{-1})
   $R = 50,000$ ohms
   $L = 0.001$ henry
   $C = 0.001$ μf

   Sketch a rough plot of the gain vs. frequency. (Make use of the curve of Prob. 5-11b if available.)

5-13   (a) Construct two electrical analogues for the mechanical system shown. Check by seeing that the impedance or admittance expressions have the same form.

   (b) Explain why the dual of this mechanical system cannot be constructed.

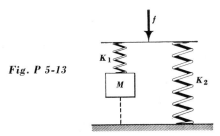

Fig. P 5-13

5-14   The thermal system shown in the figure is to be considered for the purpose of studying the effect of wall construction on the temperature inside a building. The wall and the heat-absorbing ability of the contents of the building are represented to a rough approximation by a heat-conducting wall of thermal conductivity K Btu/(hr)(°F) for each square foot of wall surface, on the inside of which is a thermal capacity of C Btu/°F for each square foot of surface.

   Let T_o and T_i represent the outside and inside temperatures, respectively, and let Q be the heat flow in Btu per hour through the wall per square foot of surface. The temperature differential $T_o - T_i$ across the wall is then Q/K. The total Btu stored inside the building for each square foot of wall surface is C times the temperature. That is,

$$\int Q \, dt = CT_i$$

Thus the equation describing the situation is

$$T_o = \frac{Q}{K} + \frac{1}{C} \int Q \, dt$$

(a) Find a mechanical and an electrical analogue for this thermal system.

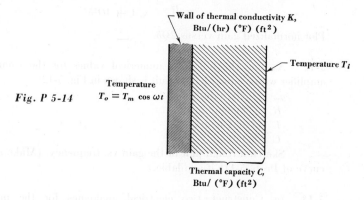

Fig. P 5-14

Temperature $T_o = T_m \cos \omega t$

Wall of thermal conductivity K, Btu/(hr) (°F) (ft^2)

Temperature T_i

Thermal capacity C, Btu/ (°F) (ft^2)

(b) Assume the outside temperature to be given by $T_o = T_m \cos \omega t$, where T_m is the maximum temperature variation from an average temperature of 70°F, t is the time in hours measured from noon, and $\omega = 2\pi/24$. Derive an expression for the temperature inside the building.

(c) Assume the values $T_m = 20°$, $K = 0.5$, $C = 1.0$. Find the maximum temperature inside the building and the time of day at which it occurs. Construct a phasor diagram.

5-4 GRAPHICAL REPRESENTATIONS IN THE COMPLEX PLANE

Graphical representations of the mathematical relations with which we deal are helpful in several ways. Primarily, they aid us in visualizing the behavior of the systems under study. This is particularly important to the engineer, since his task is not simply to analyze existing systems but to devise new systems and to find the most appropriate systems for given purposes. Thus the results of his analyses are not ends in themselves, but only means to ends. By thoroughly understanding the behavior of existing or proposed systems, the engineer conceives of other systems with desirable properties. Graphical representations are an aid to this sort of perceptual understanding.

Graphical representations also serve as a means of concisely presenting information which might otherwise be given in the form of tables, mathematical formulas, etc. Data for design purposes are often most conveniently presented in graphical form. In addition, certain types of computation can be conveniently carried out in graphical or analogue form. (The force polygon of elementary mechanics is a familiar example.)

In the study of linear systems certain representations in the complex plane are particularly helpful. We have come to appreciate, at this point, the extent to which complex numbers and complex variables appear in this work. We have made some use of representations in the complex-frequency or s plane (such as Fig. 5-2); phasor diagrams, in which sinusoidally varying quantities are represented by complex numbers; and representations in which the real and imaginary components of impedance or admittance are used as the coordinates. It will be well, now, to explore the potentialities of these representations somewhat further.

The purpose of this discussion is not so much to familiarize the reader with certain standard types of diagrams and design aids but rather to foster appreciation of the role of graphical representations in general and to cultivate the ability to devise and use them when they would be helpful.

THE COMPLEX-FREQUENCY PLANE In the course of the investigation of a spring- and dashpot-supported mass in Sec. 5-1, we found that the character of the natural behavior of this system depends upon the nature of the values of s for which the impedance is zero; more tersely, upon the location of the zeros of $\mathbf{Z}_m$ in the s plane. It will be instructive to see how these positions depend upon the magnitudes of the three system elements.

The zeros of $\mathbf{Z}_m$ are given by Eqs. (5-2) and (5-3), repeated below for convenience:

$$s_1, s_2 = -\frac{D}{2M} \pm \sqrt{\left(\frac{D}{2M}\right)^2 - \frac{1}{MK}} \tag{5-2}$$

or
$$s_1, s_2 = -\frac{D}{2M} \pm j\sqrt{\frac{1}{MK} - \left(\frac{D}{2M}\right)^2} \tag{5-3}$$

Examination of these as the spring compliance K is varied shows that the zero positions move as indicated in Fig. 5-16. For K less than $4M/D^2$, s_1 and s_2 are complex (case II). As K increases from zero, the oscillation radian frequency ω_0 (the imaginary part of s_1 and s_2) decreases, and the damping constant α remains constant. When K attains the value $4M/D^2$, the critical-damping condition (case III) is reached. As K is increased still further, the system behavior becomes nonoscilla-

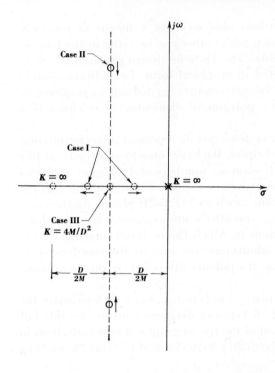

Case II

Case I

$K = \infty$ $K = \infty$

Case III
$K = 4M/D^2$

$\dfrac{D}{2M}$ $\dfrac{D}{2M}$

Fig. 5-16. Pole-zero diagram for the impedance of Eq. (5-1). Arrows indicate the changing positions of the zeros as the compliance K is increased.

tory (case I); when K is very large, s_1 approaches zero (the rate of decay of one of the exponential terms becomes very slow), and s_2 approaches $-D/M$. Finally, as K approaches infinity, the behavior of the system becomes that of a mass and dashpot alone.

Figure 5-17 shows, in similar fashion, how the zero positions move if K and M are held fixed and the frictional resistance D is varied. Very low D gives slightly damped sinusoidal oscillations at a radian frequency $1/\sqrt{MK}$. Increasing D increases the damping and lowers the

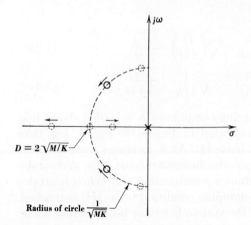

$D = 2\sqrt{M/K}$

Radius of circle $\dfrac{1}{\sqrt{MK}}$

Fig. 5-17. Pole-zero diagram for the impedance of Eq. (5-1). Arrows indicate the changing positions of the zeros as the frictional resistance D is increased.

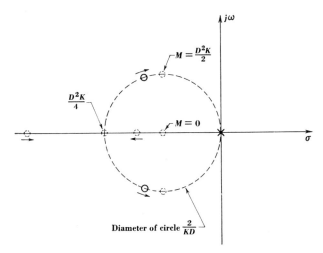

Fig. 5-18. *Pole-zero diagram of the impedance of Eq. (5-1). Arrows indicate the changing positions of the zeros as M is increased.*

oscillating frequency. If D becomes greater than the critical value $2\sqrt{M/K}$, the system exhibits nonoscillatory behavior. Finally, as D approaches infinity, corresponding to a rigid connection, motion ceases altogether. (One zero moves to infinity, and the other is canceled by the pole at the origin.)

The migration of the zeros as M is varied, D and K being fixed, is shown in Fig. 5-18. In this case it is interesting to note that as M is varied from zero to infinity, the natural-oscillation frequency ω_0 increases to a maximum value of $1/KD$ and then decreases to zero.

POLE-ZERO LOCATION AND STEADY-STATE† BEHAVIOR The forced behavior of a system, like the natural behavior, is intimately related to the location of certain points in the complex-frequency plane. To see this, let us reexamine the series-resonant electrical circuit of Sec. 5-2. The impedance is given by

$$\mathbf{Z} = sL + R + \frac{1}{sC} = \frac{s^2LC + sCR + 1}{sC} \tag{5-40}$$

Writing this as we have, in the form of a ratio of two polynomials in s, we have made it apparent that the impedance will be zero for a value of s which makes the numerator zero and will be infinite for a value of s which makes the denominator zero. These values of s we shall call the *zeros* and *poles*, respectively, of the impedance $\mathbf{Z}$.

---

† Here *steady-state* implies the response to a sinusoidally varying driving force. See footnote at the beginning of Chap. 3.

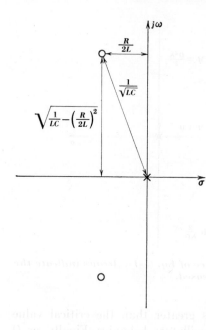

Fig. 5-19. Graphical representation of the zeros and poles of the impedance of Eq. (5-40).

This is shown even more clearly if the two polynomials are factored:

$$\mathbf{Z} = Z\underline{/\theta} = L\frac{(s - s_1)(s - s_2)}{s} \tag{5-41}$$

where

$$s_1, s_2 = -\frac{R}{2L} \pm j\sqrt{\frac{1}{LC} - \left(\frac{R}{2L}\right)^2} \tag{5-42}$$

Thus in this example $\mathbf{Z}$ has zeros at s_1 and s_2 and a pole at $s = 0$ (and also at $s \to \infty$, although this is not quite so obvious). This information is shown graphically in Fig. 5-19.

Let us now suppose that we wish to evaluate the impedance for some particular value of s—in other words, at some point s in the complex-frequency plane. Consider the factor $s - s_1$. If σ_1 and $j\omega_1$ are the real and imaginary parts of s_1 and if σ and $j\omega$ have the corresponding meaning with respect to s, then

$$s - s_1 = (\sigma - \sigma_1) + j(\omega - \omega_1) \tag{5-43}$$

But this is just the complex distance from s_1 to s; that is, its magnitude is the length of a line from s_1 to s, and its angle is the angle this line makes with the real axis.

This immediately indicates that $\mathbf{Z}$ can be computed by a graphical method, which is most easily shown with a numerical example. Let $L = 0.1$ henry, $R = 120$ ohms, $C = 10^{-5}$ farad; then

$$s_1, s_2 = -600 \pm j800$$

The impedance is to be evaluated at $s = j\omega = j200$. Interpreting Eq. (5-41) graphically leads to the result given in Fig. 5-20. Once the poles and zeros of the function to be computed are located, this method allows rapid graphical computation of curves of magnitude and angle of Z versus ω similar to those of Fig. 5-8. Distances may be scaled with a ruler and angles picked off with a protractor.

The impedance Z has a value for any value of s, of course, not merely for those on the $j\omega$ axis. To present this larger amount of data graphically, we may use the scheme of Fig. 5-21, in which, after Z is calculated for a large number of points in the s plane, lines are drawn through points for which the magnitude Z is the same and also through points for which θ is the same.

It may be helpful in visualizing the behavior of the impedance function over the complex-frequency plane to imagine the magnitude of the impedance to be represented by the height of a surface above

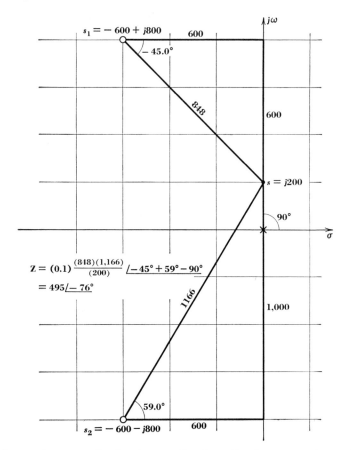

Fig. 5-20. *Illustrative example showing application of ruler-protractor method of graphical computation.*

the *s* plane (as elevation above sea level is represented on a relief map). Such a surface for the present example would look something like Fig. 5-22. The effect is somewhat as though we were to take a large elastic sheet, stake it down to the ground (representing the *s* plane) at the two points where the impedance is zero, and put a tent pole under it at the origin where the impedance is very high (approaching infinity). The sheet must also be elevated at large distances from the origin, since *Z* becomes very large when the magnitude of *s* is large.

Thus we envision a three-dimensional solid with zero elevation at the two points s_1, $s_2 = -600 \pm j800$ and a mountain peak at $s = 0$. The curve of *Z* versus ω as in Fig. 5-8 is observed if we slice this solid along the $j\omega$ axis (Fig. 5-23).

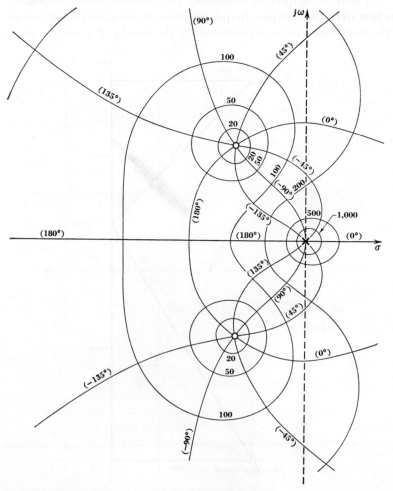

Fig. 5-21. Equal-magnitude and equal-angle contours of the impedance function of Fig. 5-20.

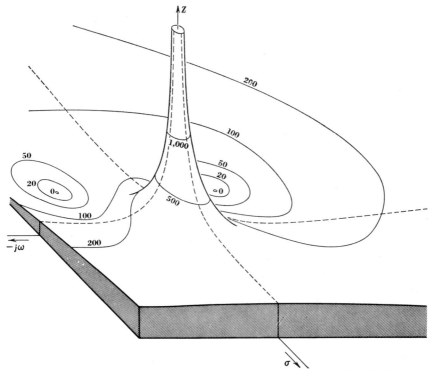

Fig. 5-22. "Relief map" of the impedance function depicted in Fig. 5-21.

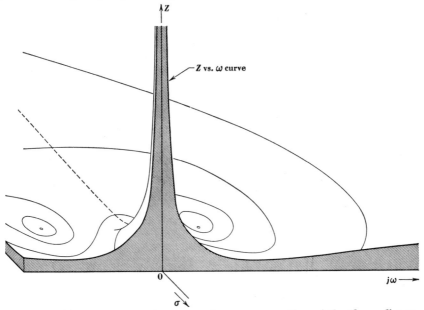

Fig. 5-23. The Z versus ω curve interpreted as a cross section of the three-dimensional solid of Fig. 5-22 along the jω axis.

Worth noting is the fact that the equal-angle contours of Fig. 5-21 are perpendicular to the equal-magnitude contours; on the "relief map" of Fig. 5-22 they would appear as lines of steepest descent. Or, continuing the topographical analogy, we might say that they are the paths which would be followed by rivulets originating in springs at the mountain peaks and flowing into sinks at the zero positions. The proof of these statements need not detain us here.

The relief-map analogy helps us visualize the approximate shape of the Z versus ω curve from the pole and zero positions without actually calculating it. Contrariwise, it can help us see what poles and zeros are needed to produce a given Z versus ω characteristic. We shall study some examples of its use in later chapters.

LOCUS DIAGRAMS   In addition to the complex-frequency plane in which the coordinates are the real and imaginary parts of s, there are diagrams in which the real and imaginary axes represent the components

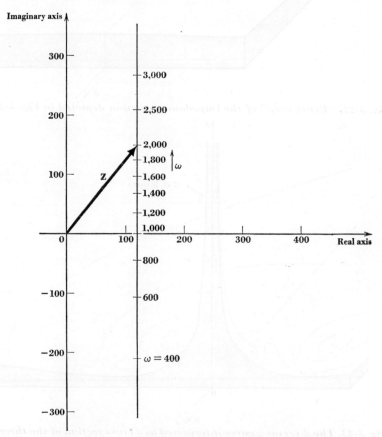

Fig. 5-24. Locus of the impedance of Fig. 5-8 as the frequency is varied.

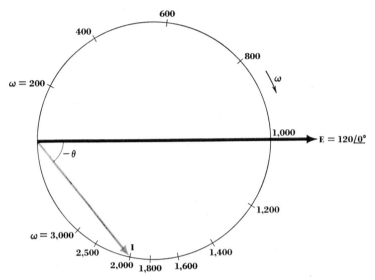

Fig. 5-25. *Phasor diagram for the circuit of Fig. 5-7 with* $\mathbf{E} = 120\underline{/0°}$*, showing the locus of the current phasor as ω is varied.*

of voltage and current phasors and others in which they represent the components of impedance or admittance. In these diagrams, which we also find occasion to use, it is often of interest to observe the consequences of varying one or another parameter.

Two examples are shown in Figs. 5-24 and 5-25, both of which pertain to the series-resonant circuit we have just studied in the complex-frequency plane. Figure 5-24 shows the locus of the impedance as the frequency is varied, and Fig. 5-25 indicates the locus of the current phasor as the frequency changes.

Additional examples illustrating the insight gained from these various graphical representations will appear in later chapters.

PROBLEMS

5-15   Verify that the zeros in Fig. 5-18 for various values of M lie on a circle, as indicated.

5-16   (*a*) Write an expression for the impedance of the three-element combination shown. Sketch a diagram of the *s* plane showing the positions of the poles and zeros of the impedance for the following values of R: ∞, $\sqrt{L/C}$, $\frac{1}{2}\sqrt{L/C}$, $\frac{1}{4}\sqrt{L/C}$, 0 (or very small). Show the locus of the pole and zero positions as R is varied from 0 to ∞.

(*b*) From the positions of the poles and zeros for the case $R = \sqrt{L/C}$ and with the aid of the relief-map analogy, sketch very roughly the shape you would expect for the curve of impedance magnitude Z (for a sinusoidal driving voltage) vs. radian frequency ω.

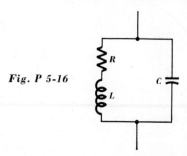

Fig. P 5-16

5-17 Considering the circuit of Prob. 5-16, assume $R = 1,000$ ohms, $L = 1$ henry, $C = 1$ μf.

(*a*) Plot accurately the pole and zero positions in the s plane. Use the ruler-protractor method of computation illustrated in Fig. 5-20 to find the magnitude of the impedance Z for $\omega = 0$, 600, 800, 1,000, 1,500, 2,000.

(*b*) Plot a curve of Z versus ω. What is the maximum value (approximately)?

(*c*) At the radian frequency for which Z is maximum, what is the approximate angle of the impedance?

5-18 A theorem which we shall not prove here states that if one complex number $\mathbf{Z}$ is related to a second s by a transformation of the form $\mathbf{Z} = (As + B)/(Cs + D)$, where A, B, C, and D are any constants whatever, and then if s varies along a circle in the complex plane, the locus of $\mathbf{Z}$ will also be a circle. (Note that a straight line is a special case of a circle with infinite radius.)

The impedance of a resistor and an inductor in parallel is $\mathbf{Z} = sRL/(R + sL)$. Making use of the above theorem, find the locus of the impedance $\mathbf{Z}$ in the complex-impedance plane as s varies along the $j\omega$ axis from 0 to ∞. [Note that if you make adequate use of the knowledge that the locus is a circle, the amount of computation required is minimized, since it never takes more than three points to define a circle and $\mathbf{Z}(0)$ and $\mathbf{Z}(\infty)$ are very simply evaluated.]

5-19 For the circuit illustrated:

(*a*) Show the locus of the impedance, in the complex-impedance plane, as R is varied from 0 to ∞, X being held constant at the value 1 ohm.

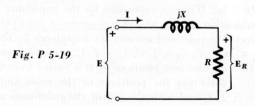

Fig. P 5-19

(*b*) Sketch the locus of the admittance (reciprocal of the impedance) as *R* varies.

(*c*) Let the voltage applied to the terminals be $\mathbf{E} = 100/\underline{0°}$. Sketch a phasor diagram showing the locus of the current phasor as *R* varies. What value of *R* gives the maximum current? What value gives the maximum power?

(*d*) Sketch the locus of the phasor $\mathbf{E}_R$ as *R* varies.

5-5   ROOT-LOCUS DETERMINATION

The zero-migration study of the preceding section (Figs. 5-16 to 5-18) can be formalized in a very useful graphical technique for obtaining insight into the effect on system behavior of varying the value of a particular parameter. This is the method of root-locus location.

We have seen that both the natural and the sinusoidal steady-state behavior of a linear network are summarized in the locations of the poles and zeros of the system function. Hence, considerable information about the influence of the magnitude of a particular parameter is furnished by the loci of these poles and zeros as that parameter is varied. Figures 5-16 to 5-18 are examples of such loci. What we seek is a more systematic method of locating them.

Let us explore this possibility by means of the example of Fig. 5-1, a mechanical network for which the impedance is

$$\mathbf{Z}_m = \frac{s^2 MK + sKD + 1}{sK} \tag{5-44}$$

The zeros of this impedance are the roots of the polynomial $s^2 MK + sKD + 1$, that is, the solutions of the equation

$$s^2 MK + sKD + 1 = 0 \tag{5-45}$$

Now we wish to see how the locations of these zeros are affected by variation of one of the parameters, say *D*. Thus let us isolate this parameter by rearranging the equation:

$$\frac{s^2 MK + 1}{sK} = -D \tag{5-46}$$

It is apparent that the desired roots are the values of *s* for which the function $(s^2 MK + 1)/sK$ is equal to the negative constant $-D$.

We need to study this function in more detail. Obviously it has zeros at $s = \pm j/\sqrt{MK}$ and a pole at the origin. It also becomes infinitely large as *s* approaches infinity. Using the ruler-protractor method illustrated in Fig. 5-20, we could locate the lines of constant magnitude and constant angle to obtain a plot such as that of Fig. 5-21. (A few of the constant-angle lines are shown in Fig. 5-26.) If we think

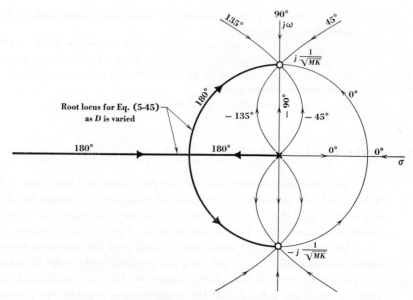

Fig. 5-26. Constant-angle lines for the function $(s^2MK + 1)/sK$.

again in terms of the relief-map analogy, in which the pole is a mountain peak and the zeros are sinkholes, the lines of constant angle are analogous to flow lines, indicating the direction water would tend to flow from melting snow on the peaks (poles) down into the sinks at the zero positions.

However, we are particularly interested in only one of these flow lines, namely, the one corresponding to an angle of $\pm 180°$, since the condition we seek is that the function under examination be equal to $-D = D\underline{/180°}$. Thus there is no need to plot all the flow lines; it is enough to locate the one of central interest. To do this, it may be helpful to imagine the mountain peaks and sinks and make a rough sketch of the anticipated flow lines. Sometimes portions of the desired 180° lines can be rather quickly located. (There should be one 180° line terminating on each pole or zero.) From these and the rough plot of anticipated positions we can get a good idea of where to explore, with the aid of a protractor, in order to locate additional points, until sufficient data are acquired to draw in the locus.

The easiest way to learn this process is to try it. Plotting a few root loci is more instructive than reading pages of descriptive text. A few simple rules for locating portions of the root locus are obvious, once seen in operation; more elaborate techniques are of interest only to the specialist.

EXAMPLE OF ROOT-LOCUS LOCATION To illustrate the location of a root locus, let us find the effect of variation of the mass M on the two roots of Eq. (5-45). Rearranging the equation to isolate the parameter M yields

$$\frac{sKD + 1}{s^2 K} = -M \tag{5-47}$$

The expression on the left has a double pole at the origin and a zero at $s = -1/KD$ (Fig. 5-27). The root locus includes the values of s which give this expression an angle of 180°.

    We shall first consider the asymptotic behavior of the root locus as $s \to \infty$. Let us imagine that we are far away from the origin; looking back, we find that the poles and zeros appear to be clustered together near the origin. The effect at this large distance is that of a net of one pole (two poles minus one zero). Hence the root locus near infinity makes an angle of 180° with the positive real axis. (A net of two poles would give $\pm 90°$ asymptotes; a net of three poles, $\pm 60°$ and 180°; etc.)

    Next, we note that along the real axis the angular contributions of any poles or zeros off the real axis always cancel out, since complex poles or zeros always occur in conjugate pairs. Thus the various segments of the real axis all correspond to multiples of 180°. In this example the positive half of the real axis corresponds to 0°, the segment of the real axis between $-1/KD$ and the origin corresponds to $-360°$, and the negative real axis to the left of $-1/KD$ corresponds to $-180°$ (and hence is a portion of the root locus).

    Very near the origin the primary angular contribution comes from

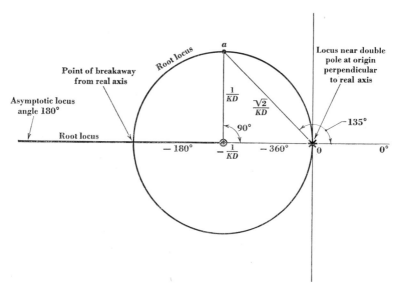

Fig. 5-27. Locus of the roots of Eq. (5-45) as M is varied, illustrating the method of locating it.

the two poles; the zero contributes little. Thus the root locus leaves the origin at an angle of $\pm 90°$.

The general shape of the locus is beginning to become apparent. Rivulets from the mountain peak circle around and meet at a point somewhere on the negative real axis. From this point they flow along the negative real axis to the sinks at $-1/KD$ and $-\infty$. The point where the locus breaks away from the negative real axis must be (we decide after some pondering) twice as far from the two poles as from the zero, in order that the angular contributions just off the real axis will add to $-180°$.

Additional points on the locus, such as point a in Fig. 5-27, can be located by trial, and the completed locus can be sketched in. (Note that the locus is symmetrical about the real axis.) This was such a simple example that the locus, which, in fact, turns out to be a combination of a circle and a straight line, could have been found by simple analytical methods. In more complicated examples the general procedure used here for approximating the location of the root locus proves to be a powerful and useful technique. Other applications of this approach will be mentioned later.

With a small added investment in labor, we can, if we wish, establish a scale on the root locus showing the values of M which correspond to the various points on the locus. To see this most clearly, we rearrange Eq. (5-47) to the form

$$D \frac{(s + 1/KD)}{s^2} = -M \tag{5-48}$$

The magnitude of the factor $s + 1/KD$ is the distance from a point s on the locus to the point $-1/KD$, whereas the magnitude of the factor s in the denominator is the distance from s to the pole at the origin. These distances can be scaled from the plot, and the value of M corresponding to any point on the locus can be easily found. For example, the value of M corresponding to point a in Fig. 5-27 is simply determined, from the distances shown, to be $M = \frac{1}{2} D^2 K$.

PROBLEMS

5-20   Use the techniques of Sec. 5-5 to find the locus of the two roots of Eq. (5-45) in the s plane as the parameter K is varied, D and M remaining constant.

Use the method of measuring distances on this plot to locate approximately the points on the locus corresponding to K equal to 1, 2, 4, 8, and 16 times M/D^2, thus establishing a scale of K values on the root locus.

5-21   The impedance function for the network of Prob. 3-27 has the value 0 at the two roots of the equation

$$s^2LCR + sL + R = 0$$

Use the techniques of Sec. 5-5 to study the locus of these roots as the parameter R is varied, L and C remaining constant.

Establish a scale of R values on the root locus by locating approximately the points on the locus corresponding to R equal to 0, to ¼, ½, and 1 times $\sqrt{L/C}$, and to ∞.

electric power circuits

The transmission and control of power are important aspects of most applications of electricity. This is so even in the field of electrical communication, where information rather than power is the commodity ultimately transmitted or processed; sufficient power must be supplied at the receiver to operate the loudspeaker or indicating device.

We shall now consider certain topics which have primarily to do with electric power. Most of them have analogues in mechanical systems, but these are not of sufficient importance or interest to take up here.

6-1 POWER AND REACTIVE POWER

Let us begin by examining the power relations in the simple circuit discussed in Sec. 3-1. The results of this discussion are summarized in Fig. 6-1. Plots of the instantaneous current and voltage are shown in Fig. 6-2.

As discussed in Sec. 1-2, the voltage between two points in a circuit is the amount of energy required, in joules per coulomb, to transfer

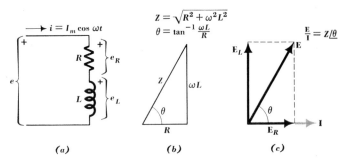

Fig. 6-1. Summary of results for a simple circuit problem. (a) Circuit diagram; (b) impedance triangle; (c) phasor diagram.

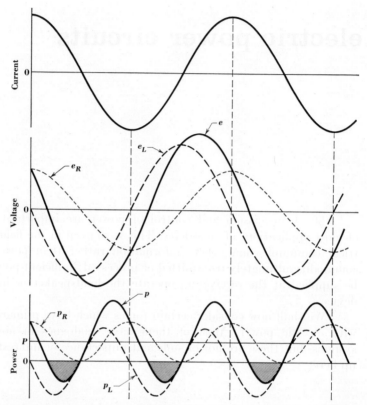

Fig. 6-2. *Instantaneous current, voltage, and power for the circuit of Fig. 6-1. The shaded regions indicate negative power flow, that is, the transfer of stored energy from the inductor back to the generator.*

charge from one point to the other. Thus, if the charge is being transferred at a rate of i coulombs/sec, the instantaneous power flow is $p = ei$ watts.†

The various powers in this example are plotted in Fig. 6-2. The power flow into the resistor is

$$p_R = e_R i = (RI_m \cos \omega t)(I_m \cos \omega t)$$
$$= I_m^2 R(\tfrac{1}{2} + \tfrac{1}{2} \cos 2\omega t) \tag{6-1}$$

† In order to use the concept of voltage between two points, it is necessary to assume that the rate of variation of the voltage and current is sufficiently slow that they do not change appreciably in the time required for an electromagnetic wave to travel from one point to the other (at a velocity of 3×10^8 m/sec). This condition is satisfied in all the usual circuit problems except those involving very high frequencies or long transmission lines. When it is not satisfied, the problem must usually be examined from a field, rather than a circuit, standpoint. There are many familiar situations, such as the reception of a radio signal from a distant transmitter, where there is a flow of power but where we cannot speak of a voltage. Thus the definition of power as voltage times current is a restricted one.

Note that this is a pulsating power, oscillating between $I_m{}^2 R$ and zero with an average value of $P = \frac{1}{2} I_m{}^2 R$. This is the average rate at which electrical energy is converted to thermal energy. The average power is usually written in terms of the effective, or rms, current $I = I_m/\sqrt{2}$:

$$P = I^2 R = EI \cos \theta \qquad \text{watts} \qquad (6\text{-}2)$$

where θ is the angle of the load impedance.

The power flow into the inductor is

$$
\begin{aligned}
p_L = e_L i &= (-\sqrt{2}\, \omega L I \sin \omega t)(\sqrt{2}\, I \cos \omega t) \\
&= -\omega L I^2 \sin 2\omega t \qquad\qquad\qquad (6\text{-}3)
\end{aligned}
$$

Notice that, although there is energy flow into the inductor (that is, into the magnetic field) during a portion of the cycle, this energy is only stored temporarily and then delivered back. The instantaneous power has no average value; it contributes nothing to the net energy transfer. Yet it is not completely undeserving of our attention, since it does represent a component of the total current flow which must be supplied by the source and which may contribute to undesired power loss in other portions of the circuit. The quantity

$$Q \triangleq \omega L I^2 = I^2 X = EI \sin \theta \qquad (6\text{-}4)$$

is a convenient measure of this effect and is termed *reactive power.* [The symbol X $(= \omega L)$ used here is a common abbreviation for the magnitude of the imaginary part of a steady-state impedance, called the *reactance.*] Reactive power is not true power and cannot be measured in watts; the units are *volt-amperes reactive,* or *vars.*

The over-all instantaneous power flow into the combination of the two elements, $p = ei$, is the sum of p_R and p_L.

The one quantity remaining here which does not yet have a name is the product EI—this is the total volt-amperes $I^2 Z$. The relations between these various quantities are summarized in Fig. 6-3.

The volt-amperes is a significant quantity, since electrical apparatus is commonly rated in volt-amperes rather than in watts. The rating is limited by heating and hence by losses in the device; these losses, in turn, are determined by the magnitudes of the voltage and current and are almost independent of the phase angle between them.

The ratio of the power to the circuit volt-amperes, the cosine of the phase angle θ between voltage and current, is termed the *power factor.* An inductive circuit in which the current lags the voltage is said to have a *lagging power factor;* a capacitive circuit in which the current leads the voltage has a *leading power factor.*

It is common to find electric-power rates dependent not only upon the power consumed but also upon the power factor (or reactive power). This is entirely logical—the turbine size and steam (or water)

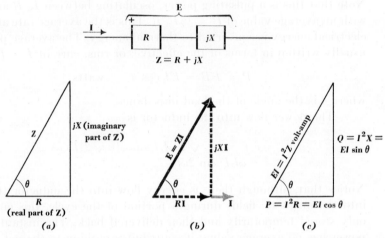

Fig. 6-3. Impedance-power relations. (a) Impedance triangle; (b) phasor diagram in which the sides of the triangle are multiplied by I; (c) volt-ampere triangle in which the sides of the triangle are multiplied by I^2.

requirements depend upon the power supplied, whereas the capacity of the electrical equipment (generators, transformers, cables, etc.) is fixed by the volt-amperes to be supplied.

PROBLEMS

6-1   In the example of Figs. 6-1 and 6-2 assume that $R = 5$ ohms, $\omega L = 12$ ohms, and $E = 130$ volts (effective). Find:

    (a) The maximum instantaneous current.

    (b) The maximum instantaneous rate of energy dissipation in the resistor.

    (c) The maximum instantaneous rate of energy storage in the magnetic field of the inductor.

    (d) The instantaneous current when the rate of energy storage and the rate of energy dissipation are equal.

6-2   A source supplying 125 volts (effective) is placed across a series combination of a 7-ohm resistance and a 24-ohm capacitive reactance.

    (a) Find the average power, the reactive power, and the power factor.

    (b) Find the maximum instantaneous power flow from the source. (Note that p_C and the fluctuating component of p_R add as two sinusoidally varying quantities 90° out of phase with each other.)

6-3   Demonstrate that the power and the reactive power associated with a voltage **E** and a current **I** may be conveniently computed by multiplying the voltage by the conjugate of the current, **I*** (that is, a complex number having the same magnitude as the current phasor but the negative of the angle of the current phasor):

$$\mathbf{E}\mathbf{I}^* = P + jQ$$

6-2   ELECTRICAL MEASUREMENT

Because we have been occupied with other things, we have rather badly neglected a most important aspect of the electrical quantities we have been dealing with, namely, how they are measured. This is a large subject, and the present discussion could at best be called introductory, and then only if one was in a charitable mood.

Let us first divide the subject of measurements into two parts: the establishing of primary standards and the practical making of everyday measurements. Measurement based directly on the defining relations for the physical quantity to be measured usually requires a greater expenditure of time and effort than is justified, unless extreme accuracy is demanded. To simplify the task, measuring instruments are constructed which make use of some observable physical phenomenon related to the quantity being measured. These are calibrated—that is, provided with some sort of scale so that numerical values can be obtained from them—by comparison with a standard which, in turn, is based on the fundamental defining relationships.

To illustrate, let us consider the measurement of mechanical force. A pound is defined as that force which will impart to a one-slug mass an acceleration of one foot per second²; a slug is equal to 14.594 kilograms, and a standard kilogram is carefully preserved at the International Bureau of Weights and Measures, near Paris, France. Thus, to measure a given force, we could perform some rather elaborate laboratory tests to find the rate of acceleration which this force would impart to a body which had previously been compared with the standard kilogram. On the other hand, for many purposes we should vastly prefer to use a simple spring or beam balance, properly calibrated.

Similarly, in the measurement of electrical quantities we are chiefly concerned with the intelligent use of such instruments as voltmeters, ammeters, wattmeters, and impedance bridges; we are less often concerned with the calibration of these meters, and usually we can let someone else worry about the primary standards of voltage, current, and resistance. Hence our main concern here will be with the sorts of measurements that we might make in the developmental laboratory or in the field and with the instruments for such measurement.

ELECTRIC CURRENT   Let us start out with the problem of measuring current. We seek some way of obtaining an indication, visual or otherwise, of the amount of this current, so that it can be compared with a standard current. To this end, let us consider various physical phenomena related to the flow of electric current which might be adapted to this measurement. The following list of phenomena is not exhaustive, but it will indicate the sort of considerations which underlie the choice of a particular type of measuring instrument:

1. An electric current passing through an electrolyte containing a metallic salt will deposit metal on the electrode toward which the current flows, at a rate which is directly proportional to the flow. Thus the current may be measured by measuring the rate of deposition. This method is capable of yielding extremely accurate results; on the other hand, it is not very attractive for, say, portable instruments. Obviously it can be used only for currents which are constant for relatively long intervals.

2. An electric current sets up a magnetic field which is directly proportional to the magnitude of the current. This magnetic field can be detected by a magnetized bar, such as a compass needle (Fig. 6-4a), and in this way an un-

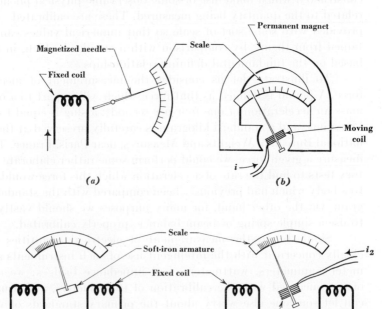

Fig. 6-4. *Some types of current-measuring instruments.* (a) *Magnetic needle;* (b) *D'Arsonval meter;* (c) *iron-vane meter;* (d) *dynamometer. In each case the force on the moving portion is opposed by a restraining spring (not shown).*

known current can be compared with a standard current. In other words, a scale may be provided so that, once the instrument is calibrated, the position of the needle on the scale will give the current at that instant. Such an instrument might be made to follow current fluctuations up to, say, several oscillations a second; at higher frequencies of alternation the inertia of the needle would prevent its accurately following the current variations.

3. A current-carrying wire in a constant magnetic field experiences a force proportional to the current. Thus a movable current-carrying coil in the field of a permanent magnet can be arranged to rotate by an amount approximately proportional to the current magnitude (Fig. 6-4*b*). An instrument operating on this principle is called a D'Arsonval meter and is widely used for measuring direct currents.

In order to reduce the inertia of the moving part, a very small one-turn coil is sometimes used, with a small mirror mounted on it. A light beam is reflected off this mirror and its motion observed visually or photographically; this instrument is called an oscillograph and may be made capable of following current fluctuations up to several hundred cycles per second.

4. A "soft" ferromagnetic material in a magnetic field has induced magnetic poles of a strength approximately proportional to the field strength. This principle is utilized in a very common type of instrument, the iron-vane meter. A soft iron armature is supported so that it is free to rotate in the field produced by the current to be measured (Fig. 6-4*c*). The field is proportional to the current, as is the induced pole strength. The total torque is proportional to the product of the induced pole strength and the magnetic flux density, that is, to the square of the current. Thus the scale in this instrument will not have equal-current divisions equally spaced; rather, they will tend to be more closely spaced at the low end of the scale. This instrument is different from those we have discussed previously, in that the observable effect of the current, depending as it does upon the square of the magnitude, is the same for current in either direction. Thus the meter will tend to read in a positive direction during both the positive and negative half-cycles of an alternating current. In fact, if the inertia of the moving element and the frequency are sufficiently high, the pointer will not respond to the rapid pulsations of the squared current but

will simply assume a position that depends upon the average squared value. Thus, here is a meter which will read the effective value of a sinusoidal current of any frequency in a wide range (typically a few to several hundred cycles per second) or direct current. As a matter of fact, if the current is periodic but nonsinusoidal, the iron-vane meter will still read the effective value.

5. The torque between two current-carrying coils (Fig. 6-4d) is proportional to the product of the two currents. Meters embodying this principle are called electro-dynamometer instruments. If the same current is passed through both coils, the resulting ammeter has characteristics similar to those of the iron-vane meter; the deflection depends upon the mean-squared value of the current.

6. Power in a resistor is converted to heat at a rate proportional to the square of the current. Thus current flow can be determined from a measurement of heat (for example, by measuring the temperature rise and flow of cooling water through the resistor). Again, the indication depends upon the mean-squared value. Obviously this method is not suitable for small, portable meters; in fact, it probably would be considered only for extremely high currents, and usually it is not very attractive, because electrical measurements are generally simpler to make than thermal measurements.

7 A thermocouple produces a voltage which depends upon the temperature of the bimetallic junction. This principle, when combined with the one immediately preceding, provides the basis for the very useful class of thermocouple instruments. In these the current passes through a resistive heating element to which is attached a thermocouple. The temperature, and hence the reading of a sensitive D'Arsonval meter attached to the thermocouple leads (Fig. 6-5), thus depends upon the mean-squared value of the current. (The frequency is assumed so high that the temperature of the thermocouple does not follow

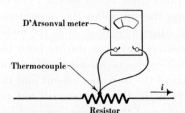

D'Arsonval meter

Thermocouple

Resistor

Fig. 6-5. Thermocouple meter.

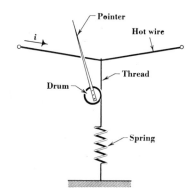

Fig. 6-6. Hot-wire ammeter.

the pulsations of thermal power but only the average value.)

Thermocouple meters are extremely useful in measuring currents at high frequencies, up to hundreds of kilocycles per second. They typically require much less power to operate than iron-vane or electrodynamometer instruments.

8. A metal expands when heated, by an amount which depends upon the temperature. This phenomenon is utilized in the hot-wire ammeter (Fig. 6-6). The current-carrying wire is heated by the current to be measured; the resulting expansion allows an attached thread to rotate a small drum, to which the pointer is attached.

9. A rectifier is a nonlinear circuit element which will pass current in only one direction. Four rectifiers can be connected in a bridge circuit with a D'Arsonval meter to make a rectifier ammeter (Fig. 6-7). In this configuration the current always passes through the meter in the same direction, although the line current is alternating. The meter reads a value which depends upon the average value of the rectified wave, which for a sinusoidal current is 0.636 of the peak value or $I_{\text{eff}}/1.11$. The scale is usually marked to read 1.11 times the actual direct current, so that effective values are read.

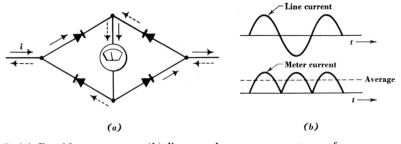

(a)   *(b)*

Fig. 6-7. (a) Rectifier ammeter; (b) line- and meter-current waveforms.

This meter will indicate the wrong effective value with nonsinusoidal current waveforms, where 1.11 is no longer the appropriate multiplying factor. On the other hand, rectifier meters, like thermocouple meters, have the advantages of high-frequency capabilities and low power drain.

The above list of ways of measuring current is not complete by any means, but perhaps enough has been said to give some perspective on the problem of measuring instruments. Practically any physical phenomenon related to electric current flow can be made the basis of some measuring instrument.

VOLTAGE AND POWER MEASUREMENT The measurement of voltage is similar to the measurement of current, in that any of a vast number of physical phenomena can be used as the basis for a measuring instrument. Many of the most common types of voltmeters are simply sensitive ammeters in series with a high value of resistance, as in Fig. 6-8a. The resistance must be high enough so that the meter does not unduly disturb the circuit to which it is connected and low enough to pass a measurable current. The meter reading then will be proportional to the average or effective value of the voltage, depending upon the type of ammeter used.

Other types of voltmeters depend upon the mechanical force between two bodies charged to high potentials, the effect on the current in a vacuum tube due to a voltage applied to its grid, the deflection of an electron beam by an electric field, the distance for sparking between two electrodes, and so on.

Power measurement is most commonly made with an electro-dynamometer wattmeter (Fig. 6-8b), in which one of the coil currents is the circuit current and the other is proportional to the circuit voltage. The instantaneous torque on the moving element is thus proportional

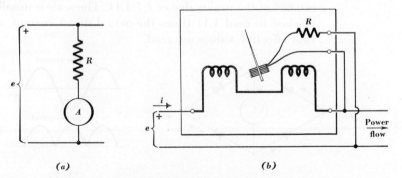

(a)   (b)

Fig. 6-8. (a) Resistance and ammeter connected together to make a voltmeter;
(b) electrodynamometer used as a wattmeter.

to the instantaneous product of current and voltage in the circuit on which the measurement is being performed. The element has too much inertia to respond to the pulsations of this torque and registers only the average value.

Thermal methods of power measurement are often used at high frequencies.

The electrodynamometer is sometimes used as a varmeter, in which case an inductor, instead of a resistor, is connected in series with the voltage coil.

PROBLEMS

6-4   Two parallel metal plates experience a mutual force approximately equal to $0.0005Ae^2/d^2$ newtons, where A is the area of the plates in square centimeters, e is the voltage applied across the plates, and d is the spacing in millimeters. Discuss the feasibility of constructing a voltmeter based on this phenomenon. Suppose the meter is constructed and calibrated with a constant voltage; if an alternating voltage is applied to the meter, will the meter read zero, effective value, peak value, or what?

6-5   An electret is the electric-field counterpart of a permanent magnet; a small bar electret placed in an electric field will tend to align itself with the field. The torque it experiences is proportional to the electric field (and hence to the voltage which produces it) and to the sine of the angle between the axis of the electret and the direction of the field.

Explain very briefly how this phenomenon might be used as the basis for a voltmeter design. Suppose such a meter is constructed and calibrated by applying known constant voltages; if an alternating voltage is applied to the meter, will it read zero, effective value, peak value, or what?

6-3   SERIES-PARALLEL-CIRCUIT EXAMPLE

One or two examples of power-circuit computation will be more effective than pages of descriptive text in imparting an ability to handle such calculations.

Consider the following problem. An induction-heating generator operates with an open-circuit voltage of 100 volts at a frequency of 10,000 cps. Its internal impedance is given by the manufacturer as $0.5 + j8.0$ ohms, and it is to be connected to a load whose impedance is found to be $0.10 + j0.80$ ohm. We wish to get as much power as possible into the load without exceeding the rating of the generator, which is 2 kva.

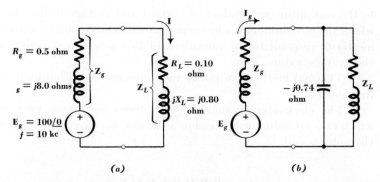

Fig. 6-9. *Induction-heating generator and load* (a) *before a capacitor has been added to increase the power into the load and* (b) *after the capacitor has been added.*

To begin with, let us find out how successful our endeavor will be if we simply connect the load impedance directly to the generator (Fig. 6-9a). The total loop impedance is then

$$\mathbf{Z}_t = (0.5 + j8.0) + (0.10 + j0.80) = 0.6 + j8.8 = 8.81\underline{/86.1°} \quad (6\text{-}5)$$

The current is (with the internal voltage of the generator taken as the reference phasor)

$$\mathbf{I} = \frac{100\underline{/0°}}{8.81\underline{/86.1°}} = 11.35\underline{/-86.1°} \quad (6\text{-}6)$$

Thus the total power supplied by the generator (including internal losses) is

$$P_t = (100)(11.35)\cos 86.1° = 77.2 \text{ watts} \quad (6\text{-}7)$$

and the power supplied to the load is

$$P_L = I^2 R_L = (11.35)^2(0.1) = 12.9 \text{ watts} \quad (6\text{-}8)$$

At this rate the load is not likely to get warm; there is little power being generated, and most of this goes to heat up the generator rather than the load.

Now, we can see that the villain here is the large internal inductive reactance of the generator, which is inherent in the construction of the machine. Even if the machine were short-circuited, the resulting current would be less than 13 amp. However, if some capacitive reactance is added in the external circuit, this will in effect cancel some of the internal inductive reactance and allow a greater current to flow.

One thing we might try is to place a capacitor in series with the load. This turns out to give some improvement, but not a great deal without exceeding the kilovolt-ampere rating of the machine.

Another possibility is to place a capacitor in parallel with the load; this we shall investigate in detail. Let us place across the load a capacitive reactance of 0.74 ohm, as in Fig. 6-9b. That this is nearly the best possible value may be ascertained by choosing a number of trial values and computing the power in each case (or by a more sophisticated analysis). Since the purpose here is to illustrate computational methods, we shall analyze only the one case.

The parallel impedance of the load and capacitor can now be computed:

$$\mathbf{Z}_{\text{par}} = \frac{(-j0.74)(0.1 + j0.8)}{0.1 + j0.8 - j0.74} = 4.03 - j3.16 \tag{6-9}$$

Thus the total impedance is

$$\mathbf{Z}_t = \mathbf{Z}_g + \mathbf{Z}_{\text{par}} = 4.53 + j4.84 = 6.63\underline{/46.8°} \tag{6-10}$$

We can now calculate the generator current:

$$\mathbf{I} = \frac{\mathbf{E}_g}{\mathbf{Z}_t} = 15.1\underline{/-46.8°} \tag{6-11}$$

The total power supplied by the generator (including internal losses) is

$$P_t = E_g I \cos \theta = (100)(15.1)(0.684) = 1{,}033 \text{ watts} \tag{6-12}$$

The power loss in the internal resistance of the generator is

$$P_R = I^2 R_g = (15.1)^2(0.5) = 113 \text{ watts} \tag{6-13}$$

The remainder of the power, about 920 watts, goes into the load. This is a considerable improvement over the power obtained without the capacitor. On the other hand, the generator is not yet loaded to its kilovolt-ampere capacity. A more elaborate coupling network, using, say, a capacitor across the load and another in series with the generator, might be used to increase the power into the load still further.

Assuming that 920 watts into the load will be sufficient, let us see what kind of capacitor we shall have to order and let us make sure that the size will be a reasonable one. The capacitive reactance is $1/2\pi f C$; so a reactance of 0.74 at 10 kc corresponds to a capacitance of

$$C = \frac{10^6}{(2\pi)(10{,}000)(0.74)} = 21.5 \ \mu\text{f} \tag{6-14}$$

The voltage rating of the capacitor will have to be

$$I Z_{\text{par}} = (15.1)(5.12) = 77.2 \text{ volts rms} \tag{6-15}$$

or about 110 volts peak as a minimum value. The current rating will have to be at least $77.2/0.74 = 104$ amp. Thus, if a capacitor with 500-volt rating is used, the kilovolt-ampere rating would have to be at least 50. This is not an unreasonable size.

PROBLEMS

6-6 An induction-heating generator has an open-circuit terminal voltage of 100 volts and an internal inductive reactance of 10 ohms. The internal resistance is to be considered negligible. It is connected to a load resistance R.

(a) Compute the average power delivered to the load resistance for $R = 0, 5, 10, 20$, and 100 ohms. Sketch a curve of power versus R.

(b) In one diagram, sketch phasors representing the internally generated voltage $100\underline{/0°}$ and the currents for the values of R given above. (Do this rather carefully, to scale.)

(c) What is the maximum power obtainable from this generator with a resistance load? How might more power be obtained from the generator?

(d) Derive a general expression for the average power P into the load as a function of R. Choose appropriate normalizing values P_n and R_n and plot a curve of normalized power as a function of normalized load resistance. (Do this in terms of a general voltage E and a reactance X, instead of using the numerical values given above.)

6-7 For the circuit shown:

(a) Assume that $E = 100$ volts, $X_L = X_C = 10$ ohms, and $R = 10$ ohms. Compute the power supplied to R.

(b) Assume $X_L = X_C$ and derive a general expression for the power into R. Plot the current and the power in the resistor as R is varied over a wide range of values.

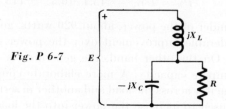

Fig. P 6-7

6-8 Find the load voltage, load power, and power loss in the source and cable impedances (a) without the capacitor (shown dashed) and (b) with the capacitor connected across the load.

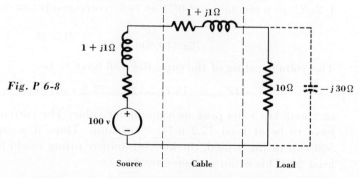

Fig. P 6-8

6-4 TWO-SOURCE EXAMPLE

For a second problem, let us solve the circuit of Fig. 6-10 in two ways, first by making use of voltage and current phasors and then by exploiting the concepts of power and reactive power.

In this circuit we have a load supplied from two generating sources G_1 and G_2 over transmission lines with the impedance Z_1 and Z_2 as shown. The load requires 10 kw at 0.80 power factor lagging. It is desired to have generator G_1 supply 5 kw total with 0.80 power factor lagging and operate with a terminal voltage of 460 volts. The operating conditions at G_2 are to be found.

In the solution of electrical circuits with complex configurations, if the available data about the circuit are in the form of numerical values for all the impedances and all the source currents or voltages, then the analysis can be completely systematized in various ways. The study of these systematic procedures forms a large part of the theory of circuit analysis.

On the other hand, if some of the data are in other forms (in this case as power and power factor), there are no such general rules, and the analysis becomes somewhat more of an art. For complicated cases the problems are often solved by constructing the system in miniature and making measurements. This example is sufficiently simple that we shall be able to solve it without difficulty.

PHASOR METHOD As a first approach, let us start with generator G_1, about which we know the most, and attempt to move out from there, finding voltage and current phasors and constructing a phasor diagram as we go. We may as well use the phase of G_1 as a reference, so that

$$\mathbf{E}_1 = 460\underline{/0°} \tag{6-16}$$

Generator G_1 supplies $5,000/0.80 = 6,250$ va, so the magnitude of the current is

$$I_1 = \frac{6,250}{460} = 13.6 \text{ amp} \tag{6-17}$$

The phase angle of the current is $\cos^{-1} 0.80 = -36.9°$.

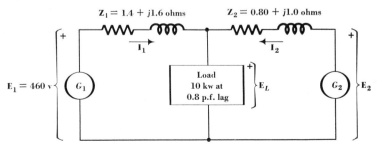

Fig. 6-10. Power circuit for the example of Sec. 6-4.

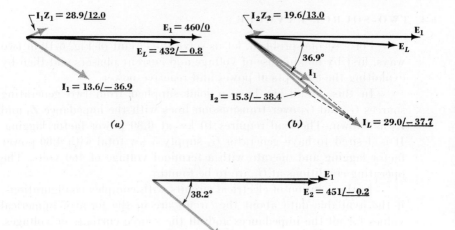

$$\mathbf{I}_1\mathbf{Z}_1 = 28.9\underline{/12.0}$$

$$\mathbf{E}_1 = 460\underline{/0}$$

$$\mathbf{E}_L = 432\underline{/-0.8}$$

$$\mathbf{I}_1 = 13.6\underline{/-36.9}$$

(a)

$$\mathbf{I}_2\mathbf{Z}_2 = 19.6\underline{/13.0}$$

$$\mathbf{E}_1$$

$$\mathbf{E}_L$$

$$36.9°$$

$$\mathbf{I}_1$$

$$\mathbf{I}_2 = 15.3\underline{/-38.4}$$

$$\mathbf{I}_L = 29.0\underline{/-37.7}$$

(b)

$$\mathbf{E}_1$$

$$\mathbf{E}_2 = 451\underline{/-0.2}$$

$$38.2°$$

$$\mathbf{I}_2$$

(c)

Fig. 6-11. Phasor diagram for Fig. 6-10, showing various stages of analysis.

With this information we are in a position to find

$$\mathbf{I}_1\mathbf{Z}_1 = (13.6\underline{/-36.9°})(1.4 + j1.6) = 28.3 + j6.0 \qquad (6\text{-}18)$$

and $$\mathbf{E}_L = \mathbf{E}_1 - \mathbf{I}_1\mathbf{Z}_1 = 431.7 - j6.0 = 432\underline{/-0.8°} \qquad (6\text{-}19)$$

These phasors are shown in diagram form in Fig. 6-11a.

Next the load current and $\mathbf{I}_2$ can be obtained. The load volt-amperes is $10,000/0.80 = 12,500$; hence the load current I_L is

$$\frac{12,500}{432} = 29.0 \text{ amp}$$

The load current lags $\mathbf{E}_L$ by $\cos^{-1} 0.80$, or $36.9°$; thus the phase angle of $\mathbf{I}_L$ is $(-36.9 - 0.8) = -37.7°$. The current $\mathbf{I}_2$ is easily found:

$$\mathbf{I}_2 = \mathbf{I}_L - \mathbf{I}_1 = (29.0\underline{/-37.7°}) - (13.6\underline{/-36.9°})$$
$$= 12.0 - j9.5 = 15.3\underline{/-38.4°} \qquad (6\text{-}20)$$

These phasors are shown in Fig. 6-11b.

The voltage drop across the impedance $\mathbf{Z}_2$ is

$$\mathbf{I}_2\mathbf{Z}_2 = (12.0 - j9.5)(0.80 + j1.0) = 19.1 + j4.4 \qquad (6\text{-}21)$$

Thus (see Fig. 6-11c):

$$\mathbf{E}_2 = \mathbf{E}_L + \mathbf{I}_2\mathbf{Z}_2 = 450.8 - j1.6 = 451\underline{/-0.2°} \qquad (6\text{-}22)$$

The power supplied by the generator G_2 is

$$P_2 = (451)(15.3)(\cos 38.2°) = 5,430 \text{ watts} \qquad (6\text{-}23)$$

The reactive power is

$$Q_2 = (451)(15.3)(\sin 38.2°) = 4{,}270 \text{ vars lagging} \qquad (6\text{-}24)$$

POWER METHOD Now let us solve this problem a second time, making use of two principles involving the concepts of power and reactive power. The first is that the total power supplied from all the sources of a system is equal to the total power consumed in the loads and losses. The second is that the total reactive power supplied is equal to the total consumed. In applying this second principle, the leading and lagging reactive power, if both appear in the system (for example, if it contains both capacitive and inductive loads), must be assigned opposite algebraic signs. (This point does not arise in the present example.)

The current associated with G_1 is found, as before, to be 13.6 amp; the power and reactive power are 5,000 watts and 3,750 vars. The power and reactive power in the first transmission line are

$$I_1{}^2R_1 = (13.6)^2(1.4) = 260 \text{ watts} \qquad I_1{}^2X_1 = (13.6)^2(1.6) = 300 \text{ vars}$$
$$(6\text{-}25)$$

Thus the power and reactive power supplied to the load by G_1 are 4,740 watts and 3,450 vars lagging.

The volt-amperes supplied to the load by G_1 is

$$\sqrt{(4{,}740)^2 + (3{,}450)^2} = 5{,}870$$

Hence the load voltage E_L is $(5{,}870/13.6) = 432$ volts.

The volt-amperes supplied to the load by G_2 is

$$\sqrt{(5{,}260)^2 + (4{,}050)^2} = 6{,}650$$

Hence the current I_2 is $(6{,}650/432) = 15.4$ amp.

The power and reactive power lost in the second transmission line are $I_2{}^2R_2 = (15.4)^2(0.80) = 190$ watts and

$$I_2{}^2X_2 = (15.4)^2(1.0) = 240 \text{ vars lagging}$$

Thus the generator G_2 must supply

$$P_2 = 5{,}260 + 190 = 5{,}450 \text{ watts}$$
$$Q_2 = 4{,}050 + 240 = 4{,}290 \text{ vars lagging} \qquad (6\text{-}26)$$

PROBLEMS

6-9 An industrial load with the parameters indicated in the figure is to be connected to the end of a long underground cable which may be approximated by the equivalent circuit shown. Compute the required source voltage, power, reactive power, and power factor.

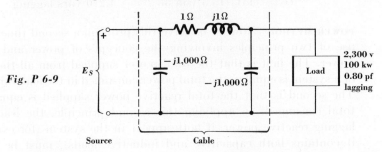

Fig. P 6-9

6-10   Generator G_2 in the figure is to supply 5 kw at 0.80 power factor lagging.

(*a*) Find the terminal voltages which must exist at the two generators.

(*b*) Find the power which must be supplied by generator G_1.

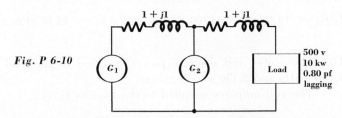

Fig. P 6-10

6-11   In a typical power system the predominant impedances in the transmission circuits are the inductive reactances of machine and transformer windings and transmission lines. Thus the impedance between two points on the system can be approximated by a pure reactance, as in the figure.

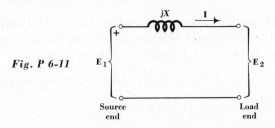

Fig. P 6-11

Let E_1 and E_2 represent the magnitudes of the source and load voltages, both of which are typically held fixed. The transmitted power is, of course, $P = E_2 I \cos \theta$, where θ is the phase angle between $\mathbf{E}_2$ and $\mathbf{I}$.

Construct a phasor diagram showing $\mathbf{E}_1$, $\mathbf{E}_2$, and $\mathbf{I}$. Show that the transmitted power is given by

$$P = \frac{E_1 E_2}{X} \sin \alpha$$

where α is the phase angle between $\mathbf{E}_1$ and $\mathbf{E}_2$, and hence that the transmitted power cannot exceed E_1E_2/X.

6-12   A single-phase induction motor is found to be represented reasonably well by an equivalent circuit consisting of a 40-ohm inductive reactance in parallel with a variable resistance to represent the effect of the mechanical load on the motor. This resistance varies from a high value for no load on the motor to 20 ohms at full load.

The motor is to be operated at the end of a long line with impedance $2 + j2$ ohms.

(*a*) Compute the sending-end voltage E_s required to give 200 volts at the motor for no-load and full-load conditions.

(*b*) Compute the motor voltage for both no-load and full-load conditions if the sending-end voltage is held constant at 220 volts.

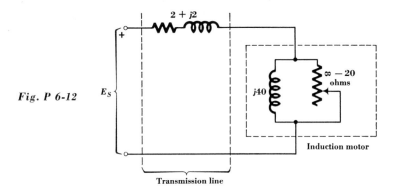

Fig. P 6-12

6-13   An industrial load varies from 10 kw at 0.90 power factor lagging to 100 kw at 0.80 power factor lagging. It is connected to a constant source voltage E_s by a transmission line with impedance $2 + j4$ ohms. The load voltage is to be maintained at 2,300 volts.

(*a*) Under the condition of lightest load, what must be the source voltage to give 2,300 volts at the load?

(*b*) Assume that the source voltage is fixed at the value found in part *a*. It is proposed that capacitance be switched in, as shown, in order to hold the load voltage constant as the load varies. What would be the total capacitance required under maximum-load conditions? (Note that it may be necessary to assume trial values for X_c.)

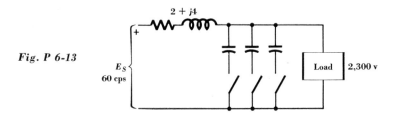

Fig. P 6-13

6-5 THREE-PHASE Y CONNECTION

The simplest possible system for a-c power transmission consists of a generator connected through two wires to a load. This is called a *single-phase* system. In such a system power flows in pulses, as we have seen (Fig. 6-2). As a result, there is an undesirable pulsating component in the torque delivered by a single-phase motor. Besides this factor, there is the problem of starting large single-phase motors, since single-phase machines are not inherently self-starting. Another disadvantage of single-phase systems is that space is used inefficiently in the construction of generators and motors.

For these reasons, and also because of certain economic and operating considerations, heavy-power generation, transmission, and utilization almost invariably involve *polyphase* systems. Of these the 3-*phase* systems are by far the most common.

THREE-PHASE VOLTAGES, CURRENTS, AND POWER Consider the three separate single-phase systems of Fig. 6-12, which are identical except that the three generators are arranged to produce voltages differing in phase by 120° from one another. Since the three load impedances are assumed identical, it follows that the three currents will also differ in phase by 120°. The phasors representing these currents and voltages are shown in Fig. 6-13, and plots of the instantaneous values are given in Fig. 6-14.

It may be seen from either of these figures that the sum of the three voltages is equal to zero at any instant; the same is true of the sum of the three currents. (In fact, this would be true for any n equal-amplitude voltages or currents spaced $360°/n$ apart in phase angle.)

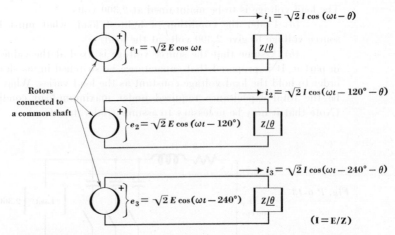

$$i_1 = \sqrt{2}\, I \cos{(\omega t - \theta)}$$

$$e_1 = \sqrt{2}\, E \cos{\omega t} \qquad Z\underline{/\theta}$$

Rotors connected to a common shaft

$$i_2 = \sqrt{2}\, I \cos{(\omega t - 120° - \theta)}$$

$$e_2 = \sqrt{2}\, E \cos{(\omega t - 120°)} \qquad Z\underline{/\theta}$$

$$i_3 = \sqrt{2}\, I \cos{(\omega t - 240° - \theta)}$$

$$e_3 = \sqrt{2}\, E \cos{(\omega t - 240°)} \qquad Z\underline{/\theta}$$

$$(\mathbf{I} = \mathbf{E}/\mathbf{Z})$$

Fig. 6-12. Three identical single-phase systems with 120° phase difference.

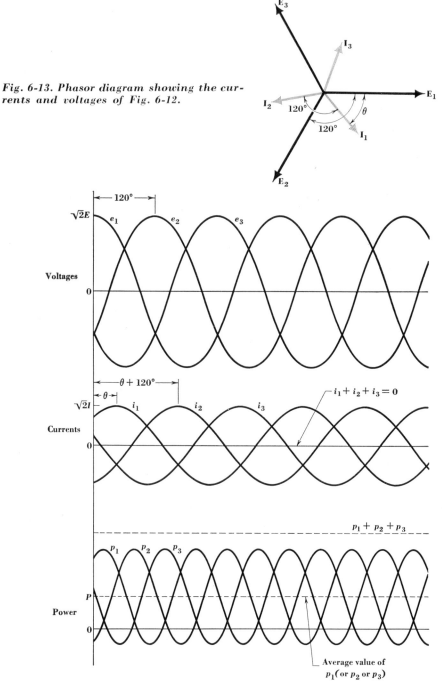

Fig. 6-13. Phasor diagram showing the currents and voltages of Fig. 6-12.

Fig. 6-14. Currents, voltages, and instantaneous power for the circuits of Fig. 6-12.

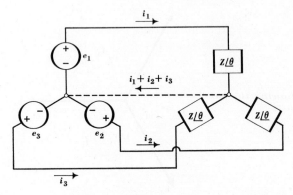

Fig. 6-15. Combination of the three single-phase systems of Fig. 6-12 into one balanced 3-phase system.

The instantaneous powers, obtained as the product of instantaneous voltage and current, as in Fig. 6-2, are also plotted in Fig. 6-14 for all three single-phase systems. These power curves, it should be noted, exhibit a very important property: the sum of the powers in the three single-phase circuits at any instant is a constant value. This value is just the sum of the average powers in the individual circuits, or three times the average power in any one of the circuits. (A similar statement could be made about n single-phase circuits in which the voltages are spaced either $180°/n$ or $360°/n$ in phase angle.)

Now these three single-phase circuits could just as well be arranged as indicated in Fig. 6-15, where a single conductor (indicated by the dashed line) is used as a return conductor for all three currents. However, we have seen that the sum of i_1, i_2, and i_3 is zero at every instant; hence this conductor carries no current and does not even need to be provided!

A 3-phase system connected in this fashion is termed a Y-Y connection, from the configuration of the generators and impedances. The

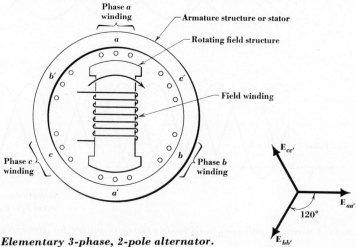

Fig. 6-16. Elementary 3-phase, 2-pole alternator.

dashed neutral connection may or may not be provided. We see here displayed the two most important characteristics of the balanced 3-phase connection: (1) only three conductors need be provided, since the current in the neutral connection is zero, and (2) the power flow is constant. (As we have seen, similar properties characterize balanced polyphase systems with other than three phases. There are 2-, 4-, 6-, 12-, and 24-phase systems which are used for special purposes, but a detailed study of these possibilities is not justified here.)

In actual practice, not only is the arrangement of Fig. 6-15 usually substituted for the three single-phase circuits of Fig. 6-12, but the three voltage sources are three windings on the same machine. The most common physical arrangement is indicated schematically in Fig. 6-16.

On the other hand, for the purpose of analyzing the Y-Y system, it is most convenient to deal with the three single-phase circuits of Fig. 6-12, which are completely equivalent. Furthermore, once the currents, voltages, and powers of one of these single-phase circuits is found, the corresponding quantities in the other two are easily derived.

Figure 6-17 is a schematic representation of the three generator windings of Fig. 6-16 arranged in a Y connection, with the terminals a', b', c' joined together to form the neutral point o. The use of double-subscript notation is illustrated here, the notation $\mathbf{E}_{ao}$ signifying "the voltage of point a with respect to point o." This is sometimes simpler than the single-subscript notation with accompanying bracket and polarity sign which we have used previously. Note that $\mathbf{E}_{oa} = -\mathbf{E}_{ao}$.

The phasor diagram of Fig. 6-17b shows the line-to-line voltages $\mathbf{E}_{ab}$, $\mathbf{E}_{bc}$, and $\mathbf{E}_{ca}$, as obtained by simple geometrical construction. Note that $E_{ab} = 2E_{ao} \cos 30°$; in words, the line-to-line voltages are equal to $\sqrt{3}$ times the phase (line-to-neutral) voltages in magnitude.

The total power transmission is just three times the power in a single phase; that is,

$$\text{Power} = 3E_{\text{phase}}I_{\text{line}} \cos \theta \tag{6-27}$$

where θ is the power-factor angle, or the angle of the load impedance. Since the line-to-line voltage is $\sqrt{3}$ times the phase voltage, this may be written

$$\text{Power} = \sqrt{3} \, E_{\text{line to line}}I_{\text{line}} \cos \theta \tag{6-28}$$

EXAMPLE To illustrate this procedure, let us compute the line current and total power if the Y-connected load impedance of Fig. 6-18 is connected to the generator of Fig. 6-17. The line-to-line voltage is assumed to be 208 volts.

The line-to-neutral voltage across any one phase, such as E_{ao}, is $208/\sqrt{3} = 120$ volts. Thus the line current is

$$I_a = \frac{E_{ao}}{Z_p} = \frac{120}{5.00} = 24.0 \text{ amp}$$

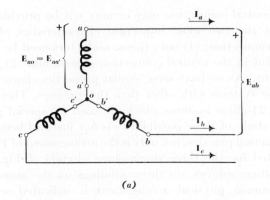

(a)

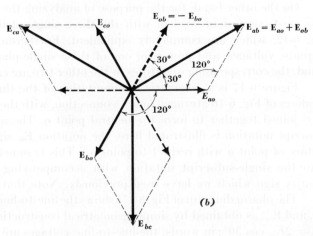

(b)

Fig. 6-17. Y connection of the three generator windings of Fig. 6-16 and phasor diagram showing line-to-line voltages.

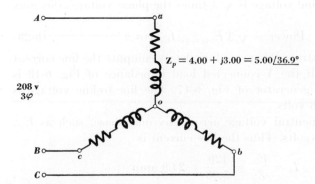

$Z_p = 4.00 + j3.00 = 5.00\underline{/36.9°}$

208 v
3φ

Fig. 6-18. Y-connected load impedance to be connected to the generator of Fig. 6-17.

This current lags the phase voltage $\mathbf{E}_{ao}$ by an angle of 36.9°. (From the phasor diagram, Fig. 6-17, it may be seen that the line current $\mathbf{I}_a$ lags the line-to-line voltage $\mathbf{E}_{ab}$ by 36.9° + 30°, or 66.9°.)

The total power is $3I_a{}^2R_p = \sqrt{3}\, E_{ab}I_a \cos \theta = 6{,}910$ watts. The reactive power and volt-amperes are

$$Q = \sqrt{3}\, E_{ab}I_a \sin \theta = 5{,}180 \text{ vars}$$
$$\text{Volt-amperes} = 3E_{ao}I_a = \sqrt{3}\, E_{ab}I_a = 8{,}640 \tag{6-29}$$

PROBLEMS

6-14   The magnitude of the balanced 3-phase line-to-neutral voltages applied to the three inductive loads as shown is 100 volts.

    (*a*) Complete the phasor diagram, showing magnitudes and angles of currents and line-to-line voltages.

    (*b*) A wattmeter connected as shown will read the product of the voltage E_{bc}, the current I_a, and the cosine of the angle between them. Predict its reading. (Note that this reading has nothing at all to do with the power absorbed by the load.)

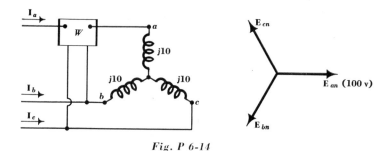

Fig. P 6-14

6-15   (*a*) Prove that the total power flow is constant in any balanced *n*-phase star-connected system (that is, any system made up of a number of identical single-phase systems connected as in Fig. 6-15) provided that the line-to-neutral voltages are equal in amplitude and spaced either 180°/*n* or 360°/*n* in phase angle.

    (*b*) Construct phasor diagrams for the line-to-neutral voltages in 2-, 4-, and 5-phase balanced systems. Find the ratio of magnitudes of line-to-line to line-to-neutral voltages in each case.

6-16   A 3-phase load consists of three equal impedances of $11 + j4$ ohms connected in Y. It connects to a 230-volt (line-to-line) source through three wires each having $1 + j1$ ohms impedance.

    (*a*) Find the line-to-line voltage at the load.

    (*b*) Find the total power in the load.

6-17   A total power of P kw at unity power factor is to be sent over a long transmission line with a voltage between conductors of V volts.

If single-phase transmission is employed, there will be two conductors with a resistance of R ohms in each conductor.

An alternative plan is to use the same number of pounds of copper in a 3-phase transmission line, in which case there will be three conductors, each with a cross-sectional area two-thirds that of the single-phase line and hence with a resistance $3R/2$.

(a) If the line-to-line voltage is the same in the two cases, compare the power loss with the 3-phase system to that with the single-phase system.

(b) Compare the drop in line-to-line voltage between source and load in the two cases.

6-6   THREE-PHASE Δ CONNECTION

To illustrate the details of computation with a Δ-connected load, let us compute the line current and power when the combination of impedances shown in Fig. 6-19 has impressed across it the same 3-phase voltages as in the previous example. The current through one of the load impedances, $\mathbf{I}_{ab}$, for example, is equal to the voltage across that impedance divided by the impedance:

$$\frac{\mathbf{E}_{ab}}{\mathbf{Z}'_p} = \frac{208}{15.00} = 13.87 \text{ amp} \qquad .$$

Thus the total power, reactive power, and volt-amperes are

$$P = 3I_{ab}^2 R = (3)(13.87)^2(12.00) = 6{,}910 \text{ watts}$$
$$Q = 3I_{ab}^2 X = (3)(13.87)^2(9.00) = 5{,}180 \text{ var} \qquad (6\text{-}30)$$
$$\text{Volt-amperes} = 3E_{ab}I_{ab} = (3)(13.87)(208) = 8{,}640$$

Now, if the three load impedances were enclosed in a box with only the three terminals a, b, c accessible, we should not be able to tell whether we had these three impedances in a Δ connection or three other impedances in a Y connection. Thus we should expect that the

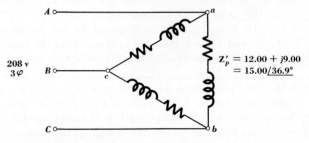

Fig. 6-19. Δ-connected load impedance.

power expression, Eq. (6-27), which was developed for the Y connection would also hold for a Δ-connected load. That this is indeed so we shall see in a moment.

Thus,

$$P = \sqrt{3}\, E_{\text{line}} I_{\text{line}} \cos \theta = 6{,}910$$
$$= \sqrt{3}\, (208) I_{\text{line}} (0.80) \tag{6-31}$$

Solving this for I_{line}, we obtain $I_{\text{line}} = 24.0$ amp.

Δ-Y EQUIVALENCE   The phasor diagram for this example can easily be constructed. Assume that the line-to-line voltages are the same as in Fig. 6-17. The currents through the three load impedances are 13.87 amp in magnitude and lag the line voltages by 36.9°.

The line current $\mathbf{I}_{Aa}$ is, by Kirchhoff's current law, the sum of the currents $\mathbf{I}_{ab}$ and $\mathbf{I}_{ac}$, or $\mathbf{I}_{ab} - \mathbf{I}_{ca}$. This is indicated on the phasor diagram of Fig. 6-20. (The other two line currents are found in similar fashion.) From the geometry of the parallelogram which indicates this subtraction, it may be seen that $I_{Aa} = 2I_{ab} \cos 30° = \sqrt{3}\, I_{ab}$. In words, the line current to a Δ-connected load is equal to $\sqrt{3}$ times the phase current in magnitude. From this it follows that the power in a Δ-connected load is

$$P = 3E_{\text{line}} I_{\text{phase}} \cos \theta = \sqrt{3}\, E_{\text{line}} I_{\text{line}} \cos \theta \tag{6-32}$$

Comparison of the results of this example of a Δ-connected load with those of the previous example of a Y-connected load leads to a valuable and interesting conclusion. It will be noted that the current,

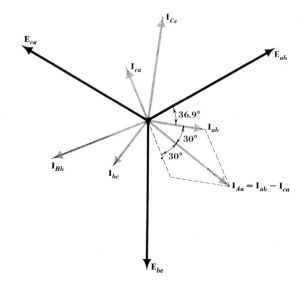

Fig. 6-20. Phasor diagram for Fig. 6-19.

power, reactive power, and volt-amperes are precisely equal in the two cases; in other words, as viewed from the terminals A, B, C, the two circuits of Figs. 6-18 and 6-19 are completely equivalent. It will also be seen that the individual impedances in the Y connection are just one-third of those in the Δ connection (the angles of the impedances being the same in the two cases).

In general, a balanced Δ-connected impedance may be replaced by a Y-connected impedance if the individual impedances have the relation

$$Z_Y = \tfrac{1}{3}Z_\Delta \qquad (6\text{-}33)$$

and the line currents and voltages will remain exactly the same. This can be shown by comparing the complete phasor diagrams for the two examples chosen here and noting that the equivalence is inherent and not dependent upon the particular numerical values chosen.

This result has important consequences in computations involving balanced 3-phase circuits. First of all, if only the line values are given and the connection is not specified, either may be assumed. Often the

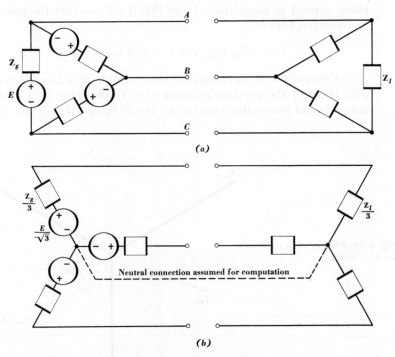

(a)

(b)

Fig. 6-21. (a) Balanced Δ-connected load and source with internal impedance and (b) equivalent Y connection. (The equivalent Y generators will differ in phase angle from the original generators by 30°.)

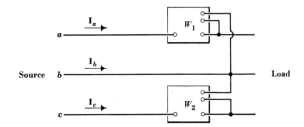

Fig. 6-22. Two-watt-meter connection for 3-phase power measurement.

choice of a Y connection is more convenient. Second, if the actual circuit is mixed, containing both Y and Δ connections, the computations may be carried out with an equivalent system in which the connections are all the same. Again, converting everything to the Y connection and performing all computations with only one of the three phases will often be the simplest procedure. (A Δ-connected generator with internal impedance may be converted to an equivalent Y connection, as is indicated in Fig. 6-21.)

THREE-PHASE POWER MEASUREMENT The use of an electrodynamometer to measure power was discussed in connection with Fig. 6-8b. In the case of a Y-connected load with the neutral connection accessible, three such meters could be used to measure the total power, one measuring the power in each phase.

The more usual situation, however, is that the neutral connection is not accessible; or, if the neutral is available, we may choose to ignore it and perform measurements using only the three lines. In this case we may arbitrarily choose to measure voltages with respect to one of the lines—line b, for example, in Fig. 6-22. We may think of two single-phase circuits, one represented by lines a and b and the other by lines b and c, line b forming the common return. These two single-phase circuits, looked at in this way, do not form a balanced polyphase system, so that in general the powers in the two (the readings W_1 and W_2 in Fig. 6-22) will not be the same. However, the sum of these two readings is the total power in the system, whether it is regarded as a balanced 3-phase system or as two separate single-phase systems.

The readings of wattmeters W_1 and W_2 in terms of the 3-phase line voltages and currents may be deduced from the phasor diagram of Fig. 6-23. Wattmeter W_1 reads the product of E_{ab}, I_a, and the cosine of the angle between them. This angle, as seen from Fig. 6-17 or 6-20, is $\theta + 30°$, where θ is the load power-factor angle. Thus W_1 reads $E_{\text{line}}I_{\text{line}}$ cos $(\theta + 30°)$. Similarly, W_2 reads $E_{\text{line}}I_{\text{line}}$ cos $(\theta - 30°)$. The sum of W_1 and W_2 is $\sqrt{3}\, E_{\text{line}}I_{\text{line}}$ cos θ, as may easily be found by making use of the trigonometric identities in Eqs. (3-3) and (3-4).

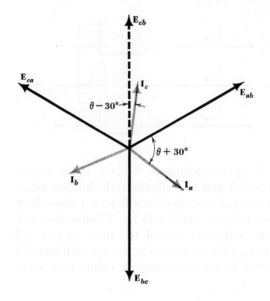

Fig. 6-23. Phasor diagram for Fig. 6-22.

PROBLEMS

6-18 Balanced 3-phase voltages are applied to a balanced 3-phase load as indicated:

$$\mathbf{E}_{ab} = 100\underline{/0^\circ} \qquad \mathbf{E}_{bc} = 100\underline{/-120^\circ} \qquad \mathbf{E}_{ca} = 100\underline{/120^\circ}$$

The three load impedances are each $\mathbf{Z} = 10\underline{/45^\circ}$.

(a) Find the current $\mathbf{I}_a$.

(b) Find the total power flow into the load.

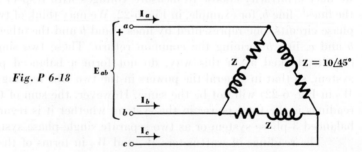

Fig. P 6-18

6-19 A 3-phase load consists of three impedances of $12 + j5$ ohms each, connected in Δ. This load is connected, through three lines of 1 ohm resistance each, to a second load consisting of three impedances of $12 + j5$ ohms each, connected in Y. The whole is supplied with 3-phase voltages measuring 230 volts from line to line.

(a) Find the current in the supply line and the current in the line to the Δ load.

(b) Find the power supplied to each load.

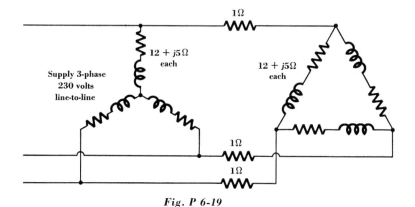

Fig. P 6-19

6-20   A balanced 3-phase motor takes 15 kw at 0.80 power factor lagging and 230 volts line to line. It is fed from a transformer through a 3-phase feeder line, and each line conductor has a resistance of 1 ohm.

     (*a*) Compute the voltage drop in each conductor.

     (*b*) Compute the line-to-line voltage required at the transformer.

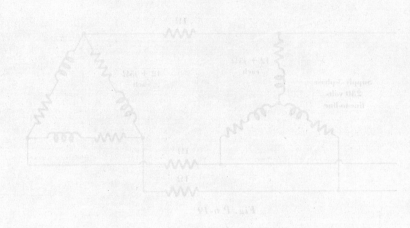

transmission networks

Much of the material of the next six chapters will be concerned with a particularly important type of system, the *transducer*. A transducer, in general, is a device or system whose function is to respond to an input force or power and to supply an output force or power which in some sense corresponds to the input. This definition is quite inclusive and hence rather vague. However, the examples of these chapters should make the concept clear.

This chapter deals with electrical and mechanical networks in which the transmission is, in general, better at some excitation frequencies than at others. Such networks are often used to separate certain frequency components from the company of other, undesired components (as in selecting a television channel). In other cases the primary function may be to eliminate from the output certain frequency components present in the input, as in a vibration-isolation mounting. If the function is primarily one of frequency selection, the network is termed a filter. On the other hand, the intended function may be that of amplification—producing an output as nearly like the input as possible but at a higher power level. (Here it may be desirable to reduce as far as practicable the variation of transmission with frequency.) The two functions may be combined in an amplifier filter.

In order to obtain certain characteristics in various transducers, it is often necessary to make them quite complex. Chapter 8 presents a number of techniques which can be utilized in analyzing complex networks. Chapter 9 extends the results of Chap. 8 in the form of a number of network theorems which simplify the analysis of transducers.

The magnetic field produced by current in one coil can affect the voltage and current in another coil located near the first. This effect, called mutual inductance, is examined in Chap. 10. Since no analogous effect occurs in mechanical systems, Chap. 10 is devoted almost exclusively to electrical devices.

Chapter 11 treats devices in which electrical energy is converted to mechanical energy, or vice versa. Examples of such energy-conversion devices are vibration pickups, loudspeakers, plunger electro-magnets, electric motors, and generators. In these devices both electrical and mechanical elements are present together. The transfer of energy from one form to the other takes place through the medium of an electric or a magnetic field.

Chapter 12 discusses a particular form of transducer, the servo-mechanism, in which the function is to cause some output quantity, such as the angular position of a shaft, to follow as closely as possible the variations of some input quantity.

7-1　VIBRATION-ISOLATION MOUNTING

For our first example of a transmission network, let us return to the vibration-isolation mounting examined in Sec. 3-4. There, it will be recalled, we dealt with a rotating machine, such as an air compressor, which produced a vibration force and the problem was to mount the machine in such a way that the force transmitted to the floor would be appreciably less than the applied force.

This is seen to be a mechanical filtering problem. The input is the applied force, and the desired output is a force which is reduced in magnitude over a range of expected excitation frequencies. One element of the network is specified, namely, the mass of the machine. Further-more, there is the practical requirement that there be some mechanical connection to the floor to support the weight of the machine. (The weight may be considered to be a second applied-force component, at zero frequency, which is considered separately from the vibrating component. Thus, in these terms, the problem is to design a filter which will pass the zero-frequency force component and afford reduced transmission of the vibration-frequency component.)

The undamped spring mounting proposed in Sec. 3-4 is, in general, somewhat unsatisfactory. To be sure, the spring compliance can be chosen to make the transmitted force at any given operating speed quite small. However, if the machine operates at varying speed, there will be, for excitation frequencies near the resonant frequency, a greatly magnified transmitted force and violent vertical oscillations of the machine base. Or, even if the operating speed is fixed, the frequency of the applied force will vary from zero to the operating value during the starting of the machine, and serious oscillations may occur during the starting period.

To alleviate this situation, a spring mounting employing some damping may be used. The damping may be in the form of separate dashpots or sliding friction, or it may be intimately associated with the spring compliance, as in a rubber mounting foot. An approximate model of such a mounting is shown in Fig. 7-1. Here K represents, as

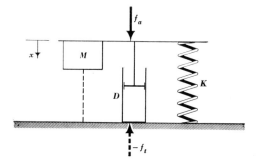

Fig. 7-1. Approximate model for a machine with vibration-isolation mounting.

before, the composite spring compliance, and D represents the combined frictional resistance of the mounting.

STEADY-STATE ANALYSIS The analysis of this system proceeds in familiar fashion. Assume that the applied force f_a, displacement x, velocity $v = dx/dt$, and transmitted force f_t all vary as e^{st}; that is, $f_a = \mathbf{F}_a e^{st}$, $v = \mathbf{V}e^{st}$, etc. (Since in this example we are interested only in a steady-state analysis, $s = j\omega$, where ω is the radian frequency of the driving force f_a, and $\mathbf{F}_a$, $\mathbf{V}$, etc., are the phasor representations of the corresponding sinusoidally varying quantities.)

The three mechanical elements are connected abreast, so that the applied force is the sum of the forces associated with the three individual elements. Thus we may write

$$f_a = f_M + f_D + f_K \tag{7-1}$$

and hence

$$\mathbf{F}_a = \left(sM + D + \frac{1}{sK} \right) \mathbf{V} \tag{7-2}$$

where $sM + D + 1/sK$ is the driving-point motional impedance.

The transmitted force is seen from Fig. 7-1 to be the sum of the dashpot and spring forces. Thus,

$$\mathbf{F}_t = \left(D + \frac{1}{sK} \right) \mathbf{V} \tag{7-3}$$

It follows that

$$\frac{\mathbf{F}_t}{\mathbf{F}_a} = \frac{D + 1/sK}{sM + D + 1/sK} = \frac{sKD + 1}{s^2MK + sKD + 1} \tag{7-4}$$

THE TRANSFER FUNCTION This sort of output-input ratio is of sufficient utility to merit a name of its own; it is called a *transfer function*. The transfer function of a linear network is defined as the ratio of an output quantity, or response, to an input quantity, or excitation, when all quantities are varying as e^{st}. Thus it is similar to an impedance or admittance, the difference being that these are ratios of quantities measured at the same point in a system, whereas the transfer function is the ratio of two quantities measured at different points. (An impedance or admittance is called, for this reason, a *driving-point function*.) The more general terms *response function* and *system function* are sometimes used for all these functions.

In the steady-state case, the transfer function is the ratio of output to input phasors. The magnitude of the transfer function is thus the ratio of the magnitudes of transmitted and applied forces, and the angle is the phase angle between the transmitted force and the applied force:

$$\frac{\mathbf{F}_t}{\mathbf{F}_a} = \frac{F_t/\underline{\theta_t}}{F_a/\underline{\theta_a}} = \frac{F_t}{F_a}/\underline{\theta_t - \theta_a} \tag{7-5}$$

In the present example the magnitude ratio F_t/F_a is of primary interest.

The magnitude ratio can be studied more easily if we first put it into a more convenient form. To begin with, the natural resonant frequency $\omega_0 = 1/\sqrt{MK}$ would seem to provide a convenient normalizing quantity for the frequency ω. If we set about manipulating the transfer-function expression so that ω will everywhere appear divided by the normalizing frequency ω_0, we obtain

$$\frac{\mathbf{F}_t}{\mathbf{F}_a} = \frac{1 + j\omega KD}{1 - \omega^2 MK + j\omega KD} = \frac{1 + j(\omega_0 KD)(\omega/\omega_0)}{1 - (\omega/\omega_0)^2 + j(\omega_0 KD)(\omega/\omega_0)} \tag{7-6}$$

The nature of the transfer function obviously depends not only upon the natural resonant frequency ω_0 but also upon the product $\omega_0 KD$, which appears in both numerator and denominator. Since the frictional dissipation D appears only in this form, we may think of this as being a normalized dissipation D/D_0, where $D_0 \triangleq 1/\omega_0 K = \sqrt{M/K}$. Thus the magnitude of $\mathbf{F}_t/\mathbf{F}_a$ may be written

$$\frac{F_t}{F_a} = \frac{\sqrt{1 + \left(\dfrac{D}{D_0}\right)^2 \left(\dfrac{\omega}{\omega_0}\right)^2}}{\sqrt{\left[1 - \left(\dfrac{\omega}{\omega_0}\right)^2\right]^2 + \left(\dfrac{D}{D_0}\right)^2 \left(\dfrac{\omega}{\omega_0}\right)^2}} \tag{7-7}$$

This is plotted in Fig. 7-2 for several values of D/D_0.

The design curves of Fig. 7-2 make it apparent that the spring compliance K should be chosen large enough that the natural resonant frequency ω_0 is well below the frequency of the applied force. The addition of the damping D is seen to increase seriously the transmission in the region $\omega/\omega_0 > \sqrt{2}$. Thus D should be no larger than is deemed necessary to reduce the resonance peak near $\omega/\omega_0 = 1$ to an acceptable amplitude.

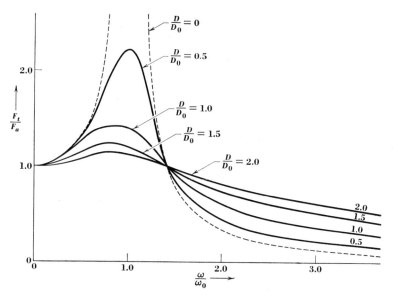

Fig. 7-2. *Relative transmission of the vibration-isolation mounting of Fig. 7-1.*

TRANSIENT ANALYSIS   The transfer function embodies information sufficient to determine the complete transient behavior as well as the
steady-state behavior. Suppose, for example, it is desired to find the
transmitted force if at time $t = 0$ a constant force is applied, equal in
magnitude to the weight of the machine, Mg. (This will be the case if
the machine is held immediately above the uncompressed spring
mounting and released at $t = 0$.)

The transmitted force will, in general, consist of a forced component plus a natural-behavior component. We find the forced component either by a physical argument or by setting $s = 0$ in the transfer
function of Eq. (7-4) (since the applied force is constant—that is, at
zero frequency). It is clearly just Mg.

The natural-behavior components of transmitted force can occur
only for values of s for which a transmitted-force component may
exist without any corresponding driving component. These are the
values of s which make the transfer function infinite, that is, make its
denominator zero. Since the denominator is a quadratic expression in s,
there are two of these:

$$s_1, s_2 = -\frac{D}{2M} \pm j\sqrt{\frac{1}{MK} - \left(\frac{D}{2M}\right)^2} \tag{7-8}$$

Thus the transmitted force is given by

$$f_t = Mg + Ae^{s_1 t} + Be^{s_2 t} \tag{7-9}$$

where A and B are constants which must be determined from the initial conditions. In this example the initial velocity v is zero (since it would require infinite force for it to be otherwise), and hence

$$f_t = Dv + \frac{1}{K} \int v \, dt \tag{7-10}$$

evaluated at $t = 0_+$ must be zero. The initial acceleration $(dv/dt)_{t=0_+}$ is g (since at this instant there is no restraining force due to either spring compliance or frictional resistance). Thus, by differentiating Eq. (7-10), we obtain

$$\frac{df_t}{dt} = D\frac{dv}{dt} + \frac{v}{K} \tag{7-11}$$

which, owing to the conditions of initial velocity and acceleration given above, reduces to

$$\left(\frac{df_t}{dt}\right)_{t=0_+} = Dg \tag{7-12}$$

These two initial conditions are sufficient to evaluate the two constants A and B in Eq. (7-9).

Before proceeding, let us note that the values of s_1 and s_2 defined by Eq. (7-8) are precisely those which we encountered in our study of mechanical oscillations in Sec. 5-1 (see Eq. 5-3). Thus we may utilize some of the results of that study to facilitate the present discussion. We notice that the critical value of D, $2\sqrt{M/K}$, marking the transition from oscillatory to nonoscillatory behavior, is just twice the normalizing value D_0 that we have used in this section. Thus the

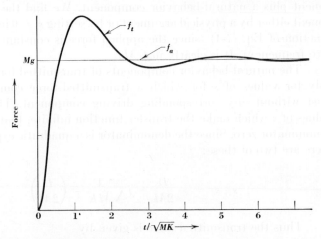

Fig. 7-3. Transient response of the system of Fig. 7-1 to a constant force Mg applied at $t = 0$, for the case $D = D_0$.

expression for transmitted force may be written in one of the three forms

$$f_t = Mg + Ae^{s_1 t} + Be^{s_2 t} \tag{7-13}$$
$$f_t = Mg + e^{-\alpha t}(A' \cos \omega_1 t + B' \sin \omega_1 t) \tag{7-14}$$
$$f_t = Mg + e^{-\alpha t}(A'' + B'' t) \tag{7-15}$$

depending upon whether D is greater than, less than, or equal to the critical value $2D_0$.

To illustrate, let us take the case of $D = D_0$. Equation (7-14) applies, and the initial conditions $f_t = 0$ and $df_t/dt = Dg$ may be used to evaluate the constants A' and B', with the result

$$f_t = Mg\left[1 - \left(\cos \frac{\sqrt{3}\,t}{2\,\sqrt{MK}} - \frac{1}{\sqrt{3}} \sin \frac{\sqrt{3}\,t}{2\,\sqrt{MK}}\right)e^{-t/2\sqrt{MK}}\right] \tag{7-16}$$

This is plotted in Fig. 7-3.

PROBLEMS

7-1   Assume the following data relating to the discussion of Sec. 7-1:
Weight of compressor and base = 64.4 lb
Composite spring constant = 24 lb/in. deflection
(a) Compute the natural radian frequency ω_0 and the critical-damping value $2D_0$.
(b) What is the minimum damping D which may be used if the ratio of transmitted to impressed force is not to exceed about 1.5 at any frequency? With this value of damping, what is the ratio of transmitted to impressed force when the frequency of the impressed force is 8 cps?

7-2   Assume the following data for the mechanical system discussed in Sec. 7-1:

$D = 5$ slugs/sec
$\omega M = 15$ slugs/sec
$\dfrac{1}{\omega K} = 3$ slugs/sec
f_a = sinusoidal, with peak amplitude 13 lb and frequency 10 cps

(a) Compute the peak instantaneous velocity and the time between the occurrence of peak force and peak velocity.
(b) Find the peak amplitude of the transmitted force.

7-3   In the design of a vibration-absorbing mounting, as discussed in Sec. 7-1, it is necessary to ensure that the motion of the base will not be so large as to bring it into direct contact with the floor. Thus the displacement x is of interest. Since $x = \int v\,dt$, it follows that $\mathbf{X} = \mathbf{V}/j\omega$.
Compute and plot curves for the peak displacement X as a function of frequency for $D/D_0 = 0, 1, 2$. Discuss the design of the spring mounting from the standpoint of these curves.

7-4   As discussed in connection with Fig. 3-18, a piston of mass m, moving vertically with a sinusoidal motion of radian frequency ω and peak displacement X_p, exerts a force through the piston rod of peak amplitude $F_a = \omega^2 m X_p$. In designing a vibration-absorbing mounting for a machine, such as a compressor, where the force F_a is a function of the operating speed of the machine, we should like to know how the peak transmitted force F_t varies with frequency.

Using the methods of Sec. 7-1, compute and sketch curves of $F_t/\omega_0^2 m X_p$ versus ω/ω_0 for $D/D_0 = 0, 1, 2, \infty$. (The quantity $\omega_0^2 m X_p$ will be found to be a convenient normalizing value for the transmitted force.) Discuss the design of the mounting in the light of these curves.

7-5   Consider the mechanical system discussed in Sec. 7-1. Assume that at $t = 0$ a constant force is applied, equal in magnitude to the weight of the machine, Mg. Let $D = 2D_0$. Find and plot the expression for the transmitted force f_t as a function of time (as in Fig. 7-3).

7-6   Find the positions of the poles and zeros of the transfer function (7-4) in the complex-frequency plane (as in the example of Sec. 5-4) for $D/D_0 = 0, 1, 2, 3, \infty$, with M and K being held constant. Discuss the shape of the curves of Fig. 7-2 in terms of the motion of these pole and zero positions. Pay particular attention to what happens as $D \to \infty$.

7-2 LOWPASS FILTER

A simple electrical lowpass filter will provide an interesting second example of a transmission network. Let us examine the configuration of Fig. 7-4, which appears to hold some promise as a moderately effective filter.

It is desired to insert between the voltage source $\mathbf{E}_1$ and the load resistance R a network which will allow low-frequency components of

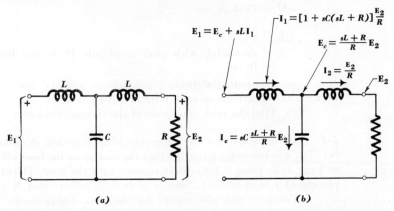

$$E_1 = E_c + sLI_1$$

$$I_1 = [1 + sC(sL + R)]\frac{E_2}{R}$$

$$E_c = \frac{sL + R}{R}E_2$$

$$I_2 = \frac{E_2}{R}$$

$$I_c = sC\frac{sL + R}{R}E_2$$

(a)   *(b)*

Fig. 7-4. (a) *Simple electrical filter and* **(b)** *example of the transfer-function calculation.*

voltage to appear across the load but will eliminate high-frequency components. Arguing roughly in justification of this choice of network, we might say that the inductors in Fig. 7-4 would tend to pass low-frequency current components and provide a barrier to higher-frequency currents, while the capacitor would serve to bypass the higher-frequency components.

The transfer function $\mathbf{E}_2/\mathbf{E}_1$ will summarize for us the filtering properties of this network. It can be easily written if we start at the load end with an assumed voltage $\mathbf{E}_2$ and work to the left. The current through the load is $\mathbf{E}_2/R$; thus the voltage across the capacitor is $(sL + R)(\mathbf{E}_2/R)$. The capacitor current is obtained by dividing this voltage by the impedance of the capacitor; this is added to the load current to find the total current. The voltage drop across the left-hand inductor is next found and added to the capacitor voltage to yield $\mathbf{E}_1$. Thus the ratio is found to be

$$\frac{\mathbf{E}_2}{\mathbf{E}_1} = \frac{R}{s^3 L^2 C + s^2 LCR + 2sL + R} \tag{7-17}$$

We have seen previously that nondimensionalizing our expressions often results in significant simplification. As has been emphasized before, there is no unique method of doing this. In the present example we may first attempt to normalize the frequency variable s with respect to some quantity having the dimensions of frequency—$\omega_0 \triangleq 1/\sqrt{LC}$, for instance. We may then observe that the combination $\sqrt{L/C}$, with the dimensions of impedance, appears. This suggests that the resistance R may be expressed in terms of this combination of L and C; thus

$$R = \alpha \sqrt{\frac{L}{C}} \tag{7-18}$$

where α is a dimensionless parameter. In this way we arrive at one possible nondimensionalized form of Eq. (7-17):

$$\frac{\mathbf{E}_2}{\mathbf{E}_1} = \frac{\alpha}{(s/\omega_0)^3 + \alpha(s/\omega_0)^2 + 2(s/\omega_0) + \alpha} \tag{7-19}$$

To see what sort of properties we can expect from this transfer function, we may examine the positions of its poles and zeros in the complex-frequency plane. There are no zeros obviously, and the pole positions are obtained by setting the cubic expression in the denominator equal to zero. The three poles are easily found to be located as indicated in Fig. 7-5.†

† There are many ways of reducing the labor involved in the location of pole and zero positions, and application of some thought and ingenuity often pays high dividends. In this case it is much simpler to assume values for the coordinate of the real root of the cubic and solve for the parameter α than to assume α and solve the cubic by a direct attack.

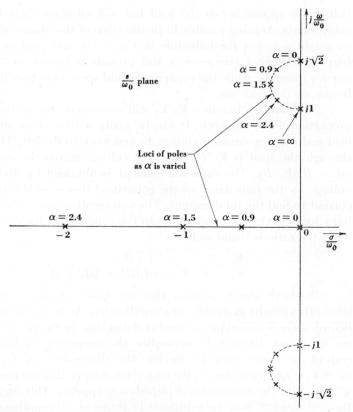

Fig. 7-5. Pole positions for the transfer function of Eq. (7-19).

Thinking in terms of the relief-map analogy discussed in Sec. 5-4, we can get some idea of what sort of filter characteristic to expect. Apparently either too high or too low a value of α will give an undesirably high resonant peak in the E_2/E_1 versus frequency curve.

Choosing several values for α near unity and substituting $j\omega$ for s in Eq. (7-19) allow us to plot the filter response curves of Fig. 7-6. The desired filtering action is obtained—the transfer-function magnitude is very low at high frequencies and is near unity for frequencies up to around 1.5 times the normalizing frequency ω_0. However, the curve is not very flat over this region, perhaps not flat enough to please us.

Of course, we have restricted ourselves by assuming that the two inductors were to have the same value. If we allow different values, as in Fig. 7-7, we complicate the problem somewhat by the introduction of a second parameter a, the ratio of the two inductance values. The transfer function is now

$$\frac{\mathbf{E}_2}{\mathbf{E}_1} = \frac{\alpha}{a(s/\omega_0)^3 + \alpha(s/\omega_0)^2 + (1+a)(s/\omega_0) + \alpha} \tag{7-20}$$

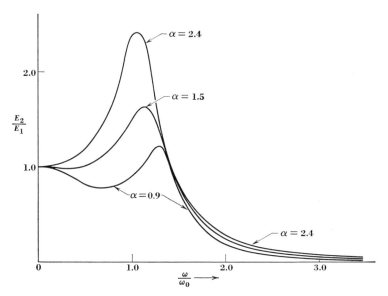

Fig. 7-6. Filter characteristic for the network of Fig. 7-4.

Again, the pole positions may be studied and the shape of the filter characteristic anticipated as the parameters α and a are varied. For example, selecting $\alpha = 1$ and $a = \frac{1}{2}$ leads to the pole positions shown in Fig. 7-7b and the rather desirable frequency response plotted in Fig. 7-8.

If this is satisfactory, the design is completed by inserting the requirements on load resistance and cutoff frequency. For instance, if the load resistance R is specified to be 1,000 ohms and the point $\omega = \omega_0$ on the curve is to correspond to 10^4 radians/sec, the remaining element values must be

$$C = 0.1 \ \mu\text{f} \qquad L = 0.1 \ \text{henry} \qquad aL = 0.05 \ \text{henry}$$

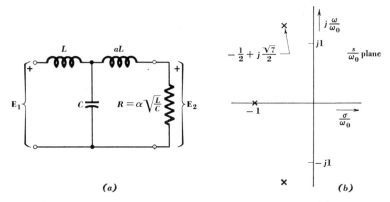

Fig. 7-7. (a) Modified filter and (b) pole positions for $\alpha = 1$, $a = \frac{1}{2}$.

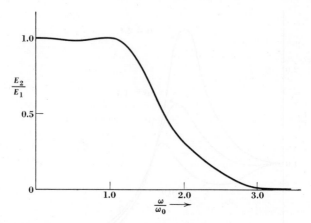

Fig. 7-8. Filter characteristic for the network of Fig. 7-7 with $\alpha = 1$, $a = \frac{1}{2}$.

On the other hand, if we are still not satisfied, we have gone about as far as we can go with only three reactive elements; to obtain a filter characteristic that cuts off the higher frequencies more sharply, it will be necessary to consider more elaborate networks.

Let us consider the effect of adding an inductance L_2 in the capacitive branch, as in Fig. 7-9. We might be led to this by arguing that at some frequency $\omega_1 = 1/\sqrt{L_2 C}$ the impedance of this branch is zero and hence that the load voltage is also zero. Strategic selection of this frequency would allow us forcibly to push the filter characteristic to zero at one point and hence bend it into a more desirable shape.

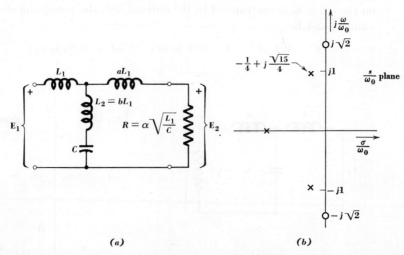

(a)　　　　　　　　　*(b)*

Fig. 7-9. (a) Modified filter and (b) pole and zero positions for $\alpha = 1$, $a = \frac{1}{2}$, $b = \frac{1}{2}$.

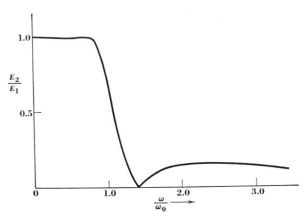

Fig. 7-10. Filter characteristic for the network of Fig. 7-9 with $\alpha = 1$, $a = \frac{1}{2}$, $b = \frac{1}{2}$.

Again taking $\omega_0 = 1/\sqrt{L_1 C}$ and defining $b \triangleq L_2/L_1 = \omega_0^2/\omega_1^2$, we can easily establish that the transfer function is

$$\frac{E_2}{E_1} = \frac{\alpha[b(s/\omega_0)^2 + 1]}{(b + a)(s/\omega_0)^3 + \alpha(b + 1)(s/\omega_0)^2 + (a + 1)(s/\omega_0) + \alpha} \quad (7\text{-}21)$$

We now have two zeros as well as three poles (Fig. 7-9b), the positions depending upon the parameters α, a, and b. Choosing a likely set of values for these parameters (on the basis of the pole and zero positions and the relief-map considerations of Sec. 5-4), we can compute the new filter characteristic by substituting $j\omega$ for s. A typical result is shown in Fig. 7-10, in which the sharpness of cutoff is seen to be markedly improved, but at the expense of having much less effective elimination of high-frequency components.

Still more elaborate networks could be considered and the filter characteristics made to approach any desired shape with any desired degree of exactness. The intent in this discussion has been, not to make the reader a designer of electrical filters, but simply to indicate in elementary fashion some of the concepts that underlie more sophisticated approaches. In this section we have again seen the advantages accruing from the study of linear systems in terms of dimensionless parameters and the use of the complex-frequency plane.

PROBLEMS

7-7   In the design of an electrical filter it is decided that the structure of Fig. 7-9 is to be used, and the shape of the transmission characteristic shown in Fig. 7-10 is acceptable. It is desired that the frequency at which there is zero transmission be located at 1,500 cps. The load resistance is 1,000 ohms.

Find the proper values for the four remaining circuit elements.

7-8   Find the transfer function E_2/E_1 for the electrical filter shown. Choose a suitable normalizing frequency ω_1 and express the transfer function in a convenient nondimensionalized form.

Show the way the poles and zeros of the transfer function E_2/E_1 move in the s plane as the load resistance R_L is varied.

For the particular case of $R_L = R$, plot a curve of E_2/E_1 versus ω/ω_1.

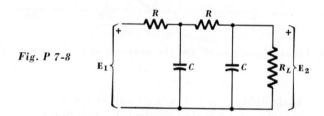

Fig. P 7-8

7-9   An equivalent circuit for a pentode filter amplifier is shown. The vacuum tube is represented by a current source supplying a current g_mE_1, where E_1 is the voltage applied to the control grid. The load is a resistance R. The purpose of the additional elements is to cause the amplifier gain-frequency curve to have the characteristic of a lowpass filter.

Obtain an expression for the gain E_2/E_1. (This is most simply done by starting with an assumed voltage E_2 and working back.) Choose suitable normalizing quantities and obtain the expression in dimensionless-ratio form. Sketch roughly the positions of the poles and zeros in the s plane.

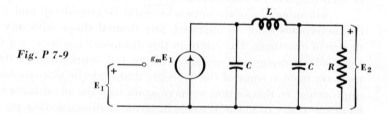

Fig. P 7-9

7-10   (a) A mass is suspended from a spring as shown, and a force, represented by F_1, is applied to a point part way up the spring. The force transmitted to a fixed frame is represented by F_2. Derive the transfer function F_2/F_1; choose a suitable normalizing frequency, and express it in a convenient dimensionless-ratio form.

(b) Assume that the frictional damping is small ($D \ll \sqrt{M/K_1}$). Sketch the location in the s plane of the poles and zeros of this transfer function for the case $K_1 = K_2$. Roughly sketch the shape of a plot of the magnitude F_2/F_1 as a function of ω, where ω is the radian frequency of an impressed sinusoidal driving force.

(c) Find an expression for the ratio of the displacement of the mass, $\mathbf{X}_m$, to the driving force $\mathbf{F}_1$; sketch a pole-zero plot.

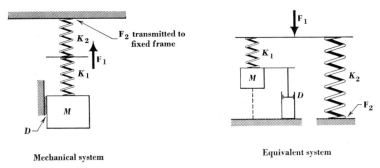

Mechanical system   Equivalent system

Fig. P 7-10

7-11   The root-locus-locating techniques of Sec. 5-5 can be used to disclose additional information regarding the effects of various parameter values on the behavior of the filter discussed in the preceding section. This problem and the following one will indicate how the effects of the parameters a and α in Eq. (7-20) can be studied by this method.

Note that Eq. (7-20) has poles for such values of s as make the denominator zero. If this denominator is set equal to zero and the resulting equation rearranged to isolate the parameter α, we obtain

$$\frac{s_1(as_1{}^2 + 1 + a)}{s_1{}^2 + 1} = -\alpha$$

[Here, for brevity, s_1 has been written for the normalized s/ω_0 of Eq. (7-20).]

The expression on the left clearly has poles at $s_1 = \pm j$ and zeros at the origin and at $s_1 = \pm j(1 + a)/a$. By plotting these pole and zero positions and applying the techniques introduced in Sec. 5-5, the root loci can be sketched in. (These loci appear in Fig. 7-5 for the case $a = 1$.)

For the case $a = \frac{1}{2}$, locate on coordinate paper the poles and zeros of the left-hand expression of the above equation and, with the aid of a protractor, find the 180° equal-angle lines for this expression, which are the loci of the three poles of the transfer function (7-20) as α is varied. (Note, as a check, that the three pole locations of Fig. 7-7b should be on these loci.)

7-12   Note that if the denominator of Eq. (7-20) is set equal to zero to determine the poles of this transfer function, the resulting equation can be rearranged to isolate the parameter a as follows:

$$\frac{\alpha s_1{}^2 + s_1 + \alpha}{s_1(s_1{}^2 + 1)} = -a$$

Locate, on coordinate paper, the two zeros and three poles of the expression on the left for the case $\alpha = 1$. Use the techniques introduced in Sec. 5-5 to locate the loci of the three poles of Eq. (7-20) as the value of a is varied. (Note, as a check, that the three pole locations of Fig. 7-7b should be on these loci.)

7-3 TABLE OF UNIT-IMPULSE RESPONSES

We wish presently to take up the study of some networks in which the transient behavior is of particular interest. The solution of these transient problems in the manner used up to the present can become rather tedious. Let us pause, therefore, to systematize the procedure by which the transient response can be obtained from knowledge of the input quantity and the driving-point or transfer function.

The solution of problems involving electrical and mechanical transients is facilitated by a tabulation of responses to unit impulses. The meaning of this statement we shall attempt to make clear in the following paragraphs.

A SIMPLE EXAMPLE To begin with, let us consider the simple example of an inductor and a resistor in series (Fig. 7-11). Suppose that a constant voltage E is applied for a time Δt starting at $t = 0$. At the end of this time the applied voltage is reduced to zero (that is, the terminals are short-circuited). In the limit as Δt becomes very small, this is termed a voltage impulse of amplitude $E\,\Delta t$. If the product $E\,\Delta t$ is 1 volt-sec and remains so as $\Delta t \to 0$, then this is called a *unit voltage impulse*.

The differential equation which relates the voltage and current is

$$e = L\frac{di}{dt} + Ri \tag{7-22}$$

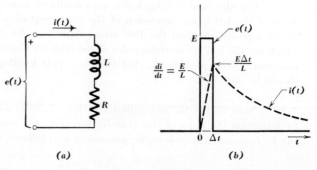

Fig. 7-11. (a) *RL circuit and* (b) *voltage impulse and resulting current.*

The instant the voltage impulse is applied, the current is zero, so that the initial rate of change of current is

$$\left(\frac{di}{dt}\right)_{t=0_+} = \frac{E}{L} \tag{7-23}$$

Thus, in a time Δt sec, the current rises to approximately $E\,\Delta t/L$.

After time Δt, the current must consist solely of natural-behavior terms, since there is no further excitation. The admittance, or ratio of i to e if both vary as e^{st}, is

$$\mathbf{Y}(s) = \frac{\mathbf{I}}{\mathbf{E}} = \frac{1}{R + sL} = \frac{1}{L}\frac{1}{s + \alpha} \tag{7-24}$$

where $\alpha \triangleq R/L$ is the reciprocal of the time constant. Thus, after time t, the current decays exponentially with time according to the equation

$$i_{t>\Delta t} = \frac{E\,\Delta t}{L}\,e^{-\alpha(t-\Delta t)} \tag{7-25}$$

Letting $\Delta t \to 0$ and $E\,\Delta t = 1$, we thus establish that the unit-impulse response of the circuit of Fig. 7-11a is

$$i = \frac{1}{L}\,e^{-\alpha t} \tag{7-26}$$

Thus a term $1/(s + \alpha)$ in the admittance function apparently corresponds to a term $e^{-\alpha t}$ in the unit-impulse response (Fig. 7-12).

But, of course, this is true whatever the symbols in the mathematical expressions happen to signify in the physical world. Thus we can say, in general, that if the ratio of any time-variable output quantity, or response (voltage, current, velocity, force, etc.), $e_o(t)$ to an input quantity, or excitation, $e_i(t)$, when both vary as e^{st}, is of the form

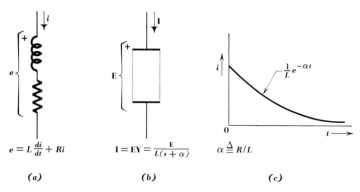

$$e = L\frac{di}{dt} + Ri \qquad\qquad \mathbf{I} = \mathbf{EY} = \frac{\mathbf{E}}{L(s + \alpha)} \qquad\qquad \alpha \triangleq R/L$$

$$(a) \qquad\qquad\qquad (b) \qquad\qquad\qquad (c)$$

Fig. 7-12. *Representation of the relation between e and i (a) in differential-equation form and (b) in admittance form; (c) current response to a unit voltage impulse.*

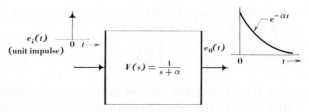

Fig. 7-13. Block-diagram representation of a simple mathematical operation.

$F(s) = 1/(s + \alpha)$, then a unit-impulse input will yield an output $e^{-\alpha t}$ for $t > 0$.

We can show this symbolically in the form of Fig. 7-13, which is termed a block diagram. In the "language" of block diagrams, the block indicates a mathematical operation to be performed on an input quantity to yield an output quantity. This output may, in turn, be the input for a second operation (Fig. 7-14a). Again, an output may be the sum of two or more components representing the results of separate operations (Fig. 7-14b). The block diagram is simply a pictorial method of representing a mathematical equation; more elaborate diagrams will be encountered in future discussions.

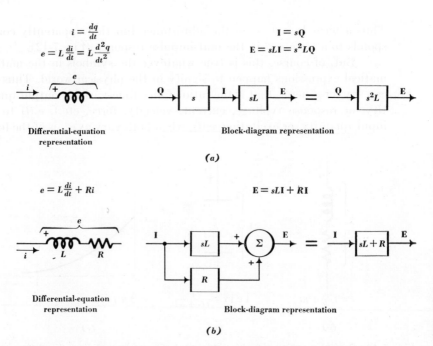

Fig. 7-14. Two examples illustrating the "language" of block diagrams.

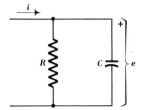

Fig. 7-15. Analogue of the circuit of Fig. 7-11a.

The solution to any analogous problem can now be written immediately. For example, consider the circuit of Fig. 7-15. The ratio of e to i when both vary as e^{st} is simply the impedance of the parallel combination of R and C:

$$\mathbf{Z}(s) = \frac{\mathbf{E}}{\mathbf{I}} = \frac{1}{sC + 1/R} = \frac{1}{C}\frac{1}{s + \alpha} \qquad (7\text{-}27)$$

where $\alpha \triangleq 1/RC$. Thus a unit impulse of current (1 coulomb of charge flowing in an infinitesimally small time) produces a voltage

$$e = \frac{1}{C}e^{-\alpha t}$$

UNIT-IMPULSE-RESPONSE TABLE   From this one relationship between a system (driving-point or transfer) function $\mathbf{F}(s)$ and its corresponding unit-impulse response $f(t)$, several others are immediately derivable. First of all, note the effect of letting α approach zero. The unit-impulse response corresponding to $\mathbf{F}(s) = 1/s$ is seen to be a unit step having value 0 prior to $t = 0$ and value 1 thereafter.

But the fact that $\int e^{st}\,dt = (1/s)e^{st}$ indicates that a factor $1/s$ in the system function corresponds to a time integration; that is, if the impulse response corresponding to the system function $\mathbf{F}(s)$ is $f(t)$, then corresponding to the system function $(1/s)\mathbf{F}(s)$ is the impulse response $\int_0^t f(t)\,dt$. This checks with the above observation that $\mathbf{F}(s) = 1/s$ corresponds to $f(t)$ being the unit-step function, since this is the integral of the unit impulse.

In like manner we establish that $\mathbf{F}(s) = 1/s^2$ corresponds to $f(t)$ being the integral of the unit step, which is zero until $t = 0$ and t thereafter. Similarly, $\mathbf{F}(s) = 1/s(s + \alpha)$ corresponds to the integral of $e^{-\alpha t}$, or $(1/\alpha)(1 - e^{-\alpha t})$.

We now have several results, and we can begin to assemble them in the form of a table for future reference. A brief tabulation of unit-impulse responses is presented in Table 7-1, and a more complete listing will be found in the Appendix.

TABLE 7-1   *Table of Unit-impulse Responses*

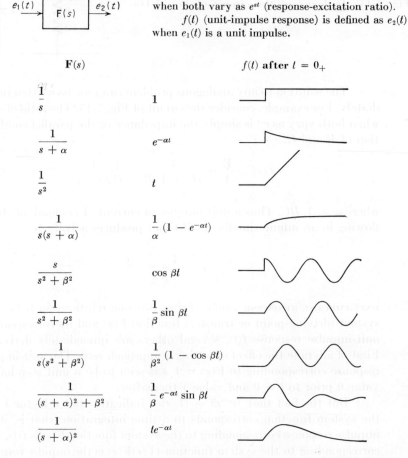

$\mathbf{F}(s)$ (system function) is defined as $e_2(t)/e_1(t)$ when both vary as e^{st} (response-excitation ratio).

$f(t)$ (unit-impulse response) is defined as $e_2(t)$ when $e_1(t)$ is a unit impulse.

$\mathbf{F}(s)$		$f(t)$ after $t = 0_+$
$\dfrac{1}{s}$	1	
$\dfrac{1}{s + \alpha}$	$e^{-\alpha t}$	
$\dfrac{1}{s^2}$	t	
$\dfrac{1}{s(s + \alpha)}$	$\dfrac{1}{\alpha}(1 - e^{-\alpha t})$	
$\dfrac{s}{s^2 + \beta^2}$	$\cos \beta t$	
$\dfrac{1}{s^2 + \beta^2}$	$\dfrac{1}{\beta} \sin \beta t$	
$\dfrac{1}{s(s^2 + \beta^2)}$	$\dfrac{1}{\beta^2}(1 - \cos \beta t)$	
$\dfrac{1}{(s + \alpha)^2 + \beta^2}$	$\dfrac{1}{\beta} e^{-\alpha t} \sin \beta t$	
$\dfrac{1}{(s + \alpha)^2}$	$te^{-\alpha t}$	

COMPUTATION OF A SAMPLE TABLE ENTRY   To illustrate further how this table might be built up, let us compute one more entry. Consider the circuit of Fig. 7-16, described by the integrodifferential equation

$$i = \frac{1}{L} \int e \, dt + C \frac{de}{dt} \qquad (7\text{-}28)$$

When e and i vary as e^{st},

$$\mathbf{Z}(s) = \frac{\mathbf{E}}{\mathbf{I}} = \frac{1}{sC + 1/sL} = \frac{1}{C} \frac{s}{s^2 + \beta^2} \qquad (7\text{-}29)$$

with $\beta \triangleq 1/\sqrt{LC}$.

Now, suppose the current assumes a value I for a time Δt starting at $t = 0$. Equation (7-28) indicates that the rate of change of voltage

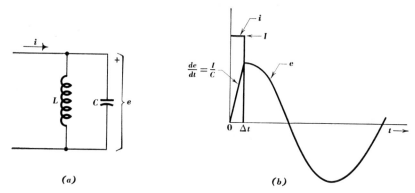

Fig. 7-16. (a) *RC circuit and* (b) *current impulse and resulting voltage.*

across the capacitor at time $t = 0_+$ is I/C (since the first term is infinitesimal). Thus the voltage reached at time Δt, if Δt is assumed to be small, is approximately $I \, \Delta t/C$. After time Δt, the voltage e can consist only of natural-behavior terms; it must thus be of the form

$$e_{t>\Delta t} = A \cos \beta(t - \Delta t) + B \sin \beta(t - \Delta t) \tag{7-30}$$

However, at $t = \Delta t_+$ the rate of change of voltage is seen from Eq. (7-28) to be

$$\left(\frac{de}{dt}\right)_{t=\Delta t_+} = \frac{1}{C}\left(0 - \frac{1}{L}\int_0^{\Delta t} e \, dt\right) \tag{7-31}$$

which approaches zero as Δt approaches zero. Thus, letting Δt approach zero and I approach infinity in such a way that the product $I \, \Delta t$ remains at unity, we obtain the condition

$$\left(\frac{de}{dt}\right)_{t=\Delta t_+} = 0 \tag{7-32}$$

from which the constants A and B can be evaluated to obtain the unit-impulse response

$$e = \frac{1}{C} \cos \beta t \tag{7-33}$$

Thus $\mathbf{F}(s) = s/(s^2 + \beta^2)$ corresponds to $f(t) = \cos \beta t$, and we have another item for Table 7-1. Since integration is equivalent to multiplying $\mathbf{F}(s)$ by $1/s$, $\mathbf{F}(s) = 1/(s^2 + \beta^2)$ corresponds to

$$f(t) = \int_0^t \cos \beta t \, dt = \frac{1}{\beta} \sin \beta t$$

In like manner, more items could be added to extend the table. Now, it may not seem that we gain very much by this tabulation. In the first place, it seems to be simply a matter of listing the answers to problems already done so that we shall not have to rework them. In the second place, it is a table of unit-impulse responses only, and it would appear that we need a similar table of responses to unit-step inputs, sinusoidal inputs, and so on.

A MORE CONVENIENT WAY OF EXTENDING THE TABLE The first objection is answered by the fact that there is a much quicker way of extending the table. It turns out that $\mathbf{F}(s)$ and $f(t)$ are related in the following way:

$$\mathbf{F}(s) = \int_0^\infty f(t)e^{-st}\, dt \tag{7-34}$$

where s is assumed to have a large enough real part to make the integral converge. This is termed the *Laplace transform* relation, and the table of unit-impulse responses is often called a table of *Laplace transforms*.

A thorough discussion of the Laplace transform is not justified here (see Chap. 13, particularly Sec. 13-6); however, the following argument may be of interest in making Eq. (7-34) appear reasonable. It will indicate the general approach; it is *not*, however, a complete and rigorous mathematical demonstration.

Suppose we have a system function $\mathbf{F}(s)$ which can be written in the form

$$\mathbf{F}(s) = \frac{A(s - s_a)(s - s_b) \cdots (s - s_m)}{(s - s_1)(s - s_2) \cdots (s - s_n)} \tag{7-35}$$

where s_a, s_b, etc., are the m values of s for which $\mathbf{F}(s)$ has zero value and s_1, s_2, etc., are the n values of s for which $\mathbf{F}(s)$ is infinite.

Let $\mathbf{F}(s)$ be expanded in partial-fraction form as follows:

$$\mathbf{F}(s) = \frac{a_1}{s - s_1} + \frac{a_2}{s - s_2} + \cdots + \frac{a_n}{s - s_n} \tag{7-36}$$

where the a's are constants. [We are assuming here that there is at least one more pole of $\mathbf{F}(s)$ than there are zeros. If there are not, the present argument can be easily extended to cover this case.]

Now recall that $\mathbf{F}(s)$ is defined as the ratio of some output quantity $e_o(t)$ to some input quantity $e_i(t)$ when both vary as e^{st}. Equation (7-36) indicates that we may think of $e_o(t)$, if we choose, as being made up of the sum of n components, the first of which is $a_1/(s - s_1)$ times the input, the second $a_2/(s - s_2)$ times the input, and so on. This may be represented in the block diagram of Fig. 7-17.

Thus, if the input is a unit impulse, the output will be the sum of a natural-behavior term corresponding to $a_1/(s - s_1)$, plus a second term corresponding to $a_2/(s - s_2)$, and so on; that is,

$$f(t) = a_1 e^{s_1 t} + a_2 e^{s_2 t} + \cdots + a_n e^{s_n t} \tag{7-37}$$

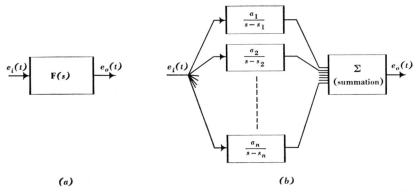

(a)   (b)

Fig. 7-17. Equivalent block-diagram representations of Eqs. (7-35) and (7-36).

But now perform the following integration involving $f(t)$:

$$\int_0^\infty f(t)e^{-st} \, dt = \int_0^\infty (a_1 e^{s_1 t} + a_2 e^{s_2 t} + \cdots + a_n e^{s_n t})e^{-st} \, dt$$

$$= \frac{a_1}{s - s_1} + \frac{a_2}{s - s_2} + \cdots + \frac{a_n}{s - s_n}$$

$$= \mathbf{F}(s) \tag{7-38}$$

(with the assumption about the real part of s that was mentioned previously). Thus we demonstrate that Eq. (7-34) may be used to generate further items for the unit-impulse response table.

RESPONSE TO OTHER INPUTS   The second point of skepticism about the utility of the unit-impulse-response table is also easily met. Suppose, for example, that the input is not a unit impulse, but rather a step of amplitude E. This is precisely the time function we would have if a unit impulse were acted upon by a transfer function E/s. Thus the response of a system characterized by the system function $\mathbf{F}(s)$ when the input is a step of amplitude E is just the unit-impulse response corresponding to the system function $(E/s)\mathbf{F}(s)$.

Similar arguments apply for inputs having any of the forms listed in Table 7-1. A few of these equivalences are shown symbolically in block-diagram form in Fig. 7-18.

AN EXAMPLE   The use of the unit-impulse-response table for non-impulsive inputs may be illustrated by applying it to the example of Sec. 4-3. In that example a voltage $\sqrt{2}\, E \cos \omega t$ was assumed applied to an RC series circuit at time $t = 0_+$; the resulting current was to be obtained. The impedance of the RC combination is $R + 1/sC$; so the block-diagram representation of the problem is as in Fig. 7-19a.

But the voltage $\sqrt{2}\, E \cos \omega t$ is the time function which would result if a unit impulse were acted upon by the transfer function

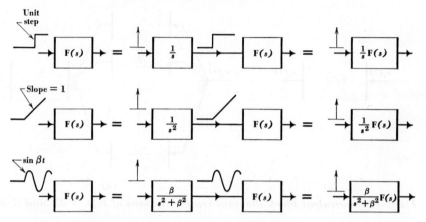

Fig. 7-18. Example of the method of handling other than unit-impulse inputs.

$$\mathbf{F}_i(s) = \frac{\sqrt{2}\,Es}{s^2 + \omega^2} \tag{7-39}$$

Thus an equivalent problem to the one we are attempting to solve is that of Fig. 7-19b. We now have, in effect, the problem of finding the unit-impulse response of the combined equivalent transfer function indicated in Fig. 7-19c.

This could be done in several ways. One would be to employ a table sufficiently complete to contain an item corresponding to the

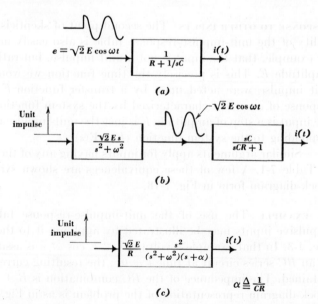

Fig. 7-19. Successive steps in the reduction of an example to a unit-impulse-response problem.

rather complicated expression

$$\mathbf{F}(s) = \frac{\sqrt{2}\,E}{R} \frac{s^2}{(s^2 + \omega^2)(s + \alpha)} \tag{7-40}$$

A second approach, which we shall employ here, is that of separating $\mathbf{F}(s)$ by partial-fraction expansion into simpler components which would be found in even a brief table.

The partial-fraction expansion can be carried out systematically with the aid of rules to be found in more advanced texts. Lacking the time to explore these, we may proceed with a more simple-minded attack. Observing the factors of the denominator, let us simply see whether we can establish an expansion of the following form:

$$\frac{s^2}{(s^2 + \omega^2)(s + \alpha)} = \frac{A}{s + \alpha} + \frac{P(s)}{s^2 + \omega^2} \tag{7-41}$$

where A is some constant, yet to be determined, and $P(s)$ is whatever remainder is required to make the equality hold.

Suppose we multiply both sides of Eq. (7-41) by the factor $s + \alpha$. Now, if the expansion is to be valid, it must hold for all values of s, including the particular value $s = -\alpha$. But when $s = -\alpha$, the factor $s + \alpha$ (which, after the multiplication, appears only in the last term) becomes zero. Thus A must be given by

$$A = \frac{\alpha^2}{\alpha^2 + \omega^2} \tag{7-42}$$

Substituting this in Eq. (7-41) leads directly to

$$P(s) = \frac{\omega^2}{\alpha^2 + \omega^2} (s - \alpha) \tag{7-43}$$

$\mathbf{F}(s)$ has now been dissociated into the sum of two simpler parts. These can be correlated with items in Table 7-1 to yield the final result

$$\begin{aligned} i(t) &= \frac{\sqrt{2}\,E}{R} \frac{\alpha^2}{\alpha^2 + \omega^2} e^{-\alpha t} + \frac{\sqrt{2}\,E}{R} \frac{\omega^2}{\alpha^2 + \omega^2} \left(\cos \omega t - \frac{\alpha}{\omega} \sin \omega t \right) \\ &= \frac{\sqrt{2}\,E}{R} \frac{\alpha^2}{\alpha^2 + \omega^2} e^{-\alpha t} + \frac{\sqrt{2}\,E}{R} \frac{1}{\omega} \left(\frac{\omega^2}{\alpha^2 + \omega^2} \right)^{\!1/2} \cos \left(\omega t + \tan^{-1} \frac{\alpha}{\omega} \right) \end{aligned} \tag{7-44}$$

If numerical values are inserted, this will be found to check with the result obtained in Sec. 4-3.

P R O B L E M S

7-13   Using partial-fraction expansion to reduce the following functions to simpler forms that can be found in Table 7-1, find the corresponding $f(t)$:

(a) $\mathbf{F}(s) = \dfrac{1}{(s + \alpha)(s + \gamma)}$

(b) $\mathbf{F}(s) = \dfrac{s}{(s + \alpha)(s + \gamma)}$

(c) $\mathbf{F}(s) = \dfrac{s}{(s^2 + \omega^2)(s + \alpha)}$

(d) $\mathbf{F}(s) = \dfrac{1}{(s^2 + \omega^2)(s + \alpha)}$

(e) $\mathbf{F}(s) = \dfrac{1}{(s + \alpha)(s + \beta)(s + \gamma)}$

7-14   Use partial-fraction expansion and Table 7-1 to find the current in the two circuits shown if the switch is closed at $t = 0$.

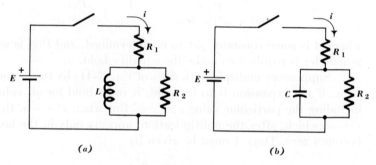

(a)   (b)

Fig. P 7-14

7-15   (a) For the mechanical system shown find the piston velocity v if the force f is a step of amplitude F.

(b) Find the force f if the velocity v is a step of amplitude V.

Fig. P 7-15

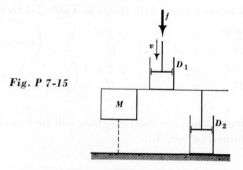

7-16   At time $t = 0$ the voltage $e = 10 \cos \omega t$ is suddenly applied to a series RC circuit. Using partial-fraction expansion and Table 7-1, find an expression for the voltage e_c which appears across the capacitor.

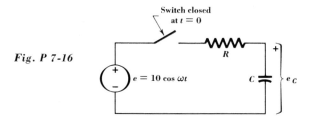

Fig. P 7-16

7-17   Solve Prob. 7-16 for $e = 10 \sin \omega t$.

7-18   Solve Prob. 7-16 for $e = 10 \cos (\omega t + 45°)$.

7-4   VIDEO AMPLIFIER STAGE

Let us now apply these methods to the problem of the design of an amplifier stage for the video (picture) signal in a television receiver. In so doing, we should bear in mind that our aim is not to learn all about electronic circuits, but to illustrate, with selected examples, techniques of analysis and ways of obtaining insight.

We have previously noted (Sec. 5-3) that a high-vacuum pentode acts essentially as a current source, the current being proportional to the input voltage applied to the control grid. However, the pentode is inherently a moderately high-voltage, low-current device, and the energy stored in electric fields cannot be ignored in all circumstances. Thus the capacitance between the anode and "ground" (that is, the main metallic structure of the receiver), C_1 in Fig. 7-20, must be considered, as must the capacitance of the grid of the following vacuum tube, C_2.

The externally observable behavior of a single amplifier stage may thus be reasonably accurately predicted on the basis of this

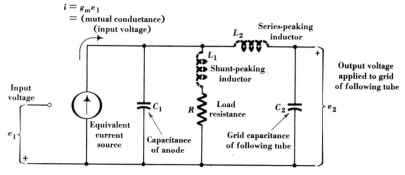

Fig. 7-20. *Equivalent circuit of a pentode video amplifier stage, showing two positions in which inductance may be added to improve the characteristics.*

equivalent circuit, or model, at least as far as alternating or fluctuating components of voltage and current are concerned. A source (representing the electron tube) supplies a current $g_m e_1$ (where e_1 represents the input voltage applied to the grid and g_m, the mutual conductance, is a proportionality constant determined by the structure of the tube) to a parallel combination of the load resistance R and the two capacitances C_1 and C_2. (Besides the fluctuating components of current and voltage which are taken into account by this model, there are also constant components which, though necessary for the operation of the electron tube, are not represented in the model. A large capacitance, not shown in Fig. 7-20, would be inserted for isolation of these constant components between successive amplifier stages. The effect of this coupling capacitor is ignored in the present discussion but is considered in the following section.)

THE UNCOMPENSATED AMPLIFIER STAGE The equivalent circuit of Fig. 7-20 is quite simple and may be analyzed by inspection. Assume, as usual, that $e_1 = \mathbf{E}_1 e^{st}$ and $e_2 = \mathbf{E}_2 e^{st}$. The output voltage is simply the product of the current with the impedance of the parallel combination of the resistance R and the capacitance $C = C_1 + C_2$:

$$\mathbf{E}_2 = g_m \mathbf{E}_1 \frac{R}{sCR + 1} \tag{7-45}$$

or, for a sinusoidal input of radian frequency ω,

$$\text{Gain} = \frac{\mathbf{E}_2}{\mathbf{E}_1} = \frac{g_m R}{1 + j\omega CR} \tag{7-46}$$

It is apparent in this expression that the effect of the distributed capacitance C is to cause the gain to become low at high values of ω. The video signal which the amplifier must handle contains, however, frequencies of the order of several megacycles per second. If typical values of g_m, say 0.009 mho, and of C, possibly 30 $\mu\mu$f, are inserted in Eq. (7-46), it becomes clear that, even when R is chosen to give a quite modest value of low-frequency gain $g_m R$, the gain is seriously down from this at frequencies of a few megacycles.

Faced with the problem of improving this situation, we might reason along the following lines. The capacitances C_1 and C_2 are, like death and taxes, items over which we have only limited control. By intensive engineering research they may be reduced; they cannot be eliminated. We recall from some of our previous studies, however, that a parallel combination of two branches, one of which is inductive and the other capacitive, may have a greater magnitude of impedance over a certain range of frequency than one of the branches alone. This may suggest adding some inductance (called *shunt-peaking inductance*) in the position marked L_1 in Fig. 7-20. The amount of added inductance should be adjusted so that the impedance is increased in the frequency range where, without L_1, the gain begins to drop off.

The known properties of a series-resonant circuit lead to a second possible solution. Note that if a *series-peaking inductance* is added in the position marked L_2 in Fig. 7-20, then near the resonant frequency of the L_2C_2 combination the voltage across C_2 (the output voltage) will be considerably greater than the voltage across the combination. Thus, by properly choosing this resonant frequency, the gain vs. frequency curve can be "lifted" in the frequency range in which it would otherwise drop off.

These two approaches sound promising; we may proceed, therefore, to make a more detailed investigation of their efficacy.

SHUNT-PEAKING COMPENSATION Considering the first approach, let us assume an inductance L_1 to be added in series with the load resistance R. The output voltage is now equal to the product of the current $g_m e_1$ with the impedance of the parallel combination of the three branches containing C_1, C_2, and RL_1, respectively. Thus the gain expression is

$$\frac{\mathbf{E}_2}{\mathbf{E}_1} = g_m \frac{(R + sL_1)(1/sC)}{R + sL_1 + 1/sC} = g_m \frac{sL_1 + R}{s^2 L_1 C + sCR + 1} \quad (7\text{-}47)$$

where $C \triangleq C_1 + C_2$.

This expression can be studied in more generality if it is arranged in dimensionless-ratio form. The fact that the gain at very low frequencies ($s \to 0$) is obviously $g_m R$ suggests that the gain might be normalized with respect to this value. The combination $1/\sqrt{L_1 C}$ has the dimensions of frequency and could be used as a normalizing frequency. On the other hand, the combination $1/RC$ also has the dimensions of frequency and has the advantage that it does not contain the parameter L_1, whose effect we wish to study. It will be well to keep separate the two variable quantities frequency and inductance L_1; hence let us choose as a normalizing frequency $\omega_1 \triangleq 1/RC$.

If the terms in Eq. (7-47) are now manipulated so that s occurs everywhere divided by ω_1, there results the dimensionless-ratio form

$$\frac{\mathbf{E}_2/\mathbf{E}_1}{g_m R} = \frac{\alpha_1(s/\omega_1) + 1}{\alpha_1(s/\omega_1)^2 + s/\omega_1 + 1} \quad (7\text{-}48)$$

where $\alpha_1 \triangleq L_1/R^2 C$ is a dimensionless parameter which gathers up the leftover symbols.

The effect of adding the inductance L_1 can be observed by studying this equation. As we have seen previously, a look at the complex-frequency-plane representation can be quite enlightening. Figure 7-21 shows the positions of the zero

$$\frac{s}{\omega_1} = -\frac{1}{\alpha_1} \quad (7\text{-}49)$$

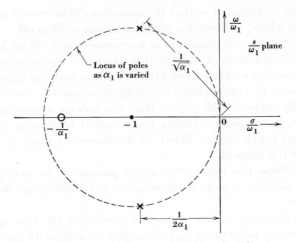

Fig. 7-21. Pole and zero positions of the gain function (7-48).

and the poles

$$\frac{s}{\omega_1} = -\frac{1}{2\alpha_1} \pm j\frac{1}{2\alpha_1}\sqrt{4\alpha_1 - 1} \qquad (7\text{-}50)$$

of the gain function.

The nature of the result of inserting L_1 is clear from this figure. For values of α_1 greater that 0.25 (that is, for L_1 greater than $0.25R^2C$) the pole positions are complex, with a resultant tendency to "lift up" the gain vs. frequency curve at high frequencies. (In other words, the addition of the inductance L_1 tends to compensate for the gain deterioration due to the capacitance C.) This is shown in the curves of Fig. 7-22, which are plots of the magnitude of Eq. (7-48). If L_1 is made

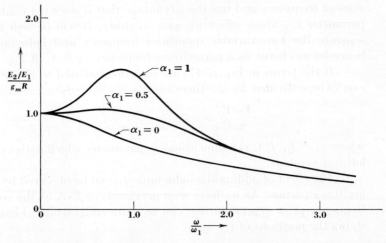

Fig. 7-22. Magnitude of the gain of a shunt-peaking compensated video amplifier stage for various values of compensating inductance.

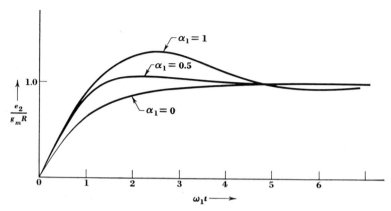

Fig. 7-23. Unit-step input response of a shunt-peaking compensated video amplifier stage for various values of compensating inductance.

too large, we can see that the poles of the gain function will move too close to the $j\omega$ axis and that the gain vs. frequency curve will exhibit an undesirably high resonance peak near the radian frequency

$$\frac{\omega_1}{\sqrt{\alpha_1}} = \frac{1}{\sqrt{L_1 C}}$$

A value of α_1 between 0.4 and 0.5 would probably be chosen.

Although it is true that a video amplifier must amplify a wide frequency range, what we are more directly interested in is its ability faithfully to reproduce the waveform, which is the electrical representation of one horizontal line of the television picture. In particular, it is important that there be no undue distortion of sudden changes in amplitude, such as occur at a vertical boundary between white and black picture areas. The response of the amplifier stage to a step input is more indicative of its ability to handle these waveforms than is its gain curve.

The unit-step response can be found from Eq. (7-48) by the methods of Sec. 7-3. Again, the qualitative behavior is discernible from the pole-zero plot of Fig. 7-21. Most important to note is that too high values of α_1 will cause the poles of the gain function to be too close to the $j\omega$ axis. This would mean long-lasting natural behavior in the form of overshoot or oscillatory transients. Computed curves of the unit-step response are shown in Fig. 7-23.

SERIES-PEAKING COMPENSATION The second proposed approach to the problem of compensating for the gain-reducing effect of the distributed capacitance C_1 and C_2 is the insertion of an inductor L_2 between the two electron tubes (Fig. 7-24). The gain expression is easily computed by the method used in the example of Sec. 7-2 (Fig. 7-4) and is found to be

$$\frac{E_2}{E_1} = \frac{g_m R}{s^3 L_2 C_1 C_2 R + s^2 L_2 C_2 + s R(C_1 + C_2) + 1} \tag{7-51}$$

For easy comparison with the shunt-peaking case, let us again choose the frequency-normalizing quantity to be $\omega_1 \triangleq 1/R(C_1 + C_2)$. The gain expression is then easily rearranged to give

$$\frac{E_2/E_1}{g_m R} = \frac{1}{\dfrac{C_1 C_2}{(C_1 + C_2)^2} \alpha_2 \left(\dfrac{s}{\omega_1}\right)^3 + \dfrac{C_2}{C_1 + C_2} \alpha_2 \left(\dfrac{s}{\omega_1}\right)^2 + \dfrac{s}{\omega_1} + 1} \tag{7-52}$$

where $\alpha_2 \triangleq \omega_1 L_2 / R$ is a convenient nondimensional parameter introducing the effect of L_2.

The form of the gain curve depends not only upon the value of α_2 but also upon the ratio of C_2 to C_1, which is normally in the neighborhood of 1 to 3. The positions of the gain-function poles and a curve of the magnitude of the gain are shown in Fig. 7-25 for the case $C_2 = C_1$, $\alpha_2 = 0.5$. It would appear that the addition of L_2 does indeed markedly improve the amplifier. The frequency range over which the amplification is reasonably uniform seems to be considerably increased over the range obtainable with the inductor in the position L_1.

However, we should not be too hasty in choosing this position for the inductor. The nature of the amplifier's response to a unit-step input is also of interest. Although this could be computed by the methods of Sec. 7-3 and plotted, if desired, this procedure would require a good deal of labor, and some information about the step response is quite readily available simply from the pole positions of the gain function. From the pole positions in Fig. 7-25a, for example, we could deduce immediately that the step-input response would contain a term of the form $e^{-1.14\omega_1 t}$ and another of the form $e^{-0.43\omega_1 t} \cos{(2.62\omega_1 t + \theta)}$. The latter, relatively slowly decaying sinusoidal term can be expected to cause oscillatory overshoot in the step response, and the undesirability of this effect may outweigh the bandwidth advantage that series compensation enjoys over shunt compensation.

We are now in a position to make as complete a study as desired of the way in which the characteristics of the video amplifier can be

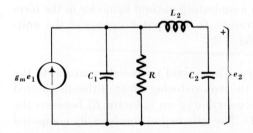

Fig. 7-24. Equivalent circuit of a series-compensated video amplifier stage.

improved by the addition of a single inductance L_1 or L_2. The choice of the design parameter α_1 or α_2 might be based on a comparison of the gain vs. frequency curves or possibly on a comparison of the responses to a unit-step input. More elaborate studies might include the effect of inductance in both positions or might consider the addition of still other circuit elements.

PROBLEMS

7-19   Using the table of unit-impulse responses (Appendix), find the response of the amplifier whose gain function is given by Eq. (7-48) when the input voltage e_1 is a unit impulse. Assume $\alpha_1 = 0.50$.

7-20   From the gain function (7-48), find mathematical expressions for the three curves of Fig. 7-23, using partial-fraction expansion and the table of unit-impulse responses (Appendix).

7-21   Show that the unit-step response of the video amplifier stage with the gain given by Eq. (7-48) is (if $\alpha_1 > 0.25$)

$$e_2 = g_m R \left\{ 1 - e^{-\omega_1 t/2\alpha_1} \left[\cos \beta t - \left(1 - \frac{1}{2\alpha_1} \right) \sin \beta t \right] \right\}$$

where $\beta \triangleq \dfrac{1}{2\alpha_1} \sqrt{4\alpha_1 - 1}\, \omega_1$

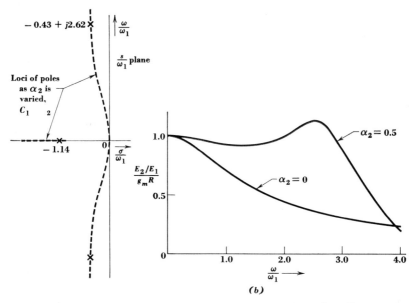

Fig. 7-25. (a) Poles of the gain expression (7-52) for the case $C_1 = C_2$, $\alpha_2 = 0.5$; (b) gain vs. frequency curve.

7-22 Making use of the techniques introduced in Sec. 5-5, find the loci of the poles of the series-peaked video-amplifier-gain expression, Eq. (7-52), for the case $C_2 = 2C_1$ as the design parameter α_2 is varied. (Compare these loci with those in Fig. 7-25 for the case $C_2 = C_1$.)

7-23 In considering the sinusoidal steady-state behavior of a network, the phase, as well as the magnitude, of the network function may be important. A convenient graphical way of summarizing the steady-state characteristics of a network is furnished by plotting the locus of the network function in the complex plane as the frequency is varied.

For example of this, consider the complex-gain function (7-48). Since sinusoidal steady-state conditions are being examined, substitute $j\omega$ for s; take the case $\alpha_1 = 1$. Now, for various values of ω/ω_1, compute the real and imaginary parts of the complex gain. Plot these values as points in the complex plane, and join them with a smooth curve. This is the locus of complex gain, and from it one can see clearly how the magnitude and phase of the gain vary with frequency.

For comparison, plot the gain locus for $\alpha_1 = 0$.

7-5 RESISTANCE-CAPACITANCE-COUPLED AMPLIFIER

In Sec. 7-4 we examined a model of an amplifier stage (Fig. 7-20) wherein the effects of the stray tube and wiring capacitances C_1 and C_2 were taken into account. As this amplifier stage is commonly constructed, there is another capacitance in the picture—this one inserted deliberately. The so-called coupling capacitor (C_c in Fig. 7-26) is placed between the anode and the grid of the following tube in order that the two may be held at different average potentials. The effect of this was disregarded in the preceding section, since it acts very nearly as a short circuit except at very low frequencies. The resistance R_2, furnishing a d-c connection to the following grid to allow control of its average potential, was also ignored in the preceding section. Analysis of the more complete resistance-capacitance-coupled amplifier model shown in Fig. 7-26, however, provides an interesting exercise. We shall be primarily interested in sinusoidal steady-state conditions.

The gain function for this network can be most simply written by starting with an assumed output voltage $\mathbf{E}_2$. The current through

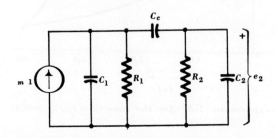

Fig. 7-26. Approximate model for the resistance-capacitance-coupled amplifier stage.

the coupling capacitor is $\mathbf{I}_c = \mathbf{E}_2(1/R_2 + sC_2)$. The voltage across R_1 is thus $\mathbf{E}_{R_1} = \mathbf{E}_2 + \mathbf{I}_c/sC_c$. Hence $g_m\mathbf{E}_1 = \mathbf{I}_c + \mathbf{E}_{R_1}(1/R_1 + sC_1)$. Combining these and rearranging yield

$$\frac{\mathbf{E}_2}{\mathbf{E}_1} = \frac{g_m sC_c R_1 R_2}{s^2 R_1 R_2 (C_1 C_2 + C_1 C_c + C_2 C_c) + s(R_1 C_c + R_2 C_c + R_1 C_1 + R_2 C_2) + 1}$$

$$(7\text{-}53)$$

The details of the amplifier properties can be explored by studying this gain function. It can be shown, by simple but tedious algebra, that the two roots of the denominator—call them s_1 and s_2—are always negative real numbers. Thus the gain function has two poles on the negative real axis and one zero at the origin (Fig. 7-27a). Thinking again in terms of the relief-map analogy, we may expect the gain curve (elevation along the $j\omega$ axis) to have more or less the shape shown in Fig. 7-27b. The exact shape for particular numerical values could be computed, of course, but it appears difficult to generalize the result with so many different element values involved.

However, this is a case in which a little consideration of the physical situation and of typical element values will yield profitable results. When we stop to think of the purpose for which this amplifier is constructed, we realize that the capacitances C_1 and C_2 are going to be as small as they can be made, since they tend to cause the gain curve to drop off at high frequencies. On the other hand, the capacitance C_c will be made as large as practicable, since otherwise the gain would tend to be poor at low frequencies.

In the mid-frequency range, therefore, the amplifier characteristics can be expected to approach those of the somewhat idealized case

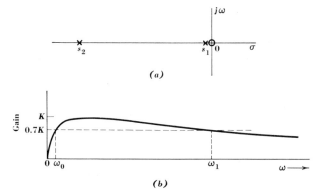

(a)

(b)

Fig. 7-27. (a) *Complex-frequency-plane representation of the gain function of Eq. (7-53); (b) typical shape of the related gain vs. frequency curve.*

in which C_1 and C_2 are both set equal to zero and C_c is replaced by a short circuit (Fig. 7-28a). The amplifier gain for this reduced model is the constant

$$K \triangleq \frac{g_m R_1 R_2}{R_1 + R_2} \tag{7-54}$$

At higher frequencies, C_1 and C_2 cannot be ignored, and the model of Fig. 7-28b is more appropriate. The gain expression is easily found to be

$$\left(\frac{E_2}{E_1}\right)_{\text{high frequency}} = \frac{K}{s/\omega_1 + 1} \tag{7-55}$$

where

$$\omega_1 \triangleq \frac{R_1 + R_2}{R_1 R_2 (C_1 + C_2)} \tag{7-56}$$

This normalizing frequency ω_1, which is essentially the same as the one used in Sec. 7-4, furnishes a convenient measure of the high-frequency limit of useful gain.

At very low frequencies, C_1 and C_2 are certainly negligible, but the capacitance C_c makes its presence known. The approximate model of Fig. 7-28c holds, and the gain expression turns out to be

$$\left(\frac{E_2}{E_1}\right)_{\text{low frequency}} = K \frac{s/\omega_0}{s/\omega_0 + 1} \tag{7-57}$$

where

$$\omega_0 \triangleq \frac{1}{(R_1 + R_2) C_c} \tag{7-58}$$

more or less indicates the low-frequency limit of useful gain.

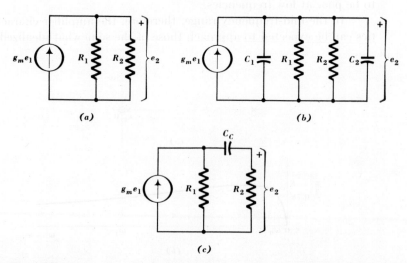

(a)   **(b)**

(c)

Fig. 7-28. (a) Mid-frequency, (b) high-frequency, and (c) low-frequency approximate models of the resistance-capacitance-coupled amplifier.

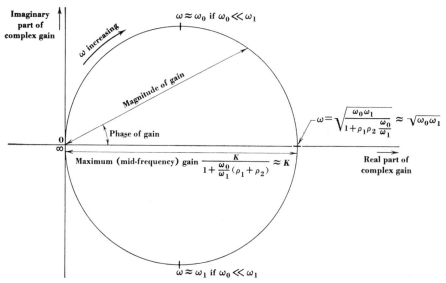

Fig. 7-29. Locus plot of the complex gain of the amplifier of Fig. 7-26 under sinusoidal steady-state conditions.

Returning to the more general gain expression, Eq. (7-53), and choosing to write this in terms of the dimensionless variable s/ω_1, we can obtain

$$\frac{E_2}{E_1} = K \frac{s/\omega_1}{\left(\dfrac{s}{\omega_1}\right)^2 \left(1 + \dfrac{\omega_0}{\omega_1}\rho_1\rho_2\right) + \left(\dfrac{s}{\omega_1}\right)\left[1 + \dfrac{\omega_0}{\omega_1}(\rho_1 + \rho_2)\right] + \dfrac{\omega_0}{\omega_1}} \tag{7-59}$$

where ρ_1 and ρ_2, defined by

$$\rho_1 \triangleq \frac{R_1 + R_2}{R_2}\frac{C_1}{C_1 + C_2}$$

$$\rho_2 \triangleq \frac{R_1 + R_2}{R_1}\frac{C_2}{C_1 + C_2}$$

gather up the leftover constants.

In this form it is not too hard to see that if $\omega_0 \ll \omega_1$, the two poles are approximately at $s_1 \approx -\omega_0$ and $s_2 \approx -\omega_1$. Though not nearly so obvious, it can be demonstrated with a little analytic geometry that the locus of the complex gain under sinusoidal steady-state conditions is a circle, as shown in Fig. 7-29.

PROBLEMS

7-24 Making use of the theorem mentioned in Prob. 5-18, find the locus of the complex-gain expression of Eq. (7-55) under sinusoidal steady-state conditions as the radian frequency ω varies from 0 to ∞. Do the same for the gain expression of Eq. (7-57).

7-25   Consider two RC-coupled amplifier stages connected in cascade, that is, with the output voltage of one forming the input voltage of the second, so that the over-all gain is the product of the two individual gain functions. Assume that the gain of each individual stage is given by Eq. (7-55). (This amounts to neglecting the effect of the coupling capacitor C_c, an approximation which might be reasonable if one were primarily interested in the high-frequency characteristics of the amplifier.) By computation of the magnitude and phase of the complex gain (under sinusoidal steady-state conditions) for several values of ω/ω_1, sketch the locus of the gain in the complex plane as ω is varied from 0 to ∞. (Notice that the shape of this locus can be anticipated from the pole-zero diagram. In the present case there are two poles at $s = -\omega_1$. If one imagines the computations to be carried out by the graphical procedure illustrated in Fig. 5-20, it becomes clear that the magnitude of the gain is greatest at $\omega = 0$ and decreases as ω increases. The phase starts at $0°$ and decreases rapidly at first, then more slowly, approaching $-180°$ as $\omega \to \infty$.)

7-26   Sketch the locus of the complex gain of two RC-coupled amplifier stages in cascade as in Prob. 7-25, but assume the gain function of Eq. (7-57) for each stage. Before performing any computations, attempt to anticipate from the pole-zero plot what the general shape of this locus will be.

7-6 VIBRATION ABSORBER

Let us examine, as a further application of the methods being studied, an interesting device known as a vibration absorber. This is an alternative approach to the vibration-isolation problem discussed in Sec. 7-1. As in that example, consider some sort of machine of mass M mounted on springs with over-all compliance K (Fig. 7-30). Assume an applied force f_a which varies sinusoidally at a radian frequency ω. If this is near the resonant frequency $\omega_0 \triangleq 1/\sqrt{MK}$, the force transmitted through the spring mounting to the floor may be considerably greater than the applied force. In Sec. 7-1 this condition was alleviated by the addition of the damping D; let us now study the effect of adding the vibration absorber shown in Fig. 7-30, consisting of a small mass m attached to the machine through a spring of compliance k and a dashpot of frictional resistance d.

In physical terms, the idea behind the vibration absorber is the following. Suppose the applied force is at a fixed radian frequency ω. If, then, the combination of the mass m and the spring compliance k is made resonant near this frequency, it can provide a counterforce which is very nearly equal to the applied force, thus in effect nearly canceling it out. In this way the net force applied to the M-K com-

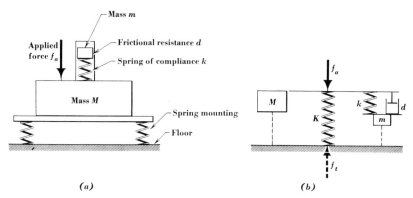

Fig. 7-30. (a) *Vibration absorber to alter the resonance characteristic of a spring-mounted machine;* (b) *alternative arrangement of elements in schematic form.*

bination is reduced, and so, therefore, is the transmitted force. It is our task to examine this scheme to see its potentialities and its limitations.

The transfer function relating the transmitted force f_t to the applied force f_a summarizes the relevant characteristics of the over-all network. With the analysis tools now at our disposal, this is quite easily obtained. From the schematic of Fig. 7-30*b* we see that the impedances of the mass M, of the spring K, and of the vibration absorber are connected abreast and hence

$$\mathbf{Z}_m(s) = \frac{\mathbf{F}_a}{\mathbf{V}} = sM + \frac{1}{sK} + \mathbf{Z}_d \qquad (7\text{-}60)$$

where $\mathbf{Z}_d$ is the impedance of the vibration damper. The spring compliance k and the dissipation d are abreast, and the two together are in tandem with the mass m; hence, using the rules for combining network elements summarized in Table 3-1, we can write

$$\mathbf{Z}_d = \frac{sm(d + 1/sk)}{sm + d + 1/sk} \qquad (7\text{-}61)$$

The only force transmitted to the floor is the spring force

$$\mathbf{F}_t = \frac{\mathbf{V}}{sK} \qquad (7\text{-}62)$$

Combining Eqs. (7-59) and (7-62) yields the desired transfer function

$$\mathbf{T}(s) = \frac{\mathbf{F}_t}{\mathbf{F}_a} = \frac{1/sK}{sM + 1/sK + \mathbf{Z}_d} \qquad (7\text{-}63)$$

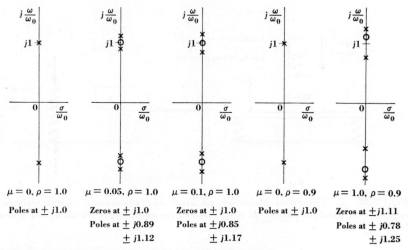

$\mu = 0, \rho = 1.0$

Poles at $\pm j1.0$

$\mu = 0.05, \rho = 1.0$

Zeros at $\pm j1.0$
Poles at $\pm j0.89$
$\pm j1.12$

$\mu = 0.1, \rho = 1.0$

Zeros at $\pm j1.0$
Poles at $\pm j0.85$
$\pm j1.17$

$\mu = 0, \rho = 0.9$

Poles at $\pm j1.0$

$\mu = 1.0, \rho = 0.9$

Zeros at $\pm j1.11$
Poles at $\pm j0.78$
$\pm j1.25$

Fig. 7-31. Poles and zeros of Eq. (7-66) in the s/ω_0 plane.

Inserting for $\mathbf{Z}_d$ from Eq. (7-61) and rationalizing (that is, rearranging in the form of the ratio of two polynomials in s) yield

$$\frac{\mathbf{F}_t}{\mathbf{F}_a} = \frac{s^2 mk + skd + 1}{s^4 mMkK + s^3(M + m)kKd + s^2(MK + mk + mK) + skd + 1}$$

(7-64)

We have seen on previous occasions the advantages which accrue from nondimensionalizing such an expression as this. We may as well choose ω_0 as the normalizing frequency; thus we may start by replacing s everywhere by $\dfrac{1}{\sqrt{MK}}\dfrac{s}{\omega_0}$. It is clear that the resonant frequency of the vibration damper is going to enter the picture, so we may replace the product mk by $\omega_d{}^2$. Various groupings of parameters in dimensionless combinations now suggest themselves, and we arrive at the following nondimensionalized form for the transfer function:

$$\frac{\mathbf{F}_t}{\mathbf{F}_a} = \frac{\rho^2(s/\omega_0)^2 + \alpha s/\omega_0 + 1}{\rho^2\left(\dfrac{s}{\omega_0}\right)^4 + \alpha(1 + \mu)\left(\dfrac{s}{\omega_0}\right)^3 + (1 + \mu + \rho^2)\left(\dfrac{s}{\omega_0}\right)^2 + \alpha\dfrac{s}{\omega_0} + 1}$$

(7-65)

where $\qquad \omega_0 \triangleq \dfrac{1}{\sqrt{MK}} \qquad \omega_d \triangleq \dfrac{1}{\sqrt{mk}} \qquad \rho \triangleq \dfrac{\omega_0}{\omega_d}$

$$\mu \triangleq \frac{m}{M} \qquad \alpha \triangleq dk\omega_0$$

This is a pretty formidable-looking expression. However, we could use it to design the vibration damper by a sort of cut-and-try approach; that is, we could assume trial values of the three design parameters μ, ρ, and α and plot the magnitude of the transfer function (with $j\omega$ substituted for s), repeating this procedure with altered values of the parameters until we obtained a satisfactory characteristic. However, we can carry out the design procedure with an added sense of direction if we first obtain insight into the effects of these parameter values by making a further examination of Eq. (7-65).

Thus, let us consider the special case of no damping, $\alpha = 0$. The transfer function then assumes the form

$$\frac{\mathbf{F}_t}{\mathbf{F}_a} = \frac{\rho^2(s/\omega_0)^2 + 1}{\rho^2(s/\omega_0)^4 + (1 + \mu + \rho^2) + 1} \tag{7-66}$$

Notice that this has two zeros at $s/\omega_0 = \pm j/\rho$ or $s = \pm j\omega_d$; that is, there is zero force transmission to the floor when the resonant frequency of the damper, ω_d, is equal to the applied frequency ω. It also has four poles at the roots of the denominator. The poles and zeros of Eq. (7-66) are shown in Fig. 7-31 for various values of μ and ρ.

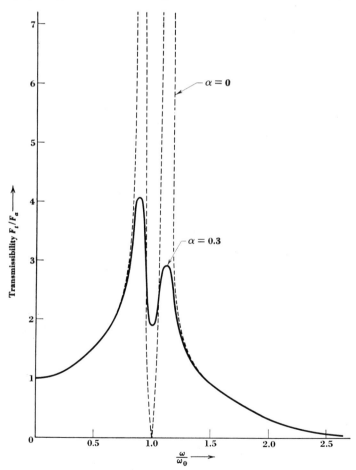

Fig. 7-32. *Transmissibility F_t/F_a of the system of Fig. 7-30 for the case $\rho = 1$, $\mu = 0.05$, $\alpha = 0.3$.*

Notice that the effect of adding the vibration absorber (increasing μ from zero) is to produce zero transmission at the resonant frequency ω_d and high transmissibility on either side of this (as in the dashed curve in Fig. 7-32). Thus the absorber does not remove the troublesome resonant frequency; in fact, it actually adds a second frequency of infinite transmission! It does, however, produce between the two frequencies of high transmissibility a region of low transmission. Hence it can be quite effective if the applied frequency ω is truly fixed. If the applied frequency varies, however—say during accelerating or decelerating conditions—the high resonant peaks which remain are extremely undesirable.

We suspect that adding dissipation in the vibration absorber (increasing α from zero) will tend to move the transfer-function poles away from the $j\omega$ axis and hence reduce the sharpness of the resonant peaks (Fig. 7-32). Again, the root-locus methods can be employed to demonstrate that this is so (Fig. 7-33). Note that too large a value of α results in the restoration of the single high resonance peak, but shifted in frequency. This corresponds to the observation that as $\alpha \to \infty$, the effect of the added elements is simply that of increasing the mass from

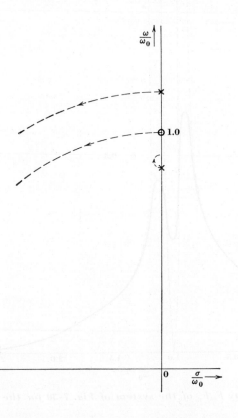

Fig. 7-33. Migration of the poles and zeros of Eq. (7-65) as α is increased from zero (sketched for $\rho = 1$, $\mu = 0.1$).

M to $(M + m)$, resulting in a new resonant frequency

$$\omega_0' = \frac{1}{\sqrt{K(M + m)}}$$

Once more let it be emphasized that the point of these studies is not to learn interesting and useful facts about RC amplifiers or vibration dampers. It is, rather, to gain some insight into the kinds of questions one might wish to ask regarding linear networks and the ways of going about finding answers.

PROBLEMS

7-27 A vibration absorber sometimes known as a *Lanchester damper* consists of a mass m attached to the machine through a frictional resistance d, somewhat as in Fig. 7-30 but without the springs. (This is equivalent to letting $k \to \infty$ in Fig. 7-30.) Find the transfer function $\mathbf{F}_t/\mathbf{F}_a$ for this case and write it in dimensionless-ratio form. (It will be convenient to introduce the dimensionless parameter $\gamma \triangleq d/m\omega_0$.)

Find the poles and zeros of this expression in the s/ω_0 plane for the parameter values $\mu = 0.21$, $\gamma = 1.0$.

Plot the magnitude of the transfer function vs. the normalized applied radian frequency ω/ω_0. Compare this with the curve for the case of no vibration absorber $(d = 0)$.

7-28 Use the root-locus techniques to study the movement of the poles of the transfer function of Prob. 7-27 when $\mu = 0.21$ as γ is varied from 0 to ∞.

7-29 In Fig. 7-30a assume that the mass M represents a scientific instrument which is mounted on the springs K in order to isolate it from the vibrations of the floor on which it rests. (The applied force f_a is not present.) The floor moves vertically with a displacement $x_0 = X_0 \cos \omega t$. The vibration absorber consisting of the elements m, k, and d is installed to reduce the undesirable oscillations which would otherwise occur if the radian frequency ω were near the resonant frequency $\omega_0 = 1/\sqrt{MK}$.

Write the transfer function $\mathbf{X}_1/\mathbf{X}_0$, where $\mathbf{X}_0$ is the phasor representation of the floor motion and $\mathbf{X}_1$ represents the motion of the mass M. Compare with Eq. (7-63).

7-7 IDEAL TIME DELAY

Some mechanical and electrical transducers behave very much like ideal time delays; that is, the output quantity is a replica of the

$f(t) \longrightarrow$ [τ] $\longrightarrow f(t-\tau)$ *Fig. 7-34. Block diagram of an ideal-delay element. The time delay is τ.*

input except for a delay time (Fig. 7-34). Two examples of transducers giving nearly ideal delay are electrical transmission lines and rigid homogeneous materials through which sound waves are transmitted. Usually, such transducers act as ideal delays over only a limited range of frequencies. For many applications, however, the ideal model of Fig. 7-34 is a reasonable approximation. This section will be devoted to a discussion of the mathematical analysis of systems which contain elements which can be represented as ideal time delays.

REPRESENTATION OF TIME DELAY IN THE s DOMAIN   We have seen in this chapter that a table of unit-impulse responses can be most helpful in solving transient problems. Various system functions $\mathbf{F}(s)$ and their corresponding impulse responses are listed in Table 7-1 and the Appendix. To derive these lists, we started with an input (a unit impulse) and a system (or response) function $\mathbf{F}(s)$ (a network) and then computed the response, or output. Now we wish to include the ideal-time-delay element as a system function in our tables. Here the problem is different. For any input, the output is known (it is just the input delayed in time). The unknown quantity is now the system function.

The problem we have set for ourselves is not too difficult if we approach it in a straightforward manner. The response function has been defined as the ratio of the response to excitation when both are varying as e^{st}. If the input to the ideal-delay element of Fig. 7-34 is e^{st}, the output must be $e^{s(t-\tau)} = e^{-s\tau}e^{st}$. Hence, the response function corresponding to an ideal delay is

$$\mathbf{F}(s) = \frac{e^{-s\tau}e^{st}}{e^{st}} = e^{-s\tau} \tag{7-67}$$

From Eq. (7-67) we conclude that the relationships of Table 7-2 could be added to Table 7-1. The last three relationships of Table 7-2 are simply derived by combining the first with various relationships from Table 7-1.

We can confirm our results by using Eq. (7-34), the integral relationship between a time-domain function $f(t)$ and its s-domain representation $\mathbf{F}(s)$. Let us apply this formulation to a function which has been delayed by a time τ. First we let $g(t)$ be $f(t)$ delayed by a time τ:

$$g(t) = f(t - \tau) \tag{7-68}$$

According to Eq. (7-34), the s-domain representation of $g(t)$ is

$$\mathbf{G}(s) = \int_0^\infty g(t)e^{-st}\,dt = \int_0^\infty f(t - \tau)e^{-st}\,dt \qquad (7\text{-}69)$$

With the change of variable $\xi = t - \tau$, Eq. (7-69) becomes

$$G(s) = e^{-s\tau}\int_{-\tau}^\infty f(\xi)e^{-s\xi}\,d\xi \qquad (7\text{-}70)$$

If we assume that $f(t) = 0$ for $t < 0$, then Eq. (7-70) can be simplified as follows:

$$\mathbf{G}(s) = e^{-s\tau}\int_0^\infty f(\xi)e^{-s\xi}\,d\xi = e^{-s\tau}\,\mathbf{F}(s) \qquad (7\text{-}71)$$

Equation (7-71) verifies the relationships of Table 7-2. It also indicates the simple way in which the s-domain representation of a delayed waveform may be derived if the s-domain representation of the undelayed waveform is known.

WAVEFORM CONSTRUCTION USING IDEAL TIME DELAY   In the following problem we shall see that the ideal time delay and its s-domain representation can be very useful in working with excitations which are pulses of various shapes. Figure 7-35a illustrates a mechanical system to which a force is applied as shown. Let the waveform of the applied

TABLE 7-2   *Table of Unit-impulse Responses in Which There Is a Delay in the System*

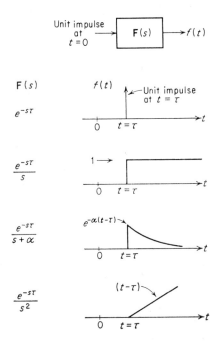

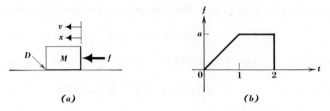

Fig. 7-35. (a) *A simple mechanical system and* (b) *the force applied to it.*

force be that shown in Fig. 7-35*b*. We have seen that the *s*-domain representation of the velocity of the mass can be found by dividing the *s*-domain representation of the applied force by the impedance of the mechanical system.† Thus,

$$\mathbf{V}(s) = \frac{\mathbf{F}(s)}{\mathbf{Z}_m(s)} = \frac{\mathbf{F}(s)}{sM + D} \tag{7-72}$$

In order to find the velocity by the method indicated in Eq. (7-72), it is first necessary to find the *s*-domain representation of the applied force. The waveform of Fig. 7-35*b* is not listed in Table 7-1 or the Appendix. The obvious method of finding $\mathbf{F}(s)$ would appear to be application of Eq. (7-34). Although this method is reasonably simple, an even easier technique is available. After a little consideration of the force waveform, we see that it is the sum of the three basic functions illustrated in Fig. 7-36. Each of these functions has a simple *s*-domain representation [$f_2(t)$ and $f_3(t)$ are functions included in Table 7-2]. Consequently, the *s*-domain representation of the applied force is the sum of the *s*-domain representations of the three functions $f_1(t)$, $f_2(t)$, and $f_3(t)$:

$$\mathbf{F}(s) = \mathbf{F}_1(s) + \mathbf{F}_2(s) + \mathbf{F}_3(s) = \frac{a}{s^2} - \frac{a}{s^2}e^{-s} - \frac{a}{s}e^{-2s} \tag{7-73}$$

It follows that the resultant velocity (*s* domain) is

$$\begin{aligned}
\mathbf{V}(s) &= a\left[\frac{1 - e^{-s}}{s^2(sM + D)} - \frac{e^{-2s}}{s(sM + D)}\right] \\
&= \frac{a}{D}\left[\left(\frac{1}{s^2} - \frac{M/D}{s} + \frac{M/D}{s + D/M}\right)(1 - e^{-s})\right. \\
&\qquad\qquad \left. - \left(\frac{1}{s} - \frac{1}{s + D/M}\right)e^{-2s}\right]
\end{aligned} \tag{7-74}$$

---

† Alternatively, we could say that the response is the product of excitation and the response, or system, function. In this case the response function is the reciprocal of the impedance.

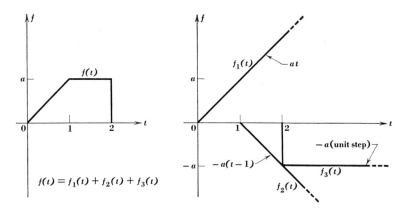

Fig. 7-36. The decomposition of a waveform into three basic functions.

Equation (7-74) is reasonably complex, but the time-domain velocity may be constructed quite simply. The technique is essentially the inverse of the decomposition of the force waveform. This reconstruction method is illustrated in Fig. 7-37.

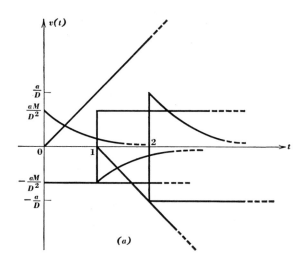

Fig. 7-37. The velocity of the mass of Fig. 7-35 with the applied force of that figure. The curve of part b is the sum of all the functions shown in part a.

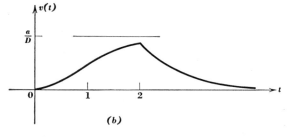

The analytic expression for the velocity, that is, the time-domain expression corresponding to Eq. (7-74), is seen to be

$$
v(t) = \begin{cases}
0 & \text{for } t < 0 \\[2mm]
\dfrac{a}{D}\left[t - \dfrac{M}{D}(1 - e^{-Dt/M})\right] & \text{for } 0 < t < 1 \\[3mm]
\dfrac{a}{D}\left[t - \dfrac{M}{D}(1 - 2^{-Dt/M}) - (t-1) + \dfrac{M}{D}(1 - e^{-D(t-1)/M})\right] & \\[2mm]
\quad = \dfrac{a}{D}\left[1 + \dfrac{M}{D}(1 - e^{D/M})e^{-Dt/M}\right] & \text{for } 1 < t < 2 \\[3mm]
\dfrac{a}{D}\left[1 + \dfrac{M}{D}(1 - e^{D/M})e^{-Dt/M} - 1 + e^{-D(t-2)/M}\right] & \\[2mm]
\quad = \dfrac{a}{D}\left[\dfrac{M}{D}(1 - e^{D/M}) + e^{2D/M}\right]e^{-Dt/M} & \text{for } 2 < t
\end{cases}
$$

$$(7\text{-}75)$$

The complete problem solution above can be related to impulse responses and illustrated diagrammatically as in Fig. 7-38.

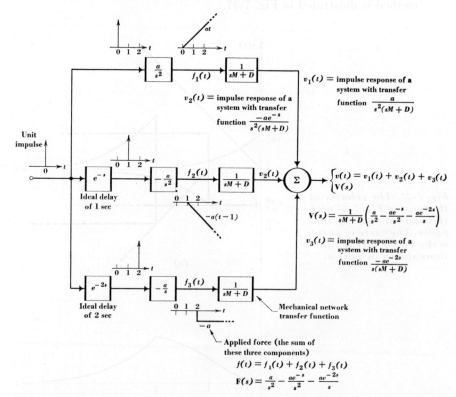

Fig. 7-38. The system of Fig. 7-35 reduced to the problem of computing impulse responses.

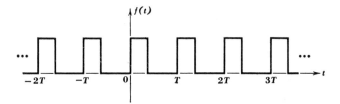

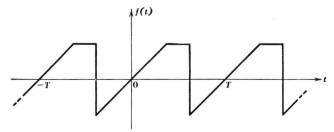

Fig. 7-39. Two examples of periodic functions.

PERIODIC EXCITATIONS A function $f(t)$ is periodic with period T if

$$f(t + T) = f(t) \qquad \text{for all } t \qquad (7\text{-}76)$$

Two examples of periodic waveforms are shown in Fig. 7-39. If a function is zero for $t < 0$ and is periodic after $t = 0$, that is, if

$$\begin{aligned} f(t) &= 0 & t &< 0 \\ f(t + T) &= f(t) & t &> 0 \end{aligned} \qquad (7\text{-}77)$$

then it may be called a one-sided periodic function. We shall henceforth generally drop the adjective *one-sided* and refer to such functions as periodic even though they do not satisfy Eq. (7-76) for all t.

The excitations applied to electrical and mechanical networks are one-sided periodic functions. If we are interested in the steady-state response after all the initial transients have died out, we may consider the excitation as having been applied for all time, and hence as a periodic function for all t. In the first part of Chap. 13, such steady-state responses to periodic excitations are discussed at some length. In the present exposition, we shall concentrate on the transient response to periodic functions.

What we shall do now is merely an extension of the technique developed in the previous problem. Let us suppose that the excitation applied to a linear network with transfer function $\mathbf{T}(s)$ is the periodic waveform of Fig. 7-40. The response of the network will be

$$\mathbf{R}(s) = \mathbf{E}(s)\mathbf{T}(s) \qquad (7\text{-}78)$$

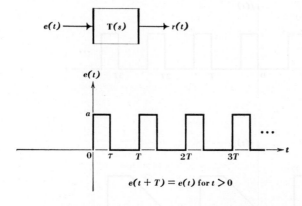

Fig. 7-40. A transducer with an applied periodic excitation $e(t)$.

where $\mathbf{E}(s)$ is the s-domain representation of the excitation $e(t)$ and $\mathbf{R}(s)$ is the s-domain representation of the response $r(t)$.

The periodic function $e(t)$ can be thought of as a sum of square pulses:

$$e(t) = e_0(t) + e_1(t) + e_2(t) + e_3(t) + \cdots$$

$$e_0(t) = \begin{cases} a & \text{for } 0 < t < \tau \\ 0 & \text{otherwise} \end{cases} \tag{7-79}$$

$$e_n(t) = e_0(t) \text{ delayed } nT \text{ sec}$$

Consequently, if $\mathbf{E}_0(s)$ is the s-domain representation of $e_0(t)$, then utilizing the transfer function of an ideal time delay, we see that

$$\mathbf{E}(s) = \mathbf{E}_0(s)(1 + e^{-sT} + e^{-2sT} + e^{-3sT} + \cdots) \tag{7-80}$$

Equation (7-80) can be modified by noting that $1/(1 - e^{-st})$ gives (by long division) the infinite summation of Eq. (7-80):

$$\mathbf{E}(s) = \frac{\mathbf{E}_0(s)}{1 - e^{-sT}} \tag{7-81}$$

The single rectangular pulse $e_0(t)$ is the sum of a step waveform and a negative delayed step of the same amplitude (Fig. 7-41). Hence

$$\mathbf{E}_0(s) = \frac{a}{s}(1 - e^{-s\tau}) \tag{7-82}$$

and $\quad \mathbf{E}(s) = \dfrac{a}{s}(1 - e^{-s\tau})(1 + e^{-sT} + e^{-2sT} + e^{-3sT} + \cdots)$

$$= \frac{a(1 - e^{-s\tau})}{s(1 - e^{-sT})} \tag{7-83}$$

The transducer response is seen to be the sum of a set of identical functions each delayed by an amount nT:

$$\mathbf{R}(s) = \frac{a\mathbf{T}(s)}{s}(1 - e^{-s\tau}) + \frac{a\mathbf{T}(s)}{s}(1 - e^{-s\tau})e^{-sT}$$

$$+ \frac{a\mathbf{T}(s)}{s}(1 - e^{-s\tau})e^{-s2T} + \cdots \tag{7-84}$$

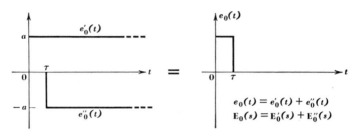

Fig. 7-41. A rectangular pulse as the sum of two step functions.

Thus, finding the response to the first period of the excitation allows us immediately to construct the total response by repeating the first-period response with the appropriate delays.

7-8 SUMMARY

This chapter serves both as a culmination of the first six chapters and as a transition and introduction to all the following chapters. In these early chapters our method has been to examine fairly simple systems, each of which led to one or two new concepts or techniques. As we progressed, the systems became progressively more complex in structure or excitation. For the most part, we have solved specific problems and then generalized our results to apply to similar situations. With increasing complexity, this method becomes less satisfactory. Consequently, our future investigations will often begin with generalizations of systems, problems, and techniques. With a general solution or technique at our disposal, we shall be able to treat any specific system to which the general solution applies.

The methods and concepts introduced in this chapter play a vital role in all later chapters. Consequently, a short review before proceeding into the last half of this text should prove valuable. An extremely important fact concerning linear networks is that their behavior can be described by a system (response) function† $F(s)$. The system function is simply an algebraic combination of the impedances of the individual network elements of the system under investigation. Although system functions were utilized in earlier chapters, it was not until the present chapter that it became clear that they were applicable to all types of excitations and not limited to natural responses and exponential and sinusoidal excitations.

---

† If the network's behavior at more than one point is of interest, more than one system function will be necessary. For example, the input impedance and the transfer function of a transducer may be necessary to describe the network adequately. For more on this topic, see Sec. 9-4.

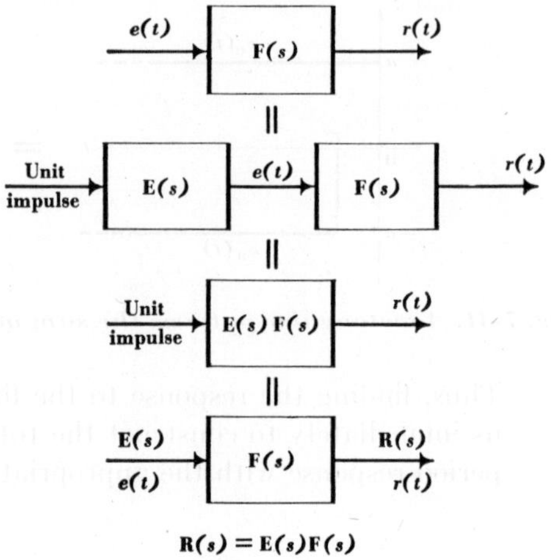

Fig. 7-42. Representation of a system response in the s domain, utilizing impulse-response concepts.

To arrive at the conclusion above, we first defined a unit impulse. Then we showed that the network impulse response is readily obtainable from the response function relating response to excitation when both vary as e^{st}; that is, for each response function there is a corresponding impulse response. The converse is also true; for each function of time (starting at $t = 0$) there is a corresponding system, or s-domain, function. As a consequence, we can construct tables of time functions and their s-domain representations such as Table 7-1 and the Appendix.

The utilization of these tables beyond impulse-response calculations is justified diagrammatically in Fig. 7-42. The final conclusion is that the response of a linear network is, in the s domain, just the product of the s-domain representation of the excitation and the appropriate network response function. This conclusion is extremely important because of the relative ease of solving linear network problems in the s domain. The response function can be readily calculated, and with the aid of tables and Eq. (7-34), the s-domain representations of time functions can be determined with facility.

Our development and investigation of these s-domain techniques are not yet complete. There are some gaps which must be filled in. Up to this point we have dealt only with networks whose structures are fairly simple. To find impedances, admittances, and other system functions for complex networks requires techniques not yet discussed. The following chapter is devoted to this problem. We have thus far used the impulse-response s-domain techniques only with networks in which there is no initial energy storage. Chapter 9 will extend these methods to networks with initial energy storage. Finally, in Chap. 13, the Laplace transform will be derived and discussed. This discussion will lead us to the same conclusions concerning the utility of s-domain techniques that we arrived at previously, but this time our approach will be more abstract mathematically and less dependent upon physical reasoning.

Because of the great utility of the s-domain concepts which have been introduced in this chapter, a large part of the discussion in later chapters will be carried out in terms of system functions and s-domain representations of time functions. Those who desire a more rigorous, mathematical development of these s-domain techniques may study Chap. 13 now, before going on to Chap. 8.

PROBLEMS

7-30 A transducer with ideal time delay $[\mathbf{T}(s) = e^{-s\tau}]$ is often called a constant-gain linear-phase network. Demonstrate the reason for this by plotting the magnitude and phase of $\mathbf{T}(s)$ for $s = j\omega$.

7-31 The transfer function $e^{-s\tau}$ of an ideal-time-delay transducer has the property of having no poles or zeros in the finite s plane. All networks composed of lumped (L, C, R, M, K, and D) network elements will have poles or zeros or both in their transfer functions unless they are purely resistive, in which case $\mathbf{T}(s)$ is just a constant. It follows that no network of lumped elements can produce an ideal delay. However, approximations to ideal-delay transducers can be made using lumped elements. The figure shows the pole and zero locations of a transfer function which can be produced by a lumped-element network. Plot the magnitude and phase angle of this transfer function for $s = j\omega$ and compare with the plot for Prob. 7-30. Discuss the properties of this transfer function as compared with the properties of ideal delays.

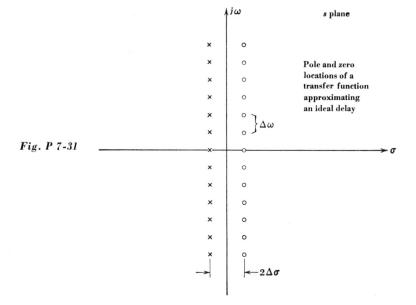

Fig. P 7-31

7-32   Find the s-domain representations of the illustrated functions.

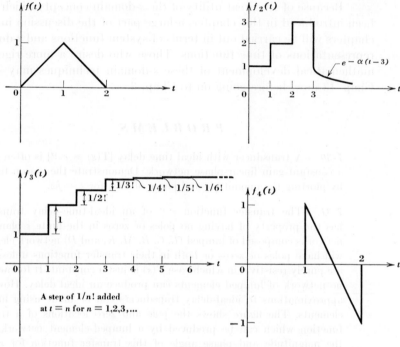

Fig. P 7-32

7-33   The figure shows four networks and four excitations. Find the indicated response of each network for each of the four excitations.

7-34   Using Eq. (7-34), find the s-domain representation of a single cycle of a sine wave starting at $t = 0$. Then use the ideal-delay method introduced in Sec. 7-7 to find the s-domain representation of a sine wave which is given in Table 7-1.

7-35   Find the s-domain representation of the square wave shown in the figure. Represent it in closed form, using Eq. (7-81). Plot the position of the poles of this function. (Note that half of the poles produced by the denominator are canceled by zeros in the numerator.) Show that by considering these poles a complex conjugate pair at a time, the s-domain representation can be written as

$$\mathbf{F}(s) = \frac{a_0}{s} + \frac{a_1}{s^2 + \omega_1{}^2} + \frac{a_3}{s^2 + (3\omega_1)^2} + \frac{a_5}{s^2 + (5\omega_1)^2} + \cdots$$

Consequently,

$$f(t) = a_0 + \frac{a_1}{\omega_1} \sin \omega_1 t + \frac{a_3}{3\omega_1} \sin 3\omega_1 t + \frac{a_5}{5\omega_1} \sin 5\omega_1 t + \cdots$$

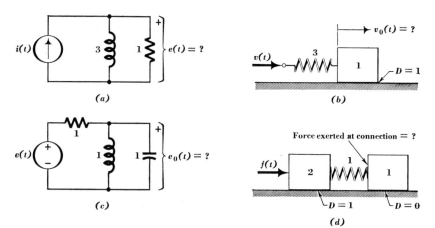

(a)

(b)

(c)

(d)

Element values in mks units (ohms, henrys, farads, kilograms, m/newton, kg/sec)

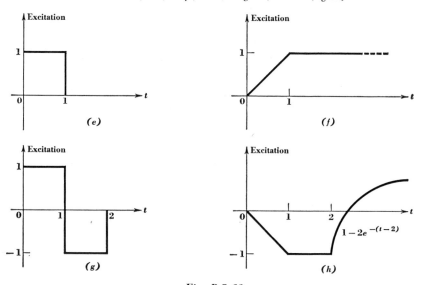

(e)

(f)

(g)

(h)

Fig. P 7-33

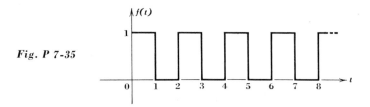

Fig. P 7-35

Find the constants ω_1, a_0, a_1, a_3, a_5, ... Discuss the significance of the developments above with reference to this periodic function as well as other periodic functions. This problem serves as a link between the s-domain methods discussed in this chapter and the Fourier-analysis methods introduced in Chap. 13.

7-36   If the square wave of Prob. 7-35 is applied to the two mechanical networks shown, find the indicated velocities.

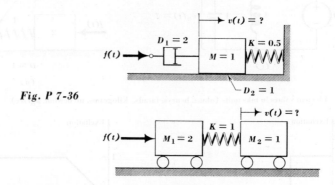

Fig. P 7-36

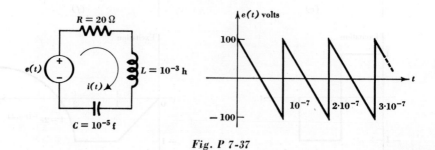

7-37   Find the current in the illustrated circuit.

Fig. P 7-37

systematic methods
of analysis

The preceding chapters have dealt with the determination of the response of a number of different mechanical and electrical systems to various driving functions. This has basically involved the solution of integrodifferential equations relating current to voltage or force to velocity. When the driving function was exponential or sinusoidal in nature, the solution of these equations reduced to the much simpler task of solving algebraic equations involving complex impedances or admittances. In the preceding examples the networks were sufficiently simple to permit easy determination of the system function.

Many of the examples merely involved the straightforward writing of network equations by Kirchhoff's laws or D'Alembert's principle, without any very systematic approach. In Figs. 3-31 and 3-32 a slightly different technique was illustrated. Here a multielement network was reduced to a single impedance to find the response at the point where the excitation was applied. (Not all networks can be reduced in this fashion; four networks which cannot be simplified in this manner are illustrated in Fig. 8-1.) Again, in Sec. 7-2 a special procedure very useful for the solution of "ladder-type" networks was demonstrated.

Many networks, however, are of sufficient complexity to require additional techniques in arriving at the appropriate integrodifferential equation or its equivalent algebraic form. A number of these techniques, together with other methods of system simplification, will be examined in this chapter and the next one.

In this chapter and the following ones free use will be made of the concepts of impulse response and the relations between functions of s and functions of time that were developed in the preceding chapter. That is to say, most of the developments and analyses that will be carried out will be in terms of impedances, admittances, voltages, currents, forces, and velocities which are expressly stated as or understood to be functions of s. Strictly speaking, we should refer to such functions as transforms or s-domain representations, that is, as voltage trans-

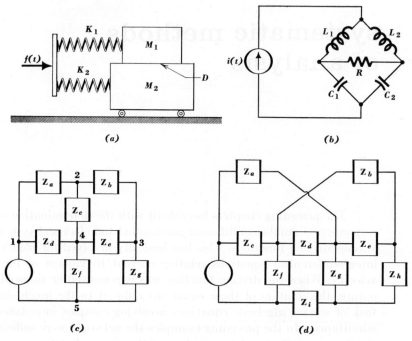

Fig. 8-1. Four networks which cannot be reduced to single equivalent imped-ances by series-parallel combination.

forms, or transforms of the voltage, etc. However, as was the case with phasors, it will be convenient to dispense with the continual use of the term *transform*. Thus, when we speak of a voltage $\mathbf{E}(s)$ or $\mathbf{E}$, or a velocity $\mathbf{V}(s)$ or $\mathbf{V}$, it should be understood that this is the s-domain representation of the voltage (velocity) and that the true time-domain voltage (velocity) can be found by transforming this function of s back to the time domain. The discussion of Sec. 7-3 indicated that, through the use of the Appendix or Eq. (7-34), any time functions which may be encountered in network analysis can be transformed into appropriate expressions in the s domain.

8-1 NODE ANALYSIS

The electrical and mechanical networks shown in Fig. 8-1a and b are analogues of each other. Although they are not complex in structure and do not possess a large number of elements, they cannot be reduced to a driving function and a single equivalent impedance by the process of combining elements in series and parallel. Similarly, the networks of Fig. 8-1c and d cannot be reduced in this manner. The latter two may be thought of as representing either mechanical or electrical systems. The impedances Z_a, Z_b, Z_c, . . . may represent individual circuit elements or series-parallel combinations of circuit elements, and the driving functions may be voltage, current, force, or velocity sources.

Systematic methods are available for analyzing networks of the most general type, including the ones in Fig. 8-1. These methods apply equally well to mechanical networks and to electrical networks. For simplicity, these methods will be developed here chiefly in terms of electrical networks. A parallel development can be obtained for mechanical networks by utilizing the mechanical-electrical analogies given in Table 5-2. *It should be noted that, when these analogies are used, mechanical impedance corresponds to electrical admittance.*

The response of an electrical network to one or more driving functions (or to initial stored energy) is known if the current through each circuit element is known. An equivalent statement is that the response is known if the voltage drop across each element is known. In determining the currents or the voltages, two methods, both based on Kirchhoff's laws, are applicable. One method will be called *loop analysis* and the other *node analysis*.

Before beginning the discussion of these two methods of analysis, a word of warning is in order: the reader should be prepared for a greater degree of abstraction than he encountered in the preceding chapters. At the level of complexity we have now reached, analysis methods can no longer be learned efficiently by studying each possible network configuration. We shall therefore develop general techniques of analysis which may be applied to any network regardless of its configuration. For the sake of efficiency, we shall not be able consistently to follow a line of reasoning and development that an investigator would follow when first encountering networks of increasing complexity. Consequently, the reader, in a number of instances, may not fully understand the motivation behind a certain line of development. This lack of understanding should be only temporary, however, and the reader should have complete comprehension when the goal of the particular development is reached.

THE GRAPH OF A CIRCUIT   The network of Fig. 8-1c will be utilized in discussing both the node and the loop methods of analysis. The simplified form of this network shown in Fig. 8-2a will be called the *graph* of the circuit. The line elements of the graph represent the circuit elements, including sources, across which the voltage varies. The small circles represent the junctions, together with the wires leading to the elements, and thus each node is considered to represent a region of the circuit at the same potential. The line sections representing the circuit elements will be called the *branches* of the graph, and the equal potential regions, the *nodes*. The same nodes in Figs. 8-1c and 8-2a are numbered from 1 to 5.

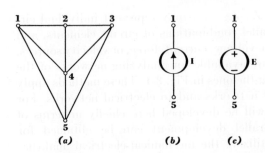

Fig. 8-2. (a) *The graph of the circuit of Fig. 8-1c;* (b) *a current source;* (c) *voltage source.*

NODE EQUATIONS Since voltage is a relative rather than an absolute measure, we may choose one node as a reference and measure all other node voltages with respect to that reference. For the circuit under consideration, we shall let node 5 be the reference node, that is, $E_5 = 0$. The other node voltages are E_1, E_2, E_3, and E_4, where the node voltages are defined as equal to the voltage drop from the particular node to the reference node. The voltage drop between two nodes, say between nodes 1 and 2, is seen to be $E_1 - E_2$ for the drop from node 1 to node 2 and $E_2 - E_1$ for the drop from node 2 to node 1.

One statement of Kirchhoff's current law is the following: *The sum of the currents leaving a node is zero.* Now let us apply this law to node 2 of our circuit. The current flowing from node 2 to node 1 is equal to the voltage drop from node 2 to node 1 divided by the impedance from node 2 to node 1. Thus

$$I_{21} = \frac{E_2 - E_1}{Z_a} \tag{8-1}$$

In the same manner, the currents flowing from node 2 to node 3 and from node 2 to node 4 are

$$I_{23} = \frac{E_2 - E_3}{Z_b} \qquad I_{24} = \frac{E_2 - E_4}{Z_d} \tag{8-2}$$

Since the sum of the three currents must be zero, we obtain the following equation:

$$\frac{E_2 - E_1}{Z_a} + \frac{E_2 - E_3}{Z_b} + \frac{E_2 - E_4}{Z_d} = 0 \tag{8-3}$$

Equation (8-3) illustrates a characteristic which is typical of all node equations. The impedances all appear in the denominator. Consequently, the equations will be simplified in appearance if we use admittances (the reciprocals of the impedances) in the equations rather than impedances. As will become obvious when we have obtained a whole set of node equations, grouping all the admittances which multiply a particular node voltage into a single admittance will simplify and systematize the node equations. This process can be illustrated on Eq. (8-3) as follows. By rearranging, Eq. (8-3) becomes

$$-\frac{1}{Z_a}E_1 + \left(\frac{1}{Z_a} + \frac{1}{Z_b} + \frac{1}{Z_d}\right)E_2 - \frac{1}{Z_b}E_3 - \frac{1}{Z_d}E_4$$
$$= Y_{21}E_1 + Y_{22}E_2 + Y_{23}E_3 + Y_{24}E_4 = 0 \quad (8\text{-}4)$$

where
$$Y_{21} = -\frac{1}{Z_a} \qquad Y_{22} = \frac{1}{Z_a} + \frac{1}{Z_b} + \frac{1}{Z_d}$$
$$Y_{23} = -\frac{1}{Z_b} \qquad Y_{24} = -\frac{1}{Z_d}$$

The reasons for the particular choice of subscripts for the admittances will become apparent shortly. If we carry out the same process at node 3, we obtain the following relations:

$$I_{32} + I_{34} + I_{35} = \frac{E_3 - E_2}{Z_b} + \frac{E_3 - E_4}{Z_e} + \frac{E_3}{Z_g}$$
$$= Y_{32}E_2 + Y_{33}E_3 + Y_{34}E_4 = 0 \quad (8\text{-}5)$$

where
$$Y_{32} = -\frac{1}{Z_b}$$
$$Y_{33} = \frac{1}{Z_b} + \frac{1}{Z_e} + \frac{1}{Z_g}$$
$$Y_{34} = -\frac{1}{Z_e}$$

Similarly, at node 4, we obtain

$$Y_{41} = -\frac{1}{Z_c} \qquad Y_{42} = -\frac{1}{Z_d} \qquad Y_{43} = -\frac{1}{Z_e}$$
$$Y_{44} = \frac{1}{Z_c} + \frac{1}{Z_d} + \frac{1}{Z_e} + \frac{1}{Z_f}$$
$$Y_{41}E_1 + Y_{42}E_2 + Y_{43}E_3 + Y_{44}E_4 = 0 \quad (8\text{-}6)$$

INCLUSION OF SOURCES Let us now turn our attention to node 1. The proper procedure at node 1 depends upon whether the source shown between nodes 1 and 5 is a current source or a voltage source. If it is a *current source*, as is illustrated in Fig. 8-2b, we may apply Kirchhoff's current law as we do at other nodes, the only difference being that one of the currents is given directly rather than as a voltage drop divided by an impedance. Thus at node 1, where $I_{15} = -I$ and the admittances are

$$Y_{11} = \frac{1}{Z_a} + \frac{1}{Z_e} \qquad Y_{12} = -\frac{1}{Z_a} \qquad Y_{14} = -\frac{1}{Z_e}$$

we obtain

$$Y_{11}E_1 + Y_{12}E_2 + Y_{14}E_4 = I \quad (8\text{-}7)$$

Grouping the equations for nodes 1 to 4 yields the following set of four simultaneous equations:

$$\begin{aligned}
\mathbf{Y}_{11}\mathbf{E}_1 + \mathbf{Y}_{12}\mathbf{E}_2 \qquad\qquad + \mathbf{Y}_{14}\mathbf{E}_4 &= \mathbf{I} \\
\mathbf{Y}_{21}\mathbf{E}_1 + \mathbf{Y}_{22}\mathbf{E}_2 + \mathbf{Y}_{23}\mathbf{E}_3 + \mathbf{Y}_{24}\mathbf{E}_4 &= 0 \\
\mathbf{Y}_{32}\mathbf{E}_2 + \mathbf{Y}_{33}\mathbf{E}_3 + \mathbf{Y}_{34}\mathbf{E}_4 &= 0 \\
\mathbf{Y}_{41}\mathbf{E}_1 + \mathbf{Y}_{42}\mathbf{E}_2 + \mathbf{Y}_{43}\mathbf{E}_3 + \mathbf{Y}_{44}\mathbf{E}_4 &= 0
\end{aligned} \qquad (8\text{-}8)$$

Thus we see that by applying Kirchhoff's current law at each of the nodes except the reference node, a set of simultaneous equations, equal in number to the unknown voltages, is obtained. These equations are all independent, since each was obtained at an independent node. By an independent node we mean one whose voltage depends upon the currents flowing, as well as upon the voltages at the other nodes. The two nodes at the terminals of a voltage source are not both independent, since specifying the voltage of one automatically specifies the voltage of the other, irrespective of current flow. A set of independent simultaneous linear equations equal in number to the unknown variables may be solved, yielding a unique value for each of the unknown quantities. The student is undoubtedly familiar with the "elimination-of-variables" method of solving a set of simultaneous equations of this type. Another method of solution, involving determinants, will be discussed later in this chapter.

The utility of our choice of subscripts to identify the various admittances now becomes apparent. The first subscript indicates the particular node to which the equation applies, and the second subscript indicates the node voltage which the admittance multiplies. This systematic notation will be very helpful in discussing general networks and in working with matrices, which are introduced later in this chapter. Before we discuss a general technique for finding any $\mathbf{Y}_{jk}$ without going through the lengthy process used so far, let us investigate the effect of a voltage source on the determination of node equations.

If the source between nodes 1 and 5 is a *voltage source*, as illustrated in Fig. 8-2c, the complexity is somewhat reduced. The voltage at node 1 is no longer an unknown quantity. The voltage source as drawn in Fig. 8-2c maintains node 1 at a potential $\mathbf{E}$ with respect to node 5. Therefore, since node 5 is the reference, the voltage at node 1, $\mathbf{E}_1$, is equal to $\mathbf{E}$. Note that if node 5 were not the reference node, we could either set $\mathbf{E}_1 = \mathbf{E}_5 + \mathbf{E}$ or set $\mathbf{E}_5 = \mathbf{E}_1 - \mathbf{E}$, which would still eliminate one of the unknown variables.

With the voltage at node 1 known, we need only three simultaneous equations to solve for the rest of the node voltages. Therefore, taking the equations for nodes 2, 3, and 4 and making use of the identity $\mathbf{E}_1 = \mathbf{E}$, we have the following set of three simultaneous equations:

$$Y_{22}E_2 + Y_{23}E_3 + Y_{24}E_4 = \frac{E}{Z_a}$$

$$Y_{32}E_2 + Y_{33}E_3 + Y_{34}E_4 = 0 \qquad (8\text{-}9)$$

$$Y_{42}E_2 + Y_{43}E_3 + Y_{44}E_4 = \frac{E}{Z_d}$$

To arrive at the appropriate simultaneous equations when one of the terminals of the voltage source is not connected to the reference node requires a slight modification in our technique. To demonstrate this, let us consider again the circuit of Figs. 8-1c and 8-2. If node 3 is the reference node for this example and the source is once again the voltage source of Fig. 8-2c, the equations at nodes 2 and 4 are obtained in exactly the same manner as is illustrated above. One more equation is needed. This equation depends upon the currents at both node 1 and node 5. To illustrate this, let us sum the currents flowing away from node 1. If the voltage at node 1 is called E_1 and the voltage at node 5 is $E_1 - E$, the current equation at node 1 is

$$\frac{E_1 - E_2}{Z_a} + \frac{E_1 - E_4}{Z_d} + I_{15} = 0 \qquad (8\text{-}10)$$

The current I_{15} flowing from node 1 to node 5 is equal to the current flowing away from node 5 through the other branches; that is,

$$I_{15} = \frac{E_1 - E}{Z_g} + \frac{E_1 - E - E_4}{Z_f} \qquad (8\text{-}11)$$

By combining Eqs. (8-10) and (8-11) and utilizing the admittances

$$Y_{11}' = \frac{1}{Z_a} + \frac{1}{Z_d} + \frac{1}{Z_g} + \frac{1}{Z_f} \qquad Y_{12}' = -\frac{1}{Z_a} \qquad Y_{14}' = -\frac{1}{Z_d} - \frac{1}{Z_f}$$

we obtain

$$Y_{11}'E_1 + Y_{12}'E_2 + Y_{14}'E_4 = E\left(\frac{1}{Z_f} + \frac{1}{Z_g}\right) \qquad (8\text{-}12)$$

The admittances above are primed to distinguish them from the previous admittances, which bear identical subscripts but may have different values.

The equations for nodes 2 and 4 together with Eq. (8-12) form the following set of simultaneous equations:

$$Y_{11}'E_1 + Y_{12}'E_2 + Y_{14}'E_4 = E\left(\frac{1}{Z_f} + \frac{1}{Z_g}\right)$$

$$Y_{21}'E_1 + Y_{22}'E_2 + Y_{24}'E_4 = 0 \qquad (8\text{-}13)$$

$$Y_{41}'E_1 + Y_{42}'E_2 + Y_{44}'E_4 = -E\left(\frac{1}{Z_f}\right)$$

where
$$Y_{21}' = Y_{12}' \qquad Y_{22}' = Y_{22} \qquad Y_{24}' = Y_{24}$$
$$Y_{41}' = Y_{14}' \qquad Y_{42}' = Y_{42} \qquad Y_{44}' = Y_{44}$$

At this point we have progressed far enough to give a general method for finding each admittance which appears in the preceding equations. The admittance $\mathbf{Y}_{jk}$ multiplies $\mathbf{E}_k$, the voltage of node k, in the current equation obtained at the jth node. The value of $\mathbf{Y}_{jk}$ is as follows:

$$\mathbf{Y}_{jk} = \mathbf{Y}_{kj} = - \text{ [admittance of branch(es) connecting nodes } j \text{ and } k]$$
$$\mathbf{Y}_{jj} = \text{ sum of admittances of all branches terminating on node } j$$
$$(8\text{-}14)$$

In calculating these admittances, current sources are treated as open circuits and voltage sources as short circuits; that is, the two terminals on either side of a voltage source are considered to coincide.

SUMMARY Before analyzing a circuit by the node method, the circuit should usually be reduced as far as possible by a series-parallel combination of impedances, although this step is not necessary and may be omitted. If there are a total of n nodes and s_v voltage sources in the circuit, then $n - 1 - s_v$ node equations must be determined and then solved simultaneously in order to find the circuit response. Each node equation has the same general form; at node j, for example,

$$\sum_{k=1}^{n-1-s_v} \mathbf{Y}_{jk}\mathbf{E}_k = \mathbf{K}_j \qquad (8\text{-}15)$$

The values of the admittances $\mathbf{Y}_{jk}$ are given by Eqs. (8-14). The right-hand side of Eq. (8-15) may be determined as follows:

1. If no source is connected to node j and conditions 3 and 4 below do not hold, $\mathbf{K}_j = 0$.

2. If one or more current sources are connected to node j, $\mathbf{K}_j$ equals the sum of the currents from the current sources flowing *into* node j.

3. If node j is connected directly by an admittance $\mathbf{Y}_v$ to a node of known voltage $\mathbf{E}$, $\mathbf{K}_j = \mathbf{Y}_v\mathbf{E}$ (or a sum of terms such as this if node j is connected to more than one known node).

4. The last possibility for $\mathbf{K}_j$ arises when node j is connected either directly or through an admittance to a voltage source neither of whose terminals is at the reference node. In this case a general expression for $\mathbf{K}_j$ may be found (see Prob. 8-7), but it is advisable to use the method followed above in finding Eqs. (8-13).

A precautionary note is in order. The summary of node-equation determination outlined above could serve as a cookbook formula for writing node equations. It is hoped, however, that it will not be used for this purpose, since blind following of methods learned by rote usually produces unsatisfactory results. Only after the reader clearly understands how the formulations above were derived should he use them in writing node equations. The summary is included mainly to indicate that, by appropriate notation, the node equations of a complex network can be expressed in a concise and systematic form. The advantages of such a formulation lie in its ability to represent not only the particular network under investigation but all networks. Consequently, statements and techniques which are applicable to one network in terms of the general formulations above can be extended to all other networks.

SOLUTION OF A MECHANICAL PROBLEM BY NODE ANALYSIS Let us consider the mechanical system consisting of the two-wheeled trailer of Fig. 8-3a. The mass of the load and trailer body combined is connected by springs and shock absorbers to the mass of the axle and wheels, which in turn is connected through the compliance of the pneumatic tires to the ground. The masses are acted upon by the force of gravity, and irregularities in the ground apply a vertical velocity to the tires as the trailer is pulled along.

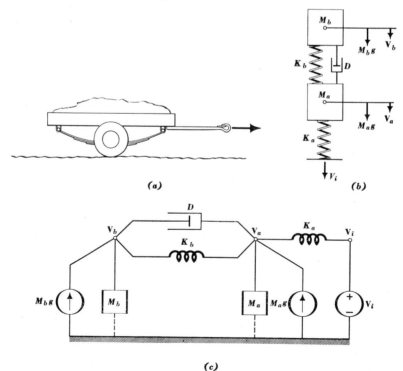

(a)   *(b)*

(c)

Fig. 8-3. *A two-wheeled trailer and the network diagram of its approximate linear model.*

The approximate mechanical network for the trailer is given in Fig. 8-3b, and a modified version of that network, more closely related in form to the analogous electrical circuit, is shown in Fig. 8-3c. Before analyzing this particular system, we should spend some time discussing the conventions used in the representation of Fig. 8-3c and the analogies to an equivalent electrical circuit. First, we see that the mechanical network consists of nodes and branches. The nodes represent regions of the system which have the same velocity, and the branches consist of the network elements connecting the nodes, either directly, as with springs and dashpots, or equivalently, as the masses are connected to the reference plane. The applied forces and velocities are represented by the same symbols as the analogous electrical sources—applied force by a current-source symbol and applied velocity by a voltage-source symbol.

Just as in electrical circuits, reference directions are very important, and unless the conventions governing them are clearly understood, errors are bound to occur. In this matter, electrical circuits may be considered one degree simpler than the mechanical systems we are analyzing, since the original assignment of negative charge to electrons in conjunction with the basic definition of voltage defines the meaning of positive current and voltage for all electrical circuits. In one-dimensional mechanical systems, on the other hand, it is first necessary to select a positive reference direction as a basis for defining positive and negative forces and velocities. In the mechanical system of Fig. 8-3, the positive reference direction has been chosen to be downward; hence it follows that velocities in the downward direction are positive and that forces acting on a node in the downward direction are positive. In order to strengthen the equivalence between the mechanical and electrical circuits, we shall represent a positive force by an arrow pointing toward the appropriate node. The convention used with the velocity source is that the positive side has a velocity V_i with respect to the negative side.

THE NODE EQUATIONS Let us now determine the appropriate node equations for the analysis of this two-wheeled trailer. Before setting up the node equations, however, we can simplify the system by applying the superposition theorem to find the system response to the two constant-force sources alone. In certain previous examples we chose to neglect such constant forces because they did not affect the system response in which we were interested. In the system under consideration here, the constant forces determine the range of applicability of our analysis and therefore cannot be neglected. Later on in this section, we shall see the significance of this statement.

The effect of the two constant forces is obviously the compression of the two springs, so that the reaction force in K_b is $M_b g$ and in K_a is

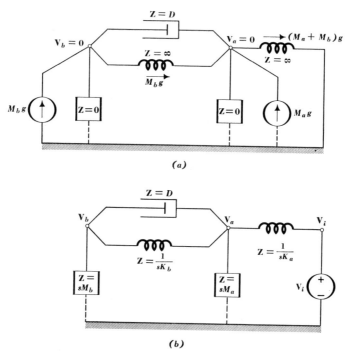

Fig. 8-4. *Approximate mechanical networks for the solution of response by superposition.*

$(M_a + M_b)g$. This result could be determined in a formal manner by calculating the various mechanical impedances of the elements in Fig. 8-3c. Since the driving functions (the force sources) are constants, $s = 0$, and hence the impedance of each spring is infinite.† Therefore, all the reaction force is developed across the springs, with the result stated above. This result is indicated graphically in Fig. 8-4a.

Now we turn to the task of determining the system response to the velocity source alone. In finding this response, we shall make use of Fig. 8-4b. We see that this system has four nodes: the reference, or ground-plane, node; the node corresponding to the connection between tire and velocity source; and the two nodes with unknown velocities V_a and V_b. It is clear that two node equations must be written, one for each unknown node velocity, in order to analyze this system.

Applying D'Alembert's principle at the V_a node is equivalent to applying Kirchhoff's law at an electrical circuit node. The statement that the sum of the reaction forces at a node is equal to the applied force is the same as saying that the sum of forces acting away from a

---

† Once again, we should realize that mechanical impedance is equivalent to electrical admittance when we make use of the mechanical-electrical analogies between force ↔ current and velocity ↔ voltage.

node (that is, negative forces) is zero. Thus, at the V_a node we obtain the following equation:

$$D(V_a - V_b) + \frac{V_a - V_b}{sK_b} + sM_aV_a + \frac{V_a - V_i}{sK_a} = 0 \qquad (8\text{-}16)$$

A similar equation can be obtained at the V_b node, and the terms of both equations can then be rearranged and properly grouped to yield the two simultaneous equations

$$\left(sM_a + D + \frac{K_a + K_b}{sK_aK_b}\right)V_a - \left(D + \frac{1}{sK_b}\right)V_b = \frac{V_i}{sK_a}$$

$$-\left(D + \frac{1}{sK_b}\right)V_a + \left(sM_b + D + \frac{1}{sK_b}\right)V_b = 0 \qquad (8\text{-}17)$$

THE TRANSFER FUNCTION Having expressed the two node equations necessary for the analysis of this system, we are now in a position to consider two aspects of the system response. One is the possibility that the trailer wheels will lose contact with the road surface, and the other is the velocity imparted to the trailer body and load by irregularities in the road. Examining the latter aspect involves the consideration of the transfer function V_b/V_i. Solving for this ratio by means of Eqs. (8-17) yields the following equation:

$$\frac{V_b}{V_i} = \frac{sDK_b + 1}{\begin{aligned}&s^4M_aM_bK_aK_b + s^3(M_a + M_b)DK_aK_b \\ &\quad + s^2[M_aK_a + M_b(K_a + K_b)] + sDK_b + 1\end{aligned}} \qquad (8\text{-}18)$$

Given any set of system parameters, this rather formidable expression will yield the desired transfer function V_b/V_i. However, for a general examination of this type of system, it is much more convenient to make use of the previously discussed method of expressing the transfer function in terms of system-parameter ratios. Thus, if we define the quantities

$$\alpha^2 \triangleq \frac{M_b}{M_a} \qquad \beta^2 \triangleq \frac{K_b}{K_a} \qquad D_0 \triangleq \sqrt{\frac{M_b}{K_b}}$$

$$\left.\begin{aligned}\omega_a &\triangleq \frac{1}{\sqrt{M_aK_a}} \\ \omega_b &\triangleq \frac{1}{\sqrt{M_bK_b}}\end{aligned}\right\} \qquad \frac{\omega_a}{\omega_b} = \alpha\beta \qquad (8\text{-}19)$$

we may write Eq. (8-18) as

$$\frac{V_b}{V_i} = \frac{(s/\omega_a)\alpha\beta(D/D_0) + 1}{\left(\dfrac{s}{\omega_a}\right)^4\alpha^2\beta^2 + \left(\dfrac{s}{\omega_a}\right)^3\alpha\beta\dfrac{D}{D_0}(1 + \alpha^2)}$$

$$+ \left(\frac{s}{\omega_a}\right)^2(1 + \alpha^2 + \alpha^2\beta^2) + \frac{s}{\omega_a}\alpha\beta\frac{D}{D_0} + 1 \qquad (8\text{-}20)$$

Equation (8-20) is still far from a simple expression, but it is now in a form which allows us to choose some typical or reasonable parameters and then determine the response as other parameters are varied. For example, suppose that the ratios α and β are set and we wish to determine the effect of varying the damping provided by the shock absorbers. To illustrate, let us assume that $\alpha^2 = 9$ and $\alpha^2\beta^2 = 25$. With these values prescribed, Eq. (8-20) becomes

$$\frac{\mathbf{V}_b}{\mathbf{V}_i} = \frac{(s/\omega_a)5(D/D_0) + 1}{(s/\omega_a)^4 25 + (s/\omega_a)^3 50(D/D_0) + (s/\omega_a)^2 35 + (s/\omega_a)5(D/D_0) + 1}$$

$$(8\text{-}21)$$

The loci of the poles and zero of the transfer function above are plotted in Fig. 8-5. As may be seen in the figure, the transfer function has two pairs of poles on the imaginary axis when there is no damping $(D/D_0 = 0)$. As the damping is increased, the poles move off the imaginary axis to the left, while the zero of the transfer function moves in along the negative real axis. As D/D_0 is further increased, the two outer poles come together on the negative real axis and then split, one moving toward 0 on the real axis and the other moving toward $-\infty$. The two inner poles curve back toward the imaginary axis,

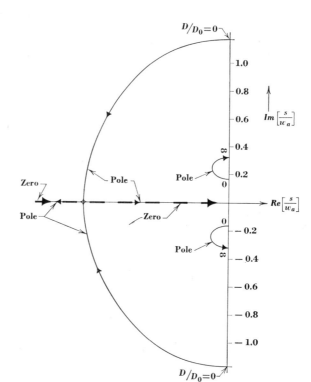

Fig. 8-5. The loci of the poles and zero of the transfer function of Eq. (8-21). The arrows indicate movement due to increasing D/D_0.

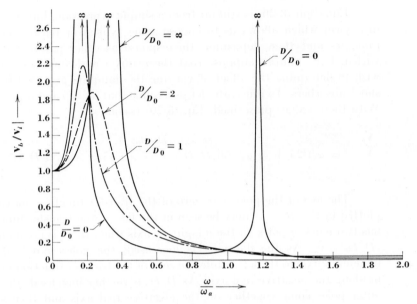

Fig. 8-6. The magnitude of the ratio V_b/V_i versus frequency.

reaching it when $D/D_0 \to \infty$. ($D/D_0 \to \infty$ corresponds to a rigid connection between the body and axle.) When $D/D_0 \to \infty$, the pole and zero moving in along the negative real axis coincide at $s = 0$ and cancel each other, while the pole moving out along the real axis reaches $-\infty$.

THE TRANSFER FUNCTION WHEN V_i IS SINUSOIDAL In Fig. 8-6 we have plotted the magnitude of the transfer function V_b/V_i versus ω/ω_a for four values of damping: $D/D_0 = 0$, $D/D_0 = 1$, $D/D_0 = 2$, $D/D_0 \to \infty$. This figure illustrates the fact that all curves (for any possible damping) have five points in common: at $\omega/\omega_a = 0$, where the magnitude is 1; at $\omega/\omega_a = 0.22$, where the magnitude is approximately 1.85; at $\omega/\omega_a = 1$, where the magnitude is approximately 0.11; at $\omega/\omega_a = 1.35$, where the magnitude is approximately 0.05; and finally at $\omega/\omega_a \to \infty$, where the transfer function goes to 0. Thus, with the values of α and β we have chosen, the maximum magnitude of the transfer function will always be at least 1.85 for one value of ω/ω_a.

Let us now take a moment to discuss ways in which the transfer function might be improved, that is, ways in which the maximum magnitude might be made less than 1.85. We see in Fig. 8-6 that the common points for all the curves occur at the crossings of the $D/D_0 = 0$ and $D/D_0 \to \infty$ curves. The first crossing occurs at a magnitude of 1.85, and it is this value which we wish to lower. It is clear that if the frequencies at which the two curves go to infinity are made farther apart, the magnitude at the crossover point will be lowered. This is equivalent to saying that the inner poles of Fig. 8-5 should move back to the imaginary axis at a point farther from where they started than they do at present. In view of the shape of the loci of the inner poles in Fig. 8-5, this last statement is synonymous with stating that the inner poles should move a greater distance to the left before returning to the imaginary axis.

It is apparent that the locations of the poles of the transfer function at the two extremes of damping are the controlling factors in this case. Let us examine the transfer function at these two extremes to see how we might influence the pole positions. With $D/D_0 = 0$,

$$\frac{V_i}{V_b} = \frac{1}{(s/\omega_a)^4 \alpha^2 \beta^2 + (s/\omega_a)^2 (1 + \alpha^2 + \alpha^2 \beta^2) + 1} \tag{8-22}$$

and with $D/D_0 \to \infty$,

$$\frac{V_i}{V_b} = \frac{1}{(s/\omega_a)^2 (1 + \alpha^2) + 1} \tag{8-23}$$

When $D/D_0 = 0$, the poles are at

$$\frac{s}{\omega_a} = \pm j \left\{ \frac{(1 + \alpha^2 + \alpha^2 \beta^2) \pm [(1 + \alpha^2 + \alpha^2 \beta^2)^2 - 4\alpha^2 \beta^2]^{\frac{1}{2}}}{2\alpha^2 \beta^2} \right\}^{\frac{1}{2}} \tag{8-24}$$

and when $D/D_0 \to \infty$, the poles are at

$$\frac{s}{\omega_a} = \pm j \sqrt{\frac{1}{1 + \alpha^2}} \tag{8-25}$$

The pole positions as given in Eq. (8-25) are seen to vary between zero and $\pm j$ as α^2 varies from infinity to zero. Equation (8-24) defines the positions of two pairs of poles on the imaginary axis. The inner ones vary in position from zero to $\pm j \sqrt{1/(1 + \alpha^2)}$ as β^2 is varied from infinity to zero, while the outer pair vary from $\pm j$ to infinity for the same variation in β^2. Thus we see that for a given α^2, increasing β^2 will increase the distance between the first infinity of the $D/D_0 = 0$ curve of Fig. 8-6 and the infinity of the $D/D_0 \to \infty$ curve. However, the increase in β^2 will at the same time decrease the distance between the second infinity of the $D/D_0 = 0$ curve and the infinity of the $D/D_0 \to \infty$ curve.

In our particular problem, a decrease in the low-frequency response at the expense of a small increase in the high-frequency response would certainly be worthwhile. Consequently, an increase in β^2 relative to α^2 is called for. Referring back to Eqs. (8-19), we see that a variation in α or β calls for a change in the ratio of trailer mass to axle mass or in the ratio of spring compliance to tire compliance.

The selection of optimum parameter values will depend upon a number of practical questions which we shall not discuss here. However, the practical problems of optimizing the system do not affect the basic techniques of analysis presented above.

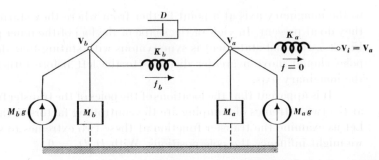

Fig. 8-7. *Approximate mechanical network for the solution of the response when the trailer has lost contact with the ground. The initial conditions consist of the force in K_b and the velocities of the masses, V_a and V_b, at the moment the wheels leave the ground.*

LIMITATIONS ON THE ABOVE ANALYSIS   As was mentioned earlier, we must consider the possibility that the trailer wheels will lose contact with the ground. In discussing the transfer function derived above, we more or less assumed that the velocity v_i could be determined from the ground contour and the forward velocity of the trailer without reference to the trailer itself. However, if the trailer wheels lose contact with the ground, then the velocity $v_i(t)$ is independent of the ground contour until contact is reestablished. When the wheels lose contact, the network diagram becomes that shown in Fig. 8-7, and the solution will involve the initial conditions of velocity and force existing at the moment contact is lost. The solution to this problem determines when contact is reestablished, together with the forces and velocities present at the moment of contact. The network reverts to that of Fig. 8-3c, and a new transient problem is established.

In order to determine whether ground contact is lost—and, if so, when—let us return our attention to Fig. 8-4 and Eqs. (8-17). Figure 8-4a indicates that the constant force developed in the tire compliance K_a is $(M_a + M_b)g$ in magnitude. The arrow direction away from node a indicates that the force is acting on node a in the negative direction. That is to say, the tires are in compression and, in the absence of other forces, would move node a in the upward, or negative, direction. The total force developed in K_a consists of this constant force plus a varying force determined by solving the network of Fig. 8-4b. If the direction of the total force ever becomes opposite to that indicated in Fig. 8-4a, the tires are in tension. But this is impossible unless the tire surfaces are attached to the ground. Thus we see that the moment at which the total force in K_a is zero, the trailer loses contact with the ground.

The force developed in K_a in a direction toward node a as a result of variations in the road is obtainable from the following equation:

$$F = (V_i - V_a)Z_{K_a} = \frac{V_i - V_a}{sK_a} \qquad (8\text{-}26)$$

Using Eqs. (8-17) to eliminate $\mathbf{V}_a$ in the equation above yields the following expression for $\mathbf{F}$:

$$\mathbf{F} = \frac{\mathbf{V}_i s[s^2 M_a M_b K_b + s(M_a + M_b)DK_b + (M_a + M_b)]}{s^4 M_a M_b K_a K_b + s^3(M_a + M_b)DK_a K_b} \\ + s^2[M_a K_a + M_b(K_a + K_b)] + sDK_b + 1 \quad (8\text{-}27)$$

Using the definitions of Eqs. (8-19), we can modify Eq. (8-27) to yield

$$\mathbf{F} = \mathbf{V}_i \frac{\dfrac{\beta}{\alpha} D_0 \dfrac{s}{\omega_a}\left[\left(\dfrac{s}{\omega_a}\right)^2 \alpha^2\beta^2 + \dfrac{s}{\omega_a}\,\alpha\beta\,\dfrac{D}{D_0}\,(1 + \alpha^2) + (1 + \alpha^2)\right]}{\left(\dfrac{s}{\omega_a}\right)^4 \alpha^2\beta^2 + \left(\dfrac{s}{\omega_a}\right)^3 \alpha\beta\,\dfrac{D}{D_0}\,(1 + \alpha^2)}$$

$$+ \left(\frac{s}{\omega_a}\right)^2 (1 + \alpha^2 + \alpha^2\beta^2) + \frac{s}{\omega_a}\,\alpha\beta\,\frac{D}{D_0} + 1 \quad (8\text{-}28)$$

This equation could, of course, be used to find the $f(t)$ resulting from any applied $v_i(t)$. (The computations could become quite tedious!) As previously noted, the trailer wheels remain in contact with the ground, and Eq. (8-28) is valid only so long as $f(t)$ remains positive. [Do not forget that $f(t)$ here must include the gravity term $(M_a + M_b)g$.]

The case of the sinusoidal steady state is of particular interest. Under what conditions will the trailer remain in continuous contact with a sinusoidally undulating road surface, and under what conditions will it hop along from bump to bump in a very jarring manner? If we assume continuous contact, the applied velocity will be sinusoidal with a maximum amplitude of, say, $V_{\max}$ (proportional to the speed with which the trailer is pulled). Making the substitution $s = j\omega$ in Eq. (8-28) (where ω is the radian frequency of the applied velocity, also proportional to the hauling speed) allows the computation of $F_{\max}$. The condition $F_{\max} = (M_a + M_b)g$ is the limiting condition for the assumption of continuous contact to be valid.

CONCLUDING COMMENTS ON THE NODE METHOD   Any linear electrical or mechanical network can be solved by obtaining an equation at each independent unknown node through the application of Kirchhoff's current law or D'Alembert's principle. A set of simultaneous equations will be formed which may be solved to find the unknown node voltages or velocities. The node equations may be written in any one of three forms: as integrodifferential equations; as equations involving impedances, admittances, and driving functions as functions of s; or, in the case of sinusoidal excitation, as equations containing complex impedances, admittances, and driving functions as functions of ω. Once the simultaneous equations are solved, the further analysis of the circuit proceeds in the same manner as has been discussed in earlier chapters.

PROBLEMS

8-1   Redraw the mechanical system of Fig. 8-1a in network form (refer to Fig. 8-3) so that its equivalence to the electrical system of Fig. 8-1b is more clearly shown. Draw the graph of the network for this system. Write the node equations necessary for solving the network, in both differential-equation form and impedance form.

8-2   Write the node equations for the circuit of Fig. 8-1b in both differential-equation form and impedance form.

8-3   For the circuit of Fig. 8-1b, find the voltage across R for the following conditions:

(a) $i(t) = \sin 1,000t$ amp

$L_1 = 10^{-3}$ henry

$L_2 = 2 \times 10^{-3}$ henry

$C_1 = 10^{-3}$ farad

$C_2 = 5 \times 10^{-4}$ farad

$R = 1$ ohm

(c) $i(t) = \begin{cases} 0 & \text{for } t < 0 \\ 10t \text{ amp} & \text{for } t > 0 \end{cases}$

$L_1 = 1$ henry

$L_2 = 2$ henrys

$C_1 = C_2 = 1$ farad

$R = 1$ ohm

(b) $i(t) = 0.01 \sin 5 \times 10^6 t$ amp

$L_1 = L_2 = 10^{-3}$ henry

$C_1 = 100$ $\mu\mu$f

$C_2 = 50$ $\mu\mu$f

$R = 1,000$ ohms

8-4   For the mechanical system of Fig. 8-1a, find the velocity of the mass M_1 under the following conditions:

(a) $f(t) = 100 \sin 10t$ newtons

$M_1 = 10$ kg

$M_2 = 20$ kg

$K_1 = 10^{-3}$ m/newton

$K_2 = 5 \times 10^{-3}$ m/newton

$D = 30$ kg/sec

(b) $f(t) = \begin{cases} 0 & \text{for } t < 0 \\ 10(1 - e^{-100t}) \text{ newtons} & \text{for } t > 0 \end{cases}$

$M_1 = 0.1$ kg

$M_2 = 0.5$ kg

$K_1 = 4 \times 10^{-3}$ m/newton

$K_2 = 2 \times 10^{-3}$ m/newton

$D = 1$ kg/sec

8-5   Draw the graph of the circuit shown in Fig. 8-1d. If the source shown is a current source, how many node equations are necessary to solve for the circuit response?

8-6   The circuits shown in the drawing are parts of more extensive networks. Write the node equation for node 1 for each of the circuits. Network element values are in henrys, farads, ohms, kilograms, meters per newton, and kilograms per second. The reference node in each circuit is numbered 0.

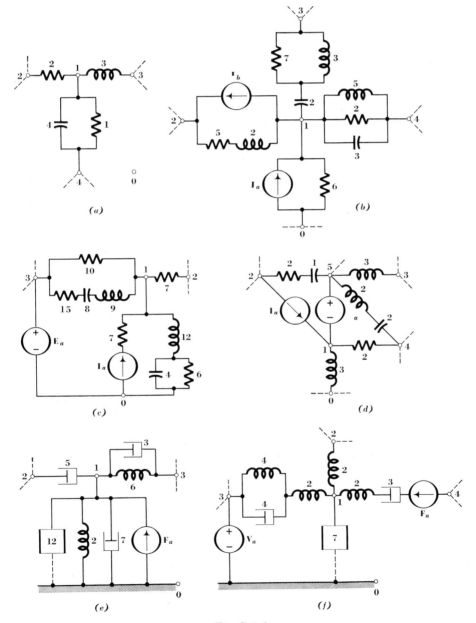

Fig. P 8-6

8-7　　In the discussion following Eq. (8-15), the value of K_j was expressed for a number of different possibilities. Complete this discussion by finding the general form of K_j when node j is connected to a voltage source with neither of its terminals at the reference node.

8-8　　As an alternative method of handling voltage sources in setting up node equations, consider the accompanying figure. Prove to your satisfaction that the three circuits are equivalent as far as solving for the node voltages E_1, E_2, E_3, E_4, and E_5 is concerned. It should be clear that this technique may be extended to any circuit containing voltage sources.

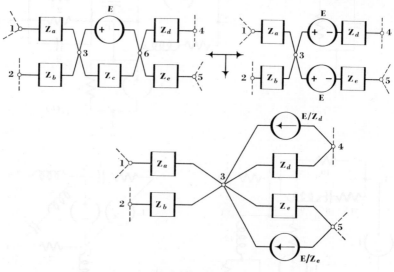

Fig. P 8-8

8-9　　Suppose that the trailer of Fig. 8-3 has the following characteristics. The weight of the body and the load it is carrying is 500 kg, and the weight of the axle and wheels is 80 kg. The compliance of the two springs combined is 50×10^{-6} m/newton, and the compliance of the two tires combined is 10×10^{-6} m/newton. The damping factor of the shock absorbers is $D/D_0 = 2$. The trailer is being pulled at a constant velocity over a road with a sinusoidal surface. The distance between troughs in this surface is 8 m, and the height from trough to peak is h m.

　　(a) Find the magnitude of the peak-to-trough swing of the trailer body at velocities of 10, 30, 60, and 80 km/hr.

　　(b) Find the value of h for each of these speeds at which the wheels begin to lose contact with the road.

8-10　　Repeat Prob. 8-9 for the case of an unloaded trailer with a body weight of 80 kg.

8-11   Consider the operation of the valves in an automobile engine. A push rod or rocker arm acts like a velocity source connected to the mass of the valve. The valve spring furnishes the restoring force, since the rod can push but not pull. Assume that the displacement of the valve is the same as a half-wave rectified sine wave. Draw the circuit diagram of the system. Discuss how you would analyze the problem of the valves' "floating" at high speed (the valves overshoot and fail to follow the push rods back down). How could this problem be alleviated? Assume some typical parameters for a modern engine and calculate the spring compliance necessary for satisfactory operation at high speed.

8-12   For the transfer function of Eq. (8-20), assume that $\alpha = 3$ and $D/D_0 = 2$. Find the value of β which yields the minimum value of the maximum of $|\mathbf{V}_b/\mathbf{V}_i|_{s=j\omega}$. Plot the magnitude of this transfer function vs. frequency using the value of β which you have found.

8-2   LOOP ANALYSIS

We have used Kirchhoff's current law to analyze an electrical circuit by the node method, and we have seen that a mechanical network can be analyzed in an analogous manner. Now it is logical to assume that Kirchhoff's voltage law could be utilized in a similar manner to obtain a set of equations which would lead to the circuit solution. The manner in which Kirchhoff's voltage law does enable us to analyze a circuit is the subject matter of this section.

BRANCH CURRENTS AND KIRCHHOFF'S VOLTAGE LAW   To develop this method of analysis, we shall use again the circuit shown in Fig. 8-1c. The graph of that circuit which was given in Fig. 8-2a is redrawn in Fig. 8-8a, with the branches numbered rather than the nodes. The branches have also been assigned arbitrary reference directions, as is illustrated in the figure.

The current flowing in each branch may be assigned the number and direction of the branch in which it occurs. Thus, in branch 1 we have a current i_1' whose positive direction is from left to right. That is, if we find, after having solved the circuit, that at a particular time the current i_1' is positive, then we know that it is actually flowing from left to right. At some other time the current may be negative, which means that it is flowing from right to left, in the negative direction.

The circuit under consideration has eight branches and thus eight branch currents: i_1', i_2', i_3', . . . , i_8'. If all eight branch currents are known, then the voltages at all points in the circuit may be immediately computed and thus the circuit response completely determined. The problem, therefore, is to determine the eight unknown branch currents. We might immediately apply Kirchhoff's voltage law, which is

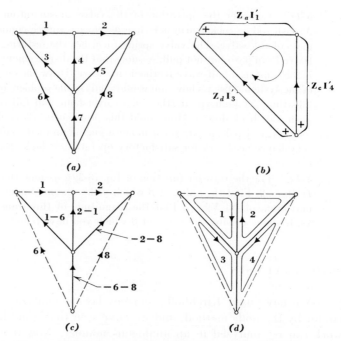

Fig. 8-8. (a) The graph of the circuit of Fig. 8-1c; (b) the loop consisting of branches 1, 3, and 4 showing the appropriate branch voltage drops; (c) one possible arrangement of independent and dependent branch currents; (d) a set of independent loop currents corresponding to the independent branch currents in part c.

stated as follows: *The sum of the voltage drops around a closed loop is zero.*† To state this law in a little more detail, we may say that if one starts at a particular node and goes along the branches from node to node, eventually returning to the original node, then the sum made up of the voltage drops across all branches traversed is zero. This is, of course, an algebraic sum, which means that the sign of each term in the sum must be taken into account. If the voltage decreases in traversing a branch, then the voltage drop is positive. If, on the other hand, the voltage increases across a branch in the direction of travel, then the voltage drop is negative.

In our circuit, the voltage across each branch may be expressed in terms of the eight unknown branch currents and the circuit impedances. Therefore, we may obtain a set of simultaneous equations by summing the voltage drops around a number of closed paths. To illustrate this, let us obtain one equation by summing the voltage drops around the loop consisting of branches 1, 3, and 4. We have arbi-

---

† Two alternative statements of this law are as follows: (1) The sum of the voltage rises around a closed loop is zero; (2) the sum of the voltage drops around a loop is equal to the sum of the applied voltages.

trarily chosen to proceed around the loop in a clockwise direction, as is illustrated in Fig. 8-8*b*. The sum of the voltage drops around this particular loop is

$$\mathbf{Z}_a\mathbf{I}_1' - \mathbf{Z}_c\mathbf{I}_4' + \mathbf{Z}_d\mathbf{I}_3' = 0 \qquad (8\text{-}29)$$

The negative sign occurs in the second term above because the reference direction of i_4' is opposite to the direction in which we are traversing branch 4. Hence i_4' produces a voltage rise (or negative voltage drop) in our summing direction.

DEPENDENCE OF BRANCH CURRENTS If we continued to form different loop equations by choosing different closed paths to sum around, we should soon have a set of equations which contained all the unknown branch currents. The number of equations, however, would be insufficient to solve for our eight unknowns. Furthermore, if we attempted to obtain more equations by choosing additional loops, we should find that the equations would not be independent; that is, they would consist of sums and differences of the equations already obtained. Since it is necessary to have eight independent simultaneous equations to solve for the eight branch currents, utilization of loop equations alone is not sufficient to analyze the circuit.

Further consideration of the branch currents and the circuit graph of Fig. 8-8*a* presents both the reason for and the solution of this impasse. We can see immediately that the branch currents are not independent; that is, a portion of the branch currents may be expressed as sums and differences of the others by applying Kirchhoff's current law at the various nodes.† Since the eight branch currents are not independent, it is impossible to obtain eight independent loop equations. However, by applying Kirchhoff's current law at all of the nodes except one, it would be possible to obtain sufficient additional independent equations to form a set of eight independent simultaneous equations.

TREES, LINKS, AND LOOP CURRENTS Rather than solve this circuit by setting up the eight equations, let us now consider a method by which we can solve the circuit by using loop equations alone. To do this, we must first express the eight dependent branch currents in terms of a set of independent currents. In order to see how this can be done, let us turn our attention to Fig. 8-8*a* again.

As was pointed out above, we can obtain a set of equations relating the branch currents to one another. After a certain amount of

---

† It may be of interest to compare this situation with that arising in node analysis. The unknown node voltages are independent. Even if all except one of the node voltages are known, a node equation must be written in order to find the last unknown voltage. This node equation will depend upon the impedances and not just upon the other node voltages.

manipulation of these equations, we would find that there is a minimum number of branch currents in terms of which all the other branch currents can be expressed. In other words, some of the branch currents can be considered independent, and the others will then be dependent upon them. To see how many independent and how many dependent branch currents we have, let us perform a small experiment on the graph of Fig. 8-8a.

If we decided to remove certain branches in an attempt to stop all current from flowing in the circuit, we would find that we would have to remove a minimum number to accomplish this. For example, removing branches 1, 2, 6, and 8 would stop all current flow. Or we could remove branches 3, 4, 5, and 6, or branches 1, 4, 7, and 8. Other combinations are possible, but in all cases at least four branches must be removed to stop all current flow. By making four branch currents zero, all other branch currents become zero.† Therefore we can say that the branch currents corresponding to the removed branches are a set of independent currents and that the remaining currents are the dependent currents.

To illustrate this last statement we may express i_3', i_4', i_5', and i_7' in terms of i_1', i_2', i_6', and i_8' by applying Kirchhoff's current law at four nodes (refer to Fig. 8-8c):

$$i_3' = i_1' - i_6' \qquad i_4' = i_2' - i_1' \qquad i_5' = -i_2' - i_8' \qquad i_7' = -i_6' - i_8' \qquad (8\text{-}30)$$

Examination of Fig. 8-8c discloses a viewpoint of considerable importance. The branch currents can be considered as a superposition of *loop currents*, each one of which is equal to one of the independent branch currents. In Fig. 8-8d we have illustrated four loop currents: i_1, i_2, i_3, and i_4, each of which may be considered to be flowing around in a loop independently of the others. We see immediately that the following equalities must hold:

$$i_1 = i_1' \qquad i_2 = i_2' \qquad i_3 = i_6' \qquad i_4 = i_8' \qquad (8\text{-}31)$$

Similarly, the dependent branch currents may be expressed in terms of the loop currents:

$$i_3' = i_1 - i_3 \qquad i_4' = i_1 - i_2 \qquad i_5' = -i_2 - i_4 \qquad i_7' = -i_3 - i_4 \qquad (8\text{-}32)$$

Equations (8-32) can be derived either by a comparison of Figs. 8-8a and 8-8d or by substituting Eqs. (8-31) into Eqs. (8-30).

The foregoing discussion has illustrated that we may express all the branch currents in a circuit in terms of a set of independent loop currents. We may then proceed to determine a set of independent loop equations containing these loop currents and equaling them in number.

† It should be noted that removal of just any four branches is not sufficient. The four must be carefully selected. For example, removal of branches 3, 4, 5, and 7 would not stop all current flow.

The simultaneous solution of these equations will then yield the circuit response. Before discussing further the determination of the loop equations, we must examine in more detail the selection of an appropriate set of loop currents.

It is clear that we must have as many loop currents as there are independent branch currents. We can determine the number of independent branch currents by seeing how many branches must be removed to stop all current flow. Let us call these removed branches the *links* and the current flowing in them the *link currents*. Without the links, the remaining circuit graph contains no closed loops and is treelike in structure. Therefore, we may consider the graph to have two parts, the *links* and the *tree*. In general, the links and the tree of a circuit are not unique. That is, each circuit will have many possible sets of links and corresponding trees. However, the number of links, which is, of course, equal to the number of independent currents, is the same for any particular circuit no matter how they are chosen.†

The number of links in any circuit is quite easy to determine. The tree consists of branches connecting all the nodes but forming no closed loops. If the circuit contains n nodes, then the tree must contain $n - 1$ branches. Therefore a circuit with a total of b branches will contain the following number of links:

$$l = b - n + 1 \tag{8-33}$$

Equation (8-33) could also be interpreted as expressing the number of independent branch currents or the number of loop currents.

In the circuit under consideration, we chose the loop currents in such a way that they could be regarded as link currents flowing in closed loops through the tree. Thus each link had only one loop current flowing through it. This procedure will always produce the correct number of independent loop currents. There is, however, another method of choosing a set of independent loop currents which may be used in seeking a circuit solution. If the loop currents are chosen consecutively in such a way that each loop current flows through at least one branch untouched by previously chosen loop currents, then they will form an independent set. Of course, with this method care must be taken to see that the number of loop currents equals the number given by Eq. (8-33). Figure 8-9 illustrates two possible sets of independent loop currents for our circuit which were determined by this method.

DETERMINATION OF THE LOOP EQUATIONS   Having chosen a set of loop currents in terms of which all the branch currents can be expressed, we

---

† We are assuming that the selection is made by removing the minimum number of branches necessary to stop all current flow.

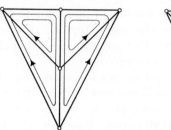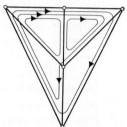

Fig. 8-9. The graph of the circuit of Fig. 8-1c showing two different sets of independent loop currents.

are left with the task of solving for them. To do this, we apply Kirchhoff's voltage law around as many loops as there are unknown loop currents. Each application yields an equation, and the set of equations so derived are solved simultaneously.

In applying Kirchhoff's voltage law, it is best to let the voltage-summation loops coincide with the paths followed by the loop currents. This procedure, although the simplest, is not the only way of choosing voltage-summation loops. For example, it would be correct to use the loop currents of one of the graphs in Fig. 8-9 while summing around the loops indicated in the other graph. The essential point is to see that the paths chosen yield a set of independent equations. Henceforth, we shall always sum around the paths followed by the loop currents.

Let us now determine the loop equations for the circuit of Fig. 8-1c using the loop currents shown in Fig. 8-8d. This circuit has been redrawn in Fig. 8-10 with the loop currents included. The loop equations are found in the manner discussed above [refer to Fig. 8-8b and Eq. (8-29)], the only variation being that the voltage drops across the branches are now due to a superposition of loop currents instead of to a single branch current. Thus, for the first loop, the summation of voltage drops yields the following equation:

$$\mathbf{Z}_a\mathbf{I}_1 + \mathbf{Z}_c(\mathbf{I}_1 - \mathbf{I}_2) + \mathbf{Z}_d(\mathbf{I}_1 - \mathbf{I}_3) = (\mathbf{Z}_a + \mathbf{Z}_c + \mathbf{Z}_d)\mathbf{I}_1 - \mathbf{Z}_c\mathbf{I}_2 - \mathbf{Z}_d\mathbf{I}_3$$
$$= \mathbf{Z}_{11}\mathbf{I}_1 + \mathbf{Z}_{12}\mathbf{I}_2 + \mathbf{Z}_{13}\mathbf{I}_3 = 0$$

$$(8\text{-}34)$$

Fig. 8-10. A circuit showing a set of loop currents applicable for solving the circuit by the loop method. The source could be either the voltage source or the current source shown to the right of the circuit.

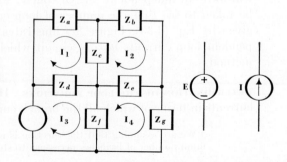

The loop equation for the second loop is

$$-\mathbf{Z}_c\mathbf{I}_1 + (\mathbf{Z}_b + \mathbf{Z}_c + \mathbf{Z}_e)\mathbf{I}_2 + \mathbf{Z}_e\mathbf{I}_4 = \mathbf{Z}_{21}\mathbf{I}_1 + \mathbf{Z}_{22}\mathbf{I}_2 + \mathbf{Z}_{24}\mathbf{I}_4 = 0 \tag{8-35}$$

The third loop contains a source in branch 6. If the source is a *voltage source*, as shown in Fig. 8-10, then the voltage drop in branch 6 in the summing direction is $-\mathbf{E}$. Therefore, the loop equation for the third loop is

$$-\mathbf{Z}_d\mathbf{I}_1 + (\mathbf{Z}_d + \mathbf{Z}_f)\mathbf{I}_3 + \mathbf{Z}_f\mathbf{I}_4 - \mathbf{E} = 0$$
$$\mathbf{Z}_{31}\mathbf{I}_1 + \mathbf{Z}_{33}\mathbf{I}_3 + \mathbf{Z}_{34}\mathbf{I}_4 = \mathbf{E} \tag{8-36}$$

The fourth and final loop equation is

$$\mathbf{Z}_e\mathbf{I}_2 + \mathbf{Z}_f\mathbf{I}_3 + (\mathbf{Z}_e + \mathbf{Z}_f + \mathbf{Z}_g)\mathbf{I}_4 = \mathbf{Z}_{42}\mathbf{I}_2 + \mathbf{Z}_{43}\mathbf{I}_3 + \mathbf{Z}_{44}\mathbf{I}_4 = 0 \tag{8-37}$$

The four loop equations form this set of simultaneous equations:

$$\begin{aligned}
\mathbf{Z}_{11}\mathbf{I}_1 + \mathbf{Z}_{12}\mathbf{I}_2 + \mathbf{Z}_{13}\mathbf{I}_3 \qquad\qquad &= 0 \\
\mathbf{Z}_{21}\mathbf{I}_1 + \mathbf{Z}_{22}\mathbf{I}_2 \qquad\qquad + \mathbf{Z}_{24}\mathbf{I}_4 &= 0 \\
\mathbf{Z}_{31}\mathbf{I}_1 \qquad\qquad + \mathbf{Z}_{33}\mathbf{I}_3 + \mathbf{Z}_{34}\mathbf{I}_4 &= \mathbf{E} \\
\mathbf{Z}_{42}\mathbf{I}_2 + \mathbf{Z}_{43}\mathbf{I}_3 + \mathbf{Z}_{44}\mathbf{I}_4 &= 0
\end{aligned} \tag{8-38}$$

If the third loop contains the *current source* rather than the voltage source, one less loop equation is needed.[†] Loop current $\mathbf{I}_3$ is seen to be identical with source current $\mathbf{I}$. Hence

$$\mathbf{I}_3 = \mathbf{I} \tag{8-39}$$

Using just the equations for loops 1, 2, and 4 and utilizing Eq. (8-39), we see that the simultaneous equations necessary to solve the circuit are

$$\begin{aligned}
\mathbf{Z}_{11}\mathbf{I}_1 + \mathbf{Z}_{12}\mathbf{I}_2 \qquad\qquad &= \mathbf{Z}_d\mathbf{I} \\
\mathbf{Z}_{21}\mathbf{I}_1 + \mathbf{Z}_{22}\mathbf{I}_2 + \mathbf{Z}_{24}\mathbf{I}_4 &= 0 \\
\mathbf{Z}_{42}\mathbf{I}_2 + \mathbf{Z}_{44}\mathbf{I}_4 &= -\mathbf{Z}_f\mathbf{I}
\end{aligned} \tag{8-40}$$

SUMMARY   In the analysis of a circuit by the loop method, it is first necessary to select a set of independent loop currents equal in number to the number of independent branch currents. Equation (8-33) constitutes a formula for determining this number. Two methods of selection are applicable. The first is to choose a tree and a set of links for the circuit and then let the loop currents correspond to the link currents flowing in a loop through the tree. The other method is to select the loop currents consecutively, so that each loop contains at least one branch which is not a part of any previously chosen loop. The latter method leads to a simpler arrangement of loop currents on a large

---

† Refer to Sec. 9-2 for a discussion of the exchange of sources.

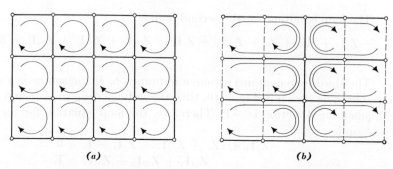

Fig. 8-11. *The graph of a circuit with loop currents found (a) by consecutive selection of loops with at least one new branch and (b) by selection of a tree and links (shown by dashed lines), with loop currents corresponding to link currents.*

mesh, or net, type of circuit than does the former method. This is illustrated in Fig. 8-11.

If there are current sources in the circuit, it is advantageous to let the branches containing the current sources be links. In this way each current source corresponds to one loop current, and the number of unknown loop currents is reduced by the number of current sources. This, of course, reduces the number of required loop equations by the same amount.

When the loop currents have been selected, a corresponding set of loop equations is obtained by summing the voltage drops around each unknown loop current path. Each loop equation will have the same general form; for example, for loop j,

$$\sum_{k=1}^{b-n+1-s_c} \mathbf{Z}_{jk}\mathbf{I}_k = \mathbf{K}_j \qquad (8\text{-}41)$$

where b = number of branches

n = number of nodes

s_c = number of current sources

$\mathbf{Z}_{jj}$ = sum of all impedances in loop j

$\mathbf{Z}_{jk} = \mathbf{Z}_{kj}$† = sum of all impedances common to both loop j and loop k (algebraic sign of $\mathbf{Z}_{jk}$ is positive if both $\qquad$ (8-42) loop currents are in same direction through $\mathbf{Z}_{jk}$ and is negative otherwise)

The term on the right-hand side of Eq. (8-41) is zero if loop j contains no voltage sources and shares no part of its path in common with a current-source loop current. Otherwise $\mathbf{K}_j$ is a summation of voltages due to voltage sources and voltage drops in common impedances due to current-source loop currents.

† The symmetrical relationship holds only if the voltage-summation paths coincide with the loop currents.

For any particular circuit, the choice of the method of analysis—either node or loop—will in general be decided in favor of the method giving fewer simultaneous equations. The number of equations to be solved by each method is as follows:

$$\text{Node equations} = n - 1 - s_v$$
$$\text{Loop equations} = b - n + 1 - s_c \qquad (8\text{-}43)$$

LOOP ANALYSIS APPLIED TO MECHANICAL SYSTEMS The methods discussed in this section may be applied to mechanical systems as well as to electrical ones. The concept of loop forces may be somewhat unsatisfying, but their usefulness in finding the network response makes them more palatable. The methods of determining a set of loop equations for a mechanical network is exactly the same as for an electrical circuit. That is, a set of independent loop forces are determined, and then the velocity drops around each loop are summed, each summation yielding a loop equation.

Loop analysis is applied infrequently to mechanical systems because the node method usually yields fewer simultaneous equations. The reason for this is that all masses are referred to "ground"; hence mechanical systems generally have more independent loops than nodes.

ANALYSIS OF A BRIDGED-T ELECTRICAL NETWORK Figure 8-12 illustrates a member of a class of circuits called *bridged*-T networks. We shall analyze this particular circuit to illustrate the loop method of analysis and to demonstrate some interesting properties of this particular circuit. Summing the voltage drops around the three loops shown yields the following set of loop equations:

$$\left(R_1 + \frac{1}{Cs}\right)\mathbf{I}_1 - R_1\mathbf{I}_2 - \frac{1}{Cs}\mathbf{I}_3 = \mathbf{E}_1$$

$$-R_1\mathbf{I}_1 + \left(R_1 + R_2 + \frac{1}{Cs}\right)\mathbf{I}_2 - \frac{1}{Cs}\mathbf{I}_3 = 0 \qquad (8\text{-}44)$$

$$-\frac{1}{Cs}\mathbf{I}_1 - \frac{1}{Cs}\mathbf{I}_2 + \left(Ls + R_L + \frac{2}{Cs}\right)\mathbf{I}_3 = 0$$

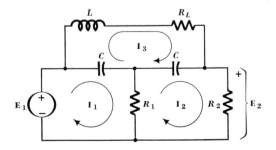

Fig. 8-12. A bridged-T electrical network.

If we wish to determine the voltage $\mathbf{E}_2$, we must solve the three equations above for $\mathbf{I}_2$. When this is accomplished, $\mathbf{I}_2$ is multiplied by R_2 to yield $\mathbf{E}_2$. The ratio of $\mathbf{E}_2$ to $\mathbf{E}_1$ is the following transfer function:

$$
\frac{\mathbf{E}_2}{\mathbf{E}_1} = \frac{R_2(R_1LC^2s^3 + R_1R_LC^2s^2 + 2R_1Cs + 1)}{\begin{array}{c} R_1R_2LC^2s^3 + (R_1R_2R_LC^2 + 2R_1LC + R_2LC)s^2 \\ + (2R_1R_2C + 2R_1R_LC + R_2R_LC + L)s + (R_2 + R_L) \end{array}}
$$

$$
= \frac{s^3 + (R_L/L)s^2 + (2/LC)s + 1/R_1LC^2}{s^3 + \left(\dfrac{R_L}{L} + \dfrac{2}{R_2C} + \dfrac{1}{R_1C}\right)s^2 \\ \quad + \left(\dfrac{2}{LC} + \dfrac{2R_L}{R_2LC} + \dfrac{RL}{R_1LC} + \dfrac{1}{R_1R_2C^2}\right)s + \dfrac{R_2 + R_L}{R_1R_2LC^2}} \tag{8-45}
$$

In Eq. (8-45) we are once again faced with an annoyingly complex expression. However, we may immediately note some facts pertaining to the poles and zeros of the transfer function, and the poles and zeros, of course, essentially determine the characteristics of a transfer function. Both the numerator and denominator of the transfer function are third-degree polynomials in s. Thus, the function has three poles and three zeros. Because of the resistors in the circuit, the poles of the transfer function will lie to the left of the imaginary axis in the s plane. This fact may be ascertained from a physical argument. In the previous chapter we saw that the positions of the poles of the transfer function determine its impulse response. Poles on the imaginary axis produce an impulse response which does not decay with time. In this circuit, the resistors must eventually dissipate all the energy supplied by the original impulse, so the poles must lie to the left of the imaginary axis.

No such argument may be applied to the numerator of the transfer function, and this results in an interesting possibility for the response of the circuit. Suppose that it was possible for a pair of zeros to lie on the imaginary axis. This would mean that at some real frequency no voltage would be produced across R_2 regardless of the magnitude of $\mathbf{E}_1$. That this would be a useful characteristic we shall soon see. To determine whether the numerator can have imaginary-axis zeros, let us consider a third-degree polynomial with zeros on the imaginary axis at $s = \pm j\beta$ and a third zero at $s = -\alpha$.

$$
(s + \alpha)(s + j\beta)(s - j\beta) = (s + \alpha)(s^2 + \beta^2) = s^3 + \alpha s^2 + \beta^2 s + \alpha\beta^2 \tag{8-46}
$$

Thus, a general third-degree polynomial

$$
s^3 + a_2s^2 + a_1s + a_0
$$

will have imaginary-axis zeros at $s = \pm j\sqrt{a_1}$ if $a_1a_2 = a_0$. Applying this last statement to the numerator of the transfer function tells us that at a frequency

$$\omega = \sqrt{\frac{2}{LC}} \tag{8-47}$$

$\mathbf{E}_2/\mathbf{E}_1$ will be zero if

$$\frac{2R_L}{L^2C} = \frac{1}{R_1LC^2} \tag{8-48}$$

Equation (8-48) can be rewritten as

$$\frac{2R_L}{L} = \frac{1}{R_1C} \tag{8-49}$$

and thus we see that, for a particular L, R_L, and ω, we can adjust C and R_1 to obtain zero output.

It is now apparent that this circuit can be used to measure inductance and its associated resistance. If R_2 is replaced by a sensitive ammeter, so that a null reading can be accurately detected, and $\mathbf{E}_1$ is a sinusoidal voltage source whose frequency ω is precisely known, then by adjusting C and R_1 for a null reading on the ammeter, the inductance and its resistance can be calculated by the following expressions:

$$\begin{aligned} L &= \frac{2}{\omega^2 C} \\ R_L &= \frac{1}{\omega^2 C^2 R_1} \end{aligned} \tag{8-50}$$

The Q of the coil is given by the following expression:

$$Q = \frac{\omega L}{R_L} = 2\omega CR_1 \tag{8-51}$$

Thus, for a particular frequency ω, the variable capacitor could be calibrated in terms of inductance values, and the variable resistance could be calibrated in terms of a factor which, multiplied by a reading of the capacitor, would yield the Q of the coil.

PROBLEMS

8-13 How many loop equations are necessary to find the response of the circuits of Fig. 8-1a, b, and d? Assume that the source in (d) is a voltage source.

8-14 The circuit shown in part a of the figure can be reduced to a circuit with the graph of part b by series-parallel combination. Find the loop impedances $\mathbf{Z}_{11}$, $\mathbf{Z}_{12}$, . . . , $\mathbf{Z}_{33}$ corresponding to the loop currents shown in part b.

8-15 The graphs of a number of electrical and mechanical circuits are shown in the figure. You may assume that the graph is for the passive

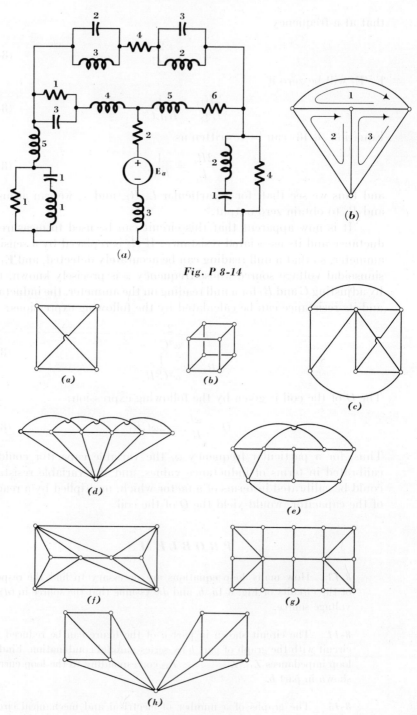

Fig. P 8-14

Fig. P 8-15

circuit elements only and that the energy is to be provided by connecting current or force sources between two nodes or by breaking a branch and inserting a voltage or velocity source. This procedure can be carried out with any number of sources without affecting the number of node or loop equations. For each graph indicate the number of node and loop equations needed to solve the circuits. Indicate your choice of loop currents in each case.

8-16   A different means of handling voltage sources in node equations was pointed out in Prob. 8-8. An analogous technique is used in the loop analysis of circuits which contain current sources. Satisfy yourself that the equivalence indicated in the figure is valid for the circuit shown and may be extended to any circuit containing current sources.

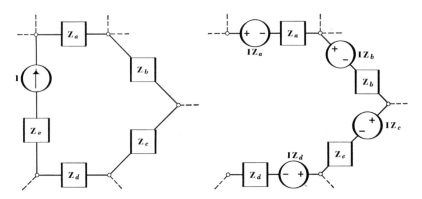

Fig. P 8-16

8-17   The bridged-T circuit of Fig. 8-12 is to be used to measure coils whose inductances range from 0.1 henry to 0.01 mh and whose Q's at a frequency of 10,000 cps range from 5 to 500. If E_1 is operating at a frequency of 10,000 cps, over what ranges must C and R_1 vary?

8-18   In Prob. 8-17, what would be the percentage error in the measured values of L and Q if a 1 per cent error occurred in the calibration of C, in the calibration of R_1, or in the frequency of E_1? What would it be if all three errors occurred simultaneously?

8-19   The circuit shown is called a twin-T or parallel-T circuit. It has properties similar to those of a bridged-T circuit. Determine the transfer

Fig. P 8-19

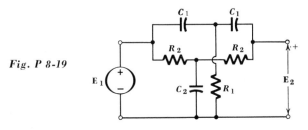

function E_2/E_1 and calculate the circumstances in which the transfer function has real frequency zeros. Can you suggest a use for such a circuit?

8-20   Suppose that somewhere within a network which you are analyzing by the loop method you have the situation pictured in part *a* of the figure. (There may be other loop currents, but they do not traverse any of the branches shown.) Prove that, as far as solving for any currents other than I_3 is concerned, the circuit of (*b*) is equivalent to that of (*a*). What are the impedance values in (*b*) in terms of those in (*a*)? This Δ-T conversion process reduces the number of loop equations by one.

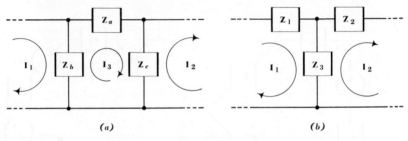

(a)   *(b)*

Fig. P 8-20

If you encountered the T circuit of (*b*) in a network which you were analyzing by the node method, it would be advantageous to convert it to the Δ circuit of (*a*), since this would reduce the number of node equations by one. Consequently, express the Δ-circuit impedances in terms of the T-circuit impedances. Use the formulas you have developed to reduce the networks of Fig. 8-1*a* and *b* to a single driving-point impedance.

8-3 MATRICES AND DETERMINANTS

We pause now in our analysis of electrical and mechanical systems to introduce some mathematical tools which will prove extremely useful in our work. Although we can only lightly touch upon the theory of matrices and determinants, this should not be considered indicative of the importance of this field of mathematics. Matrix theory is not only a highly developed and elegant subject but an extremely important one in many fields of analysis. An interested student would be well advised to study one of the many texts dealing with matrices and determinants.†

† See, for example, E. A. Guillemin, "The Mathematics of Circuit Analysis," John Wiley & Sons, Inc., New York, 1949.

Before plunging into matrix theory, a few comments should be made on the reasons for taking up this subject, since these should provide motivation for careful study of the material that follows. It should be obvious from the examples in the first two sections of this chapter that the analysis of any linear mechanical or electrical network, unless the network is quite simple, will necessitate the solution of a set of simultaneous linear equations. Furthermore, although differing in number and having different values for the coefficients of the variables, which also differ from network to network, these equations all have the same general form. Consequently, in order to avoid getting bogged down in unproductive detail, we should try to develop our analysis methods in a concise, systematic form which will have as much generality as possible. Matrix methods will help us fulfill this purpose. The investment of time and effort necessary to master matrix theory will return valuable dividends, not only in this text, but in many areas of future study.

LINEAR SIMULTANEOUS EQUATIONS IN MATRIX NOTATION We may introduce matrices through the consideration of sets of linear equations such as Eqs. (8-8), (8-17), (8-38), and (8-44). All these have the same general form, which is indicated below:

$$
\begin{aligned}
a_{11}x_1 + a_{12}x_2 + a_{13}x_3 + \cdots + a_{1n}x_n &= y_1 \\
a_{21}x_1 + a_{22}x_2 + a_{23}x_3 + \cdots + a_{2n}x_n &= y_2 \\
a_{31}x_1 + a_{32}x_2 + a_{33}x_3 + \cdots + a_{3n}x_n &= y_3 \\
\cdots\cdots\cdots\cdots\cdots\cdots\cdots\cdots\cdots\cdots \\
a_{n1}x_1 + a_{n2}x_2 + a_{n3}x_3 + \cdots + a_{nn}x_n &= y_n
\end{aligned}
\tag{8-52}
$$

Now, we could express exactly the same thing by writing Eqs. (8-52) in the following more compact form:

$$
\begin{bmatrix}
a_{11} & a_{12} & a_{13} & \cdots & a_{1n} \\
a_{21} & a_{22} & a_{23} & \cdots & a_{2n} \\
a_{31} & a_{32} & a_{33} & \cdots & a_{3n} \\
\cdots & \cdots & \cdots & \cdots & \cdots \\
a_{n1} & a_{n2} & a_{n3} & \cdots & a_{nn}
\end{bmatrix}
\times
\begin{bmatrix}
x_1 \\ x_2 \\ x_3 \\ \cdots \\ x_n
\end{bmatrix}
=
\begin{bmatrix}
y_1 \\ y_2 \\ y_3 \\ \cdots \\ y_n
\end{bmatrix}
\tag{8-53}
$$

The three arrays of elements above are called matrices, and as written above, they form a matrix equation. The matrix equation (8-53) may be represented in the following simplified notation:

$$
[A] \times x] = y]
\tag{8-54}
$$

Equation (8-53), although more concise, contains all the information present in Eqs. (8-52). The repeated writing of the x variables and the addition and equality signs have simply been eliminated. Equation (8-54) has, of course, hidden most of the information present in the preceding two equations. However, for some operations this shorthand notation is adequate, and it certainly conserves space.

Having introduced matrices through a set of linear equations, we may now define some of their general properties. A matrix $[\mathbf{A}]$,

$$[\mathbf{A}] = \begin{bmatrix} a_{11} & a_{12} & \cdots & a_{1n} \\ a_{21} & a_{22} & \cdots & a_{2n} \\ \cdots & \cdots & \cdots & \cdots \\ a_{m1} & a_{m2} & \cdots & a_{mn} \end{bmatrix} \tag{8-55}$$

is a rectangular array of elements. The elements a_{ij} may be constants, variables, or functions of some variable. The position of each element in the array is denoted by two subscripts; the first indicates the number of the row and the second the number of the column in which the element lies. The matrix above has m rows and n columns; to denote this fact, it is called an $m \times n$ matrix and is sometimes written as $[\mathbf{A}_{mn}]$.

There are three particular types of matrices which are important enough to merit special names. If a matrix has an equal number of rows and columns, it is called a *square matrix*. If a matrix consists of only one column, it is called a *column matrix*. The x and y matrices of Eq. (8-53) are examples of column matrices; as indicated in Eq. (8-54), such matrices are denoted by a single bracket rather than by two. A matrix having only one row is called a *row matrix*, and such a matrix is denoted by a single bracket underneath the symbol representing the matrix—for example, $\underline{z}$.

EQUALITY OF MATRICES   Two matrices $[\mathbf{A}]$ and $[\mathbf{B}]$ are equal if and only if $a_{ij} = b_{ij}$ for all values of i and j. Clearly, two matrices, to be equal, must have the same number of rows and columns.

ADDITION AND SUBTRACTION OF MATRICES   Two matrices are added by adding the corresponding elements. Thus, if

$$[\mathbf{A}] + [\mathbf{B}] = [\mathbf{C}] \tag{8-56}$$

then

$$c_{ij} = a_{ij} + b_{ij} \tag{8-57}$$

for all i and j. The foregoing statement applies for the subtraction of matrices if the plus signs are replaced by minus signs.

MULTIPLICATION BY A CONSTANT   Multiplying a matrix by a constant multiplies each element of that matrix by the constant. Thus, if the matrix $[\mathbf{A}]$ is defined by Eq. (8-55), then

$$k[\mathbf{A}] = \begin{bmatrix} ka_{11} & ka_{12} & \cdots & ka_{1n} \\ ka_{21} & ka_{22} & \cdots & ka_{2n} \\ \cdots & \cdots & \cdots & \cdots \\ ka_{m1} & ka_{m2} & \cdots & ka_{mn} \end{bmatrix} \tag{8-58}$$

MULTIPLICATION OF TWO OR MORE MATRICES   For the rules pertaining to the multiplication of matrices, let us return our attention to Eqs. (8-52) and (8-53). In Eq. (8-53) we have a matrix equation in which the product of two matrices equals a third. The value of each element of that third matrix is given by Eqs. (8-52). Therefore, we may derive a rule of multiplication from these equations. This rule would apply for the product of a square matrix and a column matrix, but it may be extended to the products of any types of matrices. Thus, if

$$[\mathbf{A}_{mn}] \times [\mathbf{B}_{np}] = [\mathbf{C}_{mp}] \tag{8-59}$$

then
$$c_{ij} = \sum_{k=1}^{n} a_{ik}b_{kj} \tag{8-60}$$

In words, Eq. (8-60) states that the element in the ith row and jth column of the product matrix is the sum of the products of the elements in the ith row of the first matrix times the elements in the jth column of the second matrix.

In order to carry out the summation indicated in Eq. (8-60), it is necessary for the number of elements in the rows of [A] to be equal to the number of elements in the columns of [B]. In other words, the number of columns of [A] must equal the number of rows of [B]. This fact is indicated in Eq. (8-59), where [A] has n columns and [B] has n rows. Furthermore, Eq. (8-60) indicates that i of c_{ij} may take on values up to the number of rows in [A] and that j can take on values up to the number of columns in [B]. This is also shown in Eq. (8-59). If two matrices have the property of the number of columns of one equaling the number of rows of the other, they are said to be conformable, and they may be multiplied. If they are nonconformable, their product is undefined.

The preceding discussion, together with Eqs. (8-59) and (8-60), indicates that in general

$$[\mathbf{A}] \times [\mathbf{B}] \neq [\mathbf{B}] \times [\mathbf{A}] \tag{8-61}$$

In fact, one product may exist while the other does not, because of nonconformability. In certain circumstances the equality sign in Eq. (8-61) may hold, but, in general, matrix multiplication is not commutative. However, the associative and distributive laws of multiplication do hold. That is,

$$[\mathbf{A}] \times [\mathbf{B}] \times [\mathbf{C}] = ([\mathbf{A}] \times [\mathbf{B}]) \times [\mathbf{C}] = [\mathbf{A}] \times ([\mathbf{B}] \times [\mathbf{C}]) \tag{8-62}$$
$$[\mathbf{A}] \times ([\mathbf{B}] + [\mathbf{C}]) = ([\mathbf{A}] \times [\mathbf{B}]) + ([\mathbf{A}] \times [\mathbf{C}]) \tag{8-63}$$

To illustrate the characteristics of matrix multiplication, two examples of the process are carried out below:

$$[\mathbf{A}] = \begin{bmatrix} 2 & -1 \\ 1 & 1 \\ 0 & 3 \end{bmatrix} \qquad [\mathbf{B}] = \begin{bmatrix} 2 & -3 & 1 \\ -1 & 4 & -2 \end{bmatrix}$$

$[A] \times [B] =$

$$\begin{bmatrix} (2)(2) + (-1)(-1) & (2)(-3) + (-1)(4) & (2)(1) + (-1)(-2) \\ (1)(2) + \quad (1)(-1) & (1)(-3) + \quad (1)(4) & (1)(1) + \quad (1)(-2) \\ (0)(2) + \quad (3)(-1) & (0)(-3) + \quad (3)(4) & (0)(1) + \quad (3)(-2) \end{bmatrix}$$

$$= \begin{bmatrix} 5 & -10 & 4 \\ 1 & 1 & -1 \\ -3 & 12 & -6 \end{bmatrix} \quad (8\text{-}64)$$

$[B] \times [A] =$

$$\begin{bmatrix} (2)(2) + (-3)(1) + \quad (1)(0) & (2)(-1) + (-3)(1) + \quad (1)(3) \\ (-1)(2) + \quad (4)(1) + (-2)(0) & (-1)(-1) + \quad (4)(1) + (-2)(3) \end{bmatrix}$$

$$= \begin{bmatrix} 1 & -2 \\ 2 & -1 \end{bmatrix} \quad (8\text{-}65)$$

Corresponding to the integer 1 in ordinary algebra is the unit, or identity, matrix, which is defined as follows:

$$[U] = \begin{bmatrix} 1 & 0 & 0 & 0 & \cdots & 0 \\ 0 & 1 & 0 & 0 & \cdots & 0 \\ 0 & 0 & 1 & 0 & \cdots & 0 \\ \cdots & \cdots & \cdots & \cdots & \cdots & \cdots \\ 0 & 0 & 0 & 0 & \cdots & 1 \end{bmatrix} \quad (8\text{-}66)$$

Multiplying a matrix by the unit matrix does not change the matrix in any way. That is,

$$[A] \times [U] = [U] \times [A] = [A] \quad (8\text{-}67)$$

MATRIX DIVISION Strictly speaking, matrix division does not exist. In certain circumstances an operation analogous to division may be carried out, but discussion of this must be postponed until we have examined determinants.

DETERMINANTS AND THEIR PROPERTIES It should be clear from the discussion above that a matrix is part of a representation of a set of equations and as such has no numerical value, although the matrix itself may consist wholly of numbers. This fact should be kept clearly in mind. Although a matrix has no numerical value, we may form from a square matrix a function, called a *determinant*, which does have a unique value. Indeed, the essential definition of a determinant is the method of finding its value. To illustrate these remarks, let us consider the square matrix of Eq. (8-53). Calling this matrix $[A]$, we say that the determinant of the matrix $[A]$ is $|A|$. The determinant $|A|$ is written out below:

$$|A| = \begin{vmatrix} a_{11} & a_{12} & a_{13} & \cdots & a_{1n} \\ a_{21} & a_{22} & a_{23} & \cdots & a_{2n} \\ a_{31} & a_{32} & a_{33} & \cdots & a_{3n} \\ \cdots & \cdots & \cdots & \cdots & \cdots \\ a_{n1} & a_{n2} & a_{n3} & \cdots & a_{nn} \end{vmatrix} \quad (8\text{-}68)$$

The determinant certainly looks very little different from the matrix, the only change being the replacement of the brackets by straight lines. However, as we pointed out above, the essential property of a determinant is that it has a unique value and a method of finding that value. There are several methods of finding the value of a determinant. Each method, of course, yields the same value, although the procedures followed to find that value may differ considerably. We shall first illustrate one method of evaluating a determinant and then discuss some properties which lead to a second method of evaluation.

LAPLACE'S DEVELOPMENT FOR THE EVALUATION OF A DETERMINANT The Laplace method expresses the value of a determinant in terms of the elements in a particular row or column and the minor determinants corresponding to those elements. Minor determinants are defined and denoted in the following manner.

If in a particular determinant we cancel or remove one row and one column, then the remaining elements form another determinant, which is called a minor determinant of the original. The minor is denoted by M_{ij}, where the subscripts indicate the row and column which were removed. For example, the M_{23} minor of the determinant of Eq. (8-68) is

$$M_{23} = \begin{vmatrix} a_{11} & a_{12} & a_{14} & a_{15} & \cdots & a_{1n} \\ a_{31} & a_{32} & a_{34} & a_{35} & \cdots & a_{3n} \\ a_{41} & a_{42} & a_{44} & a_{45} & \cdots & a_{4n} \\ \cdots & \cdots & \cdots & \cdots & \cdots & \cdots \\ a_{n1} & a_{n2} & a_{n4} & a_{n5} & \cdots & a_{nn} \end{vmatrix} \qquad (8\text{-}69)$$

The minor M_{ij} is also called the complement of—or the minor of or the minor corresponding to—the element a_{ij}. The *cofactor* of the element a_{ij} is denoted by $|A|_{ij}$ and is equal to the minor M_{ij}, with an algebraic sign which is determined in the following manner:

$$|A|_{ij} = M_{ij} \times (-1)^{i+j} \qquad (8\text{-}70)$$

Another way of determining the sign of the cofactor is through the use of the following sign checkerboard:

$$\begin{vmatrix} + & - & + & - & + & \cdots \\ - & + & - & + & - & \cdots \\ + & - & + & - & + & \cdots \\ - & + & - & + & - & \cdots \\ \cdots & \cdots & \cdots & \cdots & \cdots & \end{vmatrix}$$

The sign of $|A|_{ij}$ depends upon whether a_{ij} falls on a plus or a minus in the checkerboard above. Now we may state *Laplace's development: The value of a determinant is equal to the sum of the products of the elements of a particular row (or column) with their cofactors.* This statement may be represented symbolically as follows. Expanding on the ith row,

$$|A| = \sum_{k=1}^{n} a_{ik}|A|_{ik} = a_{i1}|A|_{i1} + a_{i2}|A|_{i2} + \cdots + a_{in}|A|_{in} \quad (8\text{-}71)$$

or expanding on the jth column,

$$|A| = \sum_{k=1}^{n} a_{kj}|A|_{kj} = a_{1j}|A|_{1j} + a_{2j}|A|_{2j} + \cdots + a_{nj}|A|_{nj} \quad (8\text{-}72)$$

For large determinants this development must be carried out many times. The determinant is first expanded on a row or column. If the original determinant was $n \times n$ (that is, nth order), then the development will contain a sum of n products of the form $a_{ij}|A|_{ij}$. Each cofactor is a determinant of order $n - 1$. Each of these is then expanded on a row or column, each cofactor yielding $n - 1$ products containing determinants of order $n - 2$. This process continues until the determinants in each product are of order 1. (The value of a determinant with one element is equal to that element.) It should be obvious at this point that the evaluation of large determinants, although straightforward, is exceedingly tedious and involved.

Let us illustrate Laplace's development by evaluating the following fourth-order determinant:

$$|A| = \begin{vmatrix} 1 & -1 & 3 & 2 \\ 2 & 0 & 1 & 1 \\ 4 & 3 & 2 & -1 \\ 2 & -2 & 2 & -2 \end{vmatrix} \quad (8\text{-}73)$$

Expanding on the second row yields the next expression:

$$|A| = 2 \times |A|_{21} + 0 \times |A|_{22} + 1 \times |A|_{23} + 1 \times |A|_{24} \quad (8\text{-}74)$$

$$|A|_{21} = - \begin{vmatrix} -1 & 3 & 2 \\ 3 & 2 & -1 \\ -2 & 2 & -2 \end{vmatrix} \qquad |A|_{23} = - \begin{vmatrix} 1 & -1 & 2 \\ 4 & 3 & -1 \\ 2 & -2 & -2 \end{vmatrix}$$

$$|A|_{24} = + \begin{vmatrix} 1 & -1 & 3 \\ 4 & 3 & 2 \\ 2 & -2 & 2 \end{vmatrix}$$

Expanding each of the cofactors on their first columns gives the following equations:

$$|A|_{21} = - \left[(-1) \begin{vmatrix} 2 & -1 \\ 2 & -2 \end{vmatrix} - 3 \begin{vmatrix} 3 & 2 \\ 2 & -2 \end{vmatrix} + (-2) \begin{vmatrix} 3 & 2 \\ 2 & -1 \end{vmatrix} \right]$$

$$= -\{(-1)[(2)(-2) - (2)(-1)] - 3[(3)(-2) - (2)(2)]$$
$$+ (-2)[(3)(-1) - (2)(2)]\}$$

$$= -46 \quad (8\text{-}75)$$

$$|A|_{23} = -\left[1\begin{vmatrix}3 & -1 \\ -2 & -2\end{vmatrix} - 4\begin{vmatrix}-1 & 2 \\ -2 & -2\end{vmatrix} + 2\begin{vmatrix}-1 & 2 \\ 3 & -1\end{vmatrix}\right]$$

$$= -\{1[(3)(-2) - (-2)(-1)] - 4[(-1)(-2) - (-2)(2)]$$
$$+ 2[(-1)(-1) - (3)(2)]\}$$

$$= 42 \tag{8-76}$$

$$|A|_{24} = 1\begin{vmatrix}3 & 2 \\ -2 & 2\end{vmatrix} - 4\begin{vmatrix}-1 & 3 \\ -2 & 2\end{vmatrix} + 2\begin{vmatrix}-1 & 3 \\ 3 & 2\end{vmatrix}$$

$$= 1[(3)(2) - (-2)(2)] - 4[(-1)(2) - (-2)(3)]$$
$$+ 2[(-1)(2) - (3)(3)]$$

$$= -28 \tag{8-77}$$

Substituting the results of these last three equations into Eq. (8-74) gives us the value of the determinant:

$$|A| = (2)(-46) + (1)(42) + (1)(-28) = -78 \tag{8-78}$$

FUNDAMENTAL PROPERTIES OF DETERMINANTS The following properties of determinants could be derived from the method of evaluating the determinant given above. Alternatively, they could be defined as fundamental properties, and Laplace's development and other evaluation methods could be derived from them. It is necessary to state only three fundamental properties in order to define completely the value and all other characteristics of determinants. These three properties are as follows:

> *I. The value of a determinant is unity if all the elements on the principal diagonal, that is, a_{11}, a_{22}, a_{33}, . . . , a_{nn}, are unity and all other elements are zero.*
>
> *II. The value of a determinant is multiplied by a factor k if every element in a row or column is multiplied by k.*
>
> *III. The value of a determinant is unchanged if any linear combination of other rows (columns) is added to a row (column).*

Property III may be clarified by the following illustration. Suppose we are given the following determinant:

$$|D| = \begin{vmatrix} d_{11} & d_{12} & d_{13} \\ d_{21} & d_{22} & d_{23} \\ d_{31} & d_{32} & d_{33} \end{vmatrix} \tag{8-79}$$

Now let us form a linear combination of rows one and two and add it to row three. For example, we may take 5 times row one plus -2 times row two for our linear combination. According to property III above, the value of the determinant is unchanged. Consequently,

$$|D| = \begin{vmatrix} d_{11} & d_{12} & d_{13} \\ d_{21} & d_{22} & d_{23} \\ d_{31} + 5d_{11} - 2d_{21} & d_{32} + 5d_{12} - 2d_{22} & d_{33} + 5d_{13} - 2d_{23} \end{vmatrix} \tag{8-80}$$

The three properties above may be utilized in a second method of evaluating a determinant. This method, called *diagonalization of the determinant,* can best be introduced by a numerical example. Let us use the determinant of Eq. (8-73) again. According to property III we may add -2 times row one to row two without changing the value of the determinant. Carrying this step out produces the modified determinant below:

$$|A| = \begin{vmatrix} 1 & -1 & 3 & 2 \\ 0 & 2 & -5 & -3 \\ 4 & 3 & 2 & -1 \\ 2 & -2 & 2 & -2 \end{vmatrix} \tag{8-81}$$

By adding -4 times row one to row three and -2 times row one to row four, the following modification is obtained:

$$|A| = \begin{vmatrix} 1 & -1 & 3 & 2 \\ 0 & 2 & -5 & -3 \\ 0 & 7 & -10 & -9 \\ 0 & 0 & -4 & -6 \end{vmatrix} \tag{8-82}$$

Now, adding to columns two, three, and four, column one multiplied by 1, -3, and -2, respectively, transforms the equation above into the expression

$$|A| = \begin{vmatrix} 1 & 0 & 0 & 0 \\ 0 & 2 & -5 & -3 \\ 0 & 7 & -10 & -9 \\ 0 & 0 & -4 & -6 \end{vmatrix} \tag{8-83}$$

Because of property II, we may factor a 2 out of row two, thus obtaining

$$|A| = (2)\begin{vmatrix} 1 & 0 & 0 & 0 \\ 0 & 1 & -\frac{5}{2} & -\frac{3}{2} \\ 0 & 7 & -10 & -9 \\ 0 & 0 & -4 & -6 \end{vmatrix} \tag{8-84}$$

Now we add -7 times row two to row three and then add the appropriate multiples of column two to columns three and four to produce the following modification:

$$|A| = (2)\begin{vmatrix} 1 & 0 & 0 & 0 \\ 0 & 1 & 0 & 0 \\ 0 & 0 & 15\frac{1}{2} & 3\frac{1}{2} \\ 0 & 0 & -4 & -6 \end{vmatrix} \tag{8-85}$$

Equation (8-85) is further modified by factoring row three:

$$|A| = (2)(15\frac{1}{2})\begin{vmatrix} 1 & 0 & 0 & 0 \\ 0 & 1 & 0 & 0 \\ 0 & 0 & 1 & \frac{3}{15} \\ 0 & 0 & -4 & -6 \end{vmatrix} \tag{8-86}$$

The appropriate multiples of row and column three are added to row and column four to obtain

$$|A| = (2)(15/2) \begin{vmatrix} 1 & 0 & 0 & 0 \\ 0 & 1 & 0 & 0 \\ 0 & 0 & 1 & 0 \\ 0 & 0 & 0 & -78/15 \end{vmatrix} \tag{8-87}$$

Finally, $-78/15$ is factored out of row four, and property I is utilized to complete the evaluation of the determinant.

$$|A| = (2)(15/2)(-78/15) \begin{vmatrix} 1 & 0 & 0 & 0 \\ 0 & 1 & 0 & 0 \\ 0 & 0 & 1 & 0 \\ 0 & 0 & 0 & 1 \end{vmatrix} = -78 \tag{8-88}$$

Any number of subsidiary properties may be derived from the basic three listed above. Some of the more useful ones are given below:

IV. *The value of a determinant is zero if one of its rows (columns) is equal to a linear combination of the other rows (columns) or if all the elements in a row or column are zero.*

V. *The algebraic sign of the determinant is reversed if two rows (columns) are interchanged.*

VI. *The value of a triangular determinant*

$$\begin{vmatrix} a_{11} & a_{12} & a_{13} & \cdots & a_{in} \\ 0 & a_{22} & a_{23} & \cdots & a_{2n} \\ 0 & 0 & a_{33} & \cdots & a_{3n} \\ \cdots & \cdots & \cdots & \cdots & \cdots \\ 0 & 0 & 0 & \cdots & a_{nn} \end{vmatrix}$$

is the product of the elements on its main diagonal (a_{11}, a_{22}, a_{33}, . . . , a_{nn}).

CRAMER'S RULE We shall now derive a method by which determinants may be systematically used in the solution of sets of simultaneous linear equations. Let us turn our attention once again to Eqs. (8-52). If we were to multiply the first equation through by the cofactor $|A|_{11}$, the second equation by the cofactor $|A|_{21}$, the third equation by $|A|_{31}$, . . . , and the nth equation by $|A|_{n1}$ and if we were then to add all the equations together, we should obtain the following equation:

$$\begin{aligned} (a_{11}|A|_{11} &+ a_{21}|A|_{21} + a_{31}|A|_{31} + \cdots - a_{n1}|A|_{n1})x_1 \\ &+ (a_{12}|A|_{11} + a_{22}|A|_{21} + a_{32}|A|_{31} + \cdots + a_{n2}|A|_{n1})x_2 \\ &+ (a_{13}|A|_{11} + a_{23}|A|_{21} + a_{33}|A|_{31} + \cdots + a_{n3}|A|_{n1})x_3 \\ &+ \cdots \cdots \cdots \cdots \cdots \cdots \cdots \cdots \\ &+ (a_{1n}|A|_{11} + a_{2n}|A|_{21} + a_{3n}|A|_{31} + \cdots + a_{nn}|A|_{n1})x_n \\ &= |A|_{11}y_1 + |A|_{21}y_2 + |A|_{31}y_3 + \cdots + |A|_{n1}y_n \end{aligned} \tag{8-89}$$

The coefficient of x_1 in the equation above may be recognized as the Laplace development of the determinant $|A|$ expanded on the first column. The coefficient of x_2 can be considered the Laplace development of a determinant which is the same as $|A|$ except that its first column is equal to its second column. The coefficient of x_3 is the Laplace development of a determinant which is the same as $|A|$ except that its first column is equal to its third column. As was pointed out in property IV above, determinants with two columns equal to each other have a value of zero. Consequently, the coefficients of x_2, x_3, x_4, . . . , x_n in Eq. (8-89) are all zero. Therefore, Eq. (8-89) reduces to

$$x_1 = \frac{|A|_{11}y_1 + |A|_{21}y_2 + |A|_{31}y_3 + \cdots + |A|_{n1}y_n}{|A|} \qquad (8\text{-}90)$$

A similar process could be carried out to solve for the other unknown variables; that is, x_j could be found by multiplying successive equations by $|A|_{1j}$, $|A|_{2j}$, $|A|_{3j}$, . . . , $|A|_{nj}$ and then adding. The general result may be stated as follows:

$$x_j = \sum_{k=1}^{n} \frac{|A|_{kj}y_k}{|A|} = \frac{|A|_{1j}y_1 + |A|_{2j}y_2 + |A|_{3j}y_3 + \cdots |A|_{nj}y_n}{|A|}$$

$$= \frac{\begin{vmatrix} a_{11} & a_{12} & a_{13} & \cdots & a_{1j-1} & y_1 & a_{1j+1} & \cdots & a_{1n} \\ a_{21} & a_{22} & a_{23} & \cdots & a_{2j-1} & y_2 & a_{2j+1} & \cdots & a_{2n} \\ \cdot & \cdot & & & & & & & \cdot \\ a_{n1} & a_{n2} & a_{n3} & \cdots & a_{nj-1} & y_n & a_{nj+1} & \cdots & a_{nn} \end{vmatrix}}{\begin{vmatrix} a_{11} & a_{12} & a_{13} & \cdots & a_{1n} \\ a_{21} & a_{22} & a_{23} & \cdots & a_{2n} \\ \cdot & \cdot & & & \cdot \\ a_{n1} & a_{n2} & a_{n3} & \cdots & a_{nn} \end{vmatrix}} \qquad (8\text{-}91)$$

INVERSE MATRICES   Having demonstrated the solution of simultaneous linear equations through the use of Cramer's rule, we may now define inverse matrices and the operation in matrix algebra which is analogous to division in ordinary algebra. The equations which we solved above were expressed in matrix form by Eqs. (8-53) and (8-54). The solutions, as given in Eq. (8-91), could also be expressed in matrix form. Equation (8-91) could be written

$$\frac{|A|_{11}}{|A|}y_1 + \frac{|A|_{21}}{|A|}y_2 + \frac{|A|_{31}}{|A|}y_3 + \cdots + \frac{|A|_{n1}}{|A|}y_n = x_1$$

$$\frac{|A|_{12}}{|A|}y_1 + \frac{|A|_{22}}{|A|}y_2 + \frac{|A|_{32}}{|A|}y_3 + \cdots + \frac{|A|_{n2}}{|A|}y_n = x_2 \qquad (8\text{-}92)$$

$$\frac{|A|_{1n}}{|A|}y_1 + \frac{|A|_{2n}}{|A|}y_2 + \frac{|A|_{3n}}{|A|}y_3 + \cdots + \frac{|A|_{nn}}{|A|}y_n = x_n$$

which in matrix form is

$$\begin{bmatrix} \dfrac{|A|_{11}}{|A|} & \dfrac{|A|_{21}}{|A|} & \dfrac{|A|_{31}}{|A|} & \cdots & \dfrac{|A|_{n1}}{|A|} \\ \dfrac{|A|_{12}}{|A|} & \dfrac{|A|_{22}}{|A|} & \dfrac{|A|_{32}}{|A|} & \cdots & \dfrac{|A|_{n2}}{|A|} \\ \cdots & \cdots & \cdots & \cdots & \cdots \\ \dfrac{|A|_{1n}}{|A|} & \dfrac{|A|_{2n}}{|A|} & \dfrac{|A|_{3n}}{|A|} & \cdots & \dfrac{|A|_{nn}}{|A|} \end{bmatrix} \times \begin{bmatrix} y_1 \\ y_2 \\ \cdots \\ y_n \end{bmatrix} = \begin{bmatrix} x_1 \\ x_2 \\ \cdots \\ x_n \end{bmatrix} \qquad (8\text{-}93)$$

In the shorthand notation introduced earlier, Eq. (8-93) becomes

$$[A]^{-1} \times y] = x] \qquad (8\text{-}94)$$

The matrix $[A]^{-1}$ defined in Eq. (8-94) is called the inverse of the matrix $[A]$. The reason for this may be seen if we multiply Eq. (8-94) by the matrix $[A]$:

$$[A] \times [A]^{-1} \times y] = [A] \times x] \qquad (8\text{-}95)$$

The right-hand side of Eq. (8-95) is, by Eq. (8-54), equal to $y]$. Hence

$$[A] \times [A]^{-1} \times y] = y] \qquad (8\text{-}96)$$
$$[A] \times [A]^{-1} = [U] = [A]^{-1} \times [A] \qquad (8\text{-}97)$$

If the elements of the inverse matrix are defined as a_{ij}^{-1}, then, by Eq. (8-93), we see that

$$a_{ij}^{-1} = \frac{|A|_{ji}}{|A|} \qquad (8\text{-}98)$$

The analogy to division may be seen by considering Eq. (8-54), whose solution is given by Eq. (8-94). If Eq. (8-54) were an ordinary algebraic equation, we would divide both sides of the equation by $[A]$ in order to solve for $x]$. In matrix algebra we carry out the corresponding operation by multiplying both sides of the equation by the inverse of $[A]$ to obtain the solution given by Eq. (8-94).

As was mentioned earlier, the matrix operation analogous to division can only be carried out in certain circumstances. It is necessary for the inverse of the matrix to exist, and it can exist only if the determinant of the matrix exists and is nonzero. That is to say, only square matrices with nonzero determinants have inverse matrices. The following statement is entirely equivalent to the one just given: A set of simultaneous equations has a set of unique solutions if and only if the determinant of the coefficient matrix exists and is nonzero.

SUMMARY   Matrix algebra is a systematic, condensed method of writing and carrying out various operations on simultaneous linear equations. Its value lies not only in its condensation of such expressions but in its ability to distinguish between the parameters associated with a particular set of equations and the operations which are common to all such sets of equations. Although a matrix has no numerical value, each square matrix has a corresponding function, called a determinant, which does have a unique value. If the determinant has a value other than zero, then the solutions of the simultaneous equations exist and may be found through the use of Cramer's rule. It should be noted that, although matrix and determinant methods simplify notation and aid in general proofs and developments to a great extent, they do not reduce the considerable amount of computation necessary to obtain actual numerical solutions of simultaneous equations.

PROBLEMS

8-21   For the matrices given below, find the following quantities if they exist:

(a) $[A] + [B] - [C]$ (b) $[A] \times [B]$ (c) $[C] \times [A] \times [B$
(d) $[B] \times ([A] + [C])$ (e) $[A] \times [D]$ (f) $[D] \times [A]$
(g) $[D] \times [E]$ (h) $|A|$ (i) $|B|$
(j) $|C|$ (k) $|D|$ (l) $[A]^{-1}$
(m) $[B]^{-1}$ (n) $[C]^{-1}$

$$[A] = \begin{bmatrix} 1 & 0 & -1 \\ 2 & 2 & 0 \\ -1 & 2 & 1 \end{bmatrix} \quad [B] = \begin{bmatrix} 1 & 3 & 0 \\ -1 & -2 & 1 \\ 0 & 1 & 1 \end{bmatrix}$$

$$[C] = \begin{bmatrix} 3 & -1 & -1 \\ -1 & 4 & -1 \\ -1 & -1 & 2 \end{bmatrix} \quad [D] = \begin{bmatrix} 2 & -1 \\ 0 & 3 \\ 5 & -1 \end{bmatrix} \quad [E] = \begin{bmatrix} 3 \\ -7 \end{bmatrix}$$

8-22   Show that

$$\begin{vmatrix} 1 & w & w^2 & w^3 \\ 1 & x & x^2 & x^3 \\ 1 & y & y^2 & y^3 \\ 1 & z & z^2 & z^3 \end{vmatrix} = (x - w)(y - w)(z - w)(y - x)(z - x)(z - y)$$

8-23   Consider the matrix

$$[B] = \begin{bmatrix} 1 & 3 \\ 3 & 2 \end{bmatrix}$$

which is combined with a variable times the unit matrix to form the equation

$$[B] - \lambda[U] = [B_\lambda]$$

Setting the determinant of $[B_\lambda]$ equal to zero forms a quadratic equation in λ. Show that the original matrix $[B]$ satisfies this equation. That is, if

$$|B_\lambda| = 0 = a\lambda^2 + b\lambda + c$$

then $a[B]^2 + b[B] + c[U] = [0]$

where [0] is a matrix whose elements are all zero. The equation $|B_\lambda| = 0$ is called the characteristic equation of [B]. Show that [B] satisfies its own characteristic equation no matter what its elements are.

8-24 Show that a general 3×3 matrix satisfies its own characteristic equation. (It can be shown that any $n \times n$ matrix satisfies its characteristic equation.)

8-25 Express Eqs. (8-17) in matrix form and obtain Eq. (8-18) by applying Cramer's rule.

8-26 Express Eqs. (8-44) in matrix form and obtain Eq. (8-45) by applying Cramer's rule.

8-27 For the circuits shown in the figure, determine the indicated

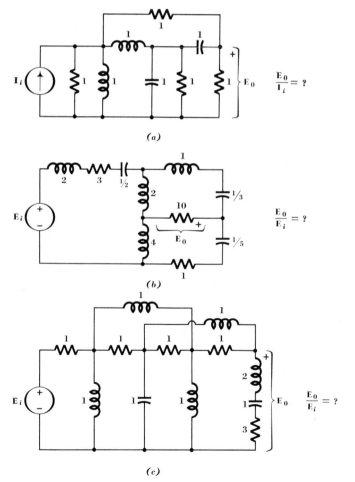

(a)

(b)

(c)

Fig. P 8-27

transfer function by matrix methods. That is, express the loop or node equations in matrix form and then apply Cramer's rule.

8-28   A symmetrical matrix is one whose elements satisfy $a_{ij} = a_{ji}$ for all i and j. Impedance and admittance matrices obtained from loop and node analysis are symmetrical. Prove that the cofactor $|A|_{ij} = |A|_{ji}$ for symmetrical matrices.

some network theorems

The previous chapter examined the two basic methods of analyzing complex networks and introduced matrix algebra, a useful tool in such analysis. The present chapter will continue the discussion of analysis, with emphasis on various methods of simplifying or reducing the networks. In addition, it will extend the impedance and impulse-response technique of finding transient responses to networks with initial stored energy.

The network theorems to be discussed are equally applicable to electrical and mechanical networks. The proofs of these theorems, particularly in the case of Thévenin's theorem, are not always the most economical, since they have been chosen to illustrate further the analysis and matrix methods of Chap. 8. The interested student is urged to examine other texts for different approaches to these proofs.

9-1 SUPERPOSITION AND RECIPROCITY THEOREMS

The first of the two theorems that we shall consider in this section is almost intuitively obvious, whereas the second is almost intuitively incorrect. The purpose of the following discussion is to make the first a little less obvious and the second more clearly correct.

THE SUPERPOSITION THEOREM Although the superposition theorem has been introduced and used extensively in the preceding chapters, it is included here for completeness, and emphasis. It is advisable not only to stress the importance of the theorem but to point out the pitfall of extending it into areas of inapplicability.

The *superposition theorem* may be stated as follows: *The response of a* linear *network containing a number of sources is the sum of the responses to the sources taken individually.*† When the response to a

† In Sec. 9-3 we shall see that initial stored energy can be treated as additional sources.

single source is being calculated, the other voltage sources are shorted, and the other current sources are open-circuited. The superposition theorem is illustrated graphically in Fig. 9-1.

The proof of this theorem lies in the linearity of the systems under investigation. As has been pointed out, the differential equations of these linear networks are linear. This is illustrated in the following three equations, where DE denotes a particular linear differential equation operating on a function of time $x(t)$. If

$$DE[x_1(t)] = y_1(t) \tag{9-1}$$
and
$$DE[x_2(t)] = y_2(t) \tag{9-2}$$
then
$$DE[x_1(t) + x_2(t)] = y_1(t) + y_2(t) \tag{9-3}$$

Thus, for a single linear differential equation, we see that the response $[x_1(t) + x_2(t)]$ to a sum of two driving functions $[y_1(t) + y_2(t)]$ is the sum of the responses to the driving functions taken individually.

The same argument extends to a set of simultaneous linear differential equations. For example, in terms of impedances, the solution for a particular current in a linear network may be expressed according to Cramer's rule as

$$\mathbf{I}_k = \frac{\mathbf{E}_1|Z|_{1k} + \mathbf{E}_2|Z|_{2k} + \cdots + \mathbf{E}_n|Z|_{nk}}{|Z|} \tag{9-4}$$

The $\mathbf{E}$'s in Eq. (9-4) are the driving functions, or sources. Equation (9-4) may be separated into a number of terms, as is illustrated below:

$$\mathbf{I}_k = \frac{\mathbf{E}_1|Z|_{1k}}{|Z|} + \frac{\mathbf{E}_2|Z|_{2k}}{|Z|} + \cdots + \frac{\mathbf{E}_n|Z|_{nk}}{|Z|} \tag{9-5}$$

Thus, we see that $\mathbf{I}_k$ may be considered as a sum of currents, each one of which is the current due to one source alone.

The superposition theorem is extremely basic and, therefore, is frequently utilized. Unfortunately, this constant usage often creates a tendency to extend the theorem into areas where it no longer applies. The word *linear* in the statement of the superposition theorem was set in distinctive type to emphasize its importance. In networks which are nonlinear, that is, networks which contain nonlinear elements, the superposition theorem can no longer be applied. Moreover, even in linear networks, the superposition theorem cannot be used in determining nonlinear responses such as power. That is to say, the total power (instantaneous or average) developed in a particular part of the circuit cannot be found by adding the powers that would be produced by the sources considered individually. The reason for this lies in the fact that power is not a linear function of the driving function. In other words, it is not directly proportional to the driving function but is proportional to its square. It should be clear that the word *response*, as used in the statement of the superposition theorem, means *linear*

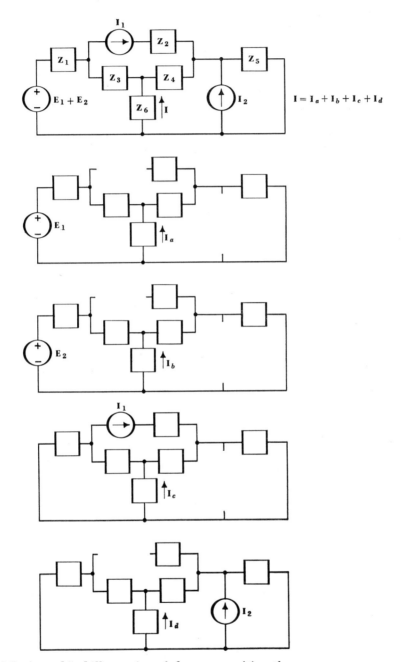

$$I = I_a + I_b + I_c + I_d$$

Fig. 9-1. A graphical illustration of the superposition theorem.

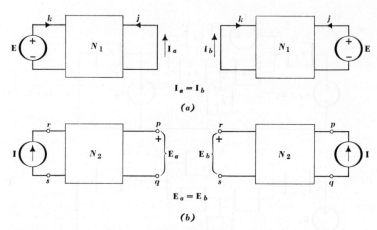

Fig. 9-2. *Graphical illustrations of the reciprocity theorem. The networks* N_1 *and* N_2 *are linear and contain no additional energy sources.*

response. Linear responses include voltage, current, force, and velocity, together with their various derivatives and integrals. The response of nonlinear circuits is discussed at greater length in Chap. 14.

THE RECIPROCITY THEOREM   The reciprocity theorem applies to *linear* networks (all-electrical or all-mechanical but not necessarily electro-mechanical) containing a single independent voltage or current (velocity or force) source. It is stated in one of two forms, depending upon the kind of source: (1) *The current response in branch j due to a voltage source in branch k is equal to the current response in branch k with the same voltage source now placed in branch j;* or (2) *the voltage response between nodes p and q due to a current source between nodes r and s is equal to the voltage response between nodes r and s with the same current source now placed between nodes p and q.* The two forms of this theorem are illustrated graphically in Fig. 9-2.

Let us prove the latter form of the theorem, leaving the voltage-source form as a problem. Referring to Fig. 9-2, we may call node s the reference node and designate nodes r, p, and q as nodes 1, 2, and 3, respectively. With the single current source, as shown on the left-hand side of the figure, the node equations in matrix form are

$$[Y] \times \begin{bmatrix} E_1 \\ E_2 \\ E_3 \\ \cdot \\ \cdot \\ \cdot \\ E_n \end{bmatrix} = \begin{bmatrix} I \\ 0 \\ 0 \\ \cdot \\ \cdot \\ \cdot \\ 0 \end{bmatrix} \qquad (9\text{-}6)$$

By Cramer's rule the solution for $\mathbf{E}_a$ is

$$\mathbf{E}_a = \mathbf{E}_2 - \mathbf{E}_3 = \frac{\mathbf{I}|Y|_{12}}{|Y|} - \frac{\mathbf{I}|Y|_{13}}{|Y|} = \frac{\mathbf{I}(|Y|_{12} - |Y|_{13})}{|Y|} \qquad (9\text{-}7)$$

Turning our attention now to the right-hand figure, we see that the node equations for this circuit will differ only in the driving-function column matrix:

$$[\mathbf{Y}] \times \begin{bmatrix} \mathbf{E}_1 \\ \mathbf{E}_2 \\ \mathbf{E}_3 \\ \cdot \\ \cdot \\ \cdot \\ \mathbf{E}_n \end{bmatrix} = \begin{bmatrix} 0 \\ \mathbf{I} \\ -\mathbf{I} \\ \cdot \\ \cdot \\ \cdot \\ 0 \end{bmatrix} \qquad (9\text{-}8)$$

Using Cramer's rule again, we see that the theorem holds and that $\mathbf{E}_a = \mathbf{E}_b$:

$$\mathbf{E}_b = \mathbf{E}_1 = \frac{\mathbf{I}|Y|_{21} + (-\mathbf{I})|Y|_{31}}{|Y|} = \frac{\mathbf{I}(|Y|_{12} - |Y|_{13})}{|Y|} = \mathbf{E}_a \quad (9\text{-}9)$$

Changing the order of the cofactor subscripts in the above equation is permissible because the admittance matrix is symmetrical, that is, $\mathbf{Y}_{jk} = \mathbf{Y}_{kj}$ [see Eq. (8-14) and Prob. 8-28].

Two notes of caution should be sounded with respect to the use of this theorem. The first is that only the single response which has exchanged places with the source remains unchanged. The other responses within the network are, in general, altered by changing the position of the source. The second note is that the theorem applies for voltage-source–current or current-source–voltage responses and not for voltage-voltage or current-current combinations.

PROBLEMS

9-1   By applying the superposition theorem, find the current in the 10-ohm resistor shown in the figure.

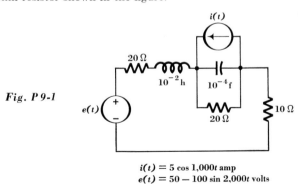

Fig. P9-1

$i(t) = 5 \cos 1{,}000t$ amp

$e(t) = 50 - 100 \sin 2{,}000t$ volts

9-2   Find the average power dissipated in the 10-ohm resistor of the problem above. Compare this with the incorrect value obtained by adding the powers due to the sources taken individually.

9-3   Use the superposition theorem to find the current through the 10-ohm resistor of Prob. 9-1 if the voltage and current sources have the following values:

$$i(t) = \begin{cases} 0 & \text{for } t < 0 \\ e^{-1\,000t} \text{ amp} & \text{for } t > 0 \end{cases}$$

$$e(t) = \begin{cases} 0 & \text{for } t < 0 \\ 10 \text{ volts} & \text{for } t > 0 \end{cases}$$

9-4   Referring to the figure, find the velocity of the mass M_1 by applying the superposition theorem. What is the total average power being dissipated in the three mechanical resistances?

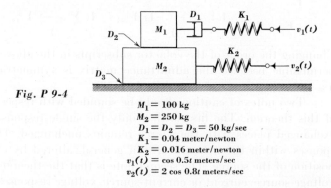

Fig. P 9-4

$$M_1 = 100 \text{ kg}$$
$$M_2 = 250 \text{ kg}$$
$$D_1 = D_2 = D_3 = 50 \text{ kg/sec}$$
$$K_1 = 0.04 \text{ meter/newton}$$
$$K_2 = 0.016 \text{ meter/newton}$$
$$v_1(t) = \cos 0.5t \text{ meters/sec}$$
$$v_2(t) = 2 \cos 0.8t \text{ meters/sec}$$

9-5   In the d-c circuit shown, find the currents in the resistors marked with a star by solving with all sources and by using the superposition theorem.

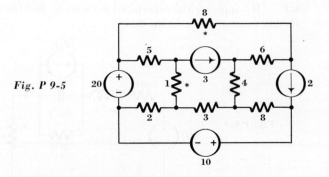

Fig. P 9-5

9-6   Prove the reciprocity theorem for linear circuits containing a single voltage source.

9-7   Referring to the figure, suppose that the impedance **Z** has a current **I** through it and a voltage **E** across it. Prove that the network of *a* may be replaced by the network of *b* or *c* without affecting any of the other voltages or currents in the circuit.

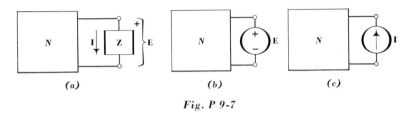

(a)   *(b)*   *(c)*

Fig. P 9-7

9-8   Show that the branch containing **Z** (in Prob. 9-7) may be replaced by any other branch which would have a voltage **E** across it when **I** was flowing through it. This property of linear circuits is called the *substitution theorem*.

9-2   EQUIVALENT-NETWORK THEOREMS

This section will cover three theorems which may be grouped together and called equivalent-network theorems. The first two, Thévenin's and Norton's theorems, furnish a means of reducing the complexity of various networks. The third, the exchange-of-sources theorem, yields a technique which is helpful in analyzing many networks.

THÉVENIN'S THEOREM   It is quite common in the analysis of complex networks to be concerned only with the response in some isolated part of the network. Often the response across a particular element when that element alone is varied is all that is needed. In such cases it is advantageous to simplify the part of the network in which we are not especially interested. Thévenin's theorem presents a method by which a complex network may be reduced to the utmost simplicity without changing the response across the particular part of the network that we wish to study.

In discussing Thévenin's theorem, we shall refer to Fig. 9-3, which represents a network that has been separated into two parts. The left-hand part, N, contains an arbitrary arrangement of passive linear elements together with any number of energy sources. We may

Fig. 9-3. A network to be analyzed through the use of Thévenin's theorem. N is a network containing linear impedances and energy sources. The response across the impedances Z_0 is to be found.

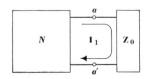

assume that the response in N itself is of no interest. The right-hand side is an impedance $\mathbf{Z}_0$, across which we wish to determine the response. The impedance $\mathbf{Z}_0$ need not be a single element. It may be any arrangement of elements, so long as no sources are included and the connections to N are limited to two, as shown.

Although the following analysis will be presented in terms of an electrical network, the theorem applies equally well to mechanical networks. The discussion may be adapted to the mechanical case by making the appropriate analogies, that is, voltage $\leftrightarrow$ velocity, current $\leftrightarrow$ force, etc.

Let us assume that we are to analyze the circuit by the loop method. We have seen that we have considerable leeway in choosing loop currents. For example, cutting or opening a set of branches effectively determines a set of loop currents. In this circuit, by cutting a branch connecting $\mathbf{Z}_0$ with N, we obtain a set of loop currents of which only one flows through $\mathbf{Z}_0$. This loop current, which we call $\mathbf{I}_1$, is shown in Fig. 9-3. When we have chosen all the loop currents and summed the voltage drops around the loops, we obtain the following set of simultaneous equations in matrix form:

$$
\begin{bmatrix}
\mathbf{Z}_0 + \mathbf{Z}_{11} & \mathbf{Z}_{12} & \mathbf{Z}_{13} & \cdots & \mathbf{Z}_{1n} \\
\mathbf{Z}_{21} & \mathbf{Z}_{22} & \mathbf{Z}_{23} & \cdots & \mathbf{Z}_{2n} \\
\cdots\cdots\cdots\cdots\cdots\cdots\cdots\cdots\cdots \\
\mathbf{Z}_{n1} & \mathbf{Z}_{n2} & \mathbf{Z}_{n3} & \cdots & \mathbf{Z}_{nn}
\end{bmatrix}
\times
\begin{bmatrix}
\mathbf{I}_1 \\
\mathbf{I}_2 \\
\cdots \\
\mathbf{I}_n
\end{bmatrix}
=
\begin{bmatrix}
\mathbf{E}_1 \\
\mathbf{E}_2 \\
\cdots \\
\mathbf{E}_n
\end{bmatrix}
\qquad (9\text{-}10)
$$

Several important properties of Eq. (9-10) should be mentioned before we proceed. The 1-1 element in the impedance matrix has been written as a sum of two elements to emphasize the fact that $\mathbf{Z}_0$ occurs in this position and in no other (since $\mathbf{I}_1$ is the only loop current flowing through $\mathbf{Z}_0$). The term $\mathbf{Z}_{11}$ is the portion of the impedance of loop 1 which is contained in N. The elements in the column matrix on the right of the equality sign are due to voltage sources or voltage drops caused by currents from current sources. As has been previously mentioned, all these sources are in N.

We may solve for the current $\mathbf{I}_1$ by using Cramer's rule. The result is shown in Eq. (9-11):

$$
\begin{aligned}
\mathbf{I}_1 &= \frac{\mathbf{E}_1|Z|_{11} + \mathbf{E}_2|Z|_{21} + \mathbf{E}_3|Z|_{31} + \cdots + \mathbf{E}_n|Z|_{n1}}{(\mathbf{Z}_0 + \mathbf{Z}_{11})|Z|_{11} + \mathbf{Z}_{21}|Z|_{21} + \mathbf{Z}_{31}|Z|_{31} + \cdots + \mathbf{Z}_{n1}|Z|_{n1}} \\
&= \frac{\mathbf{E}_1|Z|_{11} + \mathbf{E}_2|Z|_{21} + \mathbf{E}_3|Z|_{31} + \cdots + \mathbf{E}_n|Z|_{n1}}{\mathbf{Z}_0|Z|_{11} + |Z-|}
\end{aligned}
\qquad (9\text{-}11)
$$

The denominator of the expression above is, of course, the determinant of the impedance matrix of Eq. (9-10). In the second line of the equation, the denominator has been separated into two parts: $|Z-|$, which denotes the determinant of the impedance matrix with $\mathbf{Z}_0$ removed, and $\mathbf{Z}_0$ times the cofactor $|Z|_{11}$.

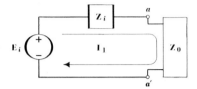

Fig. 9-4. A network which is equivalent, by Thévenin's theorem, to the network of Fig. 9-3.

If we divide the numerator and denominator of Eq. (9-11) by $|Z|_{11}$, we arrive at the following simplified expression:

$$\mathbf{I}_1 = \frac{\mathbf{E}_i}{\mathbf{Z}_0 + \mathbf{Z}_i} \tag{9-12}$$

$$\text{where}\quad \mathbf{E}_i = \frac{\mathbf{E}_1 |Z|_{11} + \mathbf{E}_2 |Z|_{21} + \mathbf{E}_3 |Z|_{31} + \cdots + \mathbf{E}_n |Z|_{n1}}{|Z|_{11}} \tag{9-13}$$

$$\mathbf{Z}_i = \frac{|Z-|}{|Z|_{11}} \tag{9-14}$$

In Eq. (9-12), $\mathbf{Z}_0$ occurs only where shown and is not hidden anywhere in $\mathbf{E}_i$ or $\mathbf{Z}_i$.

Equation (9-11) has been reduced to the form of Eq. (9-12) in order to show that it is exactly the same as the current equation which would be obtained for the circuit of Fig. 9-4 if the voltage source $\mathbf{E}_i$ and the internal impedance $\mathbf{Z}_i$ of that figure were as given in Eqs. (9-13) and (9-14). In other words, as far as the current and voltage across the impedance $\mathbf{Z}_0$ are concerned, the network of Fig. 9-3 may be replaced by the equivalent circuit shown in Fig. 9-4.

The use of such an equivalent circuit will be greatly facilitated if the quantities $\mathbf{E}_i$ and $\mathbf{Z}_i$ can be found in a simpler manner than is indicated by Eqs. (9-13) and (9-14). We can see by inspection of Fig. 9-4 or Eq. (9-12) that the voltage $\mathbf{E}_i$ is just the voltage that would be measured or calculated at the terminals $a\text{-}a'$ if $\mathbf{Z}_0$ was allowed to become very large, that is, an open circuit.

The impedance $\mathbf{Z}_i$ can be found in the equivalent circuit by shorting the voltage source† and measuring the impedance looking in at the terminals $a\text{-}a'$. To show that the same thing can be done to the original network, let us replace the impedance $\mathbf{Z}_0$ in that network by a voltage source $\mathbf{E}_0$ and then compute the current $\mathbf{I}_1$. The ratio $\mathbf{E}_0/\mathbf{I}_1$ will be the impedance of N looking in at $a\text{-}a'$. During this computation, we shall short all the voltage sources and open-circuit all the current sources in N. The shorting of the voltage sources and the opening (or removal) of the current sources will not affect the loop current paths or the impedances in each path. Therefore, the matrix equation

---

† In active networks with controlled sources only *independent* sources are removed.

for this modified circuit will have exactly the same impedance matrix as given in Eq. (9-10), except that $\mathbf{Z}_0$ will no longer be included:

$$\begin{bmatrix} \mathbf{Z}_{11} & \mathbf{Z}_{12} & \mathbf{Z}_{13} & \cdots & \mathbf{Z}_{1n} \\ \mathbf{Z}_{21} & \mathbf{Z}_{22} & \mathbf{Z}_{23} & \cdots & \mathbf{Z}_{2n} \\ \cdots & \cdots & \cdots & \cdots & \cdots \\ \mathbf{Z}_{n1} & \mathbf{Z}_{n2} & \mathbf{Z}_{n3} & \cdots & \mathbf{Z}_{nn} \end{bmatrix} \times \begin{bmatrix} \mathbf{I}_1 \\ \mathbf{I}_2 \\ \cdots \\ \mathbf{I}_n \end{bmatrix} = \begin{bmatrix} \mathbf{E}_0 \\ 0 \\ \cdots \\ 0 \end{bmatrix} \qquad (9\text{-}15)$$

Solving Eq. (9-15) for $\mathbf{I}_1$ by Cramer's rule produces the following expression:

$$\mathbf{I}_1 = \frac{\mathbf{E}_0 |Z|_{11}}{|Z-|} \qquad (9\text{-}16)$$

The impedance looking in at the terminals $a\text{-}a'$ is therefore seen to be equal to the impedance $\mathbf{Z}_i$ as defined in Eq. (9-14):

$$\frac{\mathbf{E}_0}{\mathbf{I}_1} = \frac{|Z-|}{|Z|_{11}} = \mathbf{Z}_i \qquad (9\text{-}17)$$

The foregoing discussion may be summarized in the following state-ment, which is a statement of Thévenin's theorem. *A circuit such as is shown in Fig. 9-3, with N containing any number of voltage and current sources and any arrangement of linear impedances, may be replaced by the equivalent circuit of Fig. 9-4 for the purposes of analyzing the response across* $\mathbf{Z}_0$. *The internal impedance* $\mathbf{Z}_i$ *is the impedance looking into N with all voltage sources shorted and all current sources open-circuited. The voltage source* $\mathbf{E}_i$ *is equal to the open-circuit voltage at* $a\text{-}a'$.

NORTON'S THEOREM Norton's theorem may be stated as follows: *The circuit of Fig. 9-3 may be replaced by the equivalent circuit of Fig. 9-5. The internal admittance* $\mathbf{Y}_i$ *is the admittance looking into N at* $a\text{-}a'$ *with all voltage sources shorted and all current sources open-circuited. The current source* $\mathbf{I}_i$ *is equal to the current which would flow between terminals* $a\text{-}a'$ *if they were short-circuited.*

This theorem could be proved in a manner entirely analogous to the procedure used for Thévenin's theorem. If we analyzed the original network by the node method, using terminal a' as the reference

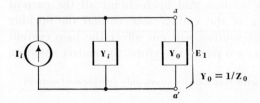

Fig. 9-5. The Norton equivalent circuit for the network of Fig. 9-3.

and terminal a as the unknown node voltage $\mathbf{E}_1$, and then solved the matrix equation, we would obtain

$$\mathbf{E}_1 = \frac{\mathbf{I}_i}{\mathbf{Y}_0 + \mathbf{Y}_i} \tag{9-18}$$

where
$$\mathbf{I}_i = \frac{\mathbf{I}_1 |Y|_{11} + \mathbf{I}_2 |Y|_{21} + \mathbf{I}_3 |Y|_{31} + \cdots + \mathbf{I}_n |Y|_{n1}}{|Y|_{11}} \tag{9-19}$$

$$\mathbf{Y}_i = \frac{|Y-|}{|Y|_{11}} \tag{9-20}$$

Equation (9-18) is the same expression as we would obtain from the circuit of Fig. 9-5. The details of the proof are left to the reader.

EXCHANGE-OF-SOURCES THEOREM The two theorems above indicate that, in relation to their effect upon the external circuit, the two types of energy sources may be freely interchanged. This last statement is illustrated graphically in Fig. 9-6. The two circuits on the left of the figure consist of a voltage source and associated passive elements (N_1) and a current source and associated passive elements (N_2). By Thévenin's and Norton's theorems, each of the circuits on the left may be represented by either of the circuits on the right. Consequently, a voltage source with associated circuitry may be replaced by a current source in parallel with an appropriate admittance. In a like manner, a current source with associated circuitry may be replaced by a voltage source in series with an appropriate impedance. The equivalence used most frequently is the exchange between a voltage source in series with an impedance and a current source in parallel with an admittance.

When a current source $\mathbf{I}_i$ in parallel with an admittance $\mathbf{Y}_i$ is to be replaced by a voltage source $\mathbf{E}_i$ in series with an impedance $\mathbf{Z}_i$, or vice versa, the following relationships, derived from Thévenin's and Nor-

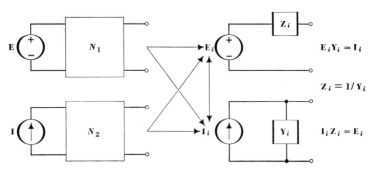

Fig. 9-6. Each of the networks on the left may be replaced by either of the two networks on the right, or, more simply, the two networks on the right may be interchanged.

ton's theorems, are employed:

$$E_i = \frac{I_i}{Y_i} \qquad Z_i = \frac{1}{Y_i} \tag{9-21}$$

DISCUSSION OF EQUIVALENT-NETWORK THEOREMS The preceding theorems, which are frequently called equivalent-network theorems, are exceedingly useful concepts which may be employed in numerous situations. It is important that the reader be familiar with the degree of generality and the restrictions on these theorems, as well as with the mechanics of applying them. The theorems were developed in terms of circuit parameters which were assumed to be functions of s. Since both the energy sources and the passive elements were assumed to be functions of s, the theorems are quite general; they hold for transient conditions, as well as sinusoidal steady-state conditions.

The restrictions which we must recognize are as follows. The theorems apply only to linear systems, that is, to systems in which the passive elements are linear and bilateral and the sources are ideal. A most important restriction in the use of such equivalent circuits is that *they are equivalent to the original circuit only in so far as their effect on the external impedance Z_0 is concerned.* The internal currents, voltages, and powers of the equivalent circuits bear no simple relation to those of the original circuit.

Thévenin-Norton equivalent networks are particularly useful in systems in which the sources are single-frequency sinusoidal steady-state sources. In these systems, phasor notation can be utilized in calculating the equivalent circuits. Consequently, the internal impedance can be represented as a simple complex number and can be found experimentally by simple measurements, even though shorting or opening the sources may be impossible. This property is illustrated in the following simple example.

EXAMPLE OF AN EQUIVALENT-NETWORK COMPUTATION Figure 9-7 illustrates the equivalent network of a power system which is delivering power to a particular installation. In order to ascertain the effect of various loads on the terminal voltage at the installation, it is necessary to determine the equivalent voltage source and the internal impedance.

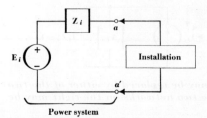

Fig. 9-7. *The equivalent network of a power system delivering power to an installation. The terminals a-a' are the only access to the power system for measurements.*

Let us assume that this is one of those often-encountered situations in which the actual internal circuit is not known† and in which it is impossible to short- or open-circuit the internal sources. However, we may find the necessary information with purely external measurements.

Let us assume that the first measurement is of the open-circuit terminal voltage. To use a numerical example, let us suppose that it is found to be 125 volts rms and 60 cps. This is, of course, the value we assign to our equivalent voltage source. Now we must devise one or more measurements to determine Z_i. One possibility is to measure the current that would flow between the terminals when they are shorted. A glance at the equivalent circuit indicates that, theoretically at least, this will yield the desired information, since

$$\frac{\mathbf{E}_{\text{open circuit}}}{\mathbf{I}_{\text{short circuit}}} = \mathbf{Z}_i \tag{9-22}$$

However, two practical problems are associated with this method which may invalidate it. The first is the possibility that the short-circuit current may be so large as to cause damage to the circuit. The second problem is that, to determine $\mathbf{Z}_i$ completely, the phase relationship between the open-circuit voltage and short-circuit current, as well as their magnitudes, must be known. This phase relationship cannot be measured with the simple voltmeters and ammeters usually available.

Both problems may be remedied by making more than one measurement at current values which can be tolerated. For example, let us suppose we have two purely resistive loads which we can connect to terminals a-a'. The first load, a 12-ohm resistance, allows a current of 8 amp to flow while the terminal voltage drops to 96 volts. The second, a 15-ohm resistance, has 6.8 amp flowing through it when connected to the terminals. Let us see what we can do with these two pieces of information.

The rms value of the current flowing through the load is equal to the rms value of the voltage source divided by the magnitude of the total impedance. Therefore, for the two loads above, we have

$$I_1 = 8 = \frac{E_i}{Z_1} = \frac{125}{\sqrt{(12 + R_i)^2 + X_i^2}} \tag{9-23}$$

$$I_2 = 6.8 = \frac{E_i}{Z_2} = \frac{125}{\sqrt{(15 + R_i)^2 + X_i^2}} \tag{9-24}$$

The terms R_i and X_i are the resistance and reactance components of the internal impedance $\mathbf{Z}_i$. The two equations above may be put into the

† However, it is assumed to be linear, which means that we may use Thévenin's theorem.

following forms by squaring and inverting:

$$R_i^2 + 24R_i + X_i^2 = \frac{125^2}{8} - 12^2 \tag{9-25}$$

$$R_i^2 + 30R_i + X_i^2 = \frac{125^2}{6.8} - 15^2 \tag{9-26}$$

The difference of these last two equations yields a solution for R_i. With a value for R_i, substitution in either equation yields X_i.

$$R_i = 2.13 \text{ ohms} \qquad X_i = \pm 6.67 \text{ ohms} \tag{9-27}$$

Equation (9-27) indicates that our two measurements are not quite sufficient to determine $\mathbf{Z}_i$ completely. The magnitude of the reactance X_i is known, but whether it is inductive or capacitive has not yet been determined. It should be clear from the form of the equations leading to the solution that any further measurements with purely resistive loads will produce no additional data of any value. However, one more measurement with a purely or partially reactive load will provide the needed information. The current through such a load can be measured, and an equation corresponding to Eqs. (9-23) and (9-24) can be established which will furnish the final solution. The determination of the sign of the reactance for this particular system is left to the student in Prob. 9-12.

PROBLEMS

9-9   Carry through in detail the proof of Norton's theorem.

9-10   Develop an argument to prove in general that the division of Eq. (9-11) by $|Z|_{11}$ is permissible. That is, show in general that $|Z|_{11} \neq 0$.

9-11   Replace each of the networks in the figure by its Thévenin and Norton equivalents.

9-12   If a 5-μf capacitor is connected in parallel with the 15-ohm resistor in the equivalent-circuit example, what will be the resultant voltage and current if the internal impedance is inductive? If the internal impedance is capacitive?

9-13   Repeat Prob. 9-12 for a 10-mh inductance in series with the 15-ohm resistor.

9-14   The n voltage sources in the figure are replaced by a single voltage source such that the terminal characteristics are unaltered. What are the values of $\mathbf{E}$ and $\mathbf{Z}$? Find $\mathbf{I}$ and $\mathbf{Y}$ for the analogous current-source circuits. The transformations demonstrated in this problem are called *Millman's theorem*.

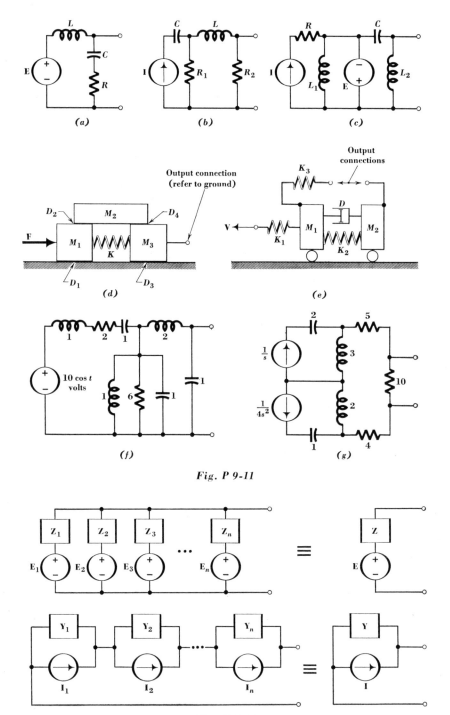

Fig. P 9-11

Fig. P 9-14

9-15   Part *a* of the figure illustrates a network in which part of one loop has been placed in evidence. Assume that the network response has been determined completely, including **I**. The exposed loop is to be opened, and the impedance shown in part *b* is to be inserted. Show that the resultant incremental change in each of the network currents and voltages can be found by inserting the circuit of part *c* in the loop and then computing the network currents and voltages with all other sources in *N* neglected. The currents and voltages so computed are the amounts that the original currents and voltages will change when **Z** is inserted.

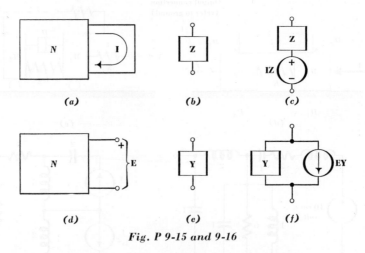

(a)   (b)   (c)

(d)   (e)   (f)

Fig. P 9-15 and 9-16

9-16   A problem analogous to the preceding one is to find the incremental changes in the voltages and currents of a network when an admittance is connected between two nodes. Assuming again that the response is known, show that the changes caused by connecting **Y** to the exposed nodes of (*d*) are determined by connecting the circuit of (*f*) to the nodes. The voltages and currents caused by (*f*) are the changes which result when **Y** alone is connected to the nodes.

Problems 9-15 and 9-16 form what is called the *compensation theorem*. Note that **Z** in Prob. 9-15 could be negative, which would indicate a reduction in the impedance of the branch. Similarly, a negative **Y** would correspond to a decreased admittance between the nodes.

9-17   Discuss the possible applications of the compensation theorem derived in the two preceding problems.

9-18   In the circuit shown, no voltage exists across the terminals *a-b* if the switch is open. Closing the switch at $t = 0$ produces a voltage across *a-b* which is $e_{ab} = 1 - e^{-4t}$. (If the switch is opened and closed again, the same voltage will occur.) When the terminals are shorted, the current which flows when the switch is closed at $t = 0$ is

$$i_{ab} = \frac{1}{2} + \frac{1}{\sqrt{2}} e^{-4t} \sin \left(4t + \frac{\pi}{4} \right)$$

Find the Thévenin and Norton equivalent circuits of this network.

Fig. P 9-18

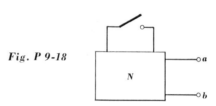

9-3 INCLUSION OF INITIAL CONDITIONS IN USING IMPEDANCE METHODS

In Chap. 7, general methods of obtaining both transient and steady-state responses to various driving functions were formulated by using the concept of impulse responses and circuit impedances in the *s* domain. Chapter 8 extended these methods to more complex networks through the use of node and loop analysis. In developing these methods, it was assumed that in the transient cases the energy-storage elements stored no initial energy. In this section, we shall see that this assumption is unnecessary and shall discuss techniques of analysis for the case of initial stored energy. The presentation of this material, which perhaps most logically should follow Sec. 7-3, was postponed until this point so that we could make use of the analysis techniques introduced in this chapter and the preceding one.

A SIMPLE MECHANICAL EXAMPLE   To introduce the technique of handling initial stored energy, let us analyze the mechanical system illustrated in Fig. 9-8. We shall assume that the force $f(t)$ is applied at $t = 0$ and that the mass has an initial velocity $v(0)$ which is known. The differential equation of this system and its solution should be

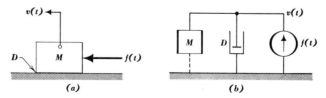

Fig. 9-8. A simple two-element mechanical system.

quite familiar by now. They are given below:

$$M \frac{dv}{dt} + Dv = f(t) \tag{9-28}$$

$$v(t) = v_f(t) + Ae^{-Dt/M} \qquad t \geq 0 \tag{9-29}$$

In Eq. (9-29), $v_f(t)$ is the forced solution due to the force $f(t)$, and the exponential term is the natural solution. The constant A may be determined through knowledge of the initial stored energy. That is,

$$v(0) = v_f(0) + A \tag{9-30}$$

Let us call A_0 the value of A which is obtained when there is no initial stored energy. Then

$$A = A_0 + A_1 \tag{9-31}$$

where $\qquad\qquad A_0 = -v_f(0) \qquad A_1 = v(0) \tag{9-32}$

Separating the constant A into the two parts given in Eq. (9-31) allows us to express Eq. (9-29) in the following form:

$$v(t) = [v_f(t) + A_0 e^{-Dt/M}] + A_1 e^{-Dt/M} \qquad t \geq 0 \tag{9-33}$$

The expression within the brackets is the response that would exist if there were no initial stored energy. This is the response which would be obtained by the impulse-response–impedance method of calculation. The last term is an additional natural response, which arises because of the initial stored energy.

We wish to enlarge the impulse-response–impedance technique to a point where it will produce the complete solution, as given in Eq. (9-33). To do this, it is helpful to utilize the superposition theorem. The network response given in Eq. (9-33) may be considered to be the response of the system, with no initial stored energy, to two sources. One source is our original-force source, which gives the response within the brackets. The other source produces the term $A_1 e^{-Dt/M}$. Therefore, we wish to find a source to apply to the network of Fig. 9-9a which will produce this response. (The original-force source has been

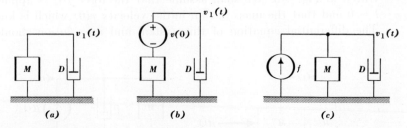

Fig. 9-9. (a) *This network, with no initial energy stored, is to have a source applied such that* $v_1(t) = A_1 e^{-Dt/M}$ *for* $t \geq 0$. *(b) This constant-velocity source applied at* $t = 0$ *satisfies the requirements. (c) This network is equivalent to that of part b if the force source is an impulse of magnitude* $Mv(0)$ *applied at* $t = 0$.

removed, as per the superposition theorem.) With such a simple response, it is not difficult to determine that the required source may be either a step-velocity source, as shown in Fig. 9-9b, or a force impulse, as shown in Fig. 9-9c.

To show that a force impulse, as applied in Fig. 9-9c, actually does satisfy our requirements, let us find the response by the impedance method. The mechanical impedance of the network is

$$\mathbf{Z}_m = Ms + D \tag{9-34}$$

The applied force is an impulse of magnitude $Mv(0)$. The velocity response (in the s domain) is

$$\mathbf{V}_1(s) = \frac{\mathbf{F}_1(s)}{\mathbf{Z}_m(s)} = \frac{Mv(0)}{Ms + D} = \frac{v(0)}{s + D/M} \tag{9-35}$$

If the corresponding response in the time domain is not recalled, it can be found in the Appendix.

$$v_1(t) = v(0)e^{-Dt/M} = A_1 e^{-Dt/M} \tag{9-36}$$

The response of the network of Fig. 9-9b can be verified in a similar manner. Note that circuits b and c of Fig. 9-9 can be derived from each other by the exchange-of-sources theorem (see Fig. 9-6).

The foregoing development has demonstrated that the network of Fig. 9-8, with the mass having an initial velocity $v(0)$, may be replaced by either of the networks in Fig. 9-10. In Fig. 9-10 the mass is considered to have no initial velocity. Although this discussion has been concerned with a very simple network, a little thought should make it obvious that the methods apply to more complex systems. That is to say, in any network a mass with an initial velocity may be replaced by an equal mass, with no stored energy, in tandem (series) with a step-velocity source or abreast (parallel) with a force-impulse source. Once this has been done, the network response may be calculated in the s domain by means of the techniques already developed. The calculations may include all the sources simultaneously or individually by superposition.

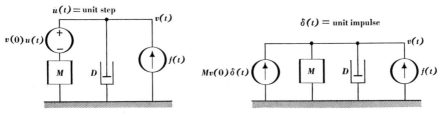

Fig. 9-10. Two circuits with zero initial stored energy which are equivalent to the circuit of Fig. 9-8.

The results of the analysis above may be applied by analogy to the other energy-storage elements. Each of the elements, when initially storing energy, may be replaced by an equal element with no stored energy in series or parallel with an appropriate source. When all such elements in a network have been replaced, the transient analysis proceeds in the usual manner. The appropriate equivalences are tabulated in Table 9-1.

A DIFFERENT APPROACH TO THE SAME PROBLEM A second approach, leading to the same result, can be evolved by considering the following example. Figure 9-11a shows a capacitor as part of a more extensive network. If the circuit is being analyzed on a loop basis, the voltage drop across the capacitor will appear in the integrodifferential equation

TABLE 9-1 *Equivalents of Elements with Initial Stored Energy*

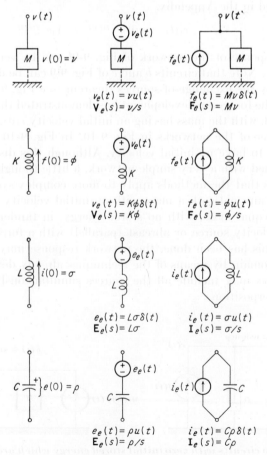

$v_e(t) = vu(t)$
$V_e(s) = v/s$

$f_e(t) = Mv\delta(t)$
$F_e(s) = Mv$

$v_e(t) = K\phi\delta(t)$
$V_e(s) = K\phi$

$f_e(t) = \phi u(t)$
$F_e(s) = \phi/s$

$e_e(t) = L\sigma\delta(t)$
$E_e(s) = L\sigma$

$i_e(t) = \sigma u(t)$
$I_e(s) = \sigma/s$

$e_e(t) = \rho u(t)$
$E_e(s) = \rho/s$

$i_e(t) = C\rho\delta(t)$
$I_e(s) = C\rho$

$u(t)$ = unit-step function $\delta(t)$ = unit-impulse function

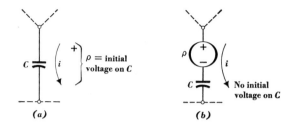

Fig. 9-11. A capacitor with an initial voltage ρ and its equivalent circuit.

of some loop as follows:

$$\cdots + \frac{1}{C} \int i \, dt + \cdots \tag{9-37}$$

The integral above is written as an indefinite integral. This results in an arbitrary constant of integration, which in the solution of the integrodifferential equation is determined by utilizing the initial conditions. The voltage across the capacitor may be more completely specified in the form of a definite integral:

$$e_c = \frac{1}{C} \int_{-\infty}^{t} i \, dt = \frac{1}{C} \int_{-\infty}^{0} i \, dt + \frac{1}{C} \int_{0}^{t} i \, dt \tag{9-38}$$

The first term in the sum above is the initial voltage across the capacitor, and the second term is the voltage that would occur if there were no initial stored voltage. Consequently, Eq. (9-37) could be written as

$$\cdots + \rho + \frac{1}{C} \int_{0}^{t} i \, dt + \cdots \tag{9-39}$$

where

$$\rho = \frac{1}{C} \int_{-\infty}^{0} i \, dt \tag{9-40}$$

Thus we see that the initial charge in Fig. 9-11a may be replaced by the voltage source in Fig. 9-11b if it is assumed, in calculating the response, that there is no initial stored energy in the capacitor.

TWO EXAMPLES OF TRANSIENT SOLUTIONS INCLUDING INITIAL STORED ENERGY   The first of the two examples in this section is concerned with a mechanical system, and the second deals with an electrical circuit. The first example demonstrates extensive use of the exchange-of-sources theorem, as well as the handling of initial conditions. Both examples are solved in the s domain, but only in the second example is the solution transformed into the time domain.

The mechanical system shown in Fig. 9-12a consists of three connected cars which have been pulled along at a constant velocity v_0 long enough to ensure steady-state conditions. The brakes of the three cars have been applied during this time, and now at $t = 0$ they are released. The velocity of the second car is to be found. The first step

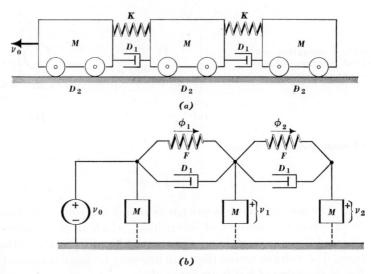

(a)

(b)

Fig. 9-12. (a) *A mechanical system consisting of three cars of mass M being pulled at a constant velocity v_0; (b) the network diagram for the system for $t \geq 0$. The brakes have been released, so $D_2 = 0$. The initial forces and velocities are ϕ_1, ϕ_2, v_1, and v_2.*

in the analysis is to redraw the system for $t \geq 0$ in network form, as is shown in Fig. 9-12b. (The reference direction is the same as the direction of the constant velocity.)

The second step is to determine the initial conditions which exist at the instant the brakes are released. Under the constant-velocity steady-state conditions, the masses may be neglected (open circuits to the "force flow"). The springs of the couplings take all the force developed across the couplings. (The springs are short circuits to force flow.) Thus, the mechanical network for the steady state, just before the brakes are released, is that shown in Fig. 9-13. From this figure the initial conditions are immediately found to be

$$\phi_1 = 2v_0 D_2 \qquad \phi_2 = v_0 D_2 \qquad v_1 = v_2 = v_0 \qquad (9\text{-}41)$$

Once the initial conditions have been determined, the appropriate equivalent networks may be selected from Table 9-1 and the response calculated in the s domain. The network equations can be set up as two

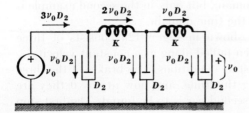

Fig. 9-13. *The network which is applicable for the steady-state conditions just before releasing the brakes (D_2).*

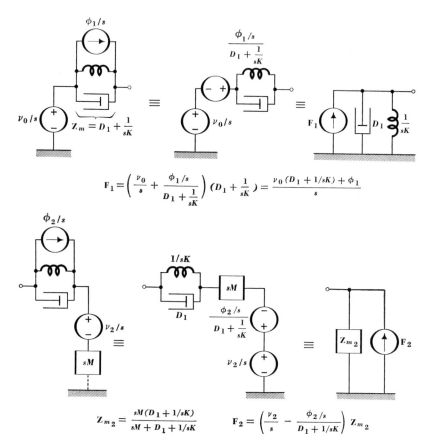

$$F_1 = \left(\frac{\nu_0}{s} + \frac{\phi_1/s}{D_1 + \frac{1}{sK}} \right) \left(D_1 + \frac{1}{sK} \right) = \frac{\nu_0 (D_1 + 1/sK) + \phi_1}{s}$$

$$Z_{m_2} = \frac{sM(D_1 + 1/sK)}{sM + D_1 + 1/sK} \qquad F_2 = \left(\frac{\nu_2}{s} - \frac{\phi_2/s}{D_1 + 1/sK} \right) Z_{m_2}$$

Fig. 9-14. *The modification of parts of the network of Fig. 9-12b by representing initial conditions as sources and by utilizing the exchange-of-sources theorem.*

node equations, or the exchange-of-sources theorem can be utilized to reduce the equations to a single node equation. Although, in this case, the reduction to a single equation hardly reduces the total computation, this method will be followed in order to demonstrate several source exchanges.

Before beginning the source exchanges, it should be noted that the first mass may be completely ignored, because the constant-velocity source is connected directly to it. The various steps in the source exchanges can best be illustrated graphically, as is done in Fig. 9-14. If the velocity of the third car, as well as that of the second car, were needed, this particular approach would not be well advised, since the velocity node of the third car is "lost in the shuffle."

Once the source exchanges have been made as indicated in Fig. 9-14, the network to be solved reduces to the one shown in Fig. 9-15.

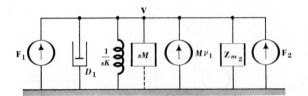

Fig. 9-15. Final equiva-
lent network for de-
termining the velocity,
after $t = 0$, of the second
car shown in Fig. 9-12a.
F_1, F_2, and Z_{m_2} are given
in Fig. 9-14.

The single node equation for this network is

$$\left(D_1 + \frac{1}{sK} + sM + Z_{m_2}\right)V = F_1 + F_2 + Mv_1 \qquad (9\text{-}42)$$

Substituting the values for Z_{m_2}, F_1, F_2, and v_1 into Eq. (9-42) yields

$$\left[D_1 + \frac{1}{sK} + sM + \frac{sM(D_1 + 1/sK)}{sM + D_1 + 1/sK}\right]V = \frac{v_0(D_1 + 1/sK) + 2v_0 D_2}{s}$$
$$+ \left(\frac{v_0}{s} - \frac{v_0 D_2/s}{D_1 + 1/sK}\right)\frac{sM(D_1 + 1/sK)}{sM + D_1 + 1/sK} + Mv_0 \qquad (9\text{-}43)$$

By placing both sides of Eq. (9-43) over a common denominator and
then simplifying as much as possible, the following equation is obtained:

$$s[(s^2 MK + sD_1 K + 1)^2 + s^2 MK(sD_1 K + 1)]V$$
$$= v_0\{(s^2 MK + sD_1 K + 1)[s^2 MK + s(D_1 + 2D_2)K + 1]$$
$$+ s^2 MK[s(D_1 - 2D_2)K + 1]\} \qquad (9\text{-}44)$$

Thus, the s-domain solution for the velocity of the second car is

$$V = \frac{v_0}{s} \frac{(s^2 MK + sD_1 K + 1)[s^2 MK + s(D_1 + 2D_2)K + 1]}{(s^2 MK + sD_1 K + 1)^2 + s^2 MK(sD_1 K + 1)} \qquad (9\text{-}45)$$

The solution above can be transformed into the time domain by
factoring the denominator and then expanding in partial-fraction form.
The time-domain response is then found by the techniques discussed in
Sec. 7-3. Before passing on to the next example, a few comments will
be made concerning Eq. (9-45). The response V has four poles in addition to the one at $s = 0$. The positions of these four poles will depend
upon the values of M, K, and D_1. With no initial braking, D_2 is zero.
Consequently, the right-hand side of Eq. (9-45) reduces to v_0/s, which
in the time domain is a constant velocity v_0. This is a partial check
on our solution, since we know that with no braking the cars will continue with no change in velocity.

AN ELECTRICAL-CIRCUIT EXAMPLE The switch in the circuit of Fig.
9-16a has been open sufficiently long for steady-state conditions to

exist. Closing the switch at $t = 0$ produces a transient response, which will be calculated below. For the purposes of this analysis the equivalent circuit shown in Fig. 9-16b will be used. The current sources in the circuit are derived from the initial $\frac{1}{2}$ amp through L_1, the initial 50 volts across C, and an exchange of a current source for the voltage source E.

The node equations for the equivalent circuit are expressed in matrix form below:

$$\begin{bmatrix} 0.01 + \dfrac{20}{s} & \dfrac{-10}{s} \\ \dfrac{-10}{s} & 10^{-6}s + 0.01 + \dfrac{10}{s} \end{bmatrix} \times \begin{bmatrix} E_1 \\ E_2 \end{bmatrix} = \begin{bmatrix} \dfrac{0.5}{s} \\ 5 \times 10^{-5} + \dfrac{0.5}{s} \end{bmatrix}$$

(9-46)

Multiplying both sides of the matrix equation by s yields the following expression:

$$\begin{bmatrix} 10^{-2}s + 20 & -10 \\ -10 & 10^{-6}s^2 + 10^{-2}s + 10 \end{bmatrix} \times \begin{bmatrix} E_1 \\ E_2 \end{bmatrix} = \begin{bmatrix} 0.5 \\ 5 \times 10^{-5}s + 0.5 \end{bmatrix}$$

(9-47)

Let us find E_2 by solving Eq. (9-47):

$$\begin{aligned} E_2 &= \frac{(10^{-2}s + 20)(5 \times 10^{-5}s + 0.5) + 5}{(10^{-2}s + 20)(10^{-6}s^2 + 10^{-2}s + 10) - 100} \\ &= \frac{50s^2 + 6 \times 10^{5}s + 15 \times 10^{8}}{s^3 + 12 \times 10^{3}s^2 + 3 \times 10^{7}s + 10^{10}} \end{aligned}$$

(9-48)

At this point the following change in variables simplifies the numerical work to some extent:

$$s = 10^{3}s_1$$ (9-49)

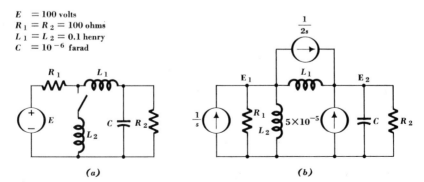

$E = 100$ volts
$R_1 = R_2 = 100$ ohms
$L_1 = L_2 = 0.1$ henry
$C = 10^{-6}$ farad

(a)   (b)

Fig. 9-16. (a) Steady-state conditions exist in this circuit before the switch is closed at $t = 0$; (b) the equivalent circuit for $t \geq 0$.

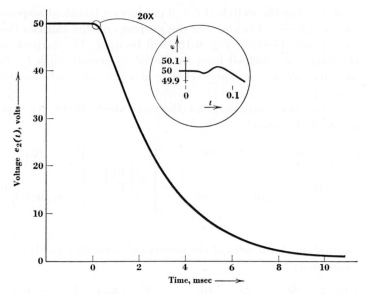

Fig. 9-17. *A plot of Eq. (9-52), the voltage across the RC combination of Fig. 9-16a after the switch is closed.*

With this change, Eq. (9-48) becomes

$$\mathbf{E}_2 = \frac{0.05s_1{}^2 + 0.6s_1 + 1.5}{s_1{}^3 + 12s_1{}^2 + 30s_1 + 10}$$
$$= \frac{0.0605}{s_1 + 0.393} - \frac{0.0117}{s_1 + 2.932} + \frac{0.0012}{s_1 + 8.674} \tag{9-50}$$

Converting back to the original variable gives

$$\mathbf{E}_2 = \frac{60.5}{s + 393} - \frac{11.7}{s + 2,932} + \frac{1.2}{s + 8,674} \tag{9-51}$$

Transforming the s-domain solution of Eq. (9-51) into the time domain gives

$$e_2(t) = 60.5e^{-393t} - 11.7e^{-2,932t} + 1.2e^{-8,674t} \tag{9-52}$$

The time response as given above is plotted in Fig. 9-17.

PROBLEMS

9-19 In each of the circuits shown, the switch has been open for a time sufficient to ensure steady-state conditions. Find the indicated quantity (s domain only) for each circuit if the switch is closed at $t = 0$.

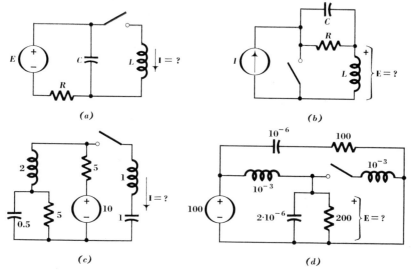

Fig. P 9-19

9-20   The boxcar shown in the figure is rolling with a velocity of 5 m/sec when it comes into contact with the bumper at $t = 0$. Find the velocity of the car for $t \geq 0$ if:

(a) The car becomes attached to the bumper after contact.

(b) The car does not become attached to the bumper.

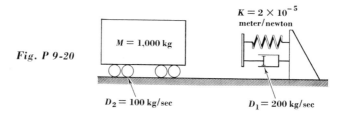

Fig. P 9-20

9-21   Suppose that the damper D_1 in Prob. 9-20 is constructed so that D_1 is zero when the bumper moves to the right and is 10^5 kg/sec when it moves to the left. Find the velocity of the boxcar under these conditions.

9-22   Find the velocity (time domain) of the second car of the example discussed in the text if $M = 1$, $K = 1$, $D_1 = 2$, and $D_2 = 1$.

9-23   Find the s-domain velocity of the second car of the example discussed in the text by setting up and solving the node equations without simplification by exchange of sources.

9-24 After being closed for a long time, the switch in the illustrated circuit is opened. Find the current through the 10-ohm resistor.

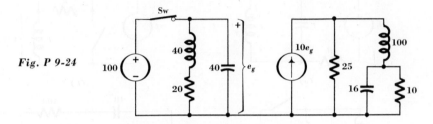

Fig. P 9-24

9-25 In the circuits shown, the initial conditions are given. Write the node or loop matrix equation for each circuit.

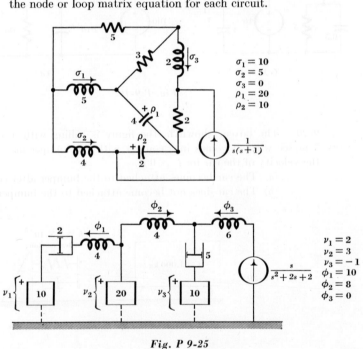

$$\sigma_1 = 10$$
$$\sigma_2 = 5$$
$$\sigma_3 = 0$$
$$\rho_1 = 20$$
$$\rho_2 = 10$$

$$\nu_1 = 2$$
$$\nu_2 = 3$$
$$\nu_3 = -1$$
$$\phi_1 = 10$$
$$\phi_2 = 8$$
$$\phi_3 = 0$$

Fig. P 9-25

9-4 TWO-PORT-NETWORK PARAMETERS

Two-port networks, which are also called four-terminal or two-terminal-pair networks, have been encountered and analyzed in previous sections of this book. For the most part, however, they have been treated as individual cases, with little attempt to generalize the analysis. The purpose of this section is to examine two-port networks as a class. The product of this examination will be sets of parameters which can be applied in the analysis of general two-port networks. Six sets

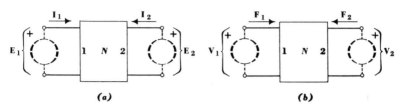

Fig. 9-18. (a) *An electrical two-port network; (b) a mechanical two-port network.*

of parameters for specifying two-port-network characteristics will be derived. All six sets are interrelated, and if one set is known, the other five can be found. Which of the six to use in analyzing a two-port network will depend upon the form of the driving function, the response function which is to be found, and the interconnections with other two-ports. The following development will be limited to two-port networks, but it can easily be extended to n-port networks.

PASSIVE TWO-PORT NETWORKS The parameters for linear passive two-ports (those with no energy sources within the network) will be derived first, and the results will then be extended to active networks. A general two-port network is illustrated in Fig. 9-18. The dashed-line source symbols indicate that sources may be connected to the terminals. Alternatively, the sources may be replaced by loads having the indicated voltages across them and currents through them. Either condition yields to the same analysis.

Analysis of the electrical two-port by the loop method results in the following equation:

$$\begin{bmatrix} Z_{11} & Z_{12} & \cdots & Z_{1n} \\ Z_{21} & Z_{22} & \cdots & Z_{2n} \\ \cdots & \cdots & \cdots & \cdots \\ Z_{n1} & Z_{n2} & \cdots & Z_{nn} \end{bmatrix} \begin{bmatrix} I_1 \\ I_2 \\ \cdots \\ I_n \end{bmatrix} = \begin{bmatrix} E_1 \\ E_2 \\ \cdots \\ E_n \end{bmatrix} \tag{9-53}$$

Since the network is passive, the following condition applies to Eq. (9-53):

$$E_3 = E_4 = \cdots = E_n = 0 \tag{9-54}$$

Therefore, the solution of Eq. (9-53) is

$$\begin{aligned} I_1 &= y_{11}E_1 + y_{12}E_2 \\ I_2 &= y_{21}E_1 + y_{22}E_2 \end{aligned} \tag{9-55}$$

where

$$y_{11} = \frac{|Z|_{11}}{|Z|} \qquad y_{22} = \frac{|Z|_{22}}{|Z|}$$

$$y_{12} = y_{21}\dagger = \frac{|Z|_{12}}{|Z|} \tag{9-56}$$

† This condition will not be generally true for active networks.

Equations (9-55) may be expressed in matrix form as follows:

$$\begin{bmatrix} y_{11} & y_{12} \\ y_{21} & y_{22} \end{bmatrix} \times \begin{bmatrix} E_1 \\ E_2 \end{bmatrix} = \begin{bmatrix} I_1 \\ I_2 \end{bmatrix} \qquad (9\text{-}57)$$

Equation (9-57) and Eqs. (9-55) express a simple but noteworthy result. As far as the terminal voltages and currents are concerned, the characteristics of the passive network, no matter how complex, are expressible in terms of just three parameters: y_{11}, y_{22}, and $y_{12} = y_{21}$. Thus, if these three parameters are known, the terminal currents corresponding to any pair of terminal voltages can be calculated immediately. The parameters derived above are called the *short-circuit admittance parameters* of the network. The reason for this appellation will be made clear shortly.

The inverse of the short-circuit admittance matrix can be found easily by the methods discussed in Sec. 8-3. This inverse matrix can be used to express the following relationship between terminal voltages and terminal currents:

$$\begin{bmatrix} z_{11} & z_{12} \\ z_{21} & z_{22} \end{bmatrix} \times \begin{bmatrix} I_1 \\ I_2 \end{bmatrix} = \begin{bmatrix} E_1 \\ E_2 \end{bmatrix} \qquad (9\text{-}58)$$

$$[\mathbf{z}] = [\mathbf{y}]^{-1} \qquad (9\text{-}59)$$

The new parameters, which are used in Eq. (9-58) and which are related to the short-circuit admittance parameters by Eq. (9-59), are called the *open-circuit impedance parameters* of the network.

It was shown in Eqs. (9-56) that the short-circuit admittance parameters are obtainable from the original-network loop impedance matrix. In a like manner, the open-circuit impedance parameters can be calculated from the admittance matrix obtained by analyzing the network on a node basis. Alternatively, there is a more direct means of determining these parameters. For example, if E_2 is made zero, that is, if port 2 is short-circuited, the following expression can be obtained from Eq. (9-57):

$$y_{11} = \frac{I_1}{E_1}\bigg]_{E_2 = 0} \qquad (9\text{-}60)$$

On the other hand, by open-circuiting port 2 and forcing I_2 to zero, z_{11} can be obtained from Eq. (9-58):

$$z_{11} = \frac{E_1}{I_1}\bigg]_{I_2 = 0} \qquad (9\text{-}61)$$

Continuing this technique yields

$$y_{11} = \frac{I_1}{E_1}\bigg]_{E_2 = 0} \qquad \text{short-circuit driving-point admittance at port 1}$$

$$y_{12} = \frac{I_1}{E_2}\bigg]_{E_1 = 0} \qquad \text{short-circuit transfer admittance with port 1 shorted}$$

$$\mathbf{y}_{21} = \frac{\mathbf{I}_2}{\mathbf{E}_1}\bigg]_{\mathbf{E}_2=0} \qquad \text{short-circuit transfer admittance with port 2 shorted}$$

$$\mathbf{y}_{22} = \frac{\mathbf{I}_2}{\mathbf{E}_2}\bigg]_{\mathbf{E}_1=0} \qquad \text{short-circuit driving-point admittance at port 2}$$

$$\mathbf{z}_{11} = \frac{\mathbf{E}_1}{\mathbf{I}_1}\bigg]_{\mathbf{I}_2=0} \qquad \text{open-circuit driving-point impedance at port 1}$$

$$\mathbf{z}_{12} = \frac{\mathbf{E}_1}{\mathbf{I}_2}\bigg]_{\mathbf{I}_1=0} \qquad \text{open-circuit transfer impedance with port 1 open}$$

$$\mathbf{z}_{21} = \frac{\mathbf{E}_2}{\mathbf{I}_1}\bigg]_{\mathbf{I}_2=0} \qquad \text{open-circuit transfer impedance with port 2 open}$$

$$\mathbf{z}_{22} = \frac{\mathbf{E}_2}{\mathbf{I}_2}\bigg]_{\mathbf{I}_1=0} \qquad \text{open-circuit driving-point impedance at port 2}$$

FOUR ADDITIONAL SETS OF PARAMETERS The short-circuit admittance parameters and open-circuit impedance parameters characterize the network by relating terminal currents to terminal voltages and vice versa. These parameters are clearly not the only ways of relating the terminal functions. In addition, the voltage and current at one port are expressible in terms of the voltage and current at the other port. Other relationships are also possible, as is illustrated below.

All possible sets of parameters, and the relations among them, are obtained by simple manipulations of the original set, Eqs. (9-55). The additional parameters are expressed below in terms of matrix equations relating the terminal functions. The short- or open-circuit measurements which also define these parameters are denoted. The relationships among all the sets of parameters are tabulated in Table 9-2.

*The **g** parameters:*

$$\begin{bmatrix} \mathbf{g}_{11} & \mathbf{g}_{12} \\ \mathbf{g}_{21} & \mathbf{g}_{22} \end{bmatrix} \times \begin{bmatrix} \mathbf{E}_1 \\ \mathbf{I}_2 \end{bmatrix} = \begin{bmatrix} \mathbf{I}_1 \\ \mathbf{E}_2 \end{bmatrix} \tag{9-62}$$

where
$$\mathbf{g}_{11} = \frac{\mathbf{I}_1}{\mathbf{E}_1}\bigg]_{\mathbf{I}_2=0} \qquad \mathbf{g}_{12} = \frac{\mathbf{I}_1}{\mathbf{I}_2}\bigg]_{\mathbf{E}_1=0}$$

$$\mathbf{g}_{21} = \frac{\mathbf{E}_2}{\mathbf{E}_1}\bigg]_{\mathbf{I}_2=0} \qquad \mathbf{g}_{22} = \frac{\mathbf{E}_2}{\mathbf{I}_2}\bigg]_{\mathbf{E}_1=0}$$

*The **h** parameters:*

$$\begin{bmatrix} \mathbf{h}_{11} & \mathbf{h}_{12} \\ \mathbf{h}_{21} & \mathbf{h}_{22} \end{bmatrix} \times \begin{bmatrix} \mathbf{I}_1 \\ \mathbf{E}_2 \end{bmatrix} = \begin{bmatrix} \mathbf{E}_1 \\ \mathbf{I}_2 \end{bmatrix} \tag{9-63}$$

where
$$\mathbf{h}_{11} = \frac{\mathbf{E}_1}{\mathbf{I}_1}\bigg]_{\mathbf{E}_2=0} \qquad \mathbf{h}_{12} = \frac{\mathbf{E}_1}{\mathbf{E}_2}\bigg]_{\mathbf{I}_1=0}$$

$$\mathbf{h}_{21} = \frac{\mathbf{I}_2}{\mathbf{I}_1}\bigg]_{\mathbf{E}_2=0} \qquad \mathbf{h}_{22} = \frac{\mathbf{I}_2}{\mathbf{E}_1}\bigg]_{\mathbf{I}_1=0}$$

The **a** *parameters:*

$$\begin{bmatrix} a_{11} & a_{12} \\ a_{21} & a_{22} \end{bmatrix} \times \begin{bmatrix} E_2 \\ -I_2 \end{bmatrix} = \begin{bmatrix} E_1 \\ I_1 \end{bmatrix} \tag{9-64}$$

where

$$a_{11} = \frac{E_1}{E_2}\bigg]_{I_2=0} \qquad a_{12} = \frac{E_1}{-I_2}\bigg]_{E_2=0}$$

$$a_{21} = \frac{I_1}{E_2}\bigg]_{I_2=} \qquad a_{22} = \frac{I_1}{-I_2}\bigg]_{E_2=0}$$

The **b** *parameters:*

$$\begin{bmatrix} b_{11} & b_{12} \\ b_{21} & b_{22} \end{bmatrix} \times \begin{bmatrix} E_1 \\ -I_1 \end{bmatrix} = \begin{bmatrix} E_2 \\ I_2 \end{bmatrix} \tag{9-65}$$

where

$$b_{11} = \frac{E_2}{E_1}\bigg]_{I_1=0} \qquad b_{12} = \frac{E_2}{-I_1}\bigg]_{E_1=0}$$

$$b_{21} = \frac{I_2}{E_1}\bigg]_{I_1=0} \qquad b_{22} = \frac{I_2}{-I_1}\bigg]_{E_1=0}$$

The six parameter matrix equations, the open- and short-circuit-parameter defining equations, and the relationships of Table 9-2 are valid for active as well as passive two-port networks. When the networks are passive, certain other relations among the parameters apply.

ADDITIONAL RELATIONSHIPS AMONG THE PARAMETERS WHEN THE NETWORKS ARE PASSIVE As has already been pointed out, passivity implies that

$$y_{12} = y_{21} \qquad z_{12} = z_{21} \tag{9-66}$$

Applying these equalities in Table 9-2 yields the following dependencies:

$$g_{12} = -g_{21} \qquad h_{12} = -h_{21} \tag{9-67}$$
$$|a| = |b| = 1 \tag{9-68}$$

In Eq. (9-68), $|a|$ and $|b|$ are the determinants of the a- and b-parameter matrices. Because of the restraints imposed by Eq. (9-68), the **a** and **b** parameters may, for passive networks, be expressed as **A, B, C, D** parameters. That is,

$$\begin{aligned} a_{11} &= b_{22} = A \\ a_{12} &= b_{12} = B \\ a_{21} &= b_{21} = C \\ a_{22} &= b_{11} = D \end{aligned} \tag{9-69}$$

As is indicated in Eqs. (9-66) and (9-67), three parameters are sufficient to specify the network. Consequently, the four parameters **A, B, C, D** cannot be independent. This is indicated by Eq. (9-68), which in terms of the parameters **A, B, C, D** is written as

$$\mathbf{AD - BC = 1} \tag{9-70}$$

TABLE 9-2   *Two-port Parameter Interrelations*

To \ From	[y]	[z]	[g]	[h]	[a]	[b]
$y_{11}\ y_{12}$	$\dfrac{I_1}{E_1}\bigg]_{E_2=0}$ $\dfrac{I_1}{E_2}\bigg]_{E_1=0}$	$\dfrac{z_{22}}{\lvert z\rvert}$ $\dfrac{-z_{12}}{\lvert z\rvert}$	$\dfrac{\lvert g\rvert}{g_{22}}$ $\dfrac{g_{12}}{g_{22}}$	$\dfrac{1}{h_{11}}$ $\dfrac{-h_{12}}{h_{11}}$	$\dfrac{a_{22}}{a_{12}}$ $\dfrac{-\lvert a\rvert}{a_{12}}$	$\dfrac{b_{11}}{b_{12}}$ $\dfrac{-1}{b_{12}}$
$y_{21}\ y_{22}$	$\dfrac{I_2}{E_1}\bigg]_{E_2=0}$ $\dfrac{I_2}{E_2}\bigg]_{E_1=0}$	$\dfrac{-z_{21}}{\lvert z\rvert}$ $\dfrac{z_{11}}{\lvert z\rvert}$	$\dfrac{-g_{21}}{g_{22}}$ $\dfrac{1}{g_{22}}$	$\dfrac{h_{21}}{h_{11}}$ $\dfrac{\lvert h\rvert}{h_{11}}$	$\dfrac{-1}{a_{12}}$ $\dfrac{a_{11}}{a_{12}}$	$\dfrac{-\lvert b\rvert}{b_{12}}$ $\dfrac{b_{22}}{b_{12}}$
$z_{11}\ z_{12}$	$\dfrac{y_{22}}{\lvert y\rvert}$ $\dfrac{-y_{12}}{\lvert y\rvert}$	$\dfrac{E_1}{I_1}\bigg]_{I_2=0}$ $\dfrac{E_1}{I_2}\bigg]_{I_1=0}$	$\dfrac{1}{g_{11}}$ $\dfrac{-g_{12}}{g_{11}}$	$\dfrac{\lvert h\rvert}{h_{22}}$ $\dfrac{h_{12}}{h_{22}}$	$\dfrac{a_{11}}{a_{21}}$ $\dfrac{\lvert a\rvert}{a_{21}}$	$\dfrac{b_{22}}{b_{21}}$ $\dfrac{1}{b_{21}}$
$z_{21}\ z_{22}$	$\dfrac{-y_{21}}{\lvert y\rvert}$ $\dfrac{y_{11}}{\lvert y\rvert}$	$\dfrac{E_2}{I_1}\bigg]_{I_2=0}$ $\dfrac{E_2}{I_2}\bigg]_{I_1=0}$	$\dfrac{g_{21}}{g_{11}}$ $\dfrac{\lvert g\rvert}{g_{11}}$	$\dfrac{-h_{21}}{h_{22}}$ $\dfrac{1}{h_{22}}$	$\dfrac{1}{a_{21}}$ $\dfrac{a_{22}}{a_{21}}$	$\dfrac{\lvert b\rvert}{b_{21}}$ $\dfrac{b_{11}}{b_{21}}$
$g_{11}\ g_{12}$	$\dfrac{\lvert y\rvert}{y_{22}}$ $\dfrac{y_{12}}{y_{22}}$	$\dfrac{1}{z_{11}}$ $\dfrac{-z_{12}}{z_{11}}$	$\dfrac{I_1}{E_1}\bigg]_{I_2=0}$ $\dfrac{I_1}{I_2}\bigg]_{E_1=0}$	$\dfrac{h_{22}}{\lvert h\rvert}$ $\dfrac{-h_{12}}{\lvert h\rvert}$	$\dfrac{a_{21}}{a_{11}}$ $\dfrac{-\lvert a\rvert}{a_{11}}$	$\dfrac{b_{21}}{b_{22}}$ $\dfrac{-1}{b_{22}}$
$g_{21}\ g_{22}$	$\dfrac{-y_{21}}{y_{22}}$ $\dfrac{1}{y_{22}}$	$\dfrac{z_{21}}{z_{11}}$ $\dfrac{\lvert z\rvert}{z_{11}}$	$\dfrac{E_2}{E_1}\bigg]_{I_2=0}$ $\dfrac{E_2}{I_2}\bigg]_{E_1=0}$	$\dfrac{-h_{21}}{\lvert h\rvert}$ $\dfrac{h_{11}}{\lvert h\rvert}$	$\dfrac{1}{a_{11}}$ $\dfrac{a_{12}}{a_{11}}$	$\dfrac{\lvert b\rvert}{b_{22}}$ $\dfrac{b_{12}}{b_{22}}$
$h_{11}\ h_{12}$	$\dfrac{1}{y_{11}}$ $\dfrac{-y_{12}}{y_{11}}$	$\dfrac{\lvert z\rvert}{z_{22}}$ $\dfrac{z_{12}}{z_{22}}$	$\dfrac{g_{22}}{\lvert g\rvert}$ $\dfrac{-g_{12}}{\lvert g\rvert}$	$\dfrac{E_1}{I_1}\bigg]_{E_2=0}$ $\dfrac{E_1}{E_2}\bigg]_{I_1=0}$	$\dfrac{a_{12}}{a_{22}}$ $\dfrac{\lvert a\rvert}{a_{22}}$	$\dfrac{b_{12}}{b_{11}}$ $\dfrac{1}{b_{11}}$
$h_{21}\ h_{22}$	$\dfrac{y_{21}}{y_{11}}$ $\dfrac{\lvert y\rvert}{y_{11}}$	$\dfrac{-z_{21}}{z_{22}}$ $\dfrac{1}{z_{22}}$	$\dfrac{-g_{21}}{\lvert g\rvert}$ $\dfrac{g_{11}}{\lvert g\rvert}$	$\dfrac{I_2}{I_1}\bigg]_{E_2=0}$ $\dfrac{I_2}{E_2}\bigg]_{I_1=0}$	$\dfrac{-1}{a_{22}}$ $\dfrac{a_{21}}{a_{22}}$	$\dfrac{-\lvert b\rvert}{b_{11}}$ $\dfrac{b_{21}}{b_{11}}$
$a_{11}\ a_{12}$	$\dfrac{-y_{22}}{y_{21}}$ $\dfrac{-1}{y_{21}}$	$\dfrac{z_{11}}{z_{21}}$ $\dfrac{\lvert z\rvert}{z_{21}}$	$\dfrac{1}{g_{21}}$ $\dfrac{g_{22}}{g_{21}}$	$\dfrac{-\lvert h\rvert}{h_{21}}$ $\dfrac{-h_{11}}{h_{21}}$	$\dfrac{E_1}{E_2}\bigg]_{I_2=0}$ $\dfrac{E_1}{-I_2}\bigg]_{E_2=0}$	$\dfrac{b_{22}}{\lvert b\rvert}$ $\dfrac{b_{12}}{\lvert b\rvert}$
$a_{21}\ a_{22}$	$\dfrac{-\lvert y\rvert}{y_{21}}$ $\dfrac{-y_{11}}{y_{21}}$	$\dfrac{1}{z_{21}}$ $\dfrac{z_{22}}{z_{21}}$	$\dfrac{g_{11}}{g_{21}}$ $\dfrac{\lvert g\rvert}{g_{21}}$	$\dfrac{-h_{22}}{h_{21}}$ $\dfrac{-1}{h_{21}}$	$\dfrac{I_1}{E_2}\bigg]_{I_2=0}$ $\dfrac{I_1}{-I_2}\bigg]_{E_2=0}$	$\dfrac{b_{21}}{\lvert b\rvert}$ $\dfrac{b_{11}}{\lvert b\rvert}$
$b_{11}\ b_{12}$	$\dfrac{-y_{11}}{y_{12}}$ $\dfrac{-1}{y_{12}}$	$\dfrac{z_{22}}{z_{12}}$ $\dfrac{\lvert z\rvert}{z_{12}}$	$\dfrac{-\lvert g\rvert}{g_{12}}$ $\dfrac{-g_{22}}{g_{12}}$	$\dfrac{1}{h_{12}}$ $\dfrac{h_{11}}{h_{12}}$	$\dfrac{a_{22}}{\lvert a\rvert}$ $\dfrac{a_{12}}{\lvert a\rvert}$	$\dfrac{E_2}{E_1}\bigg]_{I_1=0}$ $\dfrac{E_2}{-I_1}\bigg]_{E_1=0}$
$b_{21}\ b_{22}$	$\dfrac{-\lvert y\rvert}{y_{12}}$ $\dfrac{-y_{22}}{y_{12}}$	$\dfrac{1}{z_{12}}$ $\dfrac{z_{11}}{z_{12}}$	$\dfrac{-g_{11}}{g_{12}}$ $\dfrac{-1}{g_{12}}$	$\dfrac{h_{22}}{h_{12}}$ $\dfrac{\lvert h\rvert}{h_{12}}$	$\dfrac{a_{21}}{\lvert a\rvert}$ $\dfrac{a_{11}}{\lvert a\rvert}$	$\dfrac{I_2}{E_1}\bigg]_{I_1=0}$ $\dfrac{I_2}{-I_1}\bigg]_{E_1=0}$

ADDITIONAL PARAMETER CONDITIONS THAT APPLY WHEN THE NETWORKS ARE SYMMETRICAL AS WELL AS PASSIVE Symmetrical two-port networks are those networks which are exactly the same whether viewed from port 1 or port 2. That is, the numbering of the ports can be interchanged without affecting the value of any of the parameters. It is clear that in these circumstances the following additional relationships apply to the two-port-network parameters:

$$y_{11} = y_{22} \qquad z_{11} = z_{22} \qquad \lvert g\rvert = \lvert h\rvert = 1 \qquad \mathbf{A} = \mathbf{D} \qquad (9\text{-}71)$$

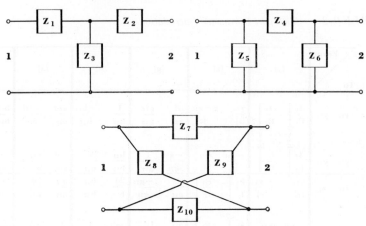

Fig. 9-19. T, Π, and lattice networks.

In Eq. (9-71), $|g|$ and $|h|$ are the determinants of the **g**- and **h**-parameter matrices. Obviously, only two independent parameters are necessary to specify completely the characteristics of a passive symmetrical two-port network.

THE TWO-PORT-NETWORK PARAMETERS OF T, Π, AND LATTICE NETWORKS The three types of networks illustrated in Fig. 9-19 are frequently encountered in electrical systems. The determination of their two-port-network parameters is straightforward. For example, the open-circuit impedance parameters of the T network may be found quite simply [refer to the definitions following Eq. (9-61)]:

$$[\mathbf{z}_\mathrm{T}] = \begin{bmatrix} \mathbf{Z}_1 + \mathbf{Z}_3 & \mathbf{Z}_3 \\ \mathbf{Z}_3 & \mathbf{Z}_2 + \mathbf{Z}_3 \end{bmatrix} \tag{9-72}$$

The short-circuit-admittance-parameter matrix of the Π network has a similar appearance:

$$[\mathbf{y}_\mathrm{\Pi}] = \begin{bmatrix} \dfrac{1}{\mathbf{Z}_5} + \dfrac{1}{\mathbf{Z}_4} & \dfrac{-1}{\mathbf{Z}_4} \\ \dfrac{-1}{\mathbf{Z}_4} & \dfrac{1}{\mathbf{Z}_6} + \dfrac{1}{\mathbf{Z}_4} \end{bmatrix} = \begin{bmatrix} \mathbf{Y}_5 + \mathbf{Y}_4 & -\mathbf{Y}_4 \\ -\mathbf{Y}_4 & \mathbf{Y}_6 + \mathbf{Y}_4 \end{bmatrix} \tag{9-73}$$

It is interesting to compare the y parameters of the T network with those of the Π network. By inverting the z matrix of Eq. (9-72), we find

$$[\mathbf{y}_\mathrm{T}] = \begin{bmatrix} \dfrac{\mathbf{Z}_2 + \mathbf{Z}_3}{|z_\mathrm{T}|} & \dfrac{-\mathbf{Z}_3}{|z_\mathrm{T}|} \\ \dfrac{-\mathbf{Z}_3}{|z_\mathrm{T}|} & \dfrac{\mathbf{Z}_1 + \mathbf{Z}_3}{|z_\mathrm{T}|} \end{bmatrix} \tag{9-74}$$

where
$$|z_\mathrm{T}| = (\mathbf{Z}_1 + \mathbf{Z}_3)(\mathbf{Z}_2 + \mathbf{Z}_3) - \mathbf{Z}_3{}^2 = \mathbf{Z}_1\mathbf{Z}_2 + \mathbf{Z}_1\mathbf{Z}_3 + \mathbf{Z}_2\mathbf{Z}_3 \tag{9-75}$$

By comparing Eqs. (9-73) and (9-74), we see that the T and the II networks have identical terminal characteristics if

$$Z_4 = \frac{Z_1 Z_2 + Z_1 Z_3 + Z_2 Z_3}{Z_3}$$

$$Z_5 = \frac{Z_1 Z_2 + Z_1 Z_3 + Z_2 Z_3}{Z_2}$$

$$Z_6 = \frac{Z_1 Z_2 + Z_1 Z_3 + Z_2 Z_3}{Z_1}$$

(9-76)

Equivalent to the equations above are the following expressions:

$$Z_1 = \frac{Z_4 Z_5}{Z_4 + Z_5 + Z_6}$$

$$Z_2 = \frac{Z_4 Z_6}{Z_4 + Z_5 + Z_6}$$

$$Z_3 = \frac{Z_5 Z_6}{Z_4 + Z_5 + Z_6}$$

(9-77)

Equations (9-76) and (9-77) are called the T-II or Y-Δ transformation equations. It is often helpful in analyzing circuits, particularly 3-phase power circuits, to replace a T by its equivalent II or vice versa.

The lattice is the third member of this trio of important basic networks. Lattice networks, like T and II networks, are commonly used as basic building blocks in the synthesis of filters. In such syntheses, the structure of a lattice permits a wider variation in the specification of its two-port characteristics than do T and II networks. This advantage is partially offset by the fact that a lattice does not possess a "common ground," as do T and II networks.

The two-port-network parameters of the lattice can be deduced readily. For example, the open-circuit voltages caused by unit currents can be calculated and, consequently, the z parameters determined (the lattice as redrawn in Fig. 9-20 may be helpful):

$$[\mathbf{z}_L] = \begin{bmatrix} \dfrac{(Z_7 + Z_9)(Z_8 + Z_{10})}{Z_7 + Z_8 + Z_9 + Z_{10}} & \dfrac{Z_8 Z_9 - Z_7 Z_{10}}{Z_7 + Z_8 + Z_9 + Z_{10}} \\[4mm] \dfrac{Z_8 Z_9 - Z_7 Z_{10}}{Z_7 + Z_8 + Z_9 + Z_{10}} & \dfrac{(Z_7 + Z_8)(Z_9 + Z_{10})}{Z_7 + Z_8 + Z_9 + Z_{10}} \end{bmatrix} \quad (9\text{-}78)$$

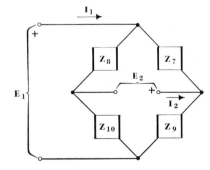

Fig. 9-20. The lattice network of Fig. 9-19 redrawn in the form of a bridge network.

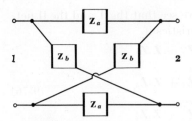

1   2   *Fig. 9-21. A symmetrical lattice.*

The **y** parameters are quite similar:

$$[\mathbf{y}_L] = \begin{bmatrix} \dfrac{(\mathbf{Y}_7 + \mathbf{Y}_8)(\mathbf{Y}_9 + \mathbf{Y}_{10})}{\mathbf{Y}_7 + \mathbf{Y}_8 + \mathbf{Y}_9 + \mathbf{Y}_{10}} & \dfrac{\mathbf{Y}_8\mathbf{Y}_9 - \mathbf{Y}_7\mathbf{Y}_{10}}{\mathbf{Y}_7 + \mathbf{Y}_8 + \mathbf{Y}_9 + \mathbf{Y}_{10}} \\ \dfrac{\mathbf{Y}_8\mathbf{Y}_9 - \mathbf{Y}_7\mathbf{Y}_{10}}{\mathbf{Y}_7 + \mathbf{Y}_8 + \mathbf{Y}_9 + \mathbf{Y}_{10}} & \dfrac{(\mathbf{Y}_7 + \mathbf{Y})_9(\mathbf{Y}_8 + \mathbf{Y}_{10})}{\mathbf{Y}_7 + \mathbf{Y}_8 + \mathbf{Y}_9 + \mathbf{Y}_{10}} \end{bmatrix} \tag{9-79}$$

Of special interest is the symmetrical lattice of Fig. 9-21. Since for the symmetrical lattice

$$\mathbf{Z}_7 = \mathbf{Z}_{10} = \mathbf{Z}_a \qquad \mathbf{Z}_8 = \mathbf{Z}_9 = \mathbf{Z}_b \tag{9-80}$$

the above expressions for the z and y parameters can be considerably simplified:

$$[\mathbf{z}_{SL}] = \begin{bmatrix} \dfrac{\mathbf{Z}_a + \mathbf{Z}_b}{2} & \dfrac{\mathbf{Z}_b - \mathbf{Z}_a}{2} \\ \dfrac{\mathbf{Z}_b - \mathbf{Z}_a}{2} & \dfrac{\mathbf{Z}_a + \mathbf{Z}_b}{2} \end{bmatrix} \tag{9-81}$$

$$[\mathbf{y}_{SL}] = \begin{bmatrix} \dfrac{\mathbf{Y}_a + \mathbf{Y}_b}{2} & \dfrac{\mathbf{Y}_b - \mathbf{Y}_a}{2} \\ \dfrac{\mathbf{Y}_b - \mathbf{Y}_a}{2} & \dfrac{\mathbf{Y}_a + \mathbf{Y}_b}{2} \end{bmatrix} \tag{9-82}$$

The other sets of parameters for the T, II, and lattice networks can be found readily by using Table 9-2.

ACTIVE TWO-PORT NETWORKS Active networks, that is, those networks which contain internal energy sources, will be separated into two types for the purpose of this discussion. The first type contains sources whose energy contributions are completely independent of the terminal functions at the two ports. These networks may be analyzed most expeditiously through the application of the superposition theorem. With internal, as well as terminal, driving functions, the response at a port is expressed as a sum of two responses. One part of the sum is the response due to the terminal functions with the internal sources removed (voltage sources shorted and current sources opened). For this response, the regular passive-two-port-network parameters are utilized. The second part of the sum is the response due to the internal sources alone.

We need say no more about this type of active network. The second type, and the more interesting of the two, consists of those networks in which the energy contributed by the internal sources is a function of the terminal quantities. More specifically, for electrical networks the voltage produced by an internal voltage source or the current produced by an internal current source is a linear function of the terminal voltages or currents. Under these conditions, the analysis of the network by the loop method would once again produce the matrix equation shown in Eq. (9-53). But in this case, Eq. (9-54) would no longer apply. Another set of conditions would replace Eq. (9-54). For example, the following constraints could apply to Eq. (9-53):

$$
\begin{aligned}
\mathbf{E}_3 &= \mathbf{F}_3(s)\mathbf{E}_1 \\
\mathbf{E}_4 &= \mathbf{F}_4(s)\mathbf{E}_1 \\
\mathbf{E}_5 &= \mathbf{F}_5(s)\mathbf{E}_2 \\
\mathbf{E}_6 &= \mathbf{E}_7 = \cdots = \mathbf{E}_n = 0
\end{aligned} \tag{9-83}
$$

For the conditions enumerated in Eqs. (9-83), the characteristics of the network may still be expressed by Eqs. (9-55). However, the $\mathbf{y}$ parameters are no longer given by Eqs. (9-56). In this case, the following set of equations replaces them:

$$
\begin{aligned}
\mathbf{y}_{11} &= \frac{|Z|_{11} + \mathbf{F}_3(s)|Z|_{31} + \mathbf{F}_4(s)|Z|_{41}}{|Z|} \\
\mathbf{y}_{12} &= \frac{|Z|_{21} + \mathbf{F}_5(s)|Z|_{51}}{|Z|} \\
\mathbf{y}_{21} &= \frac{|Z|_{12} + \mathbf{F}_3(s)|Z|_{32} + \mathbf{F}_4(s)|Z|_{42}}{|Z|} \\
\mathbf{y}_{22} &= \frac{|Z|_{22} + \mathbf{F}_5(s)|Z|_{52}}{|Z|}
\end{aligned} \tag{9-84}
$$

Equations (9-84) illustrate a statement made earlier, namely, that $\mathbf{y}_{12}$ and $\mathbf{y}_{21}$ are not necessarily equal when the network is active. Consequently, active two-port networks are completely characterized by four parameters, rather than by three. Other than this modification, all the statements and definitions concerning the parameters for passive networks are applicable to active two-ports.

AN EXAMPLE OF AN ACTIVE TWO-PORT NETWORK   A very common example of an active two-port network is a single-stage vacuum-tube amplifier. A typical single-stage amplifier is illustrated in Fig. 9-22.

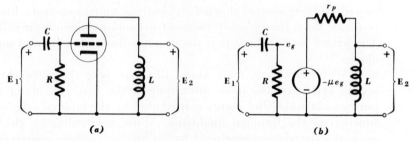

Fig. 9-22. (a) *A single-stage triode amplifier circuit;* (b) *the approximate equivalent circuit with the tube replaced by an equivalent voltage source and series plate resistance.*

Using the equivalent circuit shown in part b of this figure, we can readily determine the **Z** parameters:

$$\mathbf{z}_{11} = \left. \frac{\mathbf{E}_1}{\mathbf{I}_1} \right|_{\mathbf{I}_2=0} = R + \frac{1}{sC} \tag{9-85}$$

$$\mathbf{z}_{22} = \left. \frac{\mathbf{E}_2}{\mathbf{I}_2} \right|_{\mathbf{I}_1=0} = \frac{sr_pL}{sL + r_p} \tag{9-86}$$

$$\mathbf{z}_{12} = \left. \frac{\mathbf{E}_1}{\mathbf{I}_2} \right|_{\mathbf{I}_1=0} = 0 \tag{9-87}$$

Equations (9-85) and (9-86) are the impedances looking in at each of the ports with the opposite port open. Equation (9-87) indicates that an application of a current $\mathbf{I}_2$ at port 2 does not affect the open-circuit voltage $\mathbf{E}_1$ at port 1.

We shall calculate the last parameter, $\mathbf{z}_{21}$, by first finding $\mathbf{E}_g$ when a current $\mathbf{I}_1$ is applied at port 1:

$$\mathbf{E}_g = R\mathbf{I}_1 \tag{9-88}$$

Utilizing Eq. (9-88), we immediately deduce the open-circuit voltage at port 2:

$$\mathbf{E}_2 = \frac{-(\mu R\mathbf{I}_1)sL}{sL + r_p} \tag{9-89}$$

Consequently,
$$\mathbf{z}_{21} = \left. \frac{\mathbf{E}_2}{\mathbf{I}_1} \right|_{\mathbf{I}_2=0} = -\frac{\mu sRL}{sL + r_p} \tag{9-90}$$

$$[\mathbf{z}] = \begin{bmatrix} \dfrac{sRC + 1}{sC} & 0 \\ \dfrac{-\mu sRL}{sL + r_p} & \dfrac{sr_pL}{sL + r_p} \end{bmatrix} \tag{9-91}$$

Let us compute the **a** parameters for this circuit, since we shall shortly have use for them. They can be calculated directly from the circuit or derived from the **z** parameters through the use of Table 9-2.

$$[\mathbf{a}] = \begin{bmatrix} -\dfrac{(sRC+1)(sL+r_p)}{\mu s^2 RLC} & -\dfrac{r_p(sRC+1)}{\mu sRC} \\[3mm] -\dfrac{sL+r_p}{\mu sRL} & -\dfrac{r_p}{\mu R} \end{bmatrix} \qquad (9\text{-}92)$$

INTERCONNECTIONS OF TWO-PORT NETWORKS Both in network synthesis and in network analysis it is usually helpful, wherever possible, to treat complex two-port networks as interconnections of simpler two-ports. For this reason, we now wish to discuss the various ways of interconnecting two-ports and the parameters of such interconnected networks. Figure 9-23 illustrates the five basic interconnections of two-port networks: the series-series, parallel-parallel, series-parallel, parallel-series, and cascade connections.

The *cascade* connection will be considered first, since it is free of the restrictions encountered with some of the other interconnections. As is indicated in Fig. 9-23e, the first two-port transforms the input voltage and current to an intermediate voltage and current. The intermediate pair are then transformed by the second two-port into the output voltage and current. This port 1–to–port 2, port 1–to–port 2 process suggests that the **a** or **b** parameters should be used to analyze cascaded circuits.

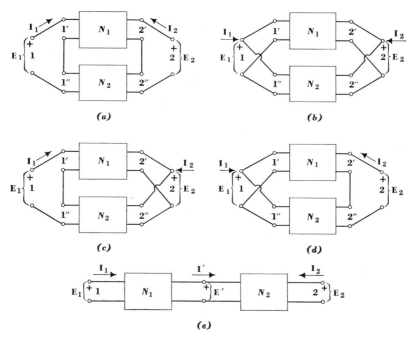

Fig. 9-23. The five ways of interconnecting two-port networks. (a) Series-series, (b) parallel-parallel, (c) series-parallel, (d) parallel-series, and (e) cascade.

Noting that $\mathbf{I}'$ is opposite to the normally assumed $\mathbf{I}_2$ direction, the input-to-output relationships are expressed by the following two matrix equations:

$$[\mathbf{a}_1] \times \begin{bmatrix} \mathbf{E}' \\ \mathbf{I}' \end{bmatrix} = \begin{bmatrix} \mathbf{E}_1 \\ \mathbf{I}_1 \end{bmatrix} \tag{9-93}$$

$$[\mathbf{a}_2] \times \begin{bmatrix} \mathbf{E}_2 \\ -\mathbf{I}_2 \end{bmatrix} = \begin{bmatrix} \mathbf{E}' \\ \mathbf{I}' \end{bmatrix} \tag{9-94}$$

Substituting Eq. (9-94) into Eq. (9-93) results in a single equation relating input to output:

$$[\mathbf{a}_1] \times [\mathbf{a}_2] \times \begin{bmatrix} \mathbf{E}_2 \\ -\mathbf{I}_2 \end{bmatrix} = \begin{bmatrix} \mathbf{E}_1 \\ \mathbf{I}_1 \end{bmatrix} \tag{9-95}$$

Equation (9-95) demonstrates that the **a** parameters for the cascade of two networks can be determined by multiplying the a-parameter matrices of the individual two-ports:

$$[\mathbf{a}] = [\mathbf{a}_1] \times [\mathbf{a}_2] \tag{9-96}$$

This result obviously is extendable to the cascade of any number of two-port networks:

$$[\mathbf{a}] = [\mathbf{a}_1] \times [\mathbf{a}_2] \times [\mathbf{a}_3] \times \cdots \times [\mathbf{a}_n] \tag{9-97}$$

By setting up equations for **b** parameters which are similar to Eqs. (9-93) and (9-94), it is easy to demonstrate that

$$[\mathbf{b}] = [\mathbf{b}_n] \times [\mathbf{b}_{n-1}] \times \cdots \times [\mathbf{b}_2] \times [\mathbf{b}_1] \tag{9-98}$$

For an example, consider the cascade of two amplifier stages identical to the one shown in Fig. 9-22. The **a** matrix for the single stage is expressed in Eq. (9-92). The **a** matrix for two stages is

$$[\mathbf{a}_2] = [\mathbf{a}_1]^2$$

$$= \begin{bmatrix} \dfrac{\begin{array}{c} R(sRC+1)^2(sL+r_p)^2 \\ + r_p(sRC+1)(sL+r_p) \end{array}}{\mu^2 s^2 R^2 LC} & \dfrac{\begin{array}{c} r_p(sRC+1)^2(sL+r_p) \\ + s^2 r_p^2 LC(sRC+1) \end{array}}{\mu^2 s^3 R^2 LC^2} \\[4ex] \dfrac{\begin{array}{c} (sRC+1)(sL+r_p)^2 \\ + s^2 r_p LC(sL+r_p) \end{array}}{\mu^2 s^3 R^2 L^2 C} & \dfrac{\begin{array}{c} r_p(sRC+1)(sL+r_p) \\ + s^2 r_p^2 LC \end{array}}{\mu^2 s^2 R^2 LC} \end{bmatrix} \tag{9-99}$$

As might be expected, the parameters of networks formed by the other four interconnections are expressible, *in some cases*, as algebraic combinations of the parameters of the two-port components. Unfortunately, the rules of combination which will be enumerated below cannot be applied with validity to the interconnections of all possible two-ports. Before discussing the reasons for this and the tests for validity, the combination rules—assuming validity—will be stated.

The parameters for a series-series and a parallel-parallel connection will be derived. The parameters for the other interconnections will merely be stated, the derivation being left to the student. The z-parameter matrix for the *series-series* connection of Fig. 9-23a is

$$[z] = [z_1] + [z_2] \tag{9-100}$$

where $[z_1]$ and $[z_2]$ are the z-parameter matrices of the two component two-ports. For the *parallel-parallel* connection of Fig. 9-23b, the y-parameter matrix is

$$[y] = [y_1] + [y_2] \tag{9-101}$$

For the *series-parallel* connection,

$$[h] = [h_1] + [h_2] \tag{9-102}$$

and for the *parallel-series* connection,

$$[g] = [g_1] + [g_2] \tag{9-103}$$

As in the case of the cascade connection, the four rules above can be extended to cover similar interconnections of any number of two-ports.

To derive Eq. (9-100), let us examine first the series-series connection as redrawn in Fig. 9-24. Expressing the characteristics of the two component two-ports in terms of their open-circuit impedance parameters produces the following two equations:

$$[z_1] \times \begin{bmatrix} I'_1 \\ I'_2 \end{bmatrix} = \begin{bmatrix} E'_1 \\ E'_2 \end{bmatrix} \tag{9-104}$$

$$[z_2] \times \begin{bmatrix} I''_1 \\ I''_2 \end{bmatrix} = \begin{bmatrix} E''_1 \\ E''_2 \end{bmatrix} \tag{9-105}$$

Noting that the voltages of the combination network are sums of the component voltages leads us to the next expression:

$$\left([z_1] \times \begin{bmatrix} I'_1 \\ I'_2 \end{bmatrix}\right) + \left([z_2] \times \begin{bmatrix} I''_1 \\ I''_2 \end{bmatrix}\right) = \begin{bmatrix} E'_1 \\ E'_2 \end{bmatrix} + \begin{bmatrix} E''_1 \\ E''_2 \end{bmatrix} = \begin{bmatrix} E_1 \\ E_2 \end{bmatrix} \tag{9-106}$$

Finally, *if*

$$I'_1 = I''_1 = I_1 \qquad I'_2 = I''_2 = I_2 \tag{9-107}$$

Fig. 9-24. A series-series connection of 2 two-port networks.

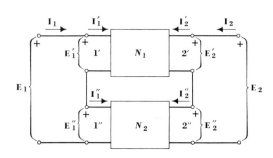

then Eq. (9-106) reduces to

$$\left([\mathbf{z}_1] + [\mathbf{z}_2] \times \begin{bmatrix} \mathbf{I}_1 \\ \mathbf{I}_2 \end{bmatrix} \right) = \begin{bmatrix} \mathbf{E}_1 \\ \mathbf{E}_2 \end{bmatrix} \tag{9-108}$$

Thus, the series-series combination rule of Eq. (9-100) has been derived. However, the proof is dependent upon the conditions stated by Eqs. (9-107). [Note that the two conditions of Eqs. (9-107) are not independent; that is, if one equality is true, then the other is also.] Furthermore, if the conditions denoted by Eqs. (9-107) are not satisfied, the original matrix equations, Eqs. (9-104) and (9-105), are not valid. The validity of such matrix equations is based upon the equality of the currents which flow in and out of the two terminals of a port.

The derivation of the parallel-parallel combination rule of Eq. (9-101) and the corresponding validity conditions are quite similar to those above. In Fig. 9-25, we see that the following equalities pertain to this parallel-parallel connection:

$$\begin{bmatrix} \mathbf{E}_1 \\ \mathbf{E}_2 \end{bmatrix} = \begin{bmatrix} \mathbf{E}_1' \\ \mathbf{E}_2' \end{bmatrix} = \begin{bmatrix} \mathbf{E}_1'' \\ \mathbf{E}_2'' \end{bmatrix} \tag{9-109}$$

$$\begin{bmatrix} \mathbf{I}_1 \\ \mathbf{I}_2 \end{bmatrix} = \begin{bmatrix} \mathbf{I}_1' \\ \mathbf{I}_2' \end{bmatrix} + \begin{bmatrix} \mathbf{I}_1'' \\ \mathbf{I}_2'' \end{bmatrix} \tag{9-110}$$

If, and this is the validity condition,

$$\mathbf{I}_1' = {}'\mathbf{I}_1 \qquad \mathbf{I}_1'' = {}''\mathbf{I}_1 \qquad \mathbf{I}_2' = {}'\mathbf{I}_2 \qquad \mathbf{I}_2'' = {}''\mathbf{I}_2 \tag{9-111}$$

the y-parameter matrix equations can be written for the component two-ports and then combined, utilizing Eqs. (9-109) and (9-110):

$$[\mathbf{y}_1] \times [\mathbf{E}'] = [\mathbf{I}'] \qquad [\mathbf{y}_2] \times [\mathbf{E}''] = [\mathbf{I}''] \tag{9-112}$$

$$([\mathbf{y}_1] \times [\mathbf{E}']) + ([\mathbf{y}_2] \times [\mathbf{E}'']) = [\mathbf{I}'] + [\mathbf{I}''] = ([\mathbf{y}_1] + [\mathbf{y}_2]) \times [\mathbf{E}] = [\mathbf{I}] \tag{9-113}$$

As in the case of the series-series validity condition, if any one of the equalities of Eqs. (9-111) is true, then they are all true. The derivations of Eqs. (9-102) and (9-103) for the series-parallel and parallel-series connections are similar to the derivations above. The validity conditions are essentially combinations of those already stated.

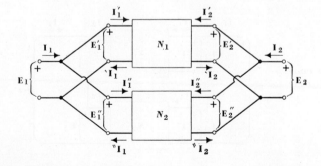

Fig. 9-25. A parallel-parallel connection of 2 two-port networks.

A few comments will now be made on the problem of ascertaining whether, for a particular combination of two-ports, the validity constraints are met. For some combinations the constraints are clearly met, and in others they clearly are not met. Figure 9-26 illustrates this fact. It is not unusual, however, to be faced with a situation in which it is not obvious whether the validity constraints are met. In such a case it is necessary to apply the tests which are outlined below.

We shall first consider the series-series connection illustrated in Fig. 9-24. The validity conditions which must be satisfied in order to apply Eq. (9-100) to this network are given by Eqs. (9-107). The conditions must hold for all possible current values, including zero. To illustrate this, I_2 has been made zero in Fig. 9-27. If the validity condition is met, no current will flow from terminal a to terminal b. If no current flows from a to b with the terminals connected, then no voltage difference can exist between a and b when they are disconnected. Herein lies the idea for a validity test: measure the open-circuit voltage from a to b with $I_2 = 0$; if this voltage is zero and if a similar measure-

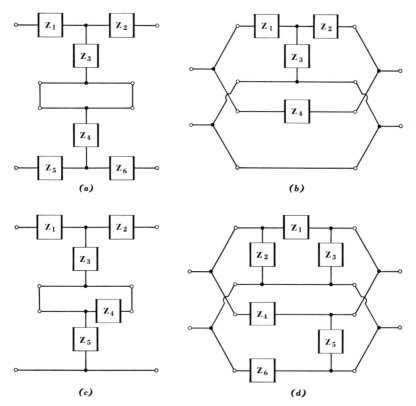

Fig. 9-26. (a, b) *Two networks in which the validity conditions are met and* (c, d) *two networks in which they are not.*

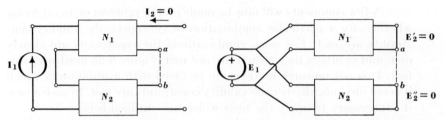

Fig. 9-27. Series-series connection with an arbitrary I_1 and with $I_2 = 0$.

Fig. 9-28. Parallel-parallel connection with an arbitrary E_1 and with $E_2' = E_2'' = 0$.

ment at port 1 with port 2 excited is also zero, then the validity conditions are satisfied.

For the parallel-parallel connection, the conditions of Eqs. (9-111) are to be met for all possible voltages at the ports, including $E_2 = 0$. When terminals a and b of Fig. 9-28 are connected, a parallel-parallel connection is achieved in which $E_2 = 0$. Before a is connected to b, the currents satisfy the validity condition. If they are to continue to satisfy this condition after the connection, no current can flow from a to b. Hence, the voltage from a to b with ports 2' and 2'' shorted must be zero. If a similar measurement at port 1 yields zero voltage, the validity test for the parallel-parallel connection is passed.

With series-parallel and parallel-series connections, the series validity test is applied at one port and the parallel validity test at the

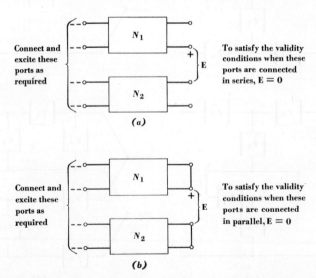

Fig. 9-29. The tests to determine whether an interconnection of 2 two-port networks will satisfy the validity conditions. Both port 1 and port 2 must be tested with the appropriate connections at the other side.

other. The validity tests are summarized in Fig. 9-29. The tests just enumerated are performed with specific currents and voltages, namely, zero. The superposition theorem is utilized to demonstrate that the tests are sufficient to indicate, for all possible values of terminal voltages and currents, whether the validity constraints are met.

Testing with various two-ports will illuminate a situation which may be somewhat disturbing. Most two-ports, when interconnected, do not satisfy the validity conditions. In synthesis techniques this situation is often remedied by the use of transformers, a procedure which will be discussed in the next chapter. If the validity conditions are not met in analysis, the standard methods of node and loop analysis must be used.

SUMMARY   It is appropriate at this juncture to summarize some of the pertinent developments which have been made in this chapter and the preceding one. It has been the plan in these two chapters to take the techniques developed in the previous chapters and apply them to systems which are more complex than those heretofore analyzed. The first products of this process were node and loop analyses. Through the utilization of either one of these two systematic methods, all the necessary simultaneous equations for finding the system response are obtainable. Because of the linear nature of these equations, their solution, although occasionally tedious, is straightforward. For example, Cramer's rule may be used in their solution. The solution in the s domain will consist, in almost all cases, of functions of s that can be expanded in partial-fraction expansions. These expansions then are transformed into the time domain.

The essence of these results is that we now have available to us tools by which we can determine the response of any linear lumped network, no matter how complex.† This remarkable result is tempered somewhat by the fact that the amount of computation necessary actually to obtain the solution in the time domain becomes enormous as the network becomes large. The two places where the amount of computation grows rapidly with system complexity are the inversion of the impedance or admittance matrix (solution by Cramer's rule) and the factorization of the numerator polynomial in s prior to partial-fraction expansion.

With these powerful tools of analysis as a foundation, we turned to the task of simplifying linear network analysis through the use of matrix methods and equivalent-circuit techniques. The final product of these efforts was the formulation of two-port-network parameters

† We are making the reasonable assumption that the driving functions, or sources, are of such a nature that their s-domain representation can be determined and then, after solution, transformed back into the time domain.

and the techniques of applying them. The paramount point of this chapter is that each new circuit or change in a network does not necessarily constitute a completely new problem. In general, it is not necessary to start from "scratch" with each network. Instead, a member of a class or type of network can be analyzed, and the results can then be applied, with a minimum of additional work, to other members of the class.

PROBLEMS

9-26   Find the **g**, **h**, **a**, and **b** parameters of the T and Π networks of Fig. 9-19.

9-27   Find the **g**, **h**, **a**, and **b** parameters of the symmetrical lattice of Fig. 9-21.

9-28   Find the **z** and **y** parameters of the networks illustrated in the figure.

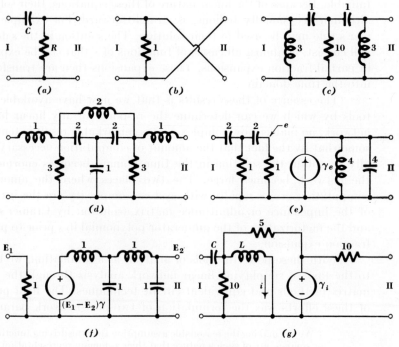

Fig. P 9-28

9-29   Find the **h** parameters of the networks shown in the figure.

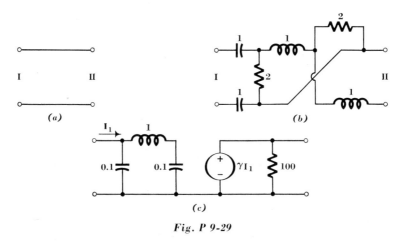

(a)   *(b)*

(c)

Fig. P 9-29

9-30   The **z** parameters of the network shown in the figure are as follows:

$$z_{11} = \frac{s^2 + s + 1}{s} \qquad z_{22} = s + 1 \qquad z_{12} = z_{21} = 1$$

Find the voltage and current at port 2 for each of the driving-function and load combinations.

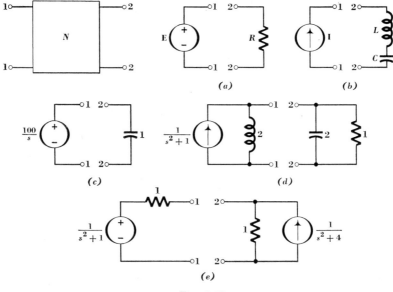

Fig. 9-30

9-31 What are the **a** parameters of the two networks shown? If they are cascaded, (b) following (a), what are the **a** parameters of the combination? What are the **a** parameters if the order of cascading is reversed?

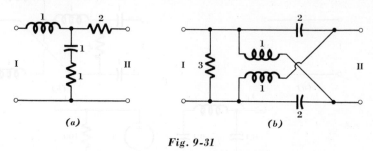

Fig. 9-31

9-32 Derive Eqs. (9-101) and (9-102). State the pertinent validity conditions.

9-33 Compute the **z** parameters of all the series-series connections of Fig. 9-26, using both the direct method and Eq. (9-100). Note that the parameters obtained by the two procedures are not equal if the validity conditions are not satisfied.

9-34 Compute the **y** parameters of the parallel-parallel connections of Fig. 9-26. Use both the direct method and Eq. (9-101).

9-35 Compute the **y** and **z** parameters of the bridged T by using the direct method and by considering the network as a series-series combination and as a parallel-parallel combination.

Fig. P 9-35

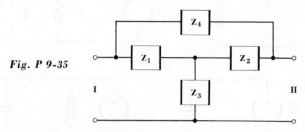

9-36 A simple a-c equivalent circuit for a junction transistor is shown in the figure. Find the y-, z-, g-, h-, a-, and b-parameter matrices for this circuit. If the source and load shown are connected to this circuit, find the power gain of this device at 10^3, 10^4, and 10^5 cps. (The power gain is the ratio of the average power developed in the load to the average power delivered by the source.) The following values are reasonable for the network elements.

$$R_b = 100 \text{ ohms} \qquad \alpha = 0.9$$
$$R_e = 30 \text{ ohms} \qquad C = 15 \ \mu\mu f$$
$$R_c = 10^6 \text{ ohms}$$

Discuss which set of parameters seem best for specifying this device.

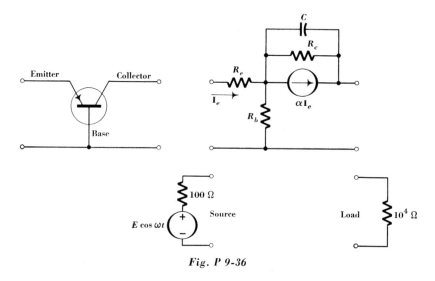

Fig. P 9-36

mutual inductance
and transformers

Mutual induction (magnetic coupling), one of the most important electrical phenomena, will be investigated in this chapter. So pervasive is its utilization that it is difficult to envisage the development of an electrical industry without it.

The present chapter consists of three sections. The first section examines the characteristics of mutual inductance (mutual induction is measured in terms of the parameter mutual inductance) and methods of dealing with it in the analysis of circuits in which it exists. The approach to this investigation will conform to that followed in previous sections of this text. That is, the results of experimental investigations will be used to formulate a mathematical model of mutual inductance, and the analysis of systems containing mutual inductance will then be based upon this model. Once again, let it be emphasized that the models used for the various circuit elements are idealizations and, under some conditions, inadequately represent the true characteristics of the elements.

The second section discusses the paramount application of mutual inductance—the transformer. Whereas a reasonably short section is adequate for the investigation of the general properties of mutual inductance, whole books have been devoted to transformers. Consequently, the discussion here can serve only to introduce some of the simplest and most basic concepts pertaining to this device.

There is no property characteristic of mechanical systems which is entirely analogous to mutual inductance. However, certain mechanical devices, such as levers and gears, have characteristics similar to those of transformers. The third section is devoted to a short discussion of such devices.

10-1 MUTUAL INDUCTANCE

In our original discussion of inductance, it will be recalled, this circuit parameter was defined in terms of the energy stored by a current-carrying element. Strictly speaking, wherever current is flowing, there is an associated stored energy in the magnetic field surrounding the current. For most purposes, it is permissible to neglect all magnetic fields with the exception of those associated with elements especially designed to enhance magnetic energy storage. These elements are called inductors or coils.

Working under the assumption that the magnetic energy is restricted to the inductors allowed us to make the following definition: The energy stored by a coil of inductance L is

$$W_L = \frac{Li^2}{2} \tag{10-1}$$

Going one step further, we might reason that the total energy stored in two coils carrying i_1 and i_2, respectively, should be

$$W_L = \frac{1}{2}(L_1 i_1^2 + L_2 i_2^2) \tag{10-2}$$

However, if we were to perform experiments with two coils of inductance L_1 and L_2, we should find that *Eq.* (10-2) *is not true generally.* In tests with the two coils widely separated, the experimental results would be in good agreement with Eq. (10-2). When the coils were brought close together, however, the measured energy could differ considerably from that predicted by Eq. (10-2).

Although the physics of electromagnetic fields is beyond the scope of this text, a brief explanation of these experimental results can be given. As has been mentioned, the inductive energy is stored in the form of a magnetic field created by the current flowing in the inductor. The magnetic field exists in the space surrounding the coil, being strongest near the coil and weakening rapidly with distance from the coil. Since the inductive energy is stored in the magnetic field, it must be considered to be stored in the space surrounding the inductor. A particular part of this space, a volume cell, is considered to have a stored-energy density which is proportional to the square of the magnetic field intensity in that cell. Consequently, the total energy stored by an inductor can be found by integrating the magnetic field energy density over all the volume containing the field.

The magnetic field produced by the current in an inductor is a vector field; that is, at every point in space the magnetic field has both magnitude and direction. Furthermore, fields produced by two or more sources are additive.† Hence, the magnetic field produced by two or more coils is the vector sum of their individual fields. Because of the vector nature of the fields, their summation can produce a stronger field by reinforcement or a weaker field by cancellation. This fact,

† This statement is valid for fields existing in linear mediums. With the exception of ferromagnetic mediums, almost all mediums are linear.

coupled with the proportionality of the energy density to the square of the magnetic field intensity, explains why the energy stored by a system of inductors can be either greater or less than the value predicted by Eq. (10-2). This effect is called mutual induction.

Now that we have an explanation of the discrepancy between Eq. (10-2) and experimental measurements, it is necessary to formulate analytic expressions which will define this phenomenon more completely and then to determine methods of including its effects in the analysis of circuits. Our first step must be to replace Eq. (10-2) by an energy equation which will include the effect of the interaction of the magnetic fields. Fortunately, the assumed linear nature of the fields allows us to express the energy stored by two inductors in the following manner:

$$W_L = \frac{L_1 i_1{}^2}{2} + \frac{L_2 i_2{}^2}{2} + M i_1 i_2 \qquad (10\text{-}3)$$

Let us examine this expression in some detail. We note first that it satisfies the necessary condition that it must reduce to Eq. (10-1) if one current is zero. The third term in Eq. (10-3) is called the mutual term, and it is in this term that the effect of mutual inductance is contained. From the experimental results and the explanation that followed, we know that M, the mutual inductance of the two coils, must depend upon the inductance of the two coils and their relative positions. If the coils are far apart, M approaches zero. As the coils are brought closer together, M becomes larger. Just how large will be discussed at the end of this section.

An important point, and one which leads to a certain amount of difficulty in circuit analysis, is that the mutual term in Eq. (10-3) need not be positive. This is due to the fact, pointed out above, that the two magnetic fields may cancel and thus store less energy than denoted by Eq. (10-2). The direction of the magnetic field produced by a current-carrying coil reverses if the current direction reverses. Consequently, the mutual term in Eq. (10-3) depends not only upon the magnitudes of the currents but also upon their direction. Clearly we are faced once again with the task of assigning and keeping track of reference directions.

Before examining the problem of reference directions in detail, let us find the *voltage-current relationships,* using the same procedure as we did in Chap. 1. Differentiating Eq. (10-3) yields the power and results in the following expression:

$$\frac{dW_L}{dt} = L_1 i_1 \frac{di_1}{dt} + L_2 i_2 \frac{di_2}{dt} + M i_1 \frac{di_2}{dt} + M i_2 \frac{di_1}{dt}$$

$$= i_1 \left(L_1 \frac{di_1}{dt} + M \frac{di_2}{dt} \right) + i_2 \left(L_2 \frac{di_2}{dt} + M \frac{di_1}{dt} \right) \qquad (10\text{-}4)$$

The power developed in an element is ei. Consequently,

$$e_1 = L_1 \frac{di_1}{dt} + M \frac{di_2}{dt}$$

$$e_2 = L_2 \frac{di_2}{dt} + M \frac{di_1}{dt}$$

(10-5)

EXTENSION TO MORE THAN TWO INDUCTANCES Equations (10-3) and (10-5) may be generalized so that they apply to mutually coupled systems containing many coils. Changing symbols slightly to conform to matrix notation, we can write the general stored-energy equation for inductances as

$$2W_L = L_{11}i_1{}^2 + L_{12}i_1i_2 + L_{13}i_1i_3 + \cdots + L_{1n}i_1i_n$$
$$+ L_{21}i_2i_1 + L_{22}i_2{}^2 + L_{23}i_2i_3 + \cdots + L_{2n}i_2i_n$$
$$\dots\dots\dots\dots\dots\dots\dots\dots\dots\dots\dots\dots\dots$$
$$+ L_{n1}i_ni_1 + L_{n2}i_ni_2 + L_{n3}i_ni_3 + \cdots + L_{nn}i_n{}^2 \quad (10\text{-}6)$$

In matrix form, Eq. (10-6) is

$$2W_L = [i_1 \quad i_2 \quad \cdots \quad i_n] \times \begin{bmatrix} L_{11} & L_{12} & L_{13} & \cdots & L_{1n} \\ L_{21} & L_{22} & L_{23} & \cdots & L_{2n} \\ \dots & \dots & \dots & & \dots \\ L_{n1} & L_{n2} & L_{n3} & \cdots & L_{nn} \end{bmatrix} \times \begin{bmatrix} i_1 \\ i_2 \\ \cdots \\ i_n \end{bmatrix}$$

$$= \underline{\mathbf{i}} \times [\mathbf{L}] \times \mathbf{i}] \quad (10\text{-}7)$$

The inductances on the main diagonal, the L_{jj} terms, are the self-inductances of each individual coil. The off-diagonal L_{jk} terms are the mutual inductances between pairs of coils. Note that the mutual term, as it appears in Eq. (10-3), has been split into two parts to produce the symmetry of Eqs. (10-6) and (10-7). Thus we have

$$M_{jk} = L_{jk} = L_{kj} \quad (10\text{-}8)$$

Differentiating Eq. (10-6) leads to the following voltage-current relationships:

$$e_1 = L_{11} \frac{di_1}{dt} + L_{12} \frac{di_2}{dt} + \cdots + L_{1n} \frac{di_n}{dt} = \sum_{k=1}^{n} L_{1k} \frac{di_k}{dt}$$
$$\dots\dots\dots\dots\dots\dots\dots\dots\dots\dots\dots\dots\dots\dots\dots \quad (10\text{-}9)$$
$$e_j = L_{j1} \frac{di_1}{dt} + L_{j2} \frac{di_2}{dt} + \cdots + L_{jn} \frac{di_n}{dt} = \sum_{k=1}^{n} L_{jk} \frac{di_k}{dt}$$
$$\dots\dots\dots\dots\dots\dots\dots\dots\dots\dots\dots\dots\dots\dots\dots$$

In words, Eqs. (10-9) tell us that the voltage developed across a coil is dependent not only upon the rate of current change in that coil but upon the rate of change of current in all coils.

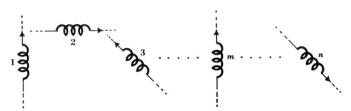

Fig. 10-1. *N mutually coupled inductors with their assigned reference directions.*

In performing circuit analyses in previous chapters, we assumed that there was no mutual inductance between coils, that is, that $L_{jk} = 0$ for $j \neq k$. We now wish to analyze circuits in which this assumption is no longer valid.

MEASUREMENT OF MUTUAL INDUCTANCE Although mutual inductance has been defined in terms of energy and explained in terms of magnetic fields, the most applicable method of measuring it is through the use of Eqs. (10-9). Let us suppose that we have a circuit containing a number of mutually coupled coils—for example, the n coils of Fig. 10-1 (these are part of a larger network which for our purposes need not be shown). Each of the coils has been assigned an arbitrary *reference direction*, indicated by the arrowheads.†

If zero current is maintained in all coils with the exception of one, say coil m, Eqs. (10-9) reduce to the following:

$$e_1 = L_{1m} \frac{di_m}{dt}$$

$$\cdots \cdots \cdots$$

$$e_j = L_{jm} \frac{di_m}{dt}$$

$$\cdots \cdots \cdots$$

(10-10)

Thus, by measuring the rate of current change in one coil and the voltages induced in all the coils, one column of the inductance matrix of Eq. (10-7) is determined. It is at this point that reference directions become necessary. Let us suppose that the current in coil m is increasing in the reference direction with a slope of 1 amp/sec. Consequently,

$$\frac{di_m}{dt} = 1$$

(10-11)

and the voltage across the jth coil is

$$e_j = L_{jm}$$

(10-12)

Now, if e_j is a positive drop in the reference direction of coil j, as is indicated in Fig. 10-2, then the mutual inductance is positive and equal

† The circuit-diagram markings must agree with corresponding directions or connections of the actual physical elements.

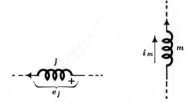

Fig. 10-2. If di_m/dt is positive and e_j is positive, then L_{jm} is positive.

to e_j in magnitude. On the other hand, if e_j is negative, that is, if the voltage across coil j rises in the direction of the arrow, then L_{jm} is negative. Additionally, if di_m/dt is negative in the reference direction with e_j negative, then L_{jm} is positive; or if di_m/dt is negative and e_j positive, then L_{jm} is negative.

CIRCUIT ANALYSIS WITH MUTUAL INDUCTANCE No new principles are involved in analyzing circuits with mutual inductance. However, greater care is necessary in the "bookkeeping" portion of the analysis. To illustrate this fact, one simple circuit will be analyzed by several techniques. Although the circuit to be analyzed contains only three inductors, the various methods extend to circuits containing any number of mutually coupled inductors.

As a first example, consider Fig. 10-3, where the three inductors are the only mutually coupled coils in a more extensive network. The loop currents have been chosen as indicated in the figure. An important condition here is the following: *There is a single loop current in the reference direction for each inductor.* The inductances have been measured and are as follows:

$$
\begin{aligned}
L_{11} &= 2 & L_{12} = L_{21} &= 1 & L_{13} = L_{31} &= 2 \\
L_{22} &= 3 & L_{23} = L_{32} &= -1 & L_{33} &= 4
\end{aligned}
\tag{10-13}
$$

In matrix form, Eq. (10-13) is

$$
[\mathbf{L}] = \begin{bmatrix} 2 & 1 & 2 \\ 1 & 3 & -1 \\ 2 & -1 & 4 \end{bmatrix}
\tag{10-14}
$$

In writing loop equations for the circuit of Fig. 10-3, the voltage drops across each of the inductors in the loop current direction must be

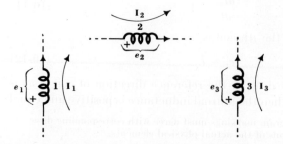

Fig. 10-3. Three mutually coupled inductors which are part of a more extensive circuit. The assigned loop currents are illustrated.

included in the appropriate loop equation. Since the loop current directions coincide with the inductor reference directions, the inductor voltage drops in the loop current direction are expressed by Eqs. (10-9). That is,

$$e_1 = L_{11}\frac{di_1}{dt} + L_{12}\frac{di_2}{dt} + L_{13}\frac{di_3}{dt} \tag{10-15}$$

which in the s domain is

$$\mathbf{e}_1 = sL_{11}\mathbf{I}_1 + sL_{12}\mathbf{I}_2 + sL_{13}\mathbf{I}_3 \tag{10-16}$$

Additionally,

$$\mathbf{e}_2 = sL_{21}\mathbf{I}_1 + sL_{22}\mathbf{I}_2 + sL_{23}\mathbf{I}_3 \tag{10-17}$$

$$\mathbf{e}_3 = sL_{31}\mathbf{I}_1 + sL_{32}\mathbf{I}_2 + sL_{33}\mathbf{I}_3 \tag{10-18}$$

The voltage drops described in Eqs. (10-16) to (10-18) are added into the appropriate loop equations, and then the solution proceeds in the usual manner. In matrix form, the loop equations for the whole circuit can be written in the following form:

$$([\mathbf{Z}-] + s[\mathbf{L}]) \times \mathbf{I}] = [\mathbf{Z}] \times \mathbf{I}] = \mathbf{E}] \tag{10-19}$$

The matrix $[\mathbf{Z}-]$ is the loop impedance matrix for the circuit with the three mutually coupled coils replaced by short circuits. The same loop currents are maintained in determining $[\mathbf{Z}-]$. If it is desired, the loop matrix equations for this circuit can be obtained in two operations. First, the impedance matrix for the circuit is determined with inductors shorted. Then the s-multiplied inductance matrix is added to this impedance matrix. This method is applicable when the loop currents agree, in both direction and numbering, with the inductors and their reference directions.

When the *loop currents do not agree in numbering or direction with the inductors*, the complexities of the loop equations increase. Using the same circuit as before, let us assume now that it is necessary to assign loop currents as indicated in Fig. 10-4. Once again, it is necessary to determine the voltage drops across the inductors in the loop current directions and add them to the loop equations. Under these conditions,

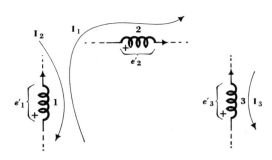

Fig. 10-4. The circuit of Fig. 10-3, but with different loop currents.

the simple expressions of the previous example no longer apply. For example, the total inductor voltage drop of loop 1 is e_1, where

$$e_1 = e_1' + e_2' \tag{10-20}$$
$$e_1' = sL_{11}(I_1 - I_2) + sL_{12}I_1 - sL_{13}I_3 \tag{10-21}$$
$$e_2' = sL_{21}(I_1 - I_2) + sL_{22}I_1 - sL_{23}I_3 \tag{10-22}$$

The voltage drop due to inductors in loop 2 is e_2, where

$$e_2 = -e_1' \tag{10-23}$$

Finally, in loop 3,

$$e_3 = -e_3' \tag{10-24}$$

where $\qquad e_3' = sL_{31}(I_1 - I_2) + sL_{32}I_1 - sL_{33}I_3 \tag{10-25}$

The minus signs occur in Eqs. (10-21), (10-22), and (10-25) wherever the loop current direction is opposite the inductor reference direction.

The matrix approach to this particular problem proceeds in the following manner. The loop equilibrium equation is

$$([Z-] \times I]) + e] = E] \tag{10-26}$$

where $\qquad e] = \begin{bmatrix} e_1 \\ e_2 \\ e_3 \end{bmatrix} \tag{10-27}$

and where $[Z-]$ once again is the impedance matrix obtained when the inductors are shorted. Now, if we denote the currents in the three inductors in the reference directions as i_1', i_2', and i_3', the following equation applies:

$$s[L] \times i'] = e'] \tag{10-28}$$

By Eqs. (10-20), (10-23), and (10-24),

$$e] = \begin{bmatrix} 1 & 1 & 0 \\ -1 & 0 & 0 \\ 0 & 0 & -1 \end{bmatrix} \times e'] \tag{10-29}$$

Furthermore, the relationships between loop currents and inductor currents are seen to be

$$i'] = \begin{bmatrix} 1 & -1 & 0 \\ 1 & 0 & 0 \\ 0 & 0 & -1 \end{bmatrix} \times I] \tag{10-30}$$

Substituting Eqs. (10-28) and (10-30) into Eq. (10-29) produces

$$e] = \begin{bmatrix} 1 & 1 & 0 \\ -1 & 0 & 0 \\ 0 & 0 & -1 \end{bmatrix} \times s[L] \times \begin{bmatrix} 1 & -1 & 0 \\ 1 & 0 & 0 \\ 0 & 0 & -1 \end{bmatrix} \times I] \tag{10-31}$$

The final step is the substitution of Eq. (10-31) into Eq. (10-26):

$$\left[[\mathbf{Z}-] + \left(\begin{bmatrix} 1 & 1 & 0 \\ -1 & 0 & 0 \\ 0 & 0 & -1 \end{bmatrix} \times s[\mathbf{L}] \times \begin{bmatrix} 1 & -1 & 0 \\ 1 & 0 & 0 \\ 0 & 0 & -1 \end{bmatrix}\right)\right] \times \mathbf{I}] = \mathbf{E}] \tag{10-32}$$

SUMMARY OF THE LOOP ANALYSIS OF MUTUALLY COUPLED CIRCUITS The preceding analysis, generalized to any mutually coupled circuit, can be neatly summarized by the following matrix equation:

$$[[\mathbf{Z}-] + ([\boldsymbol{\alpha}]_t \times s[\mathbf{L}] \times [\boldsymbol{\alpha}])] \times \mathbf{I}] = \mathbf{E}] \tag{10-33}$$

where $[\mathbf{Z}-]$ = loop impedance matrix with mutually coupled induc-
　　　　　　tors replaced by short circuits
　　$[\boldsymbol{\alpha}]$ = matrix which transforms loop currents into inductor
　　　　　currents† as per Eq. (10-30)
　$[\boldsymbol{\alpha}]_t$ = *transpose* of $[\boldsymbol{\alpha}]$; that is, the α_{jk} element of $[\boldsymbol{\alpha}]_t$ equals
　　　　the α_{kj} element of $[\boldsymbol{\alpha}]$ (see Prob. 10-14)
　　$[\mathbf{L}]$ = inductance matrix of mutually coupled inductors
　　　　If matrix methods are not employed, the loop method of analysis applied to mutually coupled circuits is summarized as follows. In summing the voltage drops around a particular loop, the voltage contributed by an inductor consists of a sum of terms. For example, if the particular inductor is number j, then its contribution to the loop voltage drops is

$$e = \pm \sum_{k=1}^{n} sL_{jk}\mathbf{i}_k \tag{10-34}$$

The current $\mathbf{i}_k$, which will normally be expressed as a sum of loop currents, is the current in the reference direction in coil k. The plus sign applies if the direction of the loop summation agrees with the reference direction of coil j. If it does not, the minus sign applies. Except for the additional terms in the voltage contributed by the inductors, the loop analysis of mutually coupled circuits is identical with that of uncoupled circuits.

NODE ANALYSIS OF MUTUALLY COUPLED CIRCUITS If Eqs. (10-9) are transformed to the s domain and then placed in matrix form, the following expression results:

$$s[\mathbf{L}] \times \mathbf{i}] = \mathbf{e}] \tag{10-35}$$

---

† The inductor currents, that is, the branch currents in the inductors, are by definition in the reference direction.

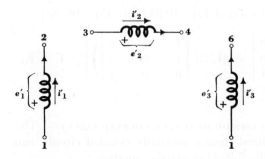

*Fig. 10-5. The circuit of Fig.
10-3, but with node numbers
assigned instead of loop currents. (Note that two nodes
coincide and that node 5 is in
some other part of the circuit.)*

The solution for the inductor currents in terms of the inductor voltages
is therefore

$$\frac{1}{s}[\mathbf{\Gamma}] \times \mathbf{e}] = \mathbf{i}] \tag{10-36}$$

where

$$[\mathbf{\Gamma}] = [\mathbf{L}]^{-1} \tag{10-37}$$

Just as Eq. (10-35) is used in circuit analysis by the loop method,
so is Eq. (10-36) used in analysis by the node method. To demonstrate
this, let us analyze by the node method the same circuit we investigated
by the loop method. Figure 10-5 illustrates this circuit with node numbers assigned rather than loop currents.

In matrix form, the node equations for this circuit are

$$([\mathbf{Y}-] \times \mathbf{E}]) + \mathbf{i}] = \mathbf{I}] \tag{10-38}$$

where

$$\mathbf{i}] = \begin{bmatrix} i_1 \\ i_2 \\ i_3 \\ i_4 \\ 0 \\ i_6 \end{bmatrix} \tag{10-39}$$

The elements in the column matrix above are the currents flowing away
from nodes 1, 2, 3, 4, and 6 through the inductors. The admittance
matrix $[\mathbf{Y}-]$ is calculated with the inductors open-circuited.

The relationships between the currents in the column matrix of
Eq. (10-39) and the inductor currents are quite simple:

$$i_1 = i_1' + i_3' \qquad i_2 = -i_1' \qquad i_3 = i_2' \qquad i_4 = -i_2' \qquad i_6 = -i_3' \tag{10-40}$$

In matrix form, Eqs. (10-40) become

$$\mathbf{i}] = \begin{bmatrix} 1 & 0 & 1 \\ -1 & 0 & 0 \\ 0 & 1 & 0 \\ 0 & -1 & 0 \\ 0 & 0 & 0 \\ 0 & 0 & -1 \end{bmatrix} \times \mathbf{i'}] \tag{10-41}$$

The inductor voltages may be expressed in terms of the node voltages as follows:

$$\mathbf{e'}] = \begin{bmatrix} 1 & -1 & 0 & 0 & 0 & 0 \\ 0 & 0 & 1 & -1 & 0 & 0 \\ 1 & 0 & 0 & 0 & 0 & -1 \end{bmatrix} \times \mathbf{E}] \qquad (10\text{-}42)$$

Finally, the inductor voltages and currents are related by Eq. (10-36):

$$\frac{1}{s} [\mathbf{\Gamma}] \times \mathbf{e'}] = \mathbf{i'}] \qquad (10\text{-}43)$$

The inverse inductance matrix of this equation is found by inverting the inductance matrix of Eq. (10-14):

$$[\mathbf{\Gamma}] = \begin{bmatrix} 1\tfrac{1}{2} & -3 & -\tfrac{7}{2} \\ -3 & 2 & 2 \\ -\tfrac{7}{2} & 2 & 5\tfrac{1}{2} \end{bmatrix} \qquad (10\text{-}44)$$

Equations (10-38) and (10-41) to (10-43) are combined to produce the next expression:

$$\left[[\mathbf{Y}-] + \left([\beta]_t \times \frac{1}{s} [\mathbf{\Gamma}] \times [\beta] \right) \right] \times \mathbf{E}] = \mathbf{I}] \qquad (10\text{-}45)$$

The matrix $[\beta]$ is the transformation matrix of Eq. (10-42). It is the matrix which transforms the node voltages to the inductor voltages in the reference direction. The matrix $[\beta]_t$, the transpose of $[\beta]$, is the transformation matrix of Eq. (10-41). Equation (10-45) effectively summarizes the analysis of mutually coupled circuits by the node method.

THE TRANSIENT ANALYSIS OF MUTUALLY COUPLED CIRCUITS WITH INITIAL STORED ENERGY presents no additional difficulties. The inductors with initial currents are replaced by inductors with no initial currents in parallel with the appropriate constant-current sources. The analysis then proceeds as outlined above.

THE COEFFICIENT OF COUPLING The question was raised earlier of how large the mutual inductance between two coils could be. The answer to that question will be deduced now. It will be recalled that the total energy stored by two coils is

$$W_L = \frac{L_1 i_1{}^2}{2} + \frac{L_2 i_2{}^2}{2} + M i_2 i_2 \qquad (10\text{-}46)$$

The total energy must always be positive; however, the mutual term may be negative. Consequently, the magnitude of M must be limited. The limitations on M are found as follows.

The minimum value of W_L, brought about by varying i_1 while holding i_2 constant, occurs when the derivative of W_L with respect to i_1 is zero:

$$\left. \frac{dW_L}{di_1} \right|_{i_2 \text{ held constant}} = L_1 i_1 + M i_2 = 0 \qquad (10\text{-}47)$$

Thus, for a particular value of i_2 the minimum of W_L occurs when

$$i_1 = -\frac{M}{L_1} i_2 \qquad (10\text{-}48)$$

Substituting this value into Eq. (10-46) gives

$$W_L = \left(\frac{M^2}{2L_1} + \frac{L_2}{2} - \frac{M^2}{L_1} \right) i_2{}^2 \qquad (10\text{-}49)$$

Clearly, W_L will remain positive for all values of i_2 if the expression within the parentheses is positive. Hence

$$M^2 \leq L_1 L_2 \qquad (10\text{-}50)$$

Equation (10-50) states an important fact: The square of the mutual inductance between two coils must be less than or equal to the product of the self-inductances. Equation (10-50) is expressed in the following modified form:

$$M = k \sqrt{L_1 L_2} \qquad |k| \leq 1 \qquad (10\text{-}51)$$

The quantity k is called the *coefficient of coupling*.

SUMMARY   The two principal questions discussed in this section were, What is mutual induction and how does it affect the analysis of circuits? In answer to the first question, mutual induction is the effect caused by the interaction of the magnetic fields of two or more current-carrying coils. This effect is analytically expressed by the equation for the energy stored by a set of mutually coupled coils, Eq. (10-6). Derivable from this energy expression are the relationships of Eqs. (10-9). These show that the voltage developed across a coil depends not only upon the current in that coil but upon the currents in all the coils.

The analysis of mutually coupled circuits differs in only one detail from the analysis heretofore employed. In loop analysis, the voltage drop across a coil is no longer a function of the current in that coil alone. The voltage drop is the function of all coil currents given by Eqs. (10-9). In node analysis, the current through a mutually coupled coil depends not only upon the voltage across that particular coil but also upon the voltages across all the coils. The last statement is expressed analytically by Eq. (10-36).

Analyses of mutually coupled circuits, although not difficult in principle, do require considerable attention to detail. This is particularly true with respect to reference directions. Because of this welter of detail, the systematic formulation provided by matrix methods is of considerable value.

PROBLEMS

10-1   The two inductors in the circuit shown are known to have self-inductances of 0.1 and 0.3 henry. The switch is moved from position a to position b, and the total energy dissipated in the resistor is found to be 15 joules. What is L_{12}?

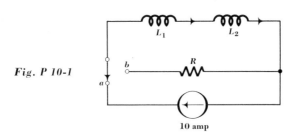

Fig. P 10-1

10 amp

10-2   A steady 1,000-cps sinusoidal voltage is applied to coil 1 in the figure. The rms current in coil 1 is measured and found to be 0.1 amp. The rms voltage across each coil is measured and the following results obtained: $E_1 = 100$ volts, $E_2 = 24$ volts, $E_3 = 77.6$ volts, $E_4 = 152$ volts. What are the magnitudes of L_{11}, L_{12}, L_{13}, and L_{14}?

Fig. P 10-2

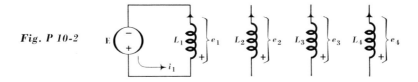

10-3   In order to determine the proper signs to associate with the mutual-inductance magnitudes found in the previous problem, the following test is performed. A current pulse of the shape indicated in the figure is applied in the reference direction to coil 1. With this current pulse applied, the induced voltages in coils 2, 3, and 4 have the shapes shown. Are L_{12}, L_{13}, and L_{14} positive or negative?

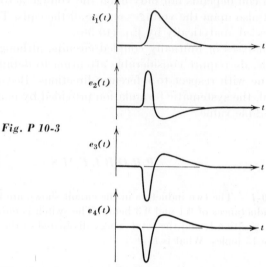

Fig. P 10-3

10-4 The sign of one of the three quantities in each of the accompanying figures is missing. What must each sign be?

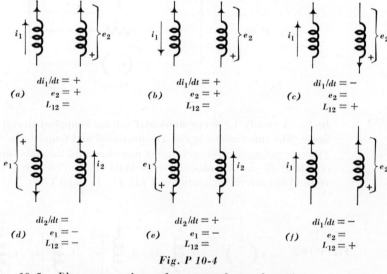

(a)
$di_1/dt = +$
$e_2 = +$
$L_{12} =$

(b)
$di_1/dt = +$
$e_2 = +$
$L_{12} =$

(c)
$di_1/dt = -$
$e_2 =$
$L_{12} = +$

(d)
$di_2/dt =$
$e_1 = -$
$L_{12} = -$

(e)
$di_2/dt = +$
$e_1 = -$
$L_{12} =$

(f)
$di_1/dt = -$
$e_2 =$
$L_{12} = +$

Fig. P 10-4

10-5 Place appropriate reference marks on the coils.

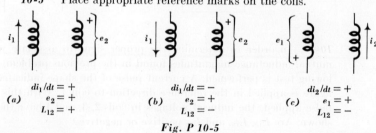

(a)
$di_1/dt = +$
$e_2 = +$
$L_{12} = +$

(b)
$di_1/dt = -$
$e_2 = +$
$L_{12} = -$

(c)
$di_2/dt = +$
$e_1 = +$
$L_{12} = -$

Fig. P 10-5

10-6   Place the appropriate signs in each of the equations.

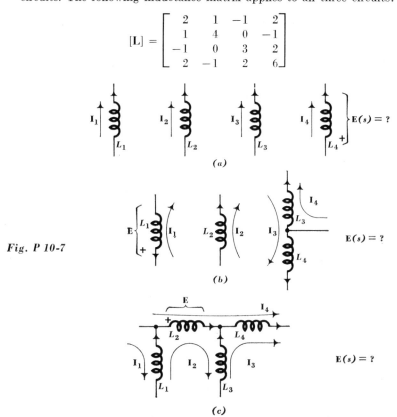

Fig. P 10-6

(a) $e = L_{31}\dfrac{di_1}{dt}$ $L_{31}\dfrac{di_2}{dt}$ $L_{32}\dfrac{di_3}{dt}$ $L_{33}\dfrac{di_4}{dt}$

(b) $\mathbf{E} = sL_{11}\mathbf{I}_1$ $sL_{12}\mathbf{I}_1$ $sL_{12}\mathbf{I}_2$ $sL_{13}\mathbf{I}_1$ $sL_{13}\mathbf{I}_3$ $sL_{14}\mathbf{I}_4$

10-7   Write an equation for the indicated voltages for each of the circuits. The following inductance matrix applies to all three circuits:

$$[\mathbf{L}] = \begin{bmatrix} 2 & 1 & -1 & 2 \\ 1 & 4 & 0 & -1 \\ -1 & 0 & 3 & 2 \\ 2 & -1 & 2 & 6 \end{bmatrix}$$

$E(s) = ?$

(a)

$E(s) = ?$

(b)

Fig. P 10-7

$E(s) = ?$

(c)

10-8   Let the complete circuit for Fig. 10-3 be as shown in the figure. Find the voltage $e_0(t)$ if $e_i(t)$ is a unit step applied at $t = 0$. The inductance matrix is given by Eq. (10-14).

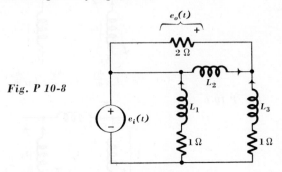

Fig. P 10-8

10-9   After steady-state conditions have been reached in the preceding problem, the voltage produced by the source falls off exponentially. That is, $e_i(t') = 1$ for $t' < 0$, $e_i(t') = e^{-t'}$ for $t' > 0$. What is the voltage $e_0(t')$ for $t' > 0$? What is the current through L_2 for $t' > 0$?

10-10   The switch in the circuit shown is closed when $t = 0$. Find the voltage $e_0(t)$ for $t > 0$. The inductance matrix is given by Eq. (10-14).

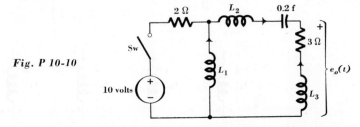

Fig. P 10-10

10-11   After the switch in Prob. 10-10 has been closed long enough to ensure steady-state conditions, it is opened again. Find the voltage $e_0(t)$ after the switch is opened.

10-12   Show that the two coils, with the same loop current through them, can be replaced by the single coil where

$$L_{11} = L_{aa} + L_{bb} - 2L_{ab} \qquad L_{12} = L_{a2} - L_{b2} \qquad L_{13} = L_{a3} - L_{b3}$$
$$\cdots \qquad L_{1n} = L_{an} - L_{bn}$$

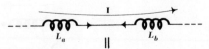

Fig. P 10-12

10-13 If the inductances in the matrix of Eq. (10-14) are in milli-henrys, find the current through the 100-ohm resistor.

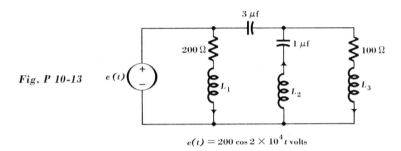

Fig. P 10-13

$e(t) = 200 \cos 2 \times 10^4 t$ volts

10-14 Prove that the matrix $[\alpha]_t$, which transforms the individual inductor voltage drops in the reference directions into the total induct-ance voltage drops for each loop, is the transpose of the matrix $[\alpha]$. The matrix $[\alpha]$ transforms the loop currents into the individual inductor currents. The matrix $[\mathbf{B}]$ is the transpose of the matrix $[\mathbf{A}]$ if $b_{jk} = a_{kj}$. Refer to Eqs. (10-29) and (10-30) and Fig. 10-4.

10-15 Find the impedance matrix for the circuits shown. Use the loop currents in the figure and use the matrix method indicated by Eq. (10-33). That is, find the $[\mathbf{Z}-]$, $[\alpha]$, and $[\alpha]_t$ matrices and then compute the total $[\mathbf{Z}]$ matrix. Use the inductance matrix of Eq. (10-14) for a and the inductance matrix of Prob. 10-7 for b.

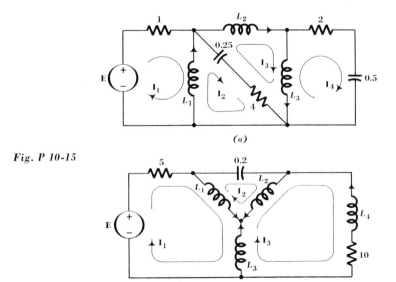

Fig. P 10-15

10-16 The matrix $[\beta]$ transforms the node voltages to inductor voltage drops. Show that its transpose, $[\beta]_t$, transforms the inductor currents to the total inductance current flowing away from the nodes.

10-17 Using the method indicated in Eq. (10-45), find the admittance matrices for the circuits shown. The inverse inductance matrix for both circuits is

$$[\Gamma] = \begin{bmatrix} 3 & -1 & -1 & 0 \\ -1 & 2 & 0 & 1 \\ -1 & 0 & 2 & -1 \\ 0 & 1 & -1 & 4 \end{bmatrix}$$

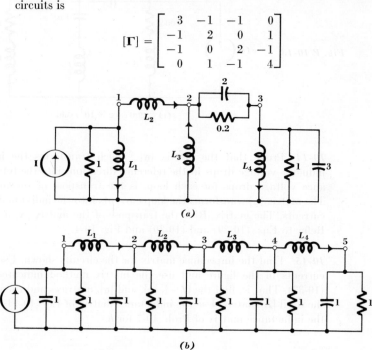

(a)

(b)

Fig. P 10-17

10-18 Find the voltage $e(t)$ if the inductance matrix for this circuit is

$$[L] = \begin{bmatrix} 1 & -1 & 0 \\ -1 & 5/3 & 1/3 \\ 0 & 1/3 & 2/3 \end{bmatrix}$$

where the element values are in millihenrys.

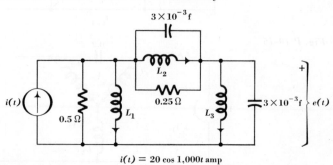

$i(t) = 20 \cos 1{,}000t \text{ amp}$

Fig. P 10-18

10-19   What conditions similar to Eq. (10-50) must apply to the mutual inductances between three coils?

10-2   TRANSFORMERS

To introduce transformers, let us contemplate the possibility of putting the phenomenon of mutual induction to practical use. One intriguing property of mutually coupled coils is that a store of energy built up by a current in one coil can be drawn upon by another coil. In other words, a pair of coils can transfer energy from one to the other without an actual physical connection. Another interesting property can be recognized by studying Eqs. (10-5) and (10-51). If the inductances of the two coils differ considerably and if they are closely coupled ($k \approx 1$), then a small voltage applied to the low-inductance coil will induce a large voltage in the other. Conversely, a high voltage applied to the high-inductance coil induces a low voltage in the other coil.

These two properties of energy transfer and voltage-level transformation, as well as other properties to be discussed shortly, suggest the usefulness of devices consisting of two or more coupled coils. Such devices are called transformers. In this section, only two-coil transformers will be discussed. However, most of their properties, with only slight modification, are shared by multicoil transformers.

NOTATION AND CONVENTION   Two classes of transformers will be discussed in this section, but before beginning this discussion, a few comments must be made concerning notation and convention. The three configurations of Fig. 10-6 illustrate various ways of drawing transformers on a circuit diagram. The two right-hand variations indicate that the transformer contains an iron core.

In the analysis of circuits with only two mutually coupled coils, it is convenient to define mutual inductance as a positive quantity and then select coil reference directions which agree with this constraint. Although the previously used arrow markings are completely applicable, the *dot convention* is more widely utilized. This convention is

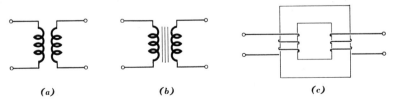

(a)   *(b)*   *(c)*

Fig. 10-6. Three circuit-diagram forms of transformers. The forms (b) and (c) denote iron-core transformers.

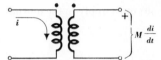

$$M\frac{di}{dt}$$

Fig. 10-7. The dot convention.

illustrated in Fig. 10-7, where the dots have the following significance. The voltage *drop* from the dotted to the undotted end of a coil, induced by a current i flowing in at the dotted end of the other coil, is $M\ di/dt$. If M is assumed positive, the four markings of Fig. 10-8a correspond exactly and may be freely interchanged. The same holds true for the four markings of Fig. 10-8b.

A TUNED TRANSFORMER-COUPLED AMPLIFIER For the purposes of this section, transformers are divided into two classifications: (1) transformers whose coupling coefficient k does not approach unity in value and (2) transformers whose coupling coefficient is very nearly unity. The amplifier under consideration utilizes a loosely coupled transformer, that is, a transformer of the first class.

Consider a radio broadcast receiver which, to be of value, must have both good selectivity and good fidelity. To clarify this last statement, consider Fig. 10-9a. This figure illustrates a part of the broadcast band in which the frequencies of three stations are close together. Each station transmits a band of frequencies centered about the "carrier" frequency. The band of a station extends from $\omega_c - \omega_a$ to $\omega_c + \omega_a$, where ω_a is the highest audio frequency that is being sent and ω_c is the carrier frequency. The receiver must have good selectivity in order to receive the signals from one station while rejecting the signals from the others. However, simply rejecting the unwanted signals is not sufficient. All the frequencies in the band belonging to the station selected must be passed equally well to prevent distortion. Conse-

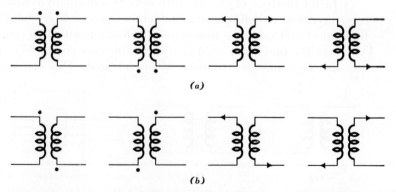

(a)

(b)

Fig. 10-8. Equivalent ways of marking reference directions. M is positive in all cases.

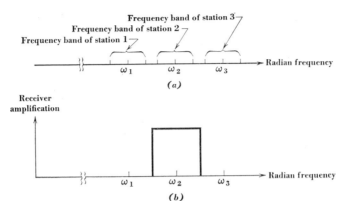

Fig. 10-9. (a) *The frequency bands occupied by three broadcast transmitters;* (b) *the ideal receiver gain vs. frequency characteristic for reception of station 2.*

quently, the ideal frequency characteristic of the receiver when tuned to station 2 is as shown in Fig. 10-9b.

　　Once again, it is possible only to approximate the ideal. One stage of an amplifier circuit resulting in a reasonably close approximation is shown in Fig. 10-10a. The circuit in Fig. 10-10b may be considered equivalent to the amplifier circuit for the purpose of computing the output voltage over the frequency range of interest.

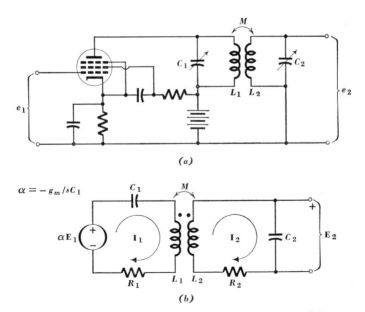

Fig. 10-10. (a) *A double-tuned transformer-coupled pentode amplifier stage;* (b) *the equivalent circuit for part a, neglecting the pentode plate resistance.* R_1 and R_2 *are the coil resistances and* $\alpha = -g_m/sC_1$.

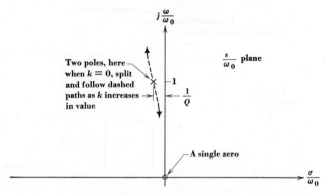

Fig. 10-11. *The pole trajectories and zero location of Eq. (10-56). The lower half plane is an image of the upper. Q has been assumed to be large.*

The loop equations for this circuit are

$$
\begin{bmatrix} sL_1 + R_1 + \dfrac{1}{sC_1} & -sM \\[2ex] -sM & sL_2 + R_2 + \dfrac{1}{sC_2} \end{bmatrix} \times \begin{bmatrix} \mathbf{I}_1 \\ \mathbf{I}_2 \end{bmatrix} = \begin{bmatrix} \alpha \mathbf{E}_1 \\ 0 \end{bmatrix} \quad (10\text{-}52)
$$

The voltage gain is found through the solution of the above equation:

$$
\frac{\mathbf{E}_2}{\mathbf{E}_1} = \frac{-sg_mM}{(s^2L_1C_1 + sR_1C_1 + 1)(s^2L_2C_2 + sR_2C_2 + 1) - s^4M^2C_1C_2} \quad (10\text{-}53)
$$

The generality of the solution is reduced only slightly by making the following assumptions:

$$
L_1 = L_2 = L \qquad C_1 = C_2 = C \qquad R_1 = R_2 = R \qquad (10\text{-}54)
$$

With these assumptions and the definitions given below [Eqs. (10-55)], Eq. (10-53) is transformed into Eq. (10-56).

$$
LC \triangleq \frac{1}{\omega_0^2} \qquad \frac{\omega_0 L}{R} \triangleq Q \qquad M \triangleq kL \qquad (10\text{-}55)
$$

$$
\frac{\mathbf{E}_2}{\mathbf{E}_1} = \frac{-sg_mkL}{\left(\dfrac{s^2}{\omega_0^2} + \dfrac{1}{Q}\dfrac{s}{\omega_0} + 1 \right)^2 - k^2 \dfrac{s^4}{\omega_0^4}} \quad (10\text{-}56)
$$

The poles and zero of this expression are illustrated in Fig. 10-11. The knowledge of the variation of pole positions facilitates the visualization of the frequency response of this circuit for various values of k. The frequency response is plotted in Fig. 10-12 for three values of k. For these curves, $Q = 10$, and the three values of k are expressed in terms of the critical coupling k_c, where $k_c = 1/Q$. The latter notation is employed because the curves for various values of k/k_c maintain the same relative shape regardless of the variation in Q.† Varying Q changes

† This is assuming that Q remains large compared with unity.

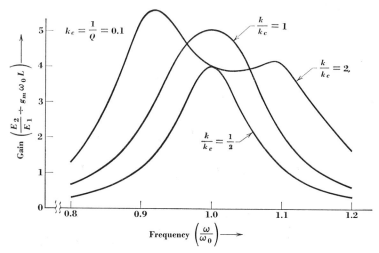

Fig. 10-12. *A plot of the magnitude of* E_2/E_1, *Eq.* (10-56), *with* $s = j\omega$ *and* $Q = 10$, *for three values of the coupling coefficient* k.

the bandwidth, whereas changing k/k_c varies the shape of the curve. It can be seen that for k/k_c equal to or slightly larger than 1, the gain curve is a reasonable approximation to the ideal of Fig. 10-9b.

The above example is a typical illustration of the use of transformers of the first class. In this example, the transformer, in conjunction with the other circuit elements, approximates the ideal bandpass filter of Fig. 10-9b. An important parameter, which controls the shape of the frequency response of this filter, is the transformer coupling coefficient. The coefficient of coupling can be adjusted by changing the position of one coil relative to the other.

TRANSFORMERS IN WHICH k APPROACHES UNITY The previous example, demonstrating the analysis of loosely coupled transformers, uses the methods developed in Sec. 10-1. For tightly coupled transformers, in which k is approximately unity, simpler techniques are applicable. To illustrate, let us analyze the circuit of Fig. 10-13.

With unity coupling, the mutual inductance is $\sqrt{L_1 L_2}$. Consequently, the loop equilibrium equations are

$$\begin{bmatrix} sL_1 & -s\sqrt{L_1L_2} \\ -s\sqrt{L_1L_2} & sL_2 + Z \end{bmatrix} \times \begin{bmatrix} I_1 \\ I_2 \end{bmatrix} = \begin{bmatrix} E \\ 0 \end{bmatrix} \qquad (10\text{-}57)$$

Fig. 10-13. *A transformer circuit in which the coefficient of coupling is unity.*

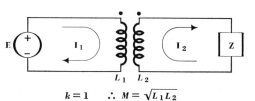

$k = 1 \qquad \therefore \ M = \sqrt{L_1 L_2}$

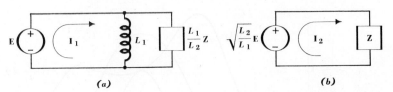

(a)   *(b)*

Fig. 10-14. *Two equivalent circuits which are applicable for finding the currents in Fig. 10-13.*

The solutions for the two loop currents are

$$\mathbf{I}_1 = \frac{\mathbf{E}(sL_2 + \mathbf{Z})}{sL_1(sL_2 + \mathbf{Z}) - s^2 L_1 L_2} = \mathbf{E}\left[\frac{1}{sL_1} + \frac{1}{(L_1/L_2)\mathbf{Z}}\right] \quad (10\text{-}58)$$

$$\mathbf{I}_2 = \frac{\mathbf{E}_s \sqrt{L_1 L_2}}{sL_1(sL_2 + \mathbf{Z}) - s^2 L_1 L_2} = \frac{\mathbf{E}}{\mathbf{Z}}\sqrt{\frac{L_2}{L_1}} \quad (10\text{-}59)$$

The current solutions are represented by the equivalent circuits of Fig. 10-14. These two equivalent circuits present a pair of revealing viewpoints. In the first equivalent circuit, the transformer, in effect, transforms the impedance $\mathbf{Z}$ on the secondary† side to an impedance $(L_1/L_2)\mathbf{Z}$ on the primary side. Alternatively, the transformer transforms the primary applied voltage $\mathbf{E}$ to a different level, $\sqrt{L_2/L_1}\,\mathbf{E}$. This is illustrated in the second of the two equivalent circuits.

Before discussing these circuits in more detail, let us further the idealization by assuming that, in addition to unity coupling, the self-inductances L_1 and L_2 are so large that they may be considered infinite. Furthermore, we shall utilize the fact that in these tightly coupled high-inductance transformers the self-inductance of each coil is proportional to the square of the number of turns in that coil. That is,

$$L_1 = \alpha N_1{}^2 \approx \infty \qquad L_2 = \alpha N_2{}^2 \approx \infty \qquad \frac{L_1}{L_2} = \left(\frac{N_1}{N_2}\right)^2 \quad (10\text{-}60)$$

These assumptions permit the representation of the transformer circuit of Fig. 10-15a by either of the two equivalent circuits shown below it. The equivalence of these two circuits can be demonstrated in a manner similar to that used to derive the equivalent circuits of Fig. 10-14. This is left to the student.

A transformer with the characteristics assumed above will be called an *ideal transformer*. The analysis of a circuit containing an ideal transformer is quite simple. Three ways of carrying out such an analysis are available. The first two, illustrated in Fig. 10-15b and c, consist in transferring impedances and sources from one side of the transformer to the other. The change in impedance or voltage level affected by this transfer is given in the figure.

† The two coils of a transformer are denoted as primary and secondary according to the following convention. The net energy flow is from primary to secondary.

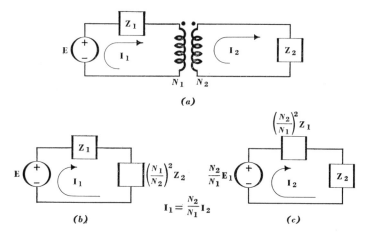

Fig. 10-15. An ideal transformer with its primary and secondary equivalent circuits. N_1 and N_2 are the number of turns of primary and secondary coils.

Occasionally a circuit will be encountered which cannot be reduced to the simple form of Fig. 10-15a. In such a case, the analysis must be carried out in the third way. Loop or node analysis is employed, with the following conditions applicable at the transformer:

$$\frac{N_2}{N_1} \mathbf{E}' \text{ (primary voltage)} = \mathbf{E}'' \text{ (secondary voltage)}$$
$$\frac{N_1}{N_2} \mathbf{I}_1 \text{ (primary current)} = \mathbf{I}_2 \text{ (secondary current)} \tag{10-61}$$

As an illustration, consider the network of Fig. 10-16, where the primary and secondary currents are now called loop currents 1 and 2. The equilibrium equations for loops 1 and 2 are as follows:

$$\sum_j \mathbf{Z}_{1j}\mathbf{I}_j + \mathbf{E}' = \mathbf{E}_1 \qquad \text{(applied voltages in loop 1)}$$
$$\sum_j \mathbf{Z}_{2j}\mathbf{I}_j - \mathbf{E}'' = \mathbf{E}_2 \qquad \text{(applied voltages in loop 2)} \tag{10-62}$$

Multiplying both sides of the loop 1 equation by N_2/N_1 and then adding to the loop 2 equation lead to

$$\sum_j \left(\frac{N_2}{N_1}\mathbf{Z}_{1j} + \mathbf{Z}_{2j}\right)\mathbf{I}_j = \frac{N_2}{N_1}\mathbf{E}_1 + \mathbf{E}_2 \tag{10-63}$$

Equation (10-63) is added to the set of equilibrium equations for loops 3, 4, 5, ... In this collection of equations, $(N_2/N_1)\mathbf{I}_2$ may be

Fig. 10-16. An ideal transformer as part of a more extensive circuit. Note the directions of the primary and secondary currents in relation to the reference dots.

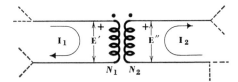

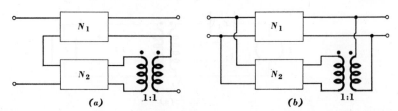

Fig. 10-17. *The utilization of ideal transformers to ensure that the validity conditions are satisfied.*

substituted for I_1 wherever it occurs. This modified set of equations is then solved by the usual methods. A process similar to that followed in obtaining Eqs. (10-62) and (10-63) is applicable to the node analysis of circuits containing ideal transformers.

THE INTERCONNECTIONS OF TWO-PORT NETWORKS USING IDEAL TRANS-FORMERS It was stated in Sec. 9-4 that the addition of **y**, **z**, **g**, or **h** parameters of the component two-ports to yield the parameters of the interconnected two-ports is not always valid. The conditions which must be satisfied in order to ensure the validity of this process are enumerated in Eqs. (9-107) and (9-111). The synthesis of a two-port network to produce a prescribed transfer function often is accomplished by interconnecting a number of two-ports, each one of which produces a part of the total transfer function. This method depends upon the simple addition of the appropriate two-port parameters. Consequently, the validity conditions must be satisfied when the component two-ports are interconnected. Ideal transformers, because of the current characteristics specified by Eqs. (10-61), provide a means of guaranteeing the validity conditions. The appropriate transformer connections to accomplish this are illustrated in Fig. 10-17.

MAXIMUM-POWER-TRANSFER THEOREMS Consider Fig. 10-18, in which Z_L is a load impedance and Z_i is an internal impedance associated with the source **E**. The source and internal impedance represent, by Thévenin's theorem, any arrangement of internal sources and impedances. The voltage source produces a single-frequency sinusoidal voltage at its terminals. Let us investigate the following problem: How can the power dissipated in Z_L be maximized through adjustment of the value of Z_L?

The solution to this problem is straightforward. First, the power in the load is expressed as the square of the magnitude of the current

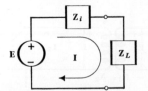

Fig. 10-18. *A circuit applicable to the development of maximum-power-transfer theorems.*

times the real part of $\mathbf{Z}_L$:

$$P = I^2R_L = \left| \frac{E}{R_i + jX_i + R_L + jX_L} \right|^2 R_L$$

$$= \frac{E^2R_L}{(R_i + R_L)^2 + (X_i + X_L)^2} \quad (10\text{-}64)$$

Load adjustment is accomplished by varying the real part R_L or the imaginary part X_L. When X_L is held constant and R_L varied, the maximum power dissipation occurs when $dP/dR_L = 0$. On the other hand, with R_L constant, the maximum power dissipation occurs when $dP/dX_L = 0$. Clearly, the maximum power dissipation for any $\mathbf{Z}_L$ occurs when both derivatives are zero simultaneously:

$$\frac{dP}{dR_L} = \frac{(R_i + R_L)^2 + (X_i + X_L)^2 - 2R_L(R_i + R_L)}{[(R_i + R_L)^2 + (X_i + X_L)^2]^2} = 0$$

$$\frac{dP}{dX_L} = \frac{-2R_L(X_i + X_L)}{[(R_i + R_L)^2 + (X_i + X_L)^2]^2} = 0 \qquad (10\text{-}65)$$

The two equations above are satisfied when

$$X_L = -X_i \qquad R_L = R_i \qquad\qquad (10\text{-}66)$$

Therefore, maximum power dissipation in the load occurs when its resistive component is equal to that of the internal impedance and when its reactive component is equal in magnitude and opposite in sign to the internal reactance. Restated, maximum power transfer from source to load takes place when internal and external impedances have equal magnitudes and phase angles which are negatives of each other.

When the phase angle of the load cannot be varied, the maximum power transfer, although less than that obtained above, occurs when the magnitudes of internal and external impedances are equal. The proof of this statement is similar to the development leading to Eqs. (10-66). This proof is left to the reader.

These theorems have been introduced in this section because of the common utilization of transformers in implementing the maximization of power transfer. A typical example of this is illustrated in Fig. 10-19, where a transformer is used to "match" the low impedance of a loudspeaker to the high source impedance of the vacuum-tube amplifier circuit.

NONIDEAL TRANSFORMERS The conditions of $k = 1$ and $L_1 \to \infty$, $L_2 \to \infty$, which were assumed in the discussion above, are approached relatively closely by carefully designed transformers. However, since these conditions can only be approximated, the method of analysis outlined above produces a certain amount of error in the circuit solution. This error is so small in most cases that it is neglected. In other situations, where more exact solutions are necessary, the techniques

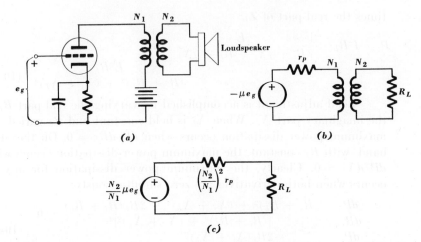

Fig. 10-19. *(a) The final stage of an audio amplifier which drives a loudspeaker. (b) The equivalent circuit corresponding to (a). The plate resistance r_p will be of the order of 1,000 to 10,000 ohms, and the effective loudspeaker resistance will be of the order of 2 to 20 ohms. (c) Final equivalent circuit referred to the secondary. For maximum power transfer $(N_2/N_1)^2 = R_L/r_p$.*

of Sec. 10-1 are applicable. However, the analysis method developed for ideal transformers is so much simpler that its extension to nonideal transformers merits considerable effort. Substantial portions of many texts and courses dealing with transformers are devoted to the application of ideal-transformer techniques to nonideal transformers. Although it would be informative to pursue these studies, our investigation here must be limited to a number of problems at the end of the chapter.

IRON-CORE TRANSFORMERS Iron, nickel, and cobalt, together with their compounds and alloys, form a group called ferromagnetic materials. A ferromagnetic core, illustrated in Fig. 10-20, is capable of increasing the inductance of a coil by a factor of several thousand over the inductance with any other material as a core. Furthermore, the coupling coefficient for a transformer with an iron core constructed as shown in Fig. 10-6c is essentially unity. The combination of high inductance and unity coupling is unobtainable in air-core transformers.

Because of the unique properties of ferromagnetic materials, they are employed in most devices which depend for their operation upon the presence of a magnetic field. Certain disadvantages, however, are

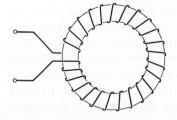

Fig. 10-20. An iron-core inductor.

concomitant with the use of these materials. They are not linear. The inductance of an iron-core coil is not constant. The inductance is a function of the current in the coil—a function not only of the magnitude of the current but also of the past history of the current. Clearly, the accurate analysis of circuits containing such devices requires methods not yet investigated in this text. Some of these methods will be discussed in Chaps. 11 and 14, and certain magnetic properties of ferromagnetic materials will be discussed more fully in later chapters.

SUMMARY The foregoing discussion placed transformers in two categories. The first contains those transformers in which the coefficient of coupling is not unity. The analysis of circuits containing transformers of this type employs the methods developed in Sec. 10-1. The second category contains transformers in which the coefficient of coupling is equal to, or very nearly equal to, unity. The analysis of these transformers can be carried out by using the equivalent circuits of Fig. 10-14.

Ideal transformers are unity-coupling infinite-inductance transformers. The analysis of an ideal transformer is aided by the fact that voltages and currents in the primary and secondary coils are related by the simple expressions of Eq. (10-16). In addition, the transformer has the effect of transforming the impedance on the primary side to the secondary side, or vice versa. This effect is illustrated in Fig. 10-15.

It should be emphasized that ideal transformers are idealizations and can only be approximated by physical transformers. Consequently, the accuracy of a circuit solution based upon the assumption that the transformer is ideal depends upon the degree to which the physical transformer approximates the ideal. This is just another of the many situations faced by an engineer in which he must decide which of the possible models representing a physical element is most appropriate for his analysis of a particular system.

PROBLEMS

10-20 Show that the circuits a and b shown in the figure are equivalent. Express L_a, L_b, and L_c in terms of L_1, L_2, and M. Would it always be physically possible to replace (a) by (b)?

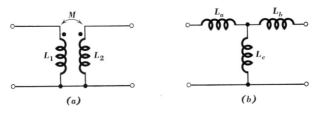

Fig. P 10-20

10-21 What are the **y, z, g, h, a,** and **b** parameters of the two transformers shown in the figure?

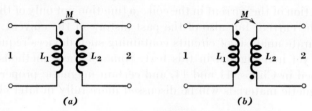

Fig. P 10-21

10-22 If the two transformers of Prob. 10-21 were ideal transformers
of turns ratio N_1/N_2, what would their **a** and **b** parameters be?

10-23 Derive the equivalent circuits of Fig. 10-15.

10-24 Find the currents I_1 and I_2 in the circuit shown. (The transformer is ideal.)

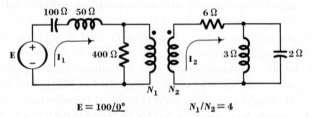

Fig. P 10-24

10-25 Find the z-parameter matrices for the circuits in the figure.
Assume that all the transformers are ideal transformers.

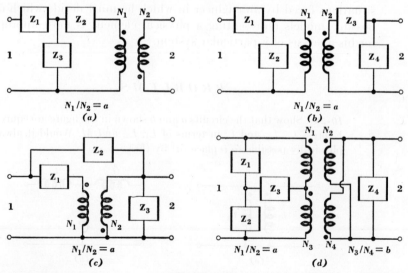

Fig. P 10-25

10-26 When the phase angle of the load cannot be varied, the maximum power transfer occurs when the magnitude of the load impedance equals the magnitude of the source impedance. Prove this statement.

10-27 The turns ratio of the ideal transformer is $N_1/N_2 = 0.2$. What is the Thévenin equivalent circuit as seen from terminals 2-2'? What is the maximum attainable power at terminals 2-2' when the current source provides a sinusoidal current with an rms value of 10 amp and a radian frequency of 500? Answer the last question for frequencies of 1,000 and 2,000 radians/sec.

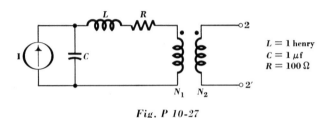

Fig. P 10-27

10-28 The voltage source produces a sinusoidal voltage with a constant radian frequency ω. The two coils can be adjusted so that k takes on any value from zero to unity. Find the k and the appropriate coil reference directions which make the load, as seen by the source, purely resistive.

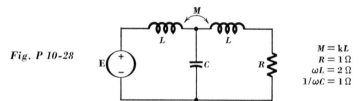

Fig. P 10-28

$$M = kL$$
$$R = 1 \, \Omega$$
$$\omega L = 2 \, \Omega$$
$$1/\omega C = 1 \, \Omega$$

10-29 The power dissipated in the secondary load is to be maximized. Specify the transformer turns ratio which will accomplish this at frequencies of 100, 1,000, and 10,000 cps. Suppose that the two-port network is to be inserted in the primary at the point x-x. How would you construct the two-port network so that the secondary power is maximized at 1,000 cps? What should the turns ratio be now? Can you construct a two-port network which maximizes the power at both 1,000 and 10,000 cps?

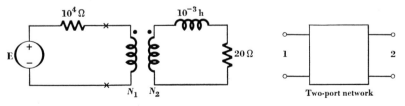

Fig. P 10-29

10-30 In the discussion of the bandpass amplifier of Fig. 10-10 it was assumed that the two coils had the same Q and were tuned to the same frequency [Eq. (10-54)]. This resulted in the pole-zero plot of Fig. 10-11. Draw a similar pole-zero plot for the following three conditions (all high Q):

    (a) The two coils have the same Q's but are tuned to slightly different frequencies.

    (b) The coils have the same frequencies but slightly different Q's.

    (c) The coils have slightly different Q's and frequencies.

10-31 Prove that the transformer whose coefficient of coupling is slightly less than unity can be approximated by the transformer with unity coupling in series with the inductance shown.

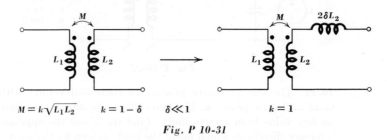

$$M = k\sqrt{L_1 L_2} \qquad k = 1 - \delta \qquad \delta \ll 1 \qquad\qquad k = 1$$

Fig. P 10-31

10-32 Let us start with an ideal transformer and then modify it, in this problem and the following ones, so that we obtain a reasonable linear model of an actual transformer. If the secondary of an ideal transformer is open-circuited, no current will flow in the primary. This is due to assuming infinite inductance for the primary and the secondary. Since these inductances can only be finite for an actual transformer, there will be some primary current even if the secondary is open-circuited. Show that this fact is accounted for in the approximate model shown in the figure. Discuss the validity of this model. How would you measure the magnetizing inductance L_m?

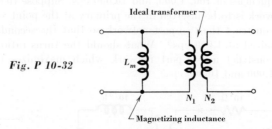

Fig. P 10-32

10-33 With the secondary open, the primary impedance is found to have a resistive component. This is due mainly to core losses. (A changing flux in ferromagnetic materials always produces some heating of the material.) Show that the illustrated modification of the previous model will account for these core losses. Note that the loss in this model depends directly upon the applied voltage rather than the total current in the primary. Discuss this fact and the means of measuring R_m.

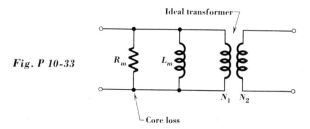

Fig. P 10-33

10-34 Not all the flux produced by the primary will link the secondary ($k < 1$). Hence there will be a primary voltage drop proportional to the total current in the primary. In addition, there will be a primary voltage drop due to the coil resistance. The same effect also will be present in the secondary. Show that the model represented in part *a* of the figure accounts for these effects. By transferring the secondary-coil impedance to the primary, show that model *b* is essentially the same as model *a*. Discuss how you would evaluate L_l, R, L_m, R_m, and N_1/N_2 for this model. (Try open-circuit and short-circuit measurements.) What are the restrictions to the validity of this model?

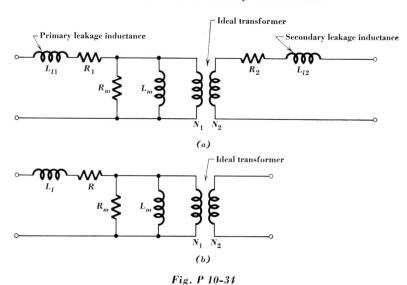

Fig. P 10-34

10-35 Consider the results of the following tests on a large 60-cps power transformer. The high-voltage side is open-circuited and 120 volts (rms) is applied to the low-voltage side. A wattmeter and ammeter in the low-voltage side read 70 watts and 1 amp, and a voltmeter across the high-voltage leads reads 2,400 volts. The low-voltage side is short-circuited, and 120 volts is applied to the high-voltage side. A wattmeter and ammeter in the high-voltage side read 225 watts and 4.5 amp. What are the values of $L_l, R, R_m,$ and L_m for model b of Prob. 10-34?

10-36 The transformer of Prob. 10-35 supplies an 8-kva load at 120 volts (from the low-voltage side).

(a) If the load is unity power factor, what must the primary voltage be to supply this requirement? What is the power factor as seen at the primary? What is the efficiency of the transformer?

(b) Answer all the questions of part a for the case in which the 8-kva load is 0.7 power factor lagging.

10-3 MECHANICAL TRANSFORMERS

As was pointed out earlier, there is no property of mechanical systems which corresponds to mutual inductance in electrical systems. However, certain mechanical devices behave very much like ideal transformers. We shall discuss some of these devices in this section.

THE LEVER The simplest example of a mechanical transformer is the lever. For small angular displacements, the ends of the lever of Fig. 10-21 may be considered to have pure translational motion only. Assuming that the lever is rigid, massless, and frictionless, we can immediately see that

$$x_2 = -\frac{a}{b} x_1 \qquad v_2 = -\frac{a}{b} v_1 \qquad f_2 = \frac{b}{a} f_1 \qquad (10\text{-}67)$$

The first two relations above are obvious from the geometry of the device. The third arises because our assumptions indicate that the lever can neither store nor dissipate energy. Hence, an increment of work done on one end of the lever must be given up at the other:

$$f_1 \Delta x_1 + f_2 \Delta x_2 = 0 \qquad (10\text{-}68)$$

Equations (10-67) are entirely analogous to the voltage and current relations of an ideal electrical transformer. The ratio a/b corresponds to the turns ratio of the electrical transformer.

A MECHANICAL SYSTEM CONTAINING AN IDEAL LEVER Let us analyze the motion of the system shown in Fig. 10-22, proceeding on the assumption that the applied force is small enough to ensure that the

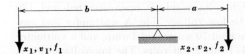

Fig. 10-21. A simple lever.

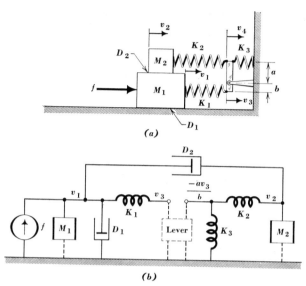

Fig. 10-22. (a) *A mechanical system containing a lever;* (b) *the network diagram of the model approximating the system.*

angular displacement of the lever will be small. In part *b* of the figure the system is represented in network form, with Eqs. (10-67) utilized to write V_4 in terms of V_3. With three unknown velocities, we must write three node equations. The node equations for the V_1 and V_2 nodes are found in the same way as in previous problems:

$$
\begin{aligned}
\left[sM_1 + (D_1 + D_2) + \frac{1}{sK_1} \right] V_1 - D_2 V_2 - \frac{V_3}{sK_1} &= F \\
- D_2 V_1 + \left(sM_2 + D_2 + \frac{1}{sK_2} \right) V_2 + \frac{aV_3}{sK_2 b} &= 0
\end{aligned}
\tag{10-69}
$$

For the equation of node velocity V_3, let us refer to Fig. 10-23. The relationships of Eqs. (10-67) tell us that the force f_4 acting on the right-hand node (tending to move it in the direction opposite to the reference direction) must equal b/a times the force f_3 acting on

Fig. 10-23. *The forces acting on the lever ends.*

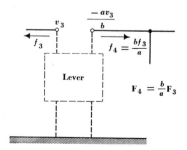

the left-hand node (tending to move it in the direction opposite to the reference direction). The force f_3 can be found from the following expression:

$$\mathbf{F}_3 = \frac{\mathbf{V}_3 - \mathbf{V}_1}{sK_1} \qquad (10\text{-}70)$$

Similarly,

$$\mathbf{F}_4 = \frac{-(a/b)\mathbf{V}_3}{sK_3} + \frac{-(a/b)\mathbf{V}_3 - \mathbf{V}_2}{sK_2} \qquad (10\text{-}71)$$

By combining the last two equations [noting that $\mathbf{F}_4 = (b/a)\mathbf{F}_3$], we form a third equation to add to the two node equations of Eqs. (10-69):

$$-\frac{b\mathbf{V}_1}{sK_1 a} + \frac{\mathbf{V}_2}{sK_2} + \left(\frac{b}{sK_1 a} + \frac{a}{sK_2 b} + \frac{a}{sK_3 b}\right)\mathbf{V}_3 = 0 \qquad (10\text{-}72)$$

In matrix notation the three node equations above reduce to the following expression:

$$
\begin{bmatrix}
sM_1 + (D_1 + D_2) + \dfrac{1}{sK_1} & -D_2 & -\dfrac{1}{sK_1} \\[2ex]
-D_2 & sM_2 + D_2 + \dfrac{1}{sK_2} & \dfrac{a}{sK_2 b} \\[2ex]
-\dfrac{b}{sK_1 a} & \dfrac{1}{sK_2} & \dfrac{b}{sK_1 a} + \dfrac{a}{sK_2 b} + \dfrac{a}{sK_3 b}
\end{bmatrix}
\times
\begin{bmatrix}
\mathbf{V}_1 \\ \mathbf{V}_2 \\ \mathbf{V}_3
\end{bmatrix}
=
\begin{bmatrix}
\mathbf{F} \\ 0 \\ 0
\end{bmatrix}
\qquad (10\text{-}73)
$$

An interesting characteristic appears in the matrix above. Unlike the nodal matrices obtained in previous problems, the one above is not symmetrical. However, it could be made symmetrical quite easily. If we had multiplied both sides of Eq. (10-72) by a/b before writing the equations in matrix form, the resultant matrix would have been symmetrical. In general, the analysis of systems containing levers will often produce unsymmetrical matrices, but the matrices can always be made symmetrical, if this is desired, by an appropriate operation, like the one outlined above.

We need not pursue the complete solution of this system any further, since the matrix equation above is similar to others that have been solved previously. However, before leaving this system, we shall carry out some manipulations of Eq. (10-73) to demonstrate that a lever transforms impedance levels just as an electrical transformer does. Let us first modify the system by setting $D_2 = 0$. Thus, the lever is the only connection between two isolated mechanical systems. Second, we shall perform the following operations on the matrix equation: (1) multiply both sides of the second node equation by a/b; (2) multiply

Fig. 10-24. A network equivalent to Fig. 10-22b. (D_2 has been assumed equal to zero.) The lever has been removed by changing the impedance level on the secondary side.

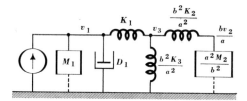

both sides of the third node equation by a/b; (3) substitute $(b/a)\mathbf{V}_2$ for $\mathbf{V}_2$ in the column matrix of velocities. This must be accompanied by a multiplication of each term in column 2 of the parameter matrix by a/b. The three operations above have not changed the three node equations, but the matrix equation does have a different appearance:

$$
\begin{bmatrix}
sM_1 + D_1 + \dfrac{1}{sK_1} & 0 & -\dfrac{1}{sK_1} \\[2ex]
0 & \dfrac{sa^2M_2}{b^2} + \dfrac{a^2}{sb^2K_2} & \dfrac{a^2}{sb^2K_2} \\[2ex]
-\dfrac{1}{sK_1} & \dfrac{a^2}{sb^2K_2} & \dfrac{1}{sK_1} + \dfrac{a^2}{sb^2K_2} + \dfrac{a^2}{sb^2K_3}
\end{bmatrix}
$$

$$
\times \begin{bmatrix} \mathbf{V}_1 \\[1ex] \dfrac{b}{a}\mathbf{V}_2 \\[1ex] \mathbf{V}_3 \end{bmatrix} = \begin{bmatrix} \mathbf{F} \\ 0 \\ 0 \end{bmatrix} \quad (10\text{-}74)
$$

As was pointed out, the three node equations are unchanged, and consequently Eq. (10-74) corresponds to Fig. 10-22b (with $D_2 = 0$). In addition, the matrix equation above is seen to conform to the network of Fig. 10-24. This figure could have been obtained directly from the original network with the appropriate change in impedance level, as is indicated.

OTHER FORMS OF MECHANICAL TRANSFORMERS A number of other mechanical devices perform in the same manner as the lever. For example, hydraulic systems, pulley systems, gears, chain and belt drives are all mechanical transformers. If these devices can be considered ideal transformers, that is, if they neither store nor dissipate energy, the analysis of systems containing them proceeds in the same manner as in the lever example above.

NONIDEAL MECHANICAL TRANSFORMERS As in the case of electrical transformers, any actual mechanical device which acts as a transformer will not be truly ideal. There will be a certain amount of energy storage and dissipation within the device itself. In some cases this energy will be so small as to be negligible. In others it cannot be neglected. In the

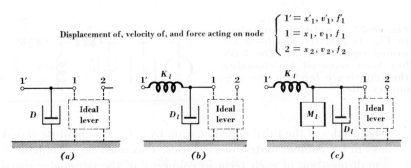

Displacement of, velocity of, and force acting on node
$$\begin{cases} 1' = x'_1, v'_1, f'_1 \\ 1 = x_1, v_1, f_1 \\ 2 = x_2, v_2, f_2 \end{cases}$$

Fig. 10-25. Three approximate models of a nonideal lever. (a) Model including only the friction, (b) model including the friction and compliance, and (c) model accounting for both forms of energy storage as well as dissipation. The ends of the actual lever are at 1' and 2.

latter cases we shall call upon techniques which are analogous to those used with electrical transformers. That is, the nonideal device will be treated as an ideal transformer in combination with appropriate values of mass, compliance, and frictional resistance.

Consider the lever of Fig. 10-21. There will be some heat loss due to friction at the pivot. Consequently, a model for this lever should include this friction. Such a model is shown in Fig. 10-25a. If one end of the lever is held fixed in one position and a force is applied at the other end, there will be some deflection due to the compliance of the lever arm. This effect can be represented by the compliance in Fig. 10-25b. The lever arm will have a finite mass and hence a moment of inertia. The kinetic energy associated with this inertia can be accounted for by adding a mass element to the ideal lever, as is shown in Fig. 10-25c. The relationships between x_1, v_1, f_1 and x_2, v_2, f_2 are those given by Eqs. (10-67). However, x_1, v_1, and f_1 are no longer the conditions at one end of the lever. They are parameters which exist only in the model. The actual conditions at the lever end are x'_1, v'_1, and f'_1. The relationships between the parameters of the two lever ends are, of course, more complex now. Nevertheless, the network solutions may be carried out by using the methods discussed above.

The other devices we have mentioned which act as mechanical transformers will also store and dissipate a certain amount of energy. Consequently, they too may be approximated by the model of Fig. 10-25c or by a similar model.

SUMMARY Although there is no property of mechanical systems which is analogous to mutual inductance, a number of mechanical devices have characteristics which correspond to those of electrical transformers. Network analysis with these devices present is carried out in a manner similar to electrical-circuit analysis with transformers present; that is, node or loop analysis can be employed, utilizing the relationships of Eqs. (10-67). Alternatively, impedance can be transferred from one side of the mechanical transformer to the other, with an appropriate change in level.

When the mechanical transformer is nonideal, it can be approximated by a model which combines an ideal mechanical transformer with other mechanical network elements.

PROBLEMS

10-37   The figure illustrates several mechanical devices which behave like transformers. If each is ideal (no energy storage or dissipation), write the expressions which relate their terminal node velocities and forces. Discuss the ways in which each is likely to deviate from the ideal and draw for each the network diagram of a model which accounts for these deviations.

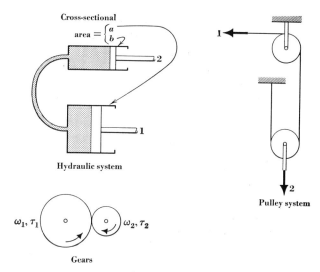

Fig. P 10-37

10-38   A lever is 1 m long and 0.2 m from end 1 to the pivot. If end 2 is held fixed and 10 newtons is applied at end 1, the lever deflects 0.01 m. With no restraint at end 2 and a sinusoidal velocity $0.05 \sin 12t$ m/sec applied at end 1, the force necessary to maintain this velocity is found to be $0.2 \sin (12t + 20°)$ newtons. Draw the approximate model for this lever, giving the values of the network parameters.

10-39   In Fig. 10-24 the secondary impedances of Fig. 10-22b have been transferred to the primary side. Redraw this equivalent network with all primary impedances and sources transferred to the secondary side. Indicate the operations that must be performed on matrix equation (10-74) in order to make it correspond to this new network.

10-40 With a nonzero D_2 in Fig. 10-22b, can the lever be eliminated by transferring impedances from one side to the other? If it can, draw the resultant network. If it cannot, explain why.

10-41 Draw network diagrams for each of the systems shown in the figure. If possible, eliminate the lever. Find the matrix equations for the networks. Redraw the networks using the nonideal model for the levers.

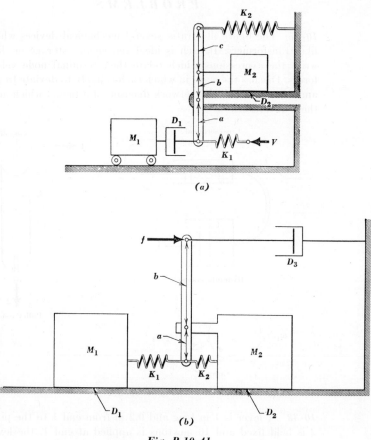

(a)

(b)

Fig. P 10-41

11

electromechanical energy conversion

The first 10 chapters of this text have dealt with methods and techniques of analyzing and characterizing mechanical and electrical systems. Our introduction to the analysis of linear lumped mechanical and electrical networks is now reasonably complete. There are a number of directions in which we could proceed at this point. Nonlinear networks, distributed parameters, more powerful and sophisticated mathematical techniques of analysis, network synthesis—these and many other topics are worthy of considerable investigation. However, rather than pursue more deeply the analysis of either mechanical or electrical systems, we shall now apply the techniques of the preceding chapters to the analysis of systems which contain both mechanical and electrical components. One reason for using parallel approaches to electrical and mechanical systems in the preceding chapters has been to develop methods which can be extended to electromechanical systems.

It is difficult to enumerate more than a few electrical systems which do not contain at some point a mechanical system that exchanges energy with the electrical system. This chapter will be devoted to an investigation of this interchange of mechanical and electrical energy. Before proceeding with this task, we must emphasize that electromechanical energy conversion need not imply only the conversion of relatively large amounts of energy in motors and generators. The conversion of very small amounts of energy, such as that involved in the conversion of sound waves into an electrical signal by a microphone or the conversion of the electric field energy in a vacuum tube to the kinetic energy of moving electrons, must be included in the category of electromechanical energy conversion.

The analysis of electromechanical systems can be based upon either of two approaches. The first starts with the laws of forces exerted on bodies by electric and magnetic fields and proceeds to a model to be analyzed. The second relies upon the conservation of energy and hence upon our ability to write energy-equilibrium equations. Both approaches will be used in the following sections, with emphasis upon the latter and more general technique.

The purpose of this chapter is to demonstrate methods of analyzing *models* of electromechanical systems. This is in keeping with the nature of the previous portion of the text, in which the major emphasis has been on the analysis of linear models of electrical and mechanical systems. The specification of the models has proceeded with a minimum of explanation of the reasons why an actual physical element or device behaves like the model which represents it. For example, it was stated that an ideal resistor dissipates energy according to the formula $p = i^2R$, but no attempt was made to discuss the movement of electrons in a solid in order to explain the generation of heat in a resistor. Detailed justifications for the models chosen have been omitted for a number of reasons. In some cases the reader has had the explanations in previous courses. In others, an adequate explanation would require a degree of technical knowledge not assumed for the readers of this book. In all cases, detailed explanations would necessitate an unreasonable expansion of the text and would obscure the primary goal of introducing techniques of linear system analysis.

This chapter in particular may be somewhat unsatisfying to some readers, since it has been necessary, in specifying various models, to draw upon a number of theorems of electromagnetic field theory with little or no explanation or justification. For those who desire further background in elementary electromagnetic field theory, there are a number of texts available in this area.†

11-1 ENERGY CONSIDERATIONS AND GENERAL PRINCIPLES

Before proceeding with the analysis of specific systems, let us examine a diagram which illustrates the features common to all electromechanical energy-conversion devices. The general electromechanical device of Fig. 11-1 consists of three systems: the electrical system, the mechanical system, and the coupling system. The electrical and mechanical systems are of the type analyzed in previous chapters.

The coupling system includes a region in which energy is stored in the form of electromagnetic fields. It is through these fields that the electrical and mechanical parts of the device are coupled. In addition to storing electromagnetic energy, the fields are capable of exerting mechanical force. If this force is allowed to produce a displacement, mechanical work results, which indicates that electromagnetic energy has been exchanged for mechanical energy. The converse is also possi-

† For example, see P. R. Clement and W. C. Johnson, "Electrical Engineering Science," McGraw-Hill Book Company, Inc., New York, 1960.

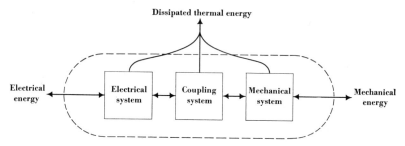

Fig. 11-1. A general electromechanical energy-conversion device.

ble. Mechanical force can be made to act through a distance in such a fashion as to increase the stored electrical energy available to the electrical system. Consequently, energy from either the electrical or the mechanical system can be taken by the coupling system, converted into the energy of the opposite system, and then transferred to that system.

ENERGY CONSERVATION AND EQUILIBRIUM It is not necessary to specify the exact process taking place in the coupling system in order to express an important equilibrium equation. This equation, based upon the law of conservation of energy, can be stated as follows: The total energy within the device is equal to the energy that has been fed into it minus the energy that has been taken from it. The energy within the device may be changed in form, but the magnitude remains the same, except for energy inputs and outputs in accordance with the preceding statement.

The energy balance stated above may be expressed in terms of changes in energy taking place over a period of time Δt:†

$$\Delta W_e + \Delta W_m + \Delta W_d + \Delta W_s = 0 \qquad (11\text{-}1)$$

where ΔW_e = electrical energy leaving device
ΔW_m = mechanical energy leaving device
ΔW_d = energy dissipated in form of heat
ΔW_s = increase in stored energy (electrical, mechanical, or both)
Clearly, one or more of the terms in Eq. (11-1) must be negative, and thus we once again encounter a situation in which care must be exercised in adopting a sign convention. We first note that energy, like mass, is always a positive quantity. However, a change in energy, and this is what Eq. (11-1) is dealing with, may be either positive or negative. The definitions and appropriate sign conventions for the last two terms of Eq. (11-1) are quite natural. The dissipated energy ΔW_d is

† We shall also consider changes in energy with respect to other variables, such as displacement. Basically, however, there must always be a finite amount of time spent in any energy change or transfer.

always positive, whereas an increase in stored energy is signified by a positive ΔW_s and a decrease by a negative ΔW_s. An arbitrary choice was made concerning the first two terms. We have chosen a flow of energy *outward* from the device to be a positive ΔW. Consequently, an inward flow of either electrical or mechanical energy is indicated by a negative sign.

Clearly, we could just as well have defined inward flow as positive, in which case negative signs would appear before ΔW_e (inward) and ΔW_m (inward) in Eq. (11-1). The energy-balance equation is often written in the following way:

$$\Delta W_{\text{in}} = \Delta W_{\text{out}} + \Delta W_d + \Delta W_s \qquad (11\text{-}2)$$

The input and output energies, which usually differ in form, are ΔW_{in} and ΔW_{out}, respectively. We shall use either Eq. (11-1) or Eq. (11-2), adopting whichever is more convenient for the particular problem.

A final comment on the diagram of Fig. 11-1 is in order. The boundary of the electromechanical energy-conversion device has been represented by the dashed line. This boundary is, of course, entirely arbitrary. It is included as a concept which may be helpful in visualizing Eq. (11-1).

A CAPACITOR ENERGY CONVERTER To illustrate the foregoing discussion, we shall now turn our attention to the parallel-plate capacitor of Fig. 11-2. One of the plates is fixed, and the other can move, so that the distance x between the two plates is variable. Let us assume that with x fixed at some particular value the capacitor is charged by the voltage source to a voltage e and a charge q. We know then that the energy stored by the capacitor is

$$W_s = \frac{Ce^2}{2} = \frac{eq}{2} = \frac{q^2}{2C} \qquad (11\text{-}3)$$

Now let us suppose that we disconnect the voltage source, removing no charge from the capacitor plates, so that the stored energy is undisturbed. We then apply a mechanical force, as illustrated, thereby producing a displacement of the movable plate. If the displacement is an infinitesimal distance dx (so that the force may be considered con-

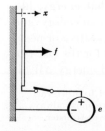

Fig. 11-2. A parallel-plate capacitor with one movable plate.

stant during the displacement), the mechanical work done on the system is

$$\Delta W_{in} = f \, dx \tag{11-4}$$

If we assume that the capacitor plate has negligible mass and that there is no energy dissipation, this increment of energy must appear as a change in the stored energy of the capacitor. Consequently,

$$f \, dx = dW_s = d\left(\frac{q^2}{2C}\right) \tag{11-5}$$

Since the capacitor is disconnected from the circuit, the charge q is not a variable, and Eq. (11-5) may be written as follows:

$$f \, dx = \frac{q^2}{2} d\left(\frac{1}{C}\right) \tag{11-6}$$

$$f = \frac{q^2}{2} \frac{d}{dx}\left(\frac{1}{C}\right) = \frac{q^2}{2}\left(-\frac{1}{C^2}\frac{dC}{dx}\right) = -\frac{e^2}{2}\frac{dC}{dx} \tag{11-7}$$

From Eq. (11-7) we deduce that the electric field existing between the plates of a capacitor must exert a force on the plates which tends to draw them together. We proceed to this deduction in the following manner. From our experience with parallel-plate capacitors, we know that the capacitance decreases as the distance between the plates is increased. As a result, dC/dx is negative. Consequently, Eq. (11-7) indicates that the mechanical force f necessary to displace the plate an incremental amount is positive. A force is necessary only if there is an equal and opposite force which must be overcome, and thus we arrive at our deduction.

It can be shown that the capacitance of a parallel-plate capacitor whose plate area A is large compared with the spacing x is, to a close degree of approximation,

$$C = \frac{\epsilon A}{x} \quad \text{farads} \tag{11-8}$$

where ϵ is the permittivity of the material between the plates. For air and vacuum the permittivity is denoted by ϵ_0 and is equal to 8.855×10^{-12} farad/m. When the value of C given above is inserted in Eq. (11-7), the result is

$$f = \frac{\epsilon A e^2}{2x^2} = \frac{q^2}{2\epsilon A} \tag{11-9}$$

The results obtained above can be acquired by a more circuitous process, which will be demonstrated below in order to point out a further application of energy-equilibrium equations. Figure 11-3 illustrates the same movable-plate capacitor, which is now charged by a voltage source through the electrical network N. Once again a force f is

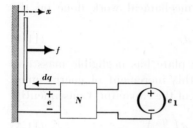

Fig. 11-3. *A movable-plate capacitor that is charged by the voltage source e_1 through the network N.*

applied so that the plate is displaced by an increment dx. In variance with the previous example, $f\,dx$ is not the only energy that is applied to the coupling system. We must include any electrical energy that is provided by the electrical system. In accordance with the figure, the incremental electrical energy input is $e\,dq$. With these two inputs and no dissipation, the equilibrium equation is

$$f\,dx + e\,dq = dW_s = d\left(\frac{Ce^2}{2}\right) \qquad (11\text{-}10)$$

Thus
$$f = -e\frac{dq}{dx} + \frac{d}{dx}\left(\frac{Ce^2}{2}\right)$$

$$= -e\frac{d}{dx}\,(Ce) + \frac{d}{dx}\left(\frac{Ce^2}{2}\right)$$

$$= -e\left(C\frac{de}{dx} + e\frac{dC}{dx}\right) + Ce\frac{de}{dx} + \frac{e^2}{2}\frac{dC}{dx}$$

$$= \frac{-e^2}{2}\frac{dC}{dx} \qquad (11\text{-}11)$$

The result above is identical to Eq. (11-7).

A CAPACITOR MICROPHONE AND LOUDSPEAKER Having derived Eq. (11-9), we shall now apply it in the analysis of two devices which are essentially parallel-plate capacitors with one movable plate. If the

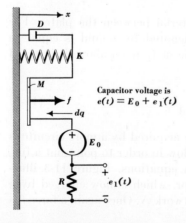

Capacitor voltage is
$e(t) = E_0 + e_1(t)$

Fig. 11-4. *A model of a capacitor microphone.*

region between the plates of our movable-plate capacitor is kept airtight, variations in air pressure on the outside due to sound waves will act as a variable force tending to displace the movable plate. Part of this force will be used in overcoming the inertia of the plate, part in overcoming the force of counterbalancing springs or elastic mounting, and part in frictional forces. The remainder of the force will be opposed by the electric field force which is established by the electrical system. Changes in the electric field caused by the applied force will be detected as variations in voltages or currents, and these variations may be amplified to the desired level.

Figure 11-4 will be referred to in the analysis of the capacitor microphone just described.† Let us first consider the equilibrium condition when no force is applied. In this case, the capacitor voltage is E_0, and the electric field force is equalized by an equal and opposite force of spring compression. This spring force will be called F_0, and its value, as prescribed by Eq. (11-9), is

$$F_0 = \frac{\epsilon A E_0{}^2}{2 X_0{}^2} \qquad (11\text{-}12)$$

where X_0 is the capacitor plate spacing under this condition.

The differential equation which describes the system response with an applied force as shown in the figure is

$$f = \frac{\epsilon A e^2}{2 x^2} + M \frac{d^2 x}{dt^2} + D \frac{dx}{dt} + \frac{x - X_0}{K} - F_0 \qquad (11\text{-}13)$$

We are now faced with an obstacle to the continued analysis of this system: Eq. (11-13) is not linear. We can meet this obstacle head on by attempting to solve this nonlinear differential equation (see Chap. 14), or we can circumvent it in such a way that we need only solve a linear differential equation. The latter will be our choice for this example.

SMALL-SIGNAL LINEAR ANALYSIS   In the systems considered in the previous chapters, the network elements have been assumed linear, that is, independent of variation in the magnitude of the current, voltage, force, or velocity applied to them. Consequently, the parameters R, L, C, D, M, and K have appeared as constants in the differential equations describing the various networks, and these equations have therefore been linear with constant coefficients. The assumption of

> † The model illustrated in this figure is a highly simplified representation of the actual device. An actual capacitor microphone will have a movable plate which is a very thin circular diaphragm clamped at its edge. The flexional motion of this diaphragm does not submit to representation by a lumped mechanical system, nor can the variation in capacity with this diaphragm be expressed in the simple form of Eq. (11-8).

linearity is usually a reasonable one for those systems—at least over the operating range of the variables in the system. Such is not the case with energy-conversion devices. The very nature of the energy conversion, as illustrated by our capacitor energy converter, generates nonlinear terms in the equations describing the device. In addition, nonlinearity is commonly produced by magnetic-core saturation, variation in spring compliance, and changes in frictional resistance with velocity.

Because of these nonlinearities, the methods of network analysis applied in previous chapters are not adaptable when we wish to find the response of energy-conversion devices to large variations in the applied quantities. However, the network parameters of many energy-conversion devices (and many other nonlinear electrical and mechanical devices) are at least approximately linear for small variations in the magnitude of the applied quantities. This is very important. Much useful information can often be obtained from the small-signal linear approximation of the device. The small-signal linear behavior of energy-conversion devices is not only an accurate approximation of the system's characteristics for a narrow range of variables but also a key to its nature over a much wider range of operation.

To illustrate the foregoing discussion, let us continue the analysis of the capacitor microphone on a small-signal basis. First, we may express each of the variables as the sum of an average term plus a variable term which is small compared with the average value. The applied force is assumed to consist of a small variable term only:

$$x(t) = X_0 + x_1(t)$$
$$e(t) = E_0 + e_1(t)$$
(11-14)

With these expressions inserted, Eq. (11-13) becomes

$$f = \frac{\epsilon A (E_0 + e_1)^2}{2(X_0 + x_1)^2} + M \frac{d^2x_1}{dt^2} + D \frac{dx_1}{dt} + \frac{x_1}{K} - F_0$$

$$= \frac{\epsilon A (E_0{}^2 + 2E_0 e_1 + e_1{}^2)}{2(X_0{}^2 + 2X_0 x_1 + x_1{}^2)} + M \frac{d^2x_1}{dt^2} + D \frac{dx_1}{dt} + \frac{x_1}{K} - F_0 \quad (11\text{-}15)$$

Now, making use of the assumption that the fluctuating components are small compared with the average values allows us to replace Eq. (11-15) by the following approximation:

$$f \cong \frac{\epsilon A E_0{}^2}{2X_0{}^2} \left(1 + \frac{2e_1}{E_0} - \frac{2x_1}{X_0}\right) + M \frac{d^2x_1}{dt^2} + D \frac{dx_1}{dt} + \frac{x_1}{K} - F_0 \quad (11\text{-}16)$$

With the definition of F_0 given by Eq. (11-12), we may further reduce Eq. (11-16):

$$f \cong \frac{\epsilon A E_0{}^2}{X_0{}^2} \left(\frac{e_1}{E_0} - \frac{x_1}{X_0}\right) + M \frac{d^2x_1}{dt^2} + D \frac{dx_1}{dt} + \frac{x_1}{K}$$

$$= \frac{\epsilon A E_0 e_1}{X_0{}^2} + M \frac{d^2x_1}{dt^2} + D \frac{dx_1}{dt} + \left(\frac{1}{K} - \frac{\epsilon A E_0{}^2}{X_0{}^3}\right) x_1 \quad (11\text{-}17)$$

Equation (11-17) is a linear approximation of Eq. (11-13). It is not yet in a form which we can solve, because it contains two unknown quantities, e_1 and x_1. A second equation is required, and this can be obtained by a consideration of the electrical system. Expressing the voltage across the resistor in terms of the current through it leads to the next equation:

$$\frac{e_1}{R} = -\frac{dq}{dt} \tag{11-18}$$

The charge on the capacitor is approximated linearly as follows:

$$q = Ce = \frac{\epsilon Ae}{x} = \frac{\epsilon A(E_0 + e_1)}{X_0 + x_1}$$

$$\cong \frac{\epsilon A}{X_0}\left(E_0 + e_1 - \frac{E_0 x_1}{X_0}\right) \tag{11-19}$$

Hence, Eq. (11-18) becomes

$$\frac{e_1}{R} + \frac{\epsilon A}{X_0}\frac{de_1}{dt} \cong \frac{\epsilon A E_0}{X_0{}^2}\frac{dx_1}{dt} \tag{11-20}$$

If the following definitions are utilized and Eqs. (11-7) and (11-20) are written in terms of impedances, we obtain Eqs. (11-22) and (11-23):

$$\frac{dx_1}{dt} = v_1 \qquad C_0 = \frac{\epsilon A}{X_0}$$

$$\beta = \frac{\epsilon A E_0}{X_0{}^2} \qquad \frac{1}{K_{eq}} = \frac{1}{K} - \frac{\epsilon A E_0{}^2}{X_0{}^3} \tag{11-21}$$

$$\mathbf{F} - \beta\mathbf{E}_1 = \left(sM + D + \frac{1}{sK_{eq}}\right)\mathbf{V}_1 \tag{11-22}$$

$$\beta\mathbf{V}_1 = \left(sC_0 + \frac{1}{R}\right)\mathbf{E}_1 \tag{11-23}$$

The last two equations can be solved algebraically to yield $\mathbf{E}_1$, the microphone output voltage (in the s domain) which is to be amplified. These equations indicate a number of equivalent-linear-network models which may be used to represent the actual device. Figure 11-5a shows a mechanical model corresponding to Eq. (11-22), and Fig. 11-5b shows an electrical model corresponding to Eq. (11-23). The two equations are combined to form the all-electrical model of Fig. 11-5c, which utilizes an ideal transformer. The transformer may be eliminated to yield the all-electrical model of Fig. 11-5d, which in turn is equivalent to the all-mechanical model of Fig. 11-5e.

The utility of these models is characteristic of small-signal models derived for other nonlinear devices. That is, after the models have been set up, a great deal of information can be obtained conveniently from them. For example, we can find the small-signal transient behavior, the sinusoidal behavior as affected by frequency, the impedance level,

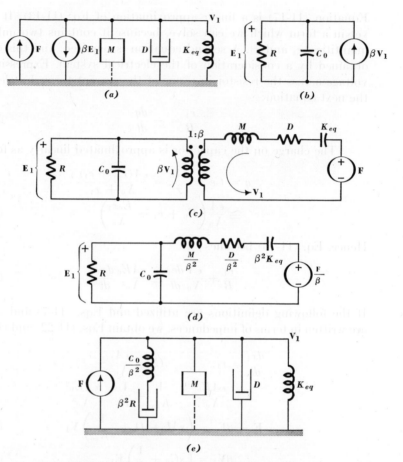

Fig. 11-5. *Various possible mechanical and electrical models corresponding to Eqs. (11-22) and (11-23).*

and the effect of variations in the magnitude of different network elements.

To illustrate the applicability of these small-signal linear models, we can refer to Fig. 11-5d and with a little computation determine the frequency characteristics of our capacitor microphone. It is clear from the figure that the response falls off at both low and high frequencies. The system transfer function has three poles, and the position of these poles will determine the shape of the frequency-response curve. The determination of this curve is left as a problem for the reader.

The small-signal model for a *capacitor loudspeaker*, which is illustrated in Fig. 11-6, differs little from that for the microphone. The microphone resistor R is replaced by a variable voltage source which provides the energy, and the applied force for the microphone is replaced by the loading of the air medium which the loudspeaker drives.

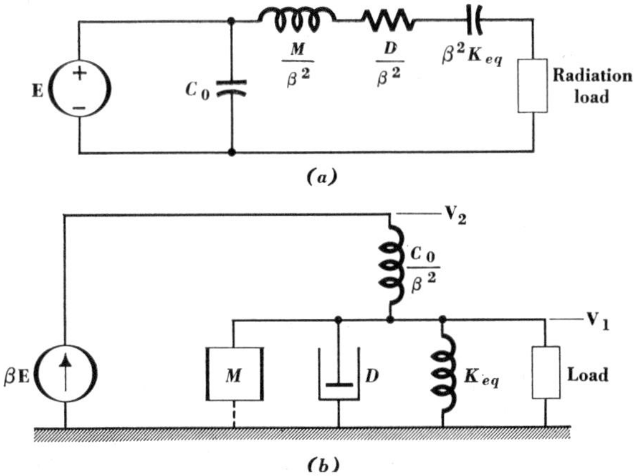

Fig. 11-6. The electrical and mechanical small-signal linear models corresponding to a capacitor loudspeaker.

This radiation load will contain a resistive component which accounts for the power actually radiated into the surrounding medium. In addition, there will be a reactive component which accounts for the energy transferred from speaker to surrounding medium and then returned later in the cycle. If the movable diaphragm is large compared with the sound wavelength in the surrounding medium, the radiation load is almost entirely resistive.

PROBLEMS

11-1 In the device shown, mechanical energy is pumped into the circuit by pushing and pulling on the capacitor plates to produce a variation in the capacity.

(a) Write an expression for the time rate of change of the stored energy in the electric fields of the capacitor as a function of C.

(b) Write an expression for the time rate of change of the stored energy in the magnetic fields.

(c) Using an energy-balance equation, calculate the instantaneous power pumped into the circuit as the capacitor plates are made to move. Write this in terms of the electrical quantities q and C.

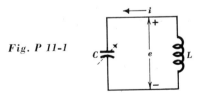

Fig. P 11-1

11-2 The capacitor shown is made of two parallel plates 1 m² in area and spaced d m apart ($d \ll 1$). A dielectric slab is partially inserted between the plates. The dielectric constant of this slab is $\epsilon = k\epsilon_0$, with $k > 1$.

(a) Assuming that there is no fringing effect, find the force exerted on the slab.

(b) If the voltage between the plates is held constant at the value E and the slab is inserted with a velocity v, what current flows in the wires supplying the plates?

Fig. P 11-2

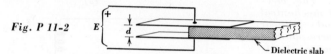

Dielectric slab

11-3 Suppose that the capacitor of the previous problem is arranged as is shown in the figure. What are the differential equations which govern this particular system? With a d-c voltage of 1,000 volts applied, the equilibrium position of the dielectric slab is just halfway into the capacitor. If the applied voltage is $1{,}000 + 25 \cos \omega t$ volts, find a set of linear equations suitable for finding the dielectric motion and circuit current. Draw an all-electrical and an all-mechanical equivalent model for this condition.

Fig. P 11-3

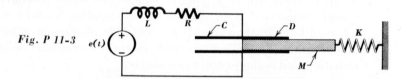

11-4 In the illustrated system the mass M is put into motion in the following way: (1) the mass M is brought to rest at the equilibrium position with no charge on the plates; (2) the mass is constrained to that position while the capacitor plates are charged to $\pm q$ as shown; (3) the constraint is removed, which permits frictionless motion. Solve for the motion of the mass after removal of the constraint.

Fig. P 11-4

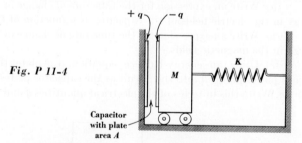

Capacitor with plate area A

11-5 The plates of a parallel-plate capacitor are submerged beneath the surface of a new and strange liquid dielectric, as shown. It is determined experimentally that the capacitor voltage, charge, and plate separation are related as follows:

$$e = aq^2 e^{-x}$$

where a is a dimensional constant. Derive an expression for the force acting to pull the plates together.

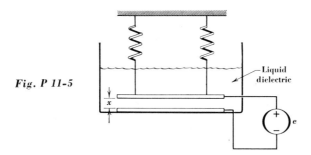

Fig. P 11-5

11-6 A capacitor loudspeaker consists of a movable diaphragm of area $A = 0.01$ m² mounted parallel to a fixed plate. The voltage applied between these two conductors consists of a signal component $E_1 \cos \omega t$ plus a polarizing voltage $E_0 = 1,000$ volts. The spacing with E_0 applied is $x_0 = 0.0001$ m.

Acoustical studies show that when sinusoidally varying sound waves are set up in air by a moving diaphragm whose dimensions are large compared with the wavelength $\lambda = c/f$, where c is the velocity of sound in air (332 m/sec at atmospheric pressure), the force required to move the diaphragm is proportional to the diaphragm velocity:

$$\text{Force} = 430Av$$

where A is the diaphragm area and v is the instantaneous velocity. Thus the acoustical loading can be treated as a mechanical dissipation element $D = 430A$.

Ignore the inertia of the diaphragm and state clearly any other assumptions made to linearize or simplify the analysis.

(a) Find the output acoustical power if the peak value of the signal voltage is $E_1 = 100$ volts.

(b) Find an equivalent electrical circuit which would represent the alternating-component, small-signal conditions at the loudspeaker terminals.

(c) Make a very rough plot of the magnitude of the input impedance over the frequency range for which the pressure-velocity relation above is valid.

(d) In order to check the approximation that the peak displacement of the diaphragm is very small compared with the spacing x_0, compute the peak displacement x_m at frequencies of 5,000, 500, and 50 cps.

11-7 The parameter values of the capacitor microphone of Fig. 11-4 are as follows: $M = 10^{-3}$, $K_{eq} = 10^{-7}$, $D = 10^{-3}$, $R = 5 \times 10^5$, $C_0 = 10^{-11}$, $\beta = 10^{-4}$, all in mks units. Find the frequency response of the microphone, that is, the voltage across R versus frequency as a constant-magnitude pressure (force) of varying frequency is applied to the microphone diaphragm.

11-8 The small-signal models (Fig. 11-5) of the capacitor microphone are not unique: by employing a different expression for the force, a different set of models can be derived. Demonstrate this fact by using the expression for the force exerted on the capacitor plate which contains q rather than x [that is, by using the right-hand quantity of Eq. (11-9)]. This q may be separated into a constant plus a small varying component, as was done with x. A set of equations replacing Eqs. (11-12) to (11-23) can then be derived which correspond to a different set of models. Draw these new models. To what extent are the new models equivalent to the old?

11-2 ENERGY CONVERSION IN COUPLING SYSTEMS WHICH UTILIZE MAGNETIC FIELDS

Several principles of analysis of energy-conversion devices have been introduced and illustrated in our discussion of the capacitor energy converter. We shall utilize these techniques as we turn our attention to conversion devices which depend upon a magnetic coupling field. Capacitor energy converters of reasonable size are incapable of converting large amounts of energy, because of the relatively small amount of energy that can be stored in their electric fields. Owing to the characteristics of ferromagnetic materials, energy-conversion devices utilizing magnetic fields can be made to convert tremendous amounts of energy. We shall investigate some of these devices and their capabilities in this section.

THE FORCE ON A MAGNETIC CORE IN AN INDUCTOR   We can derive the force exerted on the movable iron core of Fig. 11-7 by employing the same technique of virtual displacement and conservation of energy that we used to find the force exerted on the capacitor plate. Before doing this, however, we should clarify our concepts of magnetically induced voltages. We originally defined inductance in terms of the energy stored in the magnetic field associated with an inductor:

$$W_s = \tfrac{1}{2}Li^2 \tag{11-24}$$

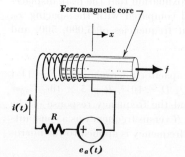

Ferromagnetic core

Fig. 11-7. A coil with a movable ferromagnetic core.

We shall retain this definition. From this expression we derived the equation for induced voltage that we used previously, that is,

$$e = L \frac{di}{dt} \tag{11-25}$$

However, this derivation was based upon the assumption that the inductance remains constant. When the inductance is also a variable, Eq. (11-25) is inadequate.

To obtain the correct expression for the induced voltage, let us recall the alternative definition of inductance given in Sec. 1-2. Inductance can be defined as the flux linkages per ampere,

$$L \triangleq \frac{\lambda}{i} \tag{11-26}$$

where λ is the flux linkages.[†] The voltage induced in a coil is $d\lambda/dt$. Consequently, the correct expression for induced voltage is

$$e = \frac{d\lambda}{dt} = \frac{d(Li)}{dt} = L \frac{di}{dt} + i \frac{dL}{dt} \tag{11-27}$$

Equations (11-24) and (11-26) can readily be shown to be compatible by computing the energy that a current source furnishes to a constant inductor. This is left to the reader.

Now we can continue our calculation of the force on the iron core of Fig. 11-7. Let us apply a force so that a displacement dx occurs. Equating the incremental energy input to the energy dissipated plus the change in field energy yields the following expression:

$$\begin{aligned} f \, dx + e_a i \, dt &= i^2 R \, dt + d(\tfrac{1}{2} Li^2) \\ &= i \left(iR + L \frac{di}{dt} + i \frac{dL}{dt} \right) dt - \frac{i^2}{2} dL \end{aligned} \tag{11-28}$$

Equation (11-27) allows us to simplify the expression above to the final form[‡]

$$f = - \frac{i^2}{2} \frac{dL}{dx} \tag{11-29}$$

[†] In linear mediums λ is linearly proportional to the current i, and thus the inductance L is independent of the current. In nonlinear mediums L will depend upon the magnitude of the current as well as upon the geometry of the inductor. Under this condition, it can validly be argued that the term inductance should not be used at all. Since our major concern is with linear systems, we shall utilize the term inductance. It should be understood, however, that flux is a basic factor, whereas inductance is a derived quantity.

[‡] The minus sign occurs because of the reference direction for measuring the displacement x.

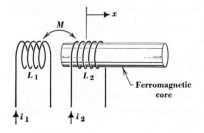

Fig. 11-8. Two mutually coupled coils with a movable ferromagnetic core.

For the same reasons that were applied to the parallel-plate capacitor, Eq. (11-29) indicates that a force is exerted by the magnetic field which tends to pull the core toward the center of the coil.

A similar development will demonstrate that the force tending to draw a magnetic core toward the center of the two mutually coupled coils of Fig. 11-8 is

$$f = -\frac{1}{2}\left(i_1{}^2 \frac{dL_1}{dx} + i_2{}^2 \frac{dL_2}{dx} + 2i_1 i_2 \frac{dM}{dx} \right) \qquad (11\text{-}30)$$

The derivation of this equation is left as a problem.

It is clear that we could construct energy-conversion devices which depend upon Eq. (11-29). Such devices could be analyzed by the same techniques that were applied to the capacitor energy convertors examined in the previous section. We shall delegate such considerations to the problems at the end of this section and direct our attention now to a more detailed study of the physical phenomena inherent in magnetic coupling systems.

THE PRINCIPAL PHENOMENA OF ENERGY CONVERSION IN A MAGNETIC FIELD

As was mentioned previously, we shall find it necessary to draw upon material which is part of electromagnetic field theory. We shall make no effort to explain the concepts of electromagnetic fields or the principles of vector calculus which serve as important tools in analyzing these fields. A complete understanding of electrical circuits and electromechanical energy-conversion devices requires a thorough knowledge of electromagnetic fields and vector calculus. But for our purposes here, a detour into field theory with vector notation can be omitted, with only a small loss of rigor and sophistication.

Despite the statement above, we cannot completely dispense with the electromagnetic field quantities and with the fact that they, together with such other parameters as force and velocity, are vector quantities, that is, quantities which have both magnitude and direction. In most of the systems we shall examine, the equations describing the system can be simplified so that they contain scalar quantities only. In the few cases where we wish to specify that a quantity is a vector, we shall use the notation described below.

The four vector field quantities, having both magnitude and direction, are

$\mathcal{E}$ = electric field strength, volts/m
$\mathcal{B}$ = magnetic flux density, webers/m^2
$\mathcal{D}$ = electric flux density, coulombs/m^2
$\mathcal{H}$ = magnetic field strength, amp-turns/m

Boldface script letters, as in the above list, are used to indicate that the field quantities are vectors. The magnitudes of these quantities will be indicated by lightface script letters. Other vector quantities in the following equations will be denoted by lower-case German letters, and the corresponding lightface italic letters will be used for the magnitudes of these quantities. For example, when it is necessary that a force be treated as a vector, it will be denoted as $\mathfrak{f}$. The magnitude of the force vector will be written as f. As was mentioned above, we shall usually be able to simplify our problems so that we need be concerned only with the magnitudes, that is, with scalar quantities.

THE FORCE ON A CURRENT-CARRYING CONDUCTOR IN A MAGNETIC FIELD
In an electric field, a point charge q will have a force exerted on it which is given by the following equation:

$$\mathfrak{f} = q\mathcal{E} \tag{11-31}$$

This is a simple vector equation with the following meaning: the magnitude of the force is

$$f = q\mathcal{E} \tag{11-32}$$

and its direction is the same as the electric field strength $\mathcal{E}$.

In a magnetic field, a point charge moving with a velocity $\mathfrak{v}_q$ will have a force exerted on it which is given by the following vector equation:†

$$\mathfrak{f} = q(\mathfrak{v}_q \times \mathcal{B}) \tag{11-33}$$

In terms of magnitudes only, Eq. (11-33) may be expressed as follows:

$$f = qv_q\mathcal{B} \sin \theta \tag{11-34}$$

The angle between the direction of $\mathfrak{v}_q$ and $\mathcal{B}$ is θ. The direction of $\mathfrak{f}$ is perpendicular to both $\mathfrak{v}_q$ and $\mathcal{B}$. A right-hand-screw rule, as is illustrated in Fig. 11-9, provides a means for determining the proper direction of $\mathfrak{f}$.

The equations above may be used to find the force exerted on the current-carrying wire of Fig. 11-10a. We may assume that the wire

---

† We include this equation to illustrate a vector equation somewhat more complex than Eq. (11-31). It is not necessary to understand the significance of the notation used here. Vector equations will be avoided from this point on.

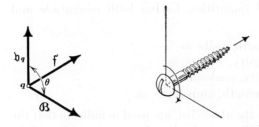

Fig. 11-9. The force exerted on a moving charge in a magnetic field is perpendicular to both the direction of motion and the direction of the magnetic field. A right-hand screw turned from the velocity direction to the field direction, as is illustrated, would advance in the direction of the force.

contains no *net* charge. It is true that the current is the result of moving charges (electrons), but within any volume of the wire, the amounts of positive and negative charge are equal. Consequently, the presence or absence of an ε field is immaterial to this problem, and we need only apply Eq. (11-34).

Since the negative charges are moving while the positive charges are essentially stationary, there is a net force exerted on the wire by the magnetic field. In the current-carrying wire there are a great number of charges moving at a great number of different velocities. Let us consider the force exerted on the moving charges (and hence upon the wire) in the incremental length of wire shown in Fig. 11-10b. For this short length, $\mathfrak{B}$ may be treated as a constant. Consequently, the total force exerted on this increment is

$$df = q_1 v_1 \mathfrak{B} \sin \theta + q_2 v_2 \mathfrak{B} \sin \theta + \cdots = \left(\sum_n q_n v_n \right) \mathfrak{B} \sin \theta \quad (11\text{-}35)$$

The summation above includes all the moving charges within the incremental length dl. A little thought will convince us that the current flowing in this increment is

$$i = \frac{\sum\limits_n q_n v_n}{dl} \quad (11\text{-}36)$$

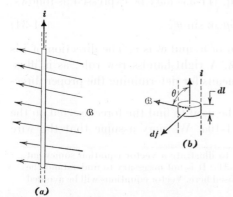

(a)

(b)

Fig. 11-10. (a) A current-carrying wire in a magnetic field; (b) an incremental length of the wire.

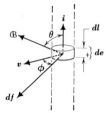

Fig. 11-11. Diagram for determining the voltage induced in a wire moving in a magnetic field.

Equation (11-35) may therefore be modified as follows:

$$df = i\mathcal{B} \sin \theta \, dl \qquad (11\text{-}37)$$

To find the total force on a length of wire, Eq. (11-37) may be integrated along this length.† Equation (11-37) indicates that the force exerted on a straight wire of length l in a uniform magnetic field is

$$f = il\mathcal{B} \sin \theta \qquad (11\text{-}38)$$

If the wire is at right angles to $\mathcal{B}$, Eq. (11-38) reduces to the following simple form:

$$f = il\mathcal{B} \qquad (11\text{-}39)$$

THE INDUCED VOLTAGE IN A CONDUCTOR MOVING IN A MAGNETIC FIELD
Let us apply the concept of energy conservation to determine the voltage induced in the incremental length of wire shown in Fig. 11-11. The whole wire is moving, but we shall consider only an increment of length dl. Let us assume that the wire is moving with a velocity $\mathfrak{v}$ in the direction shown (not necessarily the same direction as the force exerted on the wire). As this incremental length of wire moves a distance dx, the mechanical work is

$$dW_{\text{mech}} = df \, dx \cos \phi \qquad (11\text{-}40)$$

If there is no change in the stored energy of the magnetic field, this mechanical energy must be provided by the electrical system. The electrical work done on this increment of wire is

$$dW_{\text{elec}} = i \, de \, dt \qquad (11\text{-}41)$$

Assuming no heat loss allows us to combine Eqs. (11-40) and (11-41):

$$df \, dx \cos \phi = i \, de \, dt \qquad (11\text{-}42)$$

---

† If the direction of the force changes along the wire length being integrated, the simple type of integration with which we are familiar is not sufficient. In such a case, three integrations are necessary. Each integration will yield one component of the total force. If the force direction remains constant, it can be treated as a scalar, and Eq. (11-37) can be integrated in the normal manner.

Substituting the expression of Eq. (11-37) in terms of magnitudes for df and dividing both sides by i, dt, and dl yield

$$\text{ß} \sin \theta \cos \phi \frac{dx}{dt} = v\text{ß} \sin \theta \cos \phi = \frac{de}{dl} \qquad (11\text{-}43)$$

Thus, we see that there is a voltage induced in a conductor moving in a magnetic field which is independent of the current flowing in the conductor. Equations (11-37) and (11-43) are the basic motor and generator equations which will be referred to often in the following sections. Note how these two equations complement each other: Eq. (11-43) indicates that a voltage induced in a conductor moving in a magnetic field will tend to produce a current; in turn, according to Eq. (11-37), this current will produce a force which opposes the original motion. In other words, the motor action caused by a current flow tends to produce a motion which induces a voltage opposing the original current.

AN ELEMENTARY MOTOR   To illustrate some of the preceding statements, let us consider the elementary motor diagramed in Fig. 11-12a. It consists of a movable bar of mass M which slides without friction along the two rails. A voltage source causes a current i to flow through the rails and bar, as is illustrated. A uniform magnetic field ß directed downward and perpendicular to the current flowing through the length l of the bar is imposed by an external source. A small-signal assumption which simplifies and linearizes the system-response calculations is that the magnetic flux produced by the current is small compared with ß and may be neglected.

The force exerted on the bar is given by Eq. (11-39). With no friction or spring loading, this force is consumed in changing the

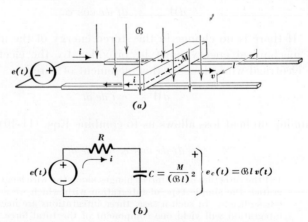

Fig. 11-12. (a) *An elementary translational motor; (b) an all-electrical model of the elementary motor.*

momentum of the bar. Thus (since in this case $\cos \phi = 1$)

$$\Re li = M \frac{dv}{dt} \tag{11-44}$$

With the resistance of the rails and bar lumped into a constant R, the electrical equilibrium equation is

$$e = iR + \Re lv \tag{11-45}$$

Equations (11-44) and (11-45) are combined into a single matrix equation using impedances (with the initial velocity assumed to be zero):

$$\begin{bmatrix} R & \Re l \\ -\Re l & sM \end{bmatrix} \times \begin{bmatrix} \mathbf{I} \\ \mathbf{V} \end{bmatrix} = \begin{bmatrix} \mathbf{E} \\ 0 \end{bmatrix} \tag{11-46}$$

The solutions of this equation are as follows:

$$\mathbf{I} = \frac{sM\mathbf{E}}{sMR + (\Re l)^2} \tag{11-47}$$

$$\mathbf{V} = \frac{\Re l\mathbf{E}}{sMR + (\Re l)^2} \tag{11-48}$$

The last two equations allow us to determine the system behavior for various applied voltages and for various changes in the system parameters. For example, if the applied voltage is a step of amplitude E applied at $t = 0$, Eq. (11-48) is transformed to give us the following time response for the velocity:

$$v(t) = \frac{E}{\Re l}(1 - e^{-(\Re l)^2 t/MR}) \qquad \text{m/sec} \tag{11-49}$$

Equation (11-47) may be modified as follows:

$$\frac{\mathbf{E}}{\mathbf{I}} = \mathbf{Z}(s) = R + \frac{1}{sM/(\Re l)^2} \tag{11-50}$$

We see, then, that the all-electrical model of Fig. 11-12b may be used to represent the system for purposes of computing the electrical response of the system. In addition, Eq. (11-48) may be written as a transfer function, and the sinusoidal frequency response of the system can be determined from the transfer function. Thus,

$$\left| \frac{V(\omega)}{E(\omega)} \right| = \frac{1}{\Re l \sqrt{1 + (MR\omega)^2/(\Re l)^4}} \tag{11-51}$$

PROBLEMS

11-9   Using Eq. (11-27), with the definition of L given by Eq. (11-26), show that Eq. (11-24) continues to hold true.

11-10   In the simple circuit shown, the d-c voltage is applied at $t = 0$. The inductance is variable and is made to vary in the following manner:

$$L(t) = e^t \qquad \text{henrys}$$

Find the current in the circuit for $t \geq 0$. What is the energy stored in the inductance at $t = 1$ sec? What energy has been supplied by the voltage source from $t = 0$ to $t = 1$? If there is a difference, explain.

Fig. P 11-10

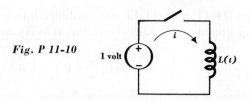

11-11   There is an initial charge q_0 on the capacitor shown in the drawing. After closing the switch at $t = 0$, a small gremlin varies the capacitor in the following manner. When all the charge is off the plates, the capacity is changed in zero time from C_0 to C_1. When the stored charge is maximum again (in the opposite direction), the capacity is changed in zero time from C_1 back to C_0. This process is repeated continuously—C_0 to C_1 at the instant of zero charge, C_1 to C_0 at the instant of maximum charge.

(*a*) Find and plot the current for the case where C_0 is somewhat greater than C_1.

(*b*) Repeat part *a* for $C_1 > C_0$.

(*c*) If a series resistance R is placed in the circuit, what relationship must exist between C_0 and C_1 to just maintain a constant level of oscillation?

Fig. P 11-11

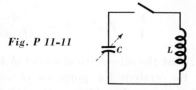

11-12   Suppose that the capacitor in the previous problem is made to vary as follows:

$$C = C_0(1 + \alpha \cos 2\omega t)$$

$$\omega = \frac{1}{\sqrt{LC_0}} \qquad \alpha < 1$$

Find the appropriate differential equation which describes the circuit response. Try to solve this differential equation. Discuss the characteristics of this circuit. Compare this problem and the previous one with the way in which a child increases the amplitude of his oscillations on a swing without anyone's pushing him.

11-13 The circuit shown has a resonant frequency $\omega_0 = 1/\sqrt{LC_0}$ and a Q of 10. The voltage source produces a sinusoidal voltage

$$e(t) = 100 \cos \omega_0 t$$

(*a*) Find the voltage across R with C constant at C_0.

(*b*) Find the voltage across R with C varied from $1.05C_0$ to $0.95C_0$ as per Prob. 11-11.

The circuit acting in this way is a simple parametric amplifier.

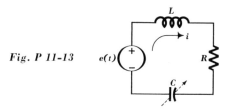

Fig. P 11-13

11-14 Derive Eq. (11-30) by virtual-displacement and energy-balance techniques.

11-15 In the system shown, the resistance is nonlinear, having the following value: $R = (i^2 + 2)$ ohms. With a constant voltage of 12 volts applied, the iron core is pulled partly into the coil, and near this equilibrium position ($x = 0$) the coil inductance is $L = (x^2 + x + 1)$ henrys. The mass of the core is $M = 1$ kg and the compliance of the spring is $K = 0.1$ m/newton.

(*a*) Find the equilibrium current when the constant 12 volts is applied.

(*b*) With $e(t) = 12 + e_1(t)$, where $e_1(t)$ is small compared with 12, find the complete differential equations governing the system.

(*c*) Find the equivalent small-signal linear differential equations from those above.

(*d*) Find the small-signal equivalent systems, all-electrical and all-mechanical.

(*e*) Find the input impedance seen by $e_1(t)$ and the transfer function $\mathbf{V}(s)/\mathbf{E}_1(s)$, where $v(t)$ is the velocity of the core.

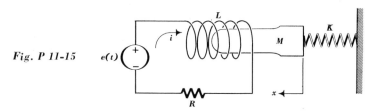

Fig. P 11-15

11-16 Imagine a portion of outer space which has the following property: a magnetic field $\mathcal{B}$ exists whose direction is always parallel to the x axis and whose magnitude increases linearly in the z direction. $\mathcal{B} = \mathcal{B}_x = z$ webers/m^2. In the yz plane, a square loop of copper, 1 m on a side, is started at the origin, as shown, with a velocity in the z direction of 10 m/sec.

(a) If the mass of the loop is 0.2 kg and the resistance is 10 ohms, calculate the motion of the loop. Neglect any flux produced by the loop.

(b) Repeat part a for the case in which the resistance is zero but the inductance is 10^{-5} henry.

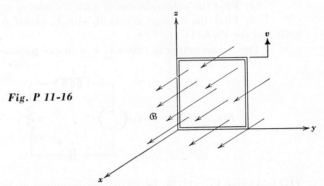

Fig. P 11-16

11-17 A group of engineers working at the north magnetic pole, where the magnetic field $\mathcal{B}$ is vertical with a magnitude of 1 weber/m², build a d-c generator by laying superconducting rails 1 m apart in a circle of very large radius. A small cart pushed by a jet engine developing 10 newtons thrust goes around the track. The cart and engine combined weigh 10 kg, and the axles and wheels have a net resistance of 1 ohm and negligible friction. With a 4-ohm resistive load connected as shown, find the motion of the cart and the current in the load for the case in which the cart starts from rest. Draw all-electrical and all-mechanical equivalent circuits.

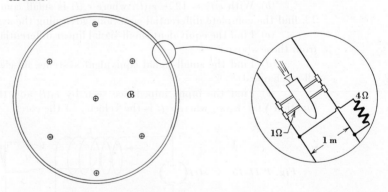

Fig. P 11-17

11-18 The device illustrated is proposed for use as a vibration pickup. The frame of the instrument and the platform on which it is placed may be assumed to move with a vertical displacement

$$x_2(t) = X_2 \cos \omega t$$

A mass M (including the attached permanent magnet) is suspended from a spring of compliance K. Assume that the generated voltage in the

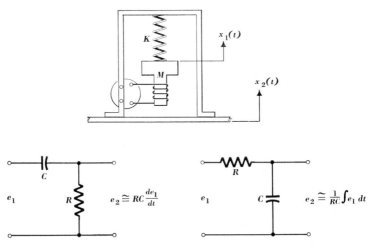

Fig. P 11-18

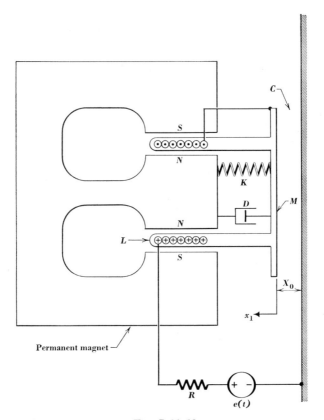

Fig. P 11-19

coil is equal to the product of a constant A and the relative velocity of the magnet and the coil, $d(x_2 - x_1)/dt$.

(*a*) Find the transfer function relating the coil voltage to the frame displacement, $\mathbf{E}(s)/\mathbf{X}_2(s)$.

(*b*) Under what conditions could the voltage be used to measure the amplitude X_2? The peak acceleration $\omega^2 X_2$? (Consider the possibility of making the natural resonant frequency of the mass and spring very much smaller or larger than the frequency ω; consider also the possibility of using a simple RC differentiating or integrating circuit to give as output the derivative or integral of the coil voltage.)

11-19 In the device illustrated (cross-sectional view), the applied voltage is $e(t) = E_0 + e_1(t)$, where $e_1 \ll E_0$. The displacement of the capacitor plate is $x(t) = X_0 + x_1(t)$, where X_0 is the average value due to E_0 and $x_1 \ll X_0$. The permanent magnet produces a uniform magnetic flux density between the pole pieces. The total length of the conductor in the magnetic field is l. Find the small-signal equivalent circuits— part-electrical and part-mechanical, all-electrical, and all-mechanical— for this device.

11-3 ENERGY CONVERSION UTILIZING FERROMAGNETIC MATERIALS

As was pointed out previously, the ability of devices with magnetic coupling fields to convert large amounts of energy is due to the unique properties of ferromagnetic materials. Although ferromagnetism has been recognized and used for centuries, the basic explanation of the phenomenon is of comparatively recent origin. The few comments below will serve merely to introduce the subject.

FERROMAGNETISM The atomic structure of ferromagnetic material is such that the spins of orbital electrons in the atoms may become aligned and produce magnetic fields. In iron, without any external fields applied, domains of alignment occur in which the electron spins in a large number of adjacent atoms become aligned. The domains themselves, which are of the order of 10^{-6} m in size, are randomly oriented with respect to one another. Consequently, an unmagnetized sample of iron will exhibit no magnetic field.

An externally applied magnetic field will tend to align the domains through a process of shifts of domain boundaries and a rotation of the direction of polarization within the domains. The magnetic fields produced by the domains will now reinforce one another and the applied field. The net effect is a magnetic field which is many times that which would be produced by the external field in the presence of a nonferromagnetic material.

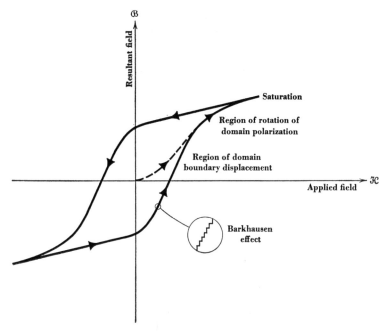

Fig. 11-13. A typical hysteresis loop (applied field vs. resultant field) for a ferro-magnetic material.

The relation between the applied and resultant fields in a ferro-magnetic medium is not a linear one. The curve relating the two fields exhibits both saturation and hysteresis, as well as minute discontinuities. A typical hysteresis loop is illustrated in Fig. 11-13. The explanation of this curve is as follows. Starting with an unmagnetized sample, the resultant field ($\mathfrak{B}$) is zero, with no applied field. As the applied field ($\mathfrak{IC}$) is increased, the resultant field increases rapidly (following the dashed line) as the domain boundaries shift, so that the domains aligned completely or partially with the applied field increase in size at the expense of unaligned domains. The slope of the curve decreases as the curve reaches the point where any further increase in alignment must be accomplished by a rotation of the polarization within the domains. Finally the curve reaches the saturation region, where essentially all the domains have been aligned. Any further increase in the applied field only increases the resultant field by an amount equal to the increment in the applied field.

When the applied field is decreased, the curve departs from the original path. This is due to the tendency of the domains to remain aligned. Thus, when the applied field is completely removed, a residual resultant field remains, and the sample acts as a permanent magnet. A reversed applied field is necessary to bring the resultant field down to zero. A further increase in the reverse direction of the applied field brings about the alignment of domains in the reverse direction until saturation is reached. The removal of the applied field and then application in the original direction result in the closure of the hysteresis loop, as is indicated in the figure.

On a microscopic scale the curve is discontinuous. This is called the *Barkhausen effect*, and it is due to the domain boundaries shifting suddenly rather than continuously.

THE RELATIONSHIP BETWEEN APPLIED AND RESULTANT FIELDS As has been discussed above, the resultant magnetic flux density $\mathcal{B}$ at any point is the result of two causes. The first is the actual flow of real current in a circuit. The second is the magnetic-dipole moments produced by the electron spins in the material medium.

The resultant flux density may be expressed as

$$\mathcal{B} = \mu_0(\mathcal{H} + \mathcal{M}) \tag{11-52}$$

where $\mathcal{H}$, the magnetic field intensity, is related to the real-current distribution and $\mathcal{M}$ is the magnetic-dipole moment per unit volume in the material. The constant μ_0 is the permeability of free space ($4\pi \times 10^{-7}$ henry/m).

From the preceding discussion, it is clear that $\mathcal{M}$ is a function of $\mathcal{H}$, but not a simple linear function. The value of $\mathcal{M}$ in a medium at a particular time depends not only upon $\mathcal{H}$ at that time but, as is indicated by the hysteresis loop, upon the whole past history of $\mathcal{H}$.

It is often convenient and practical to *assume that the material is linear*, in which case $\mathcal{M}$ and $\mathcal{H}$ are related linearly as follows:

$$\mathcal{M} = \chi\mathcal{H} \tag{11-53}$$

Consequently,

$$\mathcal{B} = \mu_0(1 + \chi)\mathcal{H} = \mu_0\mu_r\mathcal{H} = \mu\mathcal{H} \tag{11-54}$$

The constant of proportionality χ is called the susceptibility of the material; $\mu_r = 1 + \chi$ is called the relative permeability; and $\mu = \mu_0\mu_r$ is called the permeability.

IMPORTANT RELATIONSHIPS APPLICABLE TO THE SOLUTION OF MAGNETIC CIRCUITS Let us consolidate the information in the discussion to this point. In the preceding section we saw that the force exerted on current-carrying wires and the voltage induced in moving conductors depend upon the magnetic flux density $\mathcal{B}$. Consequently, it will be necessary to find, for many of the problems which we shall encounter, either $\mathcal{B}$ or some closely related quantity. (In some cases, it will be possible to bypass the computation of $\mathcal{B}$ and find forces and induced voltages by other means.) In the paragraphs above, it was pointed out that $\mathcal{B}$ depends upon the magnetic field intensity $\mathcal{H}$, which in turn depends upon the current in the circuit. Now, $\mathcal{H}$ is a vector field quantity which, with the aid of some field theory and vector-analysis experience, we could calculate from knowledge of the current distribution. However, this is no simple task, and therefore we shall seek techniques which avoid it.

It will be preferable, wherever possible, to obtain forces, induced voltages, or $\mathcal{B}$ directly in terms of the terminal quantities (current or voltage) rather than through a process involving vector analysis. In order to accomplish this, we shall state in the following equations some important relationships between the electromagnetic field quantities and the more familiar circuit parameters.

As was noted above, the voltage induced in a coil by a varying magnetic field is

$$e = \frac{d\lambda}{dt} \tag{11-55}$$

where λ is the flux linkages. If the coil has N turns and the same flux threads all the turns, then

$$\lambda = N\phi \tag{11-56}$$

where ϕ is the total flux within the coil. The total flux can be found by integrating the flux density $\mathcal{B}$ over the cross-sectional area A of the coil. When the flux density is uniform, this integration simply yields $\mathcal{B}A$. Thus, Eq. (11-55) may be written as

$$e = \frac{d\lambda}{dt} = \frac{d(N\phi)}{dt} = \frac{d(N\mathcal{B}A)}{dt} \tag{11-57}$$

The equations above relate flux density to the terminal (induced) voltage under the assumptions stated. It is also possible to relate the flux to the terminal current. Figure 11-14 shows an N-turn coil, together with a contour or path (dashed line) which goes through the coil. At each point along this contour the magnetic field intensity has a magnitude and direction, as is illustrated at one point. The integral of the field intensity completely around the contour is related to the

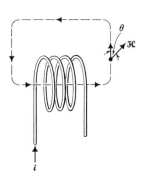

Fig. 11-14. A coil with current i and a contour of integration (dashed line) which can be used in Eq. (11-58).

coil current as follows:

$$\oint \mathfrak{IC} \cos \theta \, dl = Ni \tag{11-58}$$

The quantity above is called the magnetomotive force (mmf). In some cases, $\mathfrak{IC}$ coincides in direction with the path of integration and does not vary in magnitude along the path. Under this condition, the integration of Eq. (11-58) yields

$$\mathfrak{IC}l = Ni \tag{11-59}$$

where l is the total path length. In other cases, $\mathfrak{IC}$ may coincide with the path of integration but have a different magnitude over different sections of the path. When this occurs, Eq. (11-59) may be replaced by

$$\mathfrak{IC}_1 l_1 + \mathfrak{IC}_2 l_2 + \cdots + \mathfrak{IC}_n l_n = Ni \tag{11-60}$$

When the medium is linear, $\mathfrak{IC}$ in the equations above may be replaced by $\mathfrak{B}/\mu$.

The energy stored in a magnetic field in a linear medium can be found by the following integration:

$$W = \int \frac{\mu \mathfrak{IC}^2}{2} \, dv = \int \frac{\mathfrak{B}^2}{2\mu} \, dv \tag{11-61}$$

The integrand in each integral is termed an energy density, and the integration is carried out over the whole volume containing the magnetic field.

An important property of the magnetic flux density $\mathfrak{B}$ which is of particular value in solving magnetic circuit problems is its solenoidal characteristic. This property, which is analogous to current flow, means that the flux entering any closed volume is equal to the flux leaving the volume. An equivalent statement is that the normal component of the flux density on one side of a surface is equal to the normal component on the other side.

THE FORCE AT A MAGNETIC BOUNDARY   Consider the plunger-magnet structure shown in Fig. 11-15. The magnetic field produced by the current in the coil will exert a force upon the sliding plunger. In order to compute that force, we shall make some simplifying assumptions which, although not completely valid, will give a reasonably close approximation to the true value. First, let us assume that the permeability of the iron (μ) is so large in comparison with that of the airgap that it may be considered infinite. Second, we shall assume that the flux density $\mathfrak{B}$ is uniform within the pole piece and sliding plunger.

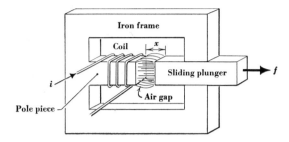

Fig. 11-15. A plunger magnet.

Because of the solenoidal property of $\mathfrak{B}$, the preceding assumption means that the flux density in the airgap will be uniform at the faces of the pole piece and plunger. If the width of the airgap x is small compared with the area of the faces, then it is valid to assume negligible fringing of the field in the airgap and hence a uniform flux density within the airgap.

Because of our assumptions, the flux density $\mathfrak{B}$ in the airgap is equal to that in the pole piece and plunger. Thus, in accordance with Eq. (11-54), we can say that the magnetic field strength in the airgap is

$$\mathfrak{K} = \frac{\mathfrak{B}}{\mu_0} \tag{11-62}$$

whereas in the iron structure it is zero, owing to the infinite permeability. Consequently, Eq. (11-60) is equivalent to the following expression:

$$\mathfrak{K}x = Ni \tag{11-63}$$

where N is the number of turns in the coil.

If the pole-face area is A, the volume of the gap is Ax, and the stored energy as given by Eq. (11-61) is

$$W = \frac{\mu_0 \mathfrak{K}^2 A x}{2} = \frac{\mu_0 N^2 i^2 A}{2x} \tag{11-64}$$

Now, if we apply the virtual-displacement method used in studying the parallel-plate capacitor, we can calculate the force exerted on the plunger. If a force is applied as shown in Fig. 11-15 and results in a displacement dx, the mechanical energy supplied to the system is $f\,dx$. To simplify the argument, imagine that the current is simultaneously changed in such a way that the total magnetic flux remains constant. This means that $\mathfrak{K}$ in the airgap remains constant. (The reason for this constraint is to ensure that the voltage drop across the coil is zero at all times, which eliminates the problem of energy being supplied or absorbed by the electrical source. If we were to assume another set of conditions, such as a constant current, the argument would just be slightly more complicated.)

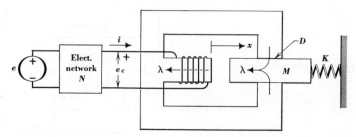

Fig. 11-16. A plunger magnet: a singly excited magnetic-field energy converter.

The only energy input or output is the mechanical energy. This energy must appear as a change in stored magnetic energy:

$$f \, dx = dW = \frac{\mu_0 \mathcal{K}^2 A \; dx}{2} = \frac{\mu_0 N^2 i^2 A}{2x^2} \, dx \qquad (11\text{-}65)$$

Thus, the force exerted on the plunger (tending to pull it toward the pole piece) is†

$$f = \frac{\mu_0 \mathcal{K}^2 A}{2} \qquad (11\text{-}66)$$

A SINGLY EXCITED MAGNETIC-FIELD CONVERTER Let us continue our investigation of the plunger magnet. Figure 11-16 illustrates the plunger magnet with a restraining spring attached to the plunger. We now have a mechanical system consisting of the spring, the mass of the plunger, and the frictional resistance between frame and plunger. This mechanical system is coupled to the electrical system through the magnetic coupling field.

We shall investigate this system first under the assumption of linearity of material and airgap field behavior and then under the conditions of nonlinearity. The force exerted toward the left on the plunger by the magnetic field is given by Eq. (11-66). Equation (11-66) has the same form as the force equation for the parallel-plate capacitor [Eq. (11-9)]. Consequently, in order to maintain linearity in our analysis, we shall make small-signal assumptions again.

The current and displacement will be represented as an average term plus a variable term which is small in comparison with the average:

$$\begin{aligned} i(t) &= I_0 + i_1(t) \\ x(t) &= X_0 + x_1(t) \end{aligned} \qquad (11\text{-}67)$$

The equilibrium spring tension F_0 is

$$F_0 = \frac{\mu_0 A}{2} \frac{N^2 I_0^2}{X_0^2} \qquad (11\text{-}68)$$

† Compare Eq. (11-66) with Eq. (11-9).

With a small applied force f, the mechanical equilibrium equation is

$$f = M\frac{d^2x}{dt^2} + D\frac{dx}{dt} + \frac{x - X_0}{K} - F_0 + \frac{\mu_0 A}{2}\frac{N^2 i^2}{x^2}$$

$$= M\frac{d^2x_1}{dt^2} + D\frac{dx_1}{dt} + \frac{x_1}{K} - F_0 + \frac{\mu_0 A N^2}{2}\frac{(I_0 + i_1)^2}{(X_0 + x_1)^2}$$

$$\cong M\frac{d^2x_1}{dt^2} + D\frac{dx_1}{dt} + \left(\frac{1}{K} - \frac{\mu_0 A N^2 I_0^2}{X_0^3}\right)x_1 + \frac{\mu_0 A N^2 I_0}{X_0^2} i_1 \quad (11\text{-}69)$$

Refer to Eqs. (11-15) to (11-17) for the intermediary steps in the derivation of Eq. (11-69).

The voltage developed across the coil can be found as follows:

$$e_c = \frac{d\lambda}{dt} = \frac{d}{dt}(N\phi) = \frac{d}{dt}(N\mathcal{B}A) = \frac{d}{dt}(N\mu_0\mathcal{H}A)$$

$$= \frac{d}{dt}\left(\mu_0 A N^2\frac{i}{x}\right) = \mu_0 A N^2\frac{d}{dt}\left(\frac{I_0 + i_1}{X_0 + x_1}\right)$$

$$\cong \mu_0 A N^2\frac{d}{dt}\left(\frac{I_0}{X_0} + \frac{i_1}{X_0} - \frac{I_0 x_1}{X_0^2}\right)$$

$$= \frac{\mu_0 A N^2}{X_0}\frac{di_1}{dt} - \frac{\mu_0 A N^2 I_0}{X_0^2}\frac{dx_1}{dt} \quad (11\text{-}70)$$

The following definitions are utilized in Eqs. (11-72) and (11-73), which correspond (in the s domain) to Eqs. (11-69) and (11-70).

$$\frac{dx_1}{dt} = v_1 \qquad\qquad L_0 = \frac{\mu_0 A N^2}{X_0}$$

$$\beta = \frac{\mu_0 A N^2 I_0}{X_0^2} \qquad \frac{1}{K_{eq}} = \frac{1}{K} - \frac{\mu_0 A N^2 I_0^2}{X_0^3} \quad (11\text{-}71)$$

$$\mathbf{F} = \left(sM + D + \frac{1}{sK_{eq}}\right)\mathbf{V}_1 + \beta\mathbf{I}_1 \quad (11\text{-}72)$$

$$\mathbf{E}_c = sL_0\mathbf{I}_1 - \beta\mathbf{V}_1 \quad (11\text{-}73)$$

As was the case with the capacitor energy converter, a number of equivalent circuits corresponding to the two equations above may be utilized. Two of these are illustrated in Fig. 11-17.

THE NONLINEAR PROPERTIES OF THE PLUNGER MAGNET The method of analysis just discussed is perfectly applicable to the device under consideration and to other similar devices in certain circumstances. For example, the variable-reluctance phonograph pickup is essentially the same as a plunger magnet and may be analyzed by the technique outlined above. Nevertheless, the small-signal linear model is not always adequate. The assumptions of a linear ferromagnetic material, infinite permeability, and uniform airgap field are not valid for the general case. For this more general condition, a graphical analysis is helpful.

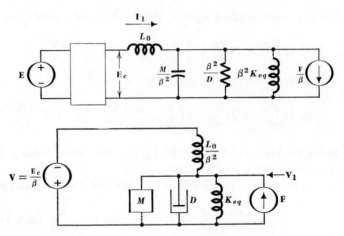

Fig. 11-17. *An electrical circuit and a mechanical system which are equivalent to the plunger magnet of Fig. 11-15 under the assumptions leading to Eqs. (11-72) and (11-73).*

To begin with, let us consider a graphical technique of determining the energy stored in the magnetic field associated with our plunger magnet. With the plunger held rigidly in one position and with the iron completely demagnetized at the start, a build-up of the coil current from zero to some final value i_f will produce the graph of flux linkages vs. excitation current shown in Fig. 11-18a. (Problem 11-23 discusses the experimental determination of this curve.)

The energy expended in establishing the final value of flux linkages λ_f is found by integrating the electric power that was supplied:

$$W_m = \int ie\, dt = \int i\frac{d\lambda}{dt}\, dt = \int_0^{\lambda_f} i\, d\lambda \qquad (11\text{-}74)$$

Thus the area to the left of the λ-i curve (the horizontally shaded portion) is the energy supplied. The vertically shaded area below the curve is called the coenergy W'_m.

$$W'_m = \int_0^{i_f} \lambda\, di \qquad (11\text{-}75)$$

Since the plunger was not allowed to move, all the energy of Eq. (11-74) must have gone into establishing the magnetic field.

If the iron were without hysteresis, all this energy could be converted back to electrical energy. However, for iron with hysteresis, when the current is returned to zero, the λ-i curve will appear as shown in Fig. 11-18b. The energy of the area to the left of this second curve will be returned to the electrical network, but the energy corresponding to the shaded area will be lost. Furthermore, an increase of current up to i_f and then a decrease to zero again will trace out curves

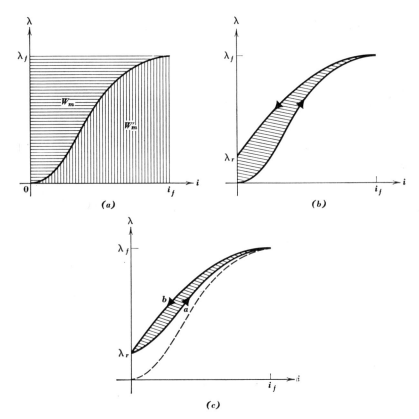

Fig. 11-18. *Flux linkages vs. excitation current for a coil with a ferromagnetic core. The areas equal to energy supplied and lost are indicated by horizontal and diagonal shading.*

a and *b* of Fig. 11-18*c*. The energy loss in this case will be equal to the shaded area. Thus, in general, any cyclic variation in the flux in a magnetic device will produce a λ-i hysteresis loop in which the energy lost per cycle will be equal to the area within the hysteresis loop. The lost energy appears in the form of heat developed in the iron. (It will be convenient in the following discussion to assume that the energy lost in increasing the flux linkages from one value to another is independent of the path taken as long as the flux does not decrease along any portion of the path.)

Let us now consider Fig. 11-19*a*, where λ-i curves are drawn for the plunger magnet with the plunger held at a number of different positions. The curve labeled 0 corresponds to zero airgap, and the curve labeled 3 is the λ-i curve for the maximum gap width. With the plunger held at the maximum airgap position, an increase in coil current from zero to i_f will trace the path from *a* to *b* along curve 3 that is shown in Fig. 11-19*b*. If the plunger is now released, it will be pulled

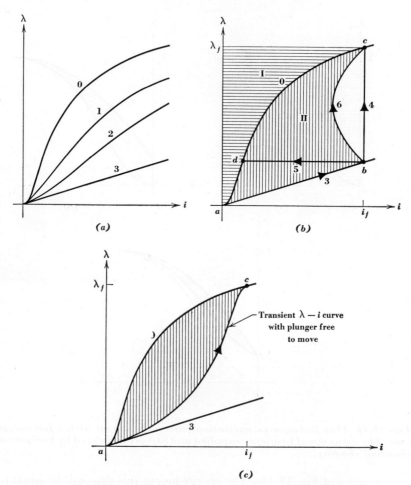

Fig. 11-19. Flux linkages vs. coil current curves for the plunger magnet.

toward the pole piece until the airgap is closed. The λ-i curve now traced out will depend upon the electrical circuit. If the current is maintained constant while the plunger is moving, the path will be from b to c along 4. If the flux linkages are maintained constant, the path will be from b to d along 5. If the circuit cannot maintain a constant current but approaches i_f again upon reaching equilibrium, the path will be of the type labeled 6 in the figure. In any case, the terminal point will be somewhere upon the zero-airgap λ-i curve.

Let us assume that path 6 was followed in reaching point c. The total energy from the electrical system is the area to the left of the path a-3-b-6-c (the horizontally and vertically shaded areas). The stored magnetic energy plus iron losses corresponding to the flux linkages at point c is equal to the area to the left of the path a-0-c. That is, except for the iron losses, this energy could be returned to the electrical network without any motion of the plunger. The difference between the total energy input and the energy corresponding to stored magnetic field energy plus iron losses is equal to the area of region II, the vertically shaded region:

$$W_t - W_I = W_{II} \tag{11-76}$$

The energy W_{II} must have gone into the mechanical system to produce the motion of the plunger. If a step of voltage is applied to the coil with the plunger initially in the maximum airgap position but free to move, the λ-i curve will appear as shown in Fig. 11-19c. The energy imparted to the mechanical system in this case is equal to the shaded area.

It is simple enough to indicate graphically the energy transfer from the electrical to the mechanical system with an assumed λ-i transient curve. Actually determining this curve and calculating the motion of the plunger are much harder. We shall discuss this problem briefly here. More detailed analyses of this type of nonlinear system are covered in texts on nonlinear system analysis (see Bibliography).

The general problem of the plunger motion may be stated as follows: at a particular time t_0 with an initial airgap x_0, an initial velocity v_0, and an initial current i_0, we wish to calculate the further motion of the plunger. The initial current and airgap specify a particular λ-i curve and a point upon it, which is indicated in Fig. 11-20a. The force exerted on the plunger at this position can be approximated by noting that the energy imparted to the mechanical system by a small displacement from x_0 to x_1 is equal to the shaded area shown in Fig. 11-20b. The energy change divided by the incremental displacement equals the mechanical force, so that†

$$f \cong \frac{\Delta W}{x_0 - x_1} \tag{11-77}$$

With accurate plots of λ-i curves for a sufficient number of airgap values, we could make reasonable approximations for the force at all positions on the λ-i chart.

Knowing the force and assuming that it remains essentially constant for small displacements, we can compute a solution for the plunger motion, valid for a small increment of time. Besides approximating the force at the initial position, we can also approximate graphically the following two quantities:

---

† It is not difficult to see that the force can also be expressed in the following two forms:

$$f = \frac{-dW_m}{dx}\bigg|_{\lambda = \text{constant}} = \frac{dW'_m}{dx}\bigg|_{i = \text{constant}}$$

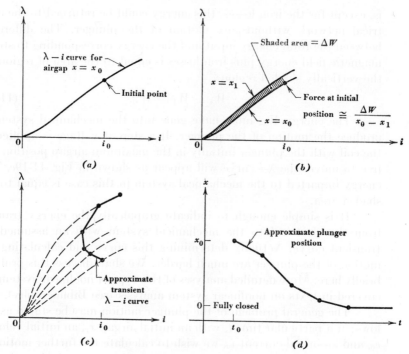

Fig. 11-20. Curves appropriate to the graphical solution for the motion of the plunger.

$$\frac{\partial \lambda}{\partial x} \cong \frac{\Delta \lambda}{\Delta x}\bigg|_{i=\text{constant}}$$

$$\frac{\partial \lambda}{\partial i} \cong \frac{\Delta \lambda}{\Delta i}\bigg|_{x=\text{constant}} \tag{11-78}$$

The coil voltage is given by the following expression:

$$e_c = \frac{d\lambda}{dt} = \frac{\partial \lambda}{\partial x}\frac{dx}{dt} + \frac{\partial \lambda}{\partial i}\frac{di}{dt} \tag{11-79}$$

Knowing dx/dt from the mechanical solution enables us to solve Eq. (11-79) for di/dt. Analysis of the four-terminal electrical network of Fig. 11-16 will give an expression for e_c as a function of i which can be equated to Eq. (11-79). The two solutions for dx/dt and di/dt will generate a new point on the λ-i chart:

$$x_n = x_0 + \frac{dx}{dt}\Delta t$$

$$i_n = i_0 + \frac{di}{dt}\Delta t \tag{11-80}$$

Starting at this new point, the process is repeated. Continued repetitions of this method will yield the final approximate solution for the motion of the plunger indicated in Fig. 11-20c and d.

DOUBLY EXCITED MAGNETIC-FIELD CONVERTERS In Sec. 11-2 we briefly discussed a doubly excited magnetic-field converter [see Fig. 11-8 and Eq. (11-30)]. We wish now to augment that discussion, with a slight change in emphasis. Figure 11-21 illustrates a doubly excited magnetic-field converter consisting of two magnetically coupled coils. Ferromagnetic material may or may not be present. If it is, we shall assume, for this development, that it is linear. That is, the λ-i curve for the material is linear with no hysteresis.

The point of departure from the previous discussion concerns the relative motion of the coils. Figure 11-8 and its legend imply that the coils remain stationary with respect to each other while the iron core moves. As a consequence, the variation in L_1, L_2, and M of Eq. (11-30) is caused by the core motion alone. The stationary nature of the coils is a restrictive assumption which will not be made in the present development.

Let us now derive Eq. (11-30) with the understanding that the coils may move. Since we have assumed linearity of the medium, the following relations hold:

$$\lambda_1 = L_1 i_1 + M i_2$$
$$\lambda_2 = L_2 i_2 + M i_1 \tag{11-81}$$

We shall assume an incremental relative motion (say dx) of one coil with respect to the other. For the general case, this will cause a change in L_1, L_2, M, i_1, and i_2 and consequently a change in the various energies of the system.

The energy added to the system by the two electrical sources is

$$dW_e = i_1 \, d\lambda_1 + i_2 \, d\lambda_2 \tag{11-82}$$

where
$$d\lambda_1 = L_1 \, di_1 + i_1 \, dL_1 + M \, di_2 + i_2 \, dM$$
$$d\lambda_2 = L_2 \, di_2 + i_2 \, dL_2 + M \, di_1 + i_1 \, dM \tag{11-83}$$

Part of this incremental energy appears as a change in the magnetic field energy, while the remainder must take the form of mechanical

Fig. 11-21. Schematic diagram of a doubly excited magnetic-field energy converter.

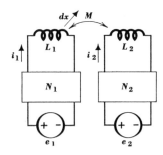

work (we are assuming no losses). The total energy stored in the magnetic field is

$$W_f = \tfrac{1}{2}L_1 i_1{}^2 + M i_1 i_2 + \tfrac{1}{2}L_2 i_2{}^2$$
$$= \tfrac{1}{2}(i_1\lambda_1 + i_2\lambda_2) \tag{11-84}$$

Thus, the incremental change in this magnetic field energy is

$$dW_f = \tfrac{1}{2}(i_1\,d\lambda_1 + \lambda_1\,di_1 + i_2\,d\lambda_2 + \lambda_2\,di_2) \tag{11-85}$$

It follows that the incremental mechanical work is

$$dW_m = dW_e - dW_f$$
$$= \tfrac{1}{2}(i_1\,d\lambda_1 + i_2\,d\lambda_2 - \lambda_1\,di_1 - \lambda_2\,di_2)$$
$$= \tfrac{1}{2}i_1{}^2\,dL_1 + \tfrac{1}{2}i_2{}^2\,dL_2 + i_1 i_2\,dM \tag{11-86}$$

Note that the final form of Eq. (11-86) contains no incremental current terms. Differential changes in current have no effect on the mechanical forces.

The mechanical work occurs over the displacement dx. Hence the force exerted on the coil (in the direction of the displacement dx) is

$$f_x = \tfrac{1}{2}i_1{}^2\frac{dL_1}{dx} + \tfrac{1}{2}i_2{}^2\frac{dL_2}{dx} + i_1 i_2\frac{dM}{dx} \tag{11-87}$$

Equation (11-87) is identical to Eq. (11-30) except for sign. The variation in sign occurs because we have chosen to define the positive direction for force differently in developing the two equations.

When no ferromagnetic materials are present, and under some conditions when they are, L_1 and L_2 will not be affected by the relative motion of the coils. In such cases, Eq. (11-87) reduces to

$$f = i_1 i_2\frac{dM}{dx} \tag{11-88}$$

Systems for which Eq. (11-88) holds will be discussed in the next section.

PROBLEMS

11-20 For the plunger magnet of Fig. 11-15, suppose that the magnetic structure has a relative permeability μ_r and a reluctance $\mathfrak{R}$ (that is, the ampere-turns Ni required to produce a flux ϕ is the gap ampere-turns $\mathfrak{K}x$ plus $\mathfrak{R}\phi$). Find an expression for the maximum force (as $x \to 0$) in terms of the current i. Compare this with the force (as $x \to 0$) for the infinite-permeability case.

11-21 The figure shows a design for an electromechanical shaker for acceleration testing of small parts and devices. The lower coil maintains a uniform flux density in the gap of $\mathcal{B}$ webers/m². The length of the coil in the gap is l. Assume the following parameter values:

$$
\left.\begin{array}{ll}
M = 0.1 \text{ kg} & L = 10^{-4} \text{ henry} \\
D \quad \text{negligible} & R \quad \text{negligible} \\
K = 0.05 \text{ m/newton} & l = 2 \text{ m}
\end{array}\right\} \begin{array}{l} \text{gap} \\ \text{coil} \end{array}
$$
$$\mathcal{B} = 0.4 \text{ weber/m}^2$$

The shaker is presumably designed to give accelerations up to 100 g (100 times the acceleration due to gravity) and to operate at frequencies from 50 to 500 cps.

(a) Find the peak displacement of the table, x_p, if the peak acceleration is 100 g and the operating frequency is 50 cps.

(b) Find the voltage and current to give a peak acceleration of 100 g at 50 cps.

(c) Find the natural resonant frequency of the mechanical portion of the system alone.

(d) Plot the magnitude of the transfer function $V(\omega)/E(\omega)$ versus ω over the frequency range 0 to 500 cps. Draw a dotted line to indicate how you would expect the shape of this curve to be modified if the effects of R and D were taken into account. Which two energy-storing elements are primarily responsible for the resonant peak?

(e) To keep this problem linear, we have assumed linear iron and have made one other assumption. What is the second assumption?

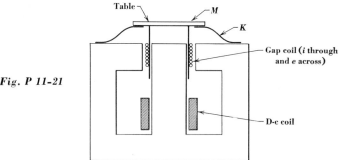

Fig. P 11-21

11-22 The device shown is proposed as an alternative design for a shaker. It consists essentially of a plunger magnet with the testing table fastened to the plunger. The coil current is to consist of a polarizing d-c component I_0 and a superposed variable component $i_1(t)$. Let the air-gap spacing with the current I_0 alone be X_0. Assume that the effective cross-sectional area of the gap is A m². Assume infinite permeability for the magnetic structure, so that the total ampere-turns Ni is used up across the airgap. Neglect leakage inductance. Include the effects of mechanical dissipation and coil resistance.

(a) Using small-signal assumptions ($i_1 \ll I_0$, $x_1 \ll X_0$) to get a linear model, find the transfer function $V_1(s)/I_1(s)$ relating the table

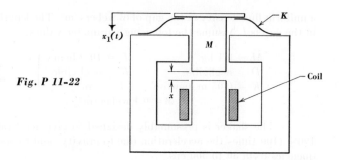

Fig. P 11-22

velocity and the coil current. Sketch a small-signal linear model consisting of separate electrical and mechanical portions.

(b) Find the input impedance $E_1(s)/I_1(s)$. Sketch an all-electrical network with the same input impedance.

(c) Assuming negligible mechanical dissipation and coil resistance, find the frequencies of maximum and minimum input impedance. Sketch the variation of the magnitude of input impedance with radian frequency ω.

(d) Find the transfer function relating table velocity $V_1(s)$ to coil voltage $E_1(s)$. Assuming negligible electrical and mechanical power loss, sketch the variation of the magnitude of this transfer function with frequency.

(e) Assume the following numerical values:

$M = 0.2$ kg (table and plunger) $K = 0.05$ m/newton
D negligible R negligible
$\mu_0 A = 10^{-9}$ henry-m $N = 100$ turns
x with zero coil current $= 1.5$ cm
I_0 adjusted to give X_0 of 1.0 cm

Find the voltage and current required to give an acceleration of 10 g at 50 cps.

(f) Compare the proposed design of this problem with the arrangement of Prob. 11-21, giving as many reasons as you can for preferring one over the other—in general rather than for the specific numerical values given.

11-23 Discuss ways by which one could determine the λ-i curves for ferromagnetic materials. Design a circuit which would enable you to display a λ-i curve for a specimen on an oscilloscope.

11-24 Suppose that the λ-i curves for a plunger magnet of the type shown in Fig. 11-16 are as given in the diagram. The mass of the plunger is 0.2 kg, the compliance K is 0.01 m/newton, and D is negligible. The equilibrium airgap with no current flowing is 14×10^{-3} m. The resistance of the coil is 2 ohms. If a d-c voltage of 6 volts is suddenly applied to the coil at $t = 0$, find the motion of the plunger and the current in the coil.

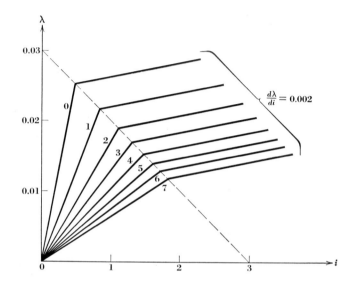

Fig. P 11-24

$$\frac{d\lambda}{di} \text{ for } \begin{cases} \text{curve } 0 = \frac{16}{3}10^{-2} \quad (\text{gap} = 0) \\[2mm] \text{curve } 1 = \frac{16}{6}10^{-2} \quad (\text{gap} = 2 \times 10^{-3}\text{m}) \\[2mm] \text{curve } 2 = \frac{16}{9}10^{-2} \quad (\text{gap} = 4 \times 10^{-3}\text{m}) \\[2mm] \text{curve } 3 = \frac{16}{12}10^{-2} \quad (\text{gap} = 6 \times 10^{-3}\text{m}) \\[2mm] \cdots\cdots\cdots\cdots\cdots\cdots\cdots\cdots\cdots\cdots \\[2mm] \text{curve } 7 = \frac{16}{24}10^{-2} \quad (\text{gap} = 14 \times 10^{-3}\text{m}) \end{cases}$$

11-4   ROTATIONAL ENERGY-CONVERSION DEVICES

    The electromechanical energy-conversion devices presented thus far in this chapter have all had mechanical systems which were translational. We shall now extend the principles developed for translational devices to rotational devices. Although the basic principles are the same for both types of device, the rotational devices lend themselves much more practically to electromechanical energy conversion. This is particularly true for the conversion of large amounts of energy.

    Although rotating devices which employ electric fields to convert energy are possible and have been built, they are not nearly so well suited to this purpose as are magnetic-field converters. For this reason, we shall limit the present investigation to magnetic-field rotational energy-conversion devices.

PARAMETERS OF ROTATING MECHANICAL SYSTEMS As a preliminary to the investigation of energy conversion, some discussion of the parameters and notation applicable to rotating devices is in order. The differential equations which govern the rotational motion of mechanical systems are identical in form to those for translational systems. Consequently, the techniques of system solution developed in the preceding sections of this text are immediately applicable to rotating devices.

The rotational parameters are listed and defined in Table 11-1.

It should be clear, from the form of Eqs. (a) through (l) of Table 11-1, just how the translational-system techniques are applied to

TABLE 11-1   *Parameters of Rotating Mechanical Systems*

Symbol	Name	Measured in	Dimensions	Analogous translational parameter
θ	Angular displacement	Radians	Dimensionless	x (displacement)
ω_r	Angular velocity	Radians/second	T^{-1}	v (velocity)
τ	Torque	Newton-meters	L^2MT^{-2}	f (force)
J	Moment of inertia	Kilogram-meters^2	L^2M	M (mass)
K_r	Rotational compliance	Radians/newton-meter	$L^{-2}M^{-1}T^2$	K (compliance)
D_r	Rotational resistance	Newton-meter-seconds	L^2MT^{-1}	D (mechanical resistance)

Interrelation of parameters:

$$\omega_r = \frac{d\theta}{dt} \tag{a}$$

$$\tau = fl \qquad \text{force} \times \text{moment arm} \tag{b}$$

$$\tau = J\frac{d\omega_r}{dt} \tag{c}$$

$$\omega_r = \frac{1}{J}\int \tau\, dt \tag{d}$$

$$\tau = \frac{1}{K_r}\int \omega_r\, dt = \frac{\theta}{K_r} \tag{e}$$

$$\omega_r = K_r\frac{d\tau}{dt} \tag{f}$$

$$\tau = D_r\omega_r \tag{g}$$

$$\omega_r = \frac{\tau}{D_r} \tag{h}$$

$$\text{Kinetic energy} = \tfrac{1}{2}J\omega_r^2 \tag{i}$$

$$\text{Potential energy} = \tfrac{1}{2}K_r\tau^2 = \frac{1}{2}\frac{\theta^2}{K_r} \tag{j}$$

$$\text{Heat loss (power)} = D_r\omega_r^2 = \frac{\tau^2}{D_r} \tag{k}$$

$$\text{Energy (work)} = \int\tau\, d\theta = \int\tau\omega_r\, dt \tag{l}$$

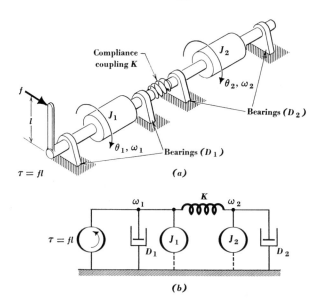

Fig. 11-22. (a) *A rotating mechanical system consisting of two rotating masses coupled by a spring, with friction provided by the bearings; (b) the equivalent network diagram for the system of part a.*

rotational systems. To illustrate, let us solve a simple problem. Figure 11-22a shows a system of two rotating masses with moments of inertia J_1 and J_2. The two masses are coupled by a spring with rotational compliance K.† The bearings contribute frictional resistances D_1† and D_2. A tangential force f with moment arm l is applied as shown.

Figure 11-22b illustrates the network diagram of the rotating system. This diagram indicates that two node equations can be written for this system. Each node equation expresses D'Alembert's law for that node; that is, we set the sum of the torques equal to zero. In differential-equation form the node equations are

$$J_1 \frac{d\omega_1}{dt} + D_1\omega_1 + \frac{1}{K} \int (\omega_1 - \omega_2)\, dl = \tau$$
$$J_2 \frac{d\omega_2}{dt} + D_2\omega_2 + \frac{1}{K} \int (\omega_2 - \omega_1)\, dl = 0$$

(11-89)

The two equations above can be transformed to the s domain and then put in matrix form to yield the following equation:‡

$$\begin{bmatrix} sJ_1 + D_1 + \dfrac{1}{sK} & -\dfrac{1}{sK} \\[2ex] -\dfrac{1}{sK} & sJ_2 + D_2 + \dfrac{1}{sK} \end{bmatrix} \times \begin{bmatrix} \omega_1(s) \\[1ex] \omega_2(s) \end{bmatrix} = \begin{bmatrix} \tau(s) \\[1ex] 0 \end{bmatrix}$$

(11-90)

† Whenever it is clear that we are dealing with rotational parameters, we shall drop the subscript r.

‡ We are assuming no initial forces or velocities.

Equation (11-90) can be readily solved. To illustrate, let us find ω_2 under the following conditions:

$$
\begin{array}{ll}
J_1 = J_2 = 10 \text{ kg-m}^2 & D_1 = 1 \text{ newton-m-sec} \\
D_2 = 0 & K = 1 \text{ radian/newton-m} \\
\tau = \begin{cases} 0 & \text{for } t < 0 \\ 2 \text{ newton-m} & \text{for } t > 0 \end{cases}
\end{array}
\tag{11-91}
$$

With the parameter values above, Eq. (11-90) becomes

$$
\begin{bmatrix} \dfrac{10s^2 + s + 1}{s} & -\dfrac{1}{s} \\[3mm] -\dfrac{1}{s} & \dfrac{10s^2 + 1}{s} \end{bmatrix} \times \begin{bmatrix} \omega_1(s) \\[3mm] \omega_2(s) \end{bmatrix} = \begin{bmatrix} \dfrac{2}{s} \\[3mm] 0 \end{bmatrix}
\tag{11-92}
$$

Thus
$$
\omega_2(s) = \frac{1}{50s(s^3 + 0.1s^2 + 0.2s + 0.01)}
$$
$$
= \frac{1}{50s(s + 0.0505)[(s + 0.0247)^2 + (0.44)^2]}
\tag{11-93}
$$

The time-domain solution corresponding to Eq. (11-93) is

$$
\omega_2(t) = 2 - 2.04e^{-0.0505t} + 0.23e^{-0.0247t} \sin(0.44t + 10°)
\tag{11-94}
$$

This response function is plotted in Fig. 11-23.

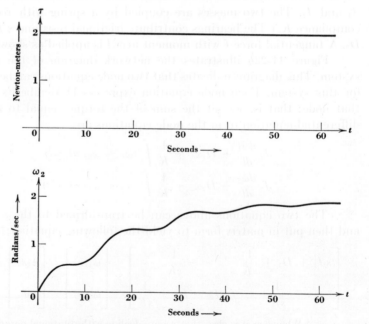

Fig. 11-23. The applied torque and resultant angular velocity of the mechanical system of Fig. 11-22. The system parameters are given by Eqs. (11-91).

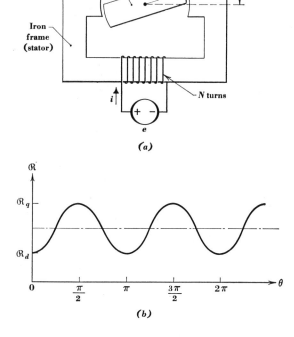

Fig. 11-24. (a) A singly excited rotational energy-conversion device; (b) the reluctance $\mathcal{R}$ of the magnetic path of part a. θ is the angle of the rotor, and the subscripts q and d stand for "quadrature" and "direct."

SINGLY EXCITED SYSTEMS We shall begin our investigation of rotational energy-conversion devices with a simple type which is commonly employed as a low-torque synchronous motor. Consider the singly excited device illustrated in Fig. 11-24a. It should be clear that this device is closely analogous to the translational devices of Figs. 11-7 and 11-15.

As the rotor (the rotating part) of the device rotates, the total magnetic flux, and hence the stored magnetic field energy, varies. This variation is due to the change in the *reluctance* of the magnetic path. A path will have low reluctance if it is entirely composed of iron and will increase in reluctance as more or larger airgaps are inserted in the path. The *reluctance* is defined as follows:†

$$\mathcal{R} = \frac{\text{magnetomotive force}}{\text{total flux}} = \frac{Ni}{\phi} \tag{11-95}$$

The reluctance of a magnetic circuit is analogous to the resistance of an electric circuit.

---

† The reciprocal of the reluctance is called the permeance. The symbol $\mathcal{R}$ is used to distinguish reluctance from the electrical resistance R, to which it is closely analogous. Reluctance is not a vector or an electromagnetic field quantity.

The variation of reluctance with rotor angle will be similar to that indicated by the graph of Fig. 11-24b. The exact shape of this curve will depend upon the geometry of the rotor and airgap, the rotor material, and, for nonlinear material, the magnitude of Ni.

Since the magnetic field energy varies with rotor position, there is an associated torque which depends upon the rate of change of the stored energy. Let us find the value of this torque and its relation to the reluctance. With the rotor held at some angle θ, the stored magnetic field energy and coenergy are, as defined in the preceding section,

$$W_m = \int_0^{\lambda_1} i \, d\lambda$$
$$W'_m = \int_0^{i_1} \lambda \, di \tag{11-96}$$

Because $\tau \, d\theta$ is incremental energy, it follows that

$$\tau = -\left[\frac{dW_m}{d\theta}\right]_{\lambda \text{ held constant}} = \left[\frac{dW'_m}{d\theta}\right]_{i \text{ held constant}} \tag{11-97}$$

For nonlinear mediums, the torque as given above can be found by graphical methods like those discussed in the previous section. The assumption of linearity simplifies the torque calculation as follows: if the magnetic material is linear, the slope of the λ-i curve is the inductance L and

$$W_m = W'_m = \tfrac{1}{2}Li_1^2 = \tfrac{1}{2}\lambda i_1 = \tfrac{1}{2}N\phi i_1 = \frac{1}{2}\frac{(Ni_1)^2}{\Re} \tag{11-98}$$

Equations (11-56) and (11-95) were used in obtaining the expression above.

The torque, under the assumption of linearity, is found by combining Eqs. (11-97) and (11-98):

$$\tau = \left[\frac{d}{d\theta}(\tfrac{1}{2}Li_1^2)\right]_{i \text{ held constant}} = \left\{\frac{d}{d\theta}\left[\frac{1}{2}\frac{(Ni_1)^2}{\Re}\right]\right\}_{i \text{ held constant}}$$
$$= \tfrac{1}{2}i_1^2 \frac{dL}{d\theta} = -\frac{1}{2}\left(\frac{Ni}{\Re}\right)^2 \frac{d\Re}{d\theta} = -\tfrac{1}{2}\,\phi^2\,\frac{d\Re}{d\theta} \tag{11-99}$$

The negative sign in the two terms above indicates that the torque is in a direction tending to decrease the reluctance. By finding the slope of the reluctance curve of Fig. 11-24b, the torque expression of Eq. (11-99) can be evaluated for each rotor angle θ.

The reluctance curve of Fig. 11-24b can be approximated by a constant plus a sinusoid:

$$\Re \cong \tfrac{1}{2}(\Re_q + \Re_d) - \tfrac{1}{2}(\Re_q - \Re_d)\cos 2\theta \tag{11-100}$$

Consequently,

$$\tau \cong -\tfrac{1}{2}\phi^2(\Re_q - \Re_d)\sin 2\theta \tag{11-101}$$

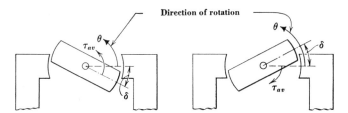

Fig. 11-25. The variation of the torque direction for negative and positive δ for a synchronously rotating rotor.

As is indicated by Eq. (11-101), this device can be used to produce a torque which is proportional to the square of the exciting current (since $\phi = Ni/\Re$). With a restraining spring and indicator, it becomes an ammeter measuring the effective value of the current (see Prob. 11-27).

This device can also be operated as a so-called "reluctance motor," delivering torque at synchronous speed. Let us see how this is accomplished. If the exciting voltage e is sinusoidal, then, since $e = d\lambda/dt$ and $\lambda = N\phi$, the flux will be sinusoidal. Let the flux be

$$\phi = \Phi \cos \beta t \qquad (11\text{-}102)$$

where Φ is the maximum value of ϕ. Now assume that the rotor is rotating at synchronous speed. That is, the angle of the rotor is

$$\theta = \beta t + \delta \qquad (11\text{-}103)$$

where δ is the rotor angle at the instant of maximum flux. Substitution of this value of θ into the torque expression yields†

$$
\begin{aligned}
\tau &= -\tfrac{1}{2}(\Phi \cos \beta t)^2(\Re_q - \Re_d) \sin 2(\beta t + \delta) \\
&= -\tfrac{1}{2}\Phi^2(\tfrac{1}{2} + \tfrac{1}{2} \cos 2\beta t)(\Re_q + \Re_d) \sin 2(\beta t + \delta) \\
&= -\tfrac{1}{4}\Phi^2(\Re_q + \Re_d)[\sin 2(\beta t + \delta) + \tfrac{1}{2} \sin 2(2\beta t + \delta) + \tfrac{1}{2} \sin 2\delta]
\end{aligned}
$$

$$(11\text{-}104)$$

This torque is fluctuating, but it does have an average value:

$$\tau_{av} = -\tfrac{1}{8}\Phi^2(\Re_q + \Re_d) \sin 2\delta \qquad (11\text{-}105)$$

The last expression calls for further discussion. Figure 11-25 illustrates two possible situations in regard to the angle δ. In the first, δ is negative and less than 90° in magnitude. In the second, δ is positive and again less than 90° in magnitude. In the first case, τ_{av} is positive, since sin 2δ is negative. Hence the torque tends to maintain the rotation of the rotor. In the second case, τ_{av} is negative and will slow the rotation until δ becomes negative. An equilibrium angle will be reached where the average torque is equal and opposite to the friction and load torque.

† We shall drop the "approximately equal" sign and use just the "equal" sign.

As the load torque is increased, δ will become more negative. The maximum average torque will be obtained when δ is $-45°$. Any increase in load torque above this maximum will cause the motor to fall out of synchronism and slow to a stop. It is not difficult to show that no average torque will exist for any other angular velocity.

Now let us turn our attention to the electrical portion of this device. Utilization of Eqs. (11-95), (11-100), and (11-102) leads to the following expression for the current:

$$i = \frac{\Re\phi}{N} = \frac{\Phi \cos \beta t}{N} [\tfrac{1}{2}(\Re_q + \Re_d) - \tfrac{1}{2}(\Re_q - \Re_d) \cos 2(\beta t + \delta)]$$

$$= \frac{\Phi}{2N} [(\Re_q + \Re_d) \cos \beta t - \tfrac{1}{2}(\Re_q - \Re_d) \cos (\beta t + 2\delta)$$

$$- \tfrac{1}{2}(\Re_q - \Re_d) \cos (3\beta t + 2\delta)]$$

$$= \frac{\Phi}{2N} [A \cos \beta t + B \sin \beta t + C \cos (3\beta t + 2\delta)] \tag{11-106}$$

where
$$A = (\Re_q + \Re_d) - \tfrac{1}{2}(\Re_q - \Re_d) \cos 2\delta$$
$$B = \tfrac{1}{2}(\Re_q - \Re_d) \sin 2\delta \tag{11-107}$$
$$C = \tfrac{1}{2}(\Re_q - \Re_d)$$

There is a third-harmonic component of current, as well as the fundamental component associated with the electric power:

$$P_{av} = -\frac{1}{2} \frac{\Phi B}{2N} N\Phi\beta$$

$$= -\tfrac{1}{8}\Phi^2\beta(\Re_q - \Re_d) \sin 2\delta$$

$$= \tau_{av}\beta \tag{11-108}$$

Equation (11-108) demonstrates that the power delivered by the source is positive if δ is negative. If δ is positive, the mechanical system yields energy to the electrical system. Consequently, an externally applied torque which maintains a positive δ will cause the device to act as a generator rather than as a motor.

Reluctance motors are used for some low-power applications where synchronous rotation is required. A familiar example is the common electric-clock motor. By special shaping of the rotor, as is shown in Fig. 11-26, the synchronous speed can be divided by an integer factor. Since reluctance motors provide torque only at synchronous speed, some provision must be made for getting their rotors

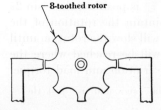

8-toothed rotor

Fig. 11-26. The rotor structure of a synchronous speed will be one-quarter of the applied flux frequency; that is, $\omega_r = \beta/4$.

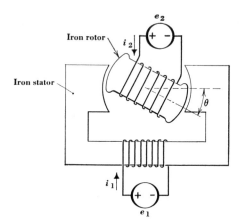

Fig. 11-27. A doubly excited rotational energy-conversion device.

up to synchronous speed. There are a number of ways of accomplishing this, but we shall not discuss them here.

Before going on to the next topic, some comments on the assumptions we have made are in order. The question naturally arises whether the operation of this reluctance motor is strongly dependent upon the assumptions. A more detailed analysis—one which would take into account the nonlinear properties of the iron, the exact form of the reluctance curve, and other effects, such as leakage flux—would give essentially the same results. The main difference would be additional higher-harmonic terms in the torque and current expressions. The general principles of operation, however, would be the same.

DOUBLY EXCITED SYSTEMS For higher-power applications and non-synchronous operation we turn from singly excited to doubly excited systems. Figure 11-27 illustrates a doubly excited rotational energy-conversion device. The derivation of the torque expression for this type of device is similar to the argument leading to Eq. (11-87). Consequently, for linear-ferromagnetic-medium devices,

$$\tau = -\left(\frac{dW_m}{d\theta}\right)_{\lambda \text{ held constant}} = \left(\frac{dW'_m}{d\theta}\right)_{i_1, i_2 \text{ held constant}}$$

$$= \tfrac{1}{2}i_1{}^2 \frac{dL_1}{d\theta} + \tfrac{1}{2}i_2{}^2 \frac{dL_2}{d\theta} + i_1 i_2 \frac{dM}{d\theta} \qquad (11\text{-}109)$$

The first two terms in the expression above are reluctance-torque terms; that is, they can be considered as being due to the superposition of two singly excited systems. Consequently, the analysis of the influence of these two terms is the same as the foregoing analysis of a singly excited device.

The third term in Eq. (11-109) is called the *interaction torque*, and it is this term which will be of the greatest interest to us. We shall

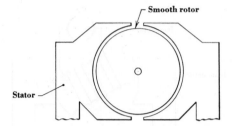

Fig. 11-28. A smooth-rotor uniform-airgap machine.

confine our analysis of doubly excited devices to those in which the reluctance-torque terms can be neglected. It is not difficult to see that a device with a smooth rotor, as is shown in Fig. 11-28, will have negligible reluctance torque, since the reluctance of the magnetic path does not vary as the rotor rotates. Most rotating electric machines are essentially smooth-rotor uniform-airgap machines in which the reluctance-torque terms are negligible. The analysis to be presented here may be extended to non-uniform-airgap machines by adding the reluctance-torque effects, as was done with the singly excited device.

ANALYSIS OF UNIFORM-AIRGAP MACHINES A detailed analysis of doubly or multiply excited rotational energy-conversion devices is made difficult by nonlinear effects and the magnetic properties of the typically complex geometry of stator, rotor, and coils. To keep our analysis from becoming hopelessly complex, we shall consider only the simplest possible model, which we shall obtain by making several simplifying assumptions and idealizations. Although our model will differ considerably from actual devices in detail, the principles of operation will be the same.

Before enumerating the idealizations and assumptions, let us examine some cross sections of rotating-machine configurations. Figure 11-29 illustrates three common configurations of stator, rotor, and coils. Although the physical arrangement and shape of the coils, rotor, and stator vary, the end result is the same: interacting magnetic fields are produced by the rotor and stator coils. Figure 11-30 shows the flux pattern produced by the rotor and stator coils for a simple 2-pole, smooth-rotor, smooth-stator device.

Examination of Fig. 11-30 gives us an indication of the behavior of the third term in Eq. (11-109). When the two fields have the same direction $\theta = 0$, M is positive and maximum. When $\theta = 90°$, M becomes zero, and when $\theta = 180°$, M is negative and maximum in magnitude again. Consequently, M and $dM/d\theta$ will have the form shown in Fig. 11-31 for this simple 2-pole device. It can be seen that this device will behave in much the same way as the singly excited synchronous device if d-c current is applied to the rotor coil and a-c current to the stator, or vice versa.

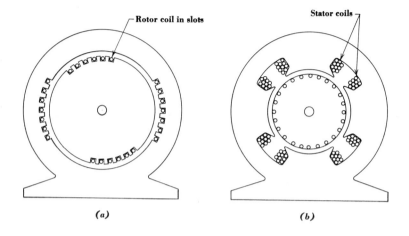

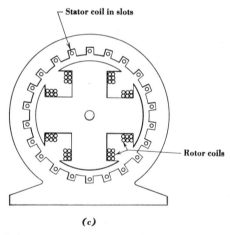

Fig. 11-29. *Cross sections of three types of rotational energy-conversion devices.*
(a) A smooth-rotor smooth-stator uniform-airgap machine; (b) a smooth-rotor
machine with a salient 4-pole stator; (c) a smooth-stator machine with a salient
4-pole rotor. Note that the salient pole devices could be considered smooth-rotor
or -stator machines with very large slots.

To demonstrate this synchronous behavior, we shall consider the
equation below, which is just Eq. (11-109) with the uniform-airgap
assumption:

$$\tau = i_1 i_2 \frac{dM}{d\theta} \tag{11-110}$$

With one current a constant (say I_1) and the other sinusoidal ($I_2 \cos \beta t$),
Eq. (11-110) becomes

$$\tau = I_1 I_2 \cos \beta t \frac{dM}{d\theta} \tag{11-111}$$

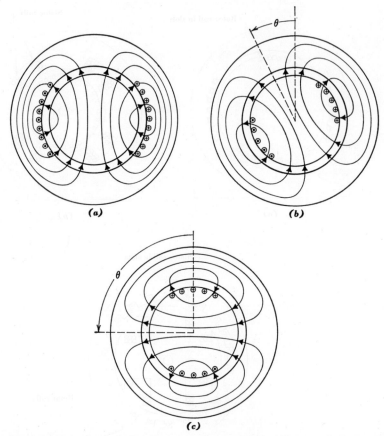

Fig. 11-30. *The magnetic-field configuration for a uniform-airgap device.* (a) *The field due to current in the stator coils;* (b, c) *the field due to rotor coil current.* ⊙ *indicates a wire with current out of the plane of the paper, and* ⊕ *indicates a wire with current into the plane of the paper.*

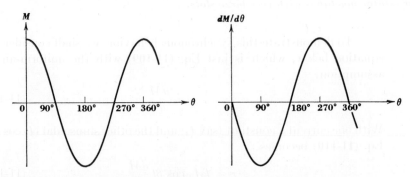

Fig. 11-31. *The variation of M and dM/dθ as θ of Fig. 11-30 is varied.*

If $dM/d\theta$ as shown in Fig. 11-31 is assumed sinusoidal and if the rotor is rotating at synchronous speed, that is,

$$\theta = \beta l + \delta \tag{11-112}$$

then Eq. (11-111) becomes

$$\tau = I_1 I_2 \cos \beta l (-M_0 \sin \theta) = -I_1 I_2 M_0 \cos \beta l \sin (\beta l + \delta)$$
$$= \frac{-I_1 I_2 M_0}{2} [\sin (2\beta l + \delta) + \sin \delta] \tag{11-113}$$

Thus, we see that when the rotor is rotating at synchronous speed, there is a constant term in the torque equation and the device will behave much like the reluctance motor we discussed previously. We shall shortly discuss methods of making this device operate as a non-synchronous motor or generator.

Rather than base the continuation of our discussion upon Eq. (11-109), we shall define a model which yields the torque equation in a different form. The new equation, although equivalent to Eq. (11-109), more readily produces quantitative results. Our idealized model will have the following properties:

    I. *The rotor and stator iron is linear with infinite permeability.*
    II. *The rotor and stator are smooth, with a uniform airgap which is small compared with the rotor radius.*
    III. *The rotor and stator currents are surface currents (on rotor and stator surfaces) flowing in the axial direction. The magnitudes of these surface currents are functions of θ.*

The reasons for specifying the above properties are as follows. Property I eliminates the complications associated with nonlinear iron. The infinite permeability restricts the $\mathcal{3C}$ field to the airgap. This allows us to utilize Eq. (11-59) without introducing complicated integrations. Property II ensures that the magnetic field in the airgap is radial and uniform across the airgap.

A more detailed explanation should clarify property III. What is meant by surface current can be elucidated by examination of Fig. 11-32. A surface current, that is, a current of zero thickness flowing on a surface, is a vector quantity. For example, in Fig. 11-32, the surface current is flowing on the xy plane. Its magnitude and direction are indicated, for various points in the plane, by the arrows. This surface current, denoted as a current density $\delta(x,y)$ amp/m, has a magnitude and direction for each value of x and y. The total current flowing across a line segment can be found by integrating the normal component of δ along that line. For the illustrated xy-plane surface current, the total current crossing the segment of the x axis between a and b is

$$i_{ab} = \int_a^b \sigma_y(x,0) \, dx \qquad \text{amp} \tag{11-114}$$

where $\sigma_y(x,0)$ is the y component of $\delta(x,y)$ along the x axis.

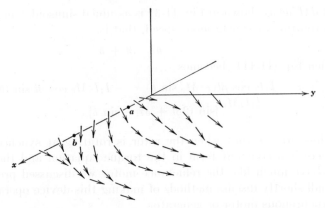

Fig. 11-32. *A graphical representation of the surface current density* $\sigma(x,y)$ *flowing on the xy plane.*

The surface currents represent the true currents flowing through the conductors in the slots of rotor and stator. For example, the rotor or stator conductor and current configuration of Fig. 11-33a could be represented by the surface current densities shown in Fig. 11-33b and c. It should be clear that if we speak of a surface current density which is, say, sinusoidal, then there is a configuration of slots and conductor currents which will be essentially equivalent to this condition.

TORQUE RELATIONSHIPS Using the properties specified above, let us now derive a torque expression which is applicable to our doubly excited device. To begin with, we shall determine the magnetic field within the airgap. Let us evaluate Eq. (11-58) along a path similar to the one illustrated in Fig. 11-34. Because of the infinite permeability of the iron, the $\mathfrak{K}$ field exists only in the airgap, and since the airgap is

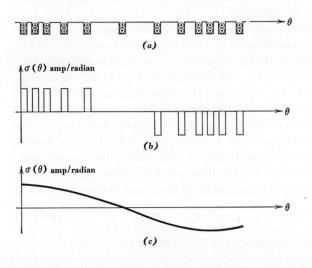

Fig. 11-33. *(a) The current flow in a segment of a rotor or stator; (b) the magnitude of the surface current density which represents (a); (c) a continuous surface current density which also represents (a).*

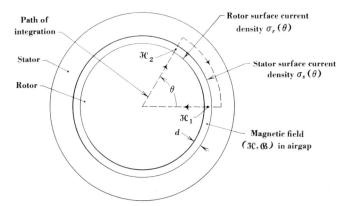

Fig. 11-34. The path of integration for finding the magnetic field in the airgap due to the rotor and stator surface currents.

small, the $\mathcal{3C}$ field across it can be considered uniform and radial. Consequently, the left-hand side of Eq. (11-58) reduces to

$$\oint \mathcal{3C} \cos \theta \, dl = (\mathcal{3C}_2 - \mathcal{3C}_1) \, d \qquad (11\text{-}115)$$

If $\sigma_r(\theta)$ and $\sigma_s(\theta)$ are the rotor and stator surface current densities (directed axially into the plane of the paper), then the total current enclosed in the path of integration (which corresponds to Ni) is

$$i_{\text{total}} = \int_{\theta_1}^{\theta_2 = \theta_1 + \theta} \sigma_r(\theta) \, d\theta + \int_{\theta_1}^{\theta_2} \sigma_s(\theta) \, d\theta \qquad (11\text{-}116)$$

This last expression is the right-hand side of Eq. (11-58). At some angle, which we shall call $\theta = 0$, the magnetic field in the airgap is zero. Letting one radial of our path of integration be at this angle, we obtain

$$\mathcal{3C}(\theta) \, d = \int_0^\theta \sigma_r(\theta) \, d\theta + \int_0^\theta \sigma_s(\theta) \, d\theta \qquad (11\text{-}117)$$

The airgap fields for various types of surface current distributions are illustrated in Fig. 11-35.

In our further discussion, we shall limit our attention to sinusoidal surface current densities and hence to sinusoidally distributed airgap fields. For example, the current density on the surface of a stator with a 2-pole winding will be assumed to be $\sigma_s = A_s \cos \theta$, where A_s is a constant. The field due to this current will be $\mathcal{3C}_s = (A_s \sin \theta)/d$. The current density for a 4-pole stator would be $\sigma_s = A_s \cos 2\theta$.

Let us find the torque exerted on the rotor by summing the incremental forces exerted on strips of the rotor surface current. Figure 11-36 illustrates a rotor of radius r and length l. The radial magnetic field at the rotor surface is $\mathcal{B}(\theta) = \mu_0 \mathcal{3C}(\theta)$. According to Eq. (11-39),

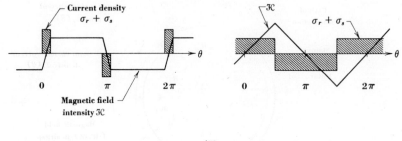

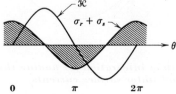

Fig. 11-35. Surface current distributions and the resulting magnetic field intensities.

the force exerted on the illustrated current strip is

$$f_\Delta = -\mathcal{B}(\theta)li = -\mathcal{B}(\theta)l\sigma_r(\theta)\,d\theta \qquad (11\text{-}118)$$

The negative sign occurs because we chose to measure positive force (or torque) in the positive θ direction. With the current and field directions shown in Fig. 11-36, the force is in the negative θ direction.

If the stator and rotor surface current densities are

$$\sigma_s(\theta) = A_s \cos \theta$$
$$\sigma_r(\theta) = A_r \cos (\theta + \delta) \qquad (11\text{-}119)$$

then the torque due to the current strip is

$$\tau_\Delta = f_\Delta r = \frac{-\mu_0 rl}{d} [A_s \sin \theta + A_r \sin (\theta + \delta)]A_r \cos (\theta + \delta)\,d\theta$$

$$(11\text{-}120)$$

Now, if we integrate the torques of all the strips around the rotor, the

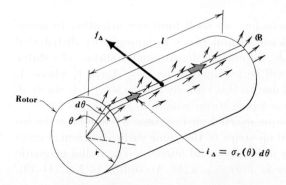

Fig. 11-36. A diagram applicable to the determination of the torque exerted on the rotor.

second term in the brackets above yields no net torque, and the total torque is

$$\tau = \int_0^{2\pi} \tau_\Delta \, d\theta = \frac{-\mu_0 r l}{d} A_s A_r \int_0^{2\pi} \sin\theta \cos(\theta + \delta) \, d\theta$$

$$= \frac{\pi\mu_0 r l A_s A_r \sin\delta}{d} \tag{11-121}$$

For the 2-pole device the total magnetic flux from each stator pole is

$$\Phi_p = \frac{\text{flux}}{\text{pole}} = \int_0^\pi r l \mathcal{B}_s(\theta) \, d\theta = \frac{2\mu_0 r l A_s}{d} \tag{11-122}$$

Using Eq. (11-122), we may rewrite Eq. (11-121) as follows:

$$\tau = \frac{\pi}{2} A_r \Phi_p \sin\delta \tag{11-123}$$

The constant A_r in Eq. (11-123) is directly proportional to the current in the rotor coil. Thus, Eq. (11-123) may be rewritten as

$$\tau = k_r i_r \Phi_p \sin\delta \tag{11-124}$$

where i_r is the rotor current and k_r is a constant of proportionality.

The diagram of Fig. 11-37 should be helpful in interpreting the torque equations above. It indicates the directions in space of the maxima of rotor and stator current distributions for the distributions given by Eqs. (11-119). Note that a positive δ in the rotor current equation corresponds to a space lag, as is indicated in the diagram. With such a δ, the torque as given by Eqs. (11-123) and (11-124) is positive; that is, it is in the positive θ direction, as is shown in the diagram. This torque tends to decrease δ. In other words, it tends to align the magnetic fields of the rotor and stator.

CONTROL OF THE TORQUE ANGLE δ It is clear that, since the torque tends to decrease δ, some method must be used to maintain a torque angle,

Fig. 11-37. A diagram showing the directions in space of the maxima of the rotor and stator current distributions [see Eqs. (11-119)] and the maxima of the corresponding flux distributions.

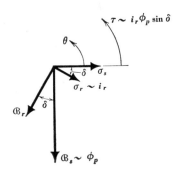

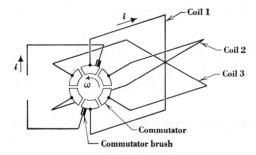

Fig. 11-38. An elementary form of commutator for maintaining a stationary rotor current distribution.

even though the rotor is allowed to rotate. Basically, there are two ways of doing this, both of which we shall briefly discuss. In all d-c machines and in certain a-c machines, the rotor and stator flux distributions are kept stationary in space by *commutation*. Sections of the rotor coils are connected to a *commutator*, which, in turn, is connected, by brushes riding on the commutator, to an external source of current. As the rotor and commutator rotate, the coil connections are changed in such a way that the space distribution of current remains stationary and δ is constant at about 90°. A very elementary commutator is illustrated in Fig. 11-38.

We shall continue the investigation of d-c-machines shortly. Before doing this, let us introduce the other method of maintaining a torque angle. This introduction will be extended in Sec. 11-6. In the machines discussed above, the stator flux was stationary in space. Consequently, rotation of the rotor, due to the torque, tended to align the rotor flux and stator flux, with a resultant decrease in torque angle and torque. Commutation prevents this by maintaining a stationary rotor flux even though the rotor itself is in motion. Another method of maintaining a torque angle is to make both the stator flux and the rotor flux rotate. If the stator flux is "kept ahead" of the rotor flux, the torque angle is maintained. Such a rotating stator flux is possible with a-c voltages applied to properly wound stator coils. We shall discuss how this is accomplished in Sec. 11-6.

INDUCED VOLTAGES   It has been shown that a magnetic field will induce a voltage in a conductor whenever there is relative motion between field and conductor. Consequently, movement of the rotor relative to the stator flux will result in induced voltages in the rotor coils. We can find the magnitude of these voltages by applying Eq. (11-43). Since the magnetic field, the conductor, and the conductor motion are all mutually perpendicular in our model and since the magnetic field does not vary over the rotor length l, the voltage induced in a single conductor length is

$$e_1 = \mathcal{B}(\theta)lv = \mathcal{B}(\theta)lr\omega_r \qquad (11\text{-}125)$$

A number of conductor lengths will be connected in series to form a rotor coil. Consequently, the voltage induced in a coil will be

$$e_c = lr\omega_r \sum_k \mathcal{B}(\theta_k) \tag{11-126}$$

where $\mathcal{B}(\theta_k)$ is the flux density at the position of each section of conductor in the coil.

In an a-c machine, $\mathcal{B}(\theta_k)$ will vary sinusoidally with time. Hence e_c will be sinusoidal. The commutation in d-c machines removes the time dependence. In a d-c machine the flux due to the rotor current will affect the induced voltage. However, for our purposes, we may write, with a reasonable degree of accuracy, that the induced rotor voltage is

$$e = k_e \Phi_p \omega_r \tag{11-127}$$

where k_e is a constant of proportionality, Φ_p is the flux per pole as given in Eq. (11-122), and ω_r is the angular velocity of the rotor. Equations (11-124) and (11-127) will be taken as our basic equations for the discussion of the dynamics of d-c machines, which constitutes the subject of the following section.

SUMMARY In this brief introduction to rotational energy-conversion devices we have attempted to stress basic principles, while eliminating the wealth of detail inherent in the practical examples of such devices. This attempt is consistent with the procedure, used throughout this text, of determining a simple mathematical model of a physical system and then studying the system in terms of the model. More approximations and idealizations were necessary for rotational energy-conversion devices than for previous systems. Nevertheless, the equations we have derived under these assumptions provide reasonable approximations to the actual characteristics of the various devices.

Basically, two effects must be considered in determining the torque produced by the devices under consideration. The first is the variation in the stored magnetic energy due to positional changes in the ferromagnetic material of the device. This variation produces what has been called the reluctance torque. A complete analysis of this effect would require the techniques used in our analysis of the plunger magnet. The analysis was simplified here by assuming linearity. Reluctance motors make use of this effect alone.

The second effect which produces torque is the variation in stored magnetic energy as two current-carrying coils rotate with respect to each other. This effect may be studied in isolation by eliminating reluctance torques. This was done by limiting our study to uniform-airgap devices. Equation (11-124) demonstrated that the torque developed by a uniform-airgap machine depends upon the angle δ between the stator flux direction and the rotor flux direction. The torque angle δ is maintained in d-c machines by commutation and in a-c machines by rotating fields or by commutation.

Since the interchange of electromechanical energy in these devices is bilateral, all may serve as motors or as generators. Associated with the torque production is an induced voltage in the rotor or stator coils.

PROBLEMS

11-25 In a ballistic galvanometer, a moving element, with moment of inertia J, is mounted in a magnetic field, as is indicated in the sketch. It is suspended by a wire with torsional compliance k. For simplicity, the frictional resistance may be ignored. If the angular displacement θ is small, the magnetic flux density at the coil sides may be considered a constant, independent of θ. Under this condition a current i flowing

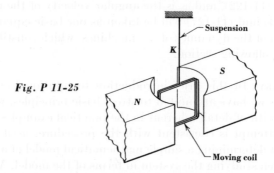

Fig. P 11-25

through the moving coil produces a torque $k_T i$. Thus the differential equation governing the motion of the moving coil is

$$k_T i = J \frac{d^2\theta}{dt^2} + \frac{\theta}{K}$$

Assume that the coil has a resistance R. The effect of the magnetic flux set up by the coil current can be approximated, so long as θ remains small, by assuming that the coil has a constant inductance L. Assume that the voltage induced by the coil's motion is negligibly small compared with the voltage drop across the coil impedance.

(a) Find the transfer function $\Theta(s)/\mathbf{I}(s)$ relating the angular position to the current. Show that the angular position for a unit-step input current is

$$\theta = k_T K(1 - \cos \beta t) \qquad \text{where } \beta = \frac{1}{\sqrt{JK}}$$

(b) Find the transfer function relating the angular position θ to the voltage applied across the moving coil. (It will be convenient to introduce the parameter $\alpha = R/L$.)

(c) Using the technique of partial-fraction expansion, find θ as a function of time if a unit impulse of voltage is applied to the moving coil. (Make rough sketches of θ versus t for the three conditions $\alpha \ll \beta$, $\alpha = \beta$, $\alpha \gg \beta$.)

(d) Thus far the coil voltage induced by the coil's motion in the magnetic field has been neglected. If this is included, it turns out that the differential equation relating the terminal voltage to the current and angular velocity is

$$e = Ri + L\frac{di}{dt} + k_T\frac{d\theta}{dt}$$

Taking into account this additional term, find the transfer function called for in part b. Show that the condition under which this term may be neglected is $k_T{}^2 \ll L/K$.

11-26 In a variable-reluctance type of torque motor, similar to the one shown in Fig. 11-24, the reluctance may be assumed to be given by the expression

$$\mathfrak{R} = \tfrac{1}{2}(\mathfrak{R}_q + \mathfrak{R}_d) - \tfrac{1}{2}(\mathfrak{R}_q - \mathfrak{R}_d)\cos 2\theta$$

$\mathfrak{R}_q$ and $\mathfrak{R}_d$ indicate the reluctance values for the quadrature axis ($\theta = \pi/2$) and for the direct axis ($\theta = 0$), and θ is the rotor angle, as shown in the figure.

Assume the values $\mathfrak{R}_q = 10^6$ henry^{-1} and $\mathfrak{R}_d = 2 \times 10^5$ henry^{-1}. The current is held constant at 1 amp; the winding has 100 turns.

(a) How much energy is converted from the electrical, or magnetic-field, form to the mechanical form if the rotor is allowed to rotate from the position $\theta = -\pi/2$ to the position $\theta = 0$?

(b) Suppose that the rotor, which has a moment of inertia of $J = 10^{-4}$ kg-m^2, is disconnected from any load, so that it can turn freely. If it is displaced from the direct-axis position ($\theta = 0$) by a small angle and released, it will oscillate about the position $\theta = 0$. What will be the frequency of this oscillation in cycles per second?

11-27 The device shown in the sketch is to be used as an ammeter. It is designed to give a linear variation in reluctance over a small range of

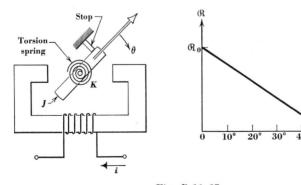

Fig. P 11-27

rotation (0 to 40°), as is shown in the graph. If $\mathfrak{R}_0$ is 10^7 henry^{-1}, and J is 5×10^{-6} kg-m^2, find the torsional compliance K and the number of turns, N, necessary to make the device meet the following requirements: full-scale deflection (40°) is to occur when the rms value of i is 1 amp; the low-frequency fluctuation of the pointer is to be no more than ± 10 per cent of the rms reading at 10 cps.

Draw a curve showing deflection vs. current for this device. What is the inductance of the coil at full-scale deflection? What is the maximum usable frequency if the coil impedance must be less than 10 ohms?

11-28   Assume that the reluctance variation in the single-phase reluctance motor of Fig. 11-24 is as shown in the graph. Assume that the flux is $\Phi \cos \omega t$ and that the rotor is rotating at synchronous speed, $\theta = \omega t + \delta$.

(a) Sketch curves of the instantaneous torque for $\delta = 0°$, $\pm 30°$, $\pm 45°$.

(b) Derive an expression for the average torque in terms of Φ, $\mathfrak{R}_d$, $\mathfrak{R}_q$, and δ.

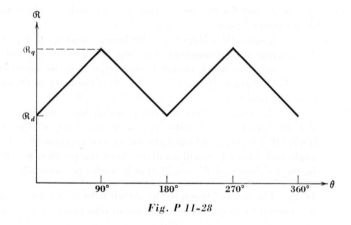

Fig. P 11-28

11-29   For the reluctance motor of Fig. 11-24, prove that no average torque exists for any rotational frequency other than the synchronous frequency.

11-30   For the reluctance motor of Fig. 11-24, derive an expression for the power-factor angle as seen by the voltage source which drives it.

11-31   Consider a rotating machine having two windings, one on the stator and one on the rotor. The windings are distributed in such a way that, when the rotor revolves, the mutual inductance between stator and rotor windings varies as the cosine of the angle between their magnetic axes. The maximum value of the mutual inductance is M. The airgap is uniform, so that the self-inductances L_1 and L_2 of stator and rotor can be considered constant, independent of the angular position of the rotor. The shaft is coupled to a device which can be made to absorb or deliver mechanical torque over a wide range of speeds. This machine can be connected and operated in several ways. For example, suppose the rotor is excited with direct current and the stator is connected to a single-phase 60-cps system which can either absorb or deliver power. The machine then has the basic features of an idealized single-phase synchronous machine.

(a) Describe the nature of the torque developed by the machine as the speed is varied by control of the device connected to its shaft.

(b) Is there a synchronous speed?

(c) If there is a synchronous speed, how many rpm?

(d) Is average torque developed at any speed other than the synchronous speed?

(e) Derive an expression for the average torque in terms of the d-c rotor current, the rms value of the 60-cps stator current (assumed sinusoidal in waveform), the maximum value M of the mutual inductance between stator and rotor, and any other variables that you need.

(f) Under the assumed conditions of sinusoidal variation of mutual inductance, sinusoidal stator current, and constant d-c rotor current, what can you say regarding the waveforms of the voltages at the stator and rotor terminals?

(g) What would you expect regarding waveforms if the rotor were excited from a low-impedance source, such as a storage battery?

11-32 Suppose that the stator and rotor windings of the machine of Prob. 11-31 are connected in series and energized from a 60-cps source. For convenience, the current can be considered sinusoidal.

(a) What is the nature of the torque produced when the rotor is stationary?

(b) Is a starting torque produced?

(c) Is there a synchronous speed? If so, how many rpm?

(d) Derive an expression for the average torque in terms of the rms current I, the maximum value M of the mutual inductance, and any other variables that you may need.

11-33 Consider a machine consisting of a 2-pole steel rotor mounted concentrically inside a hollow cylindrical steel stator core. The rotor carries the single winding marked a in the figure. The stator carries two identical windings marked bb and cc arranged in quadrature as shown. Obviously the reluctance for the two sets of magnetic fields produced by the stator windings varies with the angular position of the rotor. Likewise, the self- and mutual inductances of the stator windings are functions of θ and can be expressed as follows:

$$L_b = L_0 - L \cos 2\theta \qquad L_c = L_0 + L \cos 2\theta \qquad M_{bc} = L \sin 2\theta$$

where L_0 and L are positive constants. The mutual inductances between the rotor and the stator windings are also functions of θ as follows:

$$M_{ab} = M \sin \theta \qquad M_{ac} = M \cos \theta$$

where M is a positive constant. The self-inductance of the rotor is constant. The rotor winding is excited with a direct current I_a, and the currents to the stator windings are

$$i_b = \sqrt{2}\, I_b \sin \omega t \qquad i_c = \sqrt{2}\, I_b \cos \omega t$$

Assume that the rotor is revolving at synchronous speed, so that

$$\theta = \omega t + \delta$$

(a) Derive an expression for the torque acting on the rotor.

(b) Can the machine be operated as a motor? As a generator? Explain.

(c) Will the machine continue to run if I_a is reduced to zero? Explain.

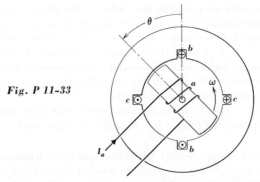

Fig. P 11-33

11-34 Consider a uniform-airgap machine in which a single-phase winding on the stator produces an airgap flux density component $\mathfrak{B}$:

$$\mathfrak{B} = \mathfrak{B}_m \sin 2\pi f t \sin \theta$$

Assume that the rotor is of radius r and length l and that it has a single-coil winding of N turns. Let θ_r be the angular position of the rotor measured from the position where it links the maximum flux. Assume that the rotor is rotating at the speed n rps ($d\theta_r/dt = 2\pi n$). Find the voltage $e_r(t)$ generated in the rotor coil. Identify the transformer component (proportional to f) and the speed component (proportional to n). Make a rough sketch of the waveforms of these components for the case $n = \frac{1}{2}f$. What frequencies are present?

11-35 The figure shows a 2-pole rotor revolving inside a smooth stator which carries a coil of 100 turns. The rotor produces a sinusoidal space distribution of flux at the stator surface, the peak value of the flux-density wave being 0.80 weber/m² when the current in the rotor is

10 amp. The magnetic circuit is linear. The inside diameter of the stator is 0.10 m, and the axial length is 0.10 m. The rotor is driven at a speed of 60 rps.

(*a*) The rotor is excited by a direct current of 10 amp. Taking zero time as the instant when the axis of the rotor is vertical, find the expression for the instantaneous voltage generated in the open-circuited stator coil.

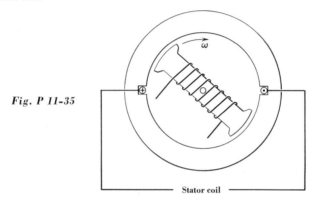

Fig. P 11-35

Stator coil

(*b*) The rotor is now excited by a 60-cps sinusoidal alternating current whose rms value is 7.07 amp. Consequently, the rotor current reverses every half-revolution; it is timed to go through zero whenever the axis of the rotor is vertical. Taking zero time as the instant when the axis of the rotor is vertical, find the expression for the instantaneous voltage generated in the open-circuited stator coil.

It is sometimes suggested that the device described in this problem be used as a d-c generator without a commutator, the thought being that if alternate half-cycles of the alternating voltage generated in part *a* are reversed by reversal of the polarity of the field (rotor) winding, then a pulsating direct voltage will be generated in the stator. Explain whether or not this invention will work as described.

11-5   THE DYNAMICS OF ROTATIONAL D-C MACHINES

The d-c machines to be discussed will be illustrated graphically, as is shown in Fig. 11-39*a*. Four possible methods of connecting these machines to electrical sources are illustrated in Fig. 11-39*b* to *e*. When running as a motor, the machine will be connected to a mechanical load. The general case, covering both mechanical and electrical load, is represented in Fig. 11-40.

THE QUESTION OF LINEARITY   In Fig. 11-40, a d-c machine is used to couple a two-port electrical network and a two-port mechanical system. We assume that both these two-port systems are linear. If the d-c machine is linear, that is, if the relationships among voltage, current,

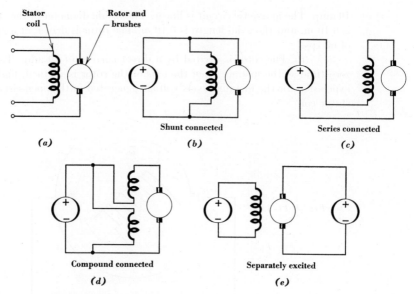

Fig. 11-39. Diagrammatic representation of a d-c machine and four possible connections of such a machine.

torque, and angular velocity are linear, then the whole electromechanical system will submit to linear analysis. Under this condition, all-electrical or all-mechanical equivalent systems can be derived, and transient and steady-state responses can be found in the usual way. If the d-c machine is nonlinear, more complex techniques of analysis will be necessary.

Let us examine Eqs. (11-124) and (11-127) to determine the linearity of our d-c machines. Because of the construction of the d-c machines, the torque angle δ is maintained constant at 90°. Consequently, our two basic equations become

$$\tau = k_\tau i \Phi \tag{11-128}$$
$$e = k_e \omega \Phi \tag{11-129}$$

We note first that the relationships above are linear if the stator flux Φ is not a function of i or e. This will be true for the separately excited

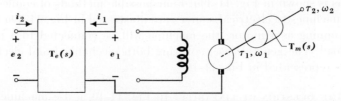

Fig. 11-40. *A d-c machine as the coupling between a two-port electrical network and a two-port rotational mechanical system. $T_e(s)$ and $T_m(s)$ represent the two-port system parameters or transfer functions which are applicable to the systems.*

connection of Fig. 11-39e. With the other connections, the stator coil current—and hence the flux Φ—will be a function of the rotor current or voltage. We shall limit our analysis here to the linear situation achieved by separate excitation of the stator coil.

Before discussing the dynamics of the linear version of our d-c machine system, we shall demonstrate that the constants k_τ and k_e in Eqs. (11-128) and (11-129) are equal. The electrical energy supplied to the machine for transformation to mechanical energy is

$$W_e = \int ei \, dt \qquad (11\text{-}130)$$

where e is the induced rotor voltage given by Eq. (11-129) and i is the rotor current appearing in Eq. (11-128). The mechanical energy produced is

$$W_m = \int \tau \, d\theta = \int \tau \omega \, dt \qquad (11\text{-}131)$$

The two energies must be equal. In order to satisfy this condition, we see that

$$k_\tau = k_e \qquad (11\text{-}132)$$

EQUIVALENT SYSTEMS FOR THE SEPARATELY EXCITED D-C MACHINE
Within the machine itself, we must consider the inductance and resistance of the rotor coils and the moment of inertia of the rotor and the bearing and other friction. Including these effects, a separately excited d-c machine can be represented by the model shown in Fig. 11-41a. An all-electrical equivalent is shown in Fig. 11-41b. This equivalent was found in a manner analogous to the method used in deriving the models of Fig. 11-5. Additional electrical or mechanical

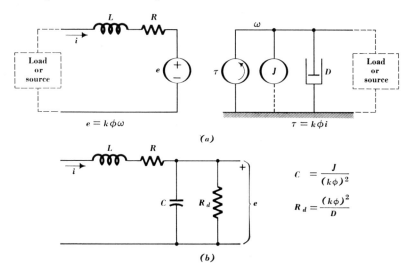

Fig. 11-41. (a) *A combined electrical and mechanical model of a separately excited d-c machine; (b) an all-electrical equivalent circuit.*

loads and sources could obviously be included in the equivalent circuit. An all-mechanical equivalent could also be derived for this system. This is left as a problem for the reader.

Clearly, from here on, analysis of this type of system can be accomplished by application of techniques which by now should be familiar.

PROBLEMS

11-36 Figure 11-41b is an all-electrical model of a separately excited d-c machine. Find the equivalent all-mechanical model.

11-37 Although not so common, a second way of connecting a d-c machine so that it acts as a linear device is to connect the rotor to a constant-current source and the stator coil to a variable source. Draw equivalent models for this connection, including the inductance and resistance of the stator coil. Discuss the ways in which the two types of connections are similar and dissimilar.

11-38 The sketch represents a stator field-controlled servomotor driving an inertial load. The torque of the motor is given by $\tau = kI_a i_f$, where I_a is the constant armature (rotor) current and i_f is the time-variable field current. The voltage induced in the rotor is $e_a = k_a \omega i_f$. The field current is limited only by the resistance R and the inductance L of the field winding. The load is assumed to be only the moment of inertia J. Find an expression for the shaft angular velocity as a function of time if the signal voltage e_f is a unit step.

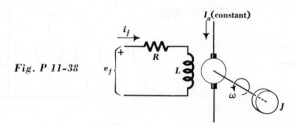

Fig. P 11-38

11-39 Suppose that a constant voltage is applied in the three connections shown in Fig. 11-39b to d. Make plots and discuss how the motor speed in each of these connections must vary as the load torque is varied.

11-40 For the separately excited d-c motor of Fig. 11-39e, state how the rotor current and speed would be affected by each of the following changes in the operating conditions:

(a) Halving the rotor terminal voltage, the field current and load torque remaining constant.

(b) Halving the rotor terminal voltage, the field current and horsepower output remaining constant.

(c) Doubling the field flux, the rotor terminal voltage and load torque remaining constant.

(d) Halving both the field flux and the rotor terminal voltage, the horsepower output remaining constant.

(e) Halving the rotor terminal voltage, the field flux remaining constant and the load torque varying as the square of the speed.

11-41 For each of the systems illustrated, draw the equivalent all-electrical and all-mechanical models. Also, find the indicated transfer

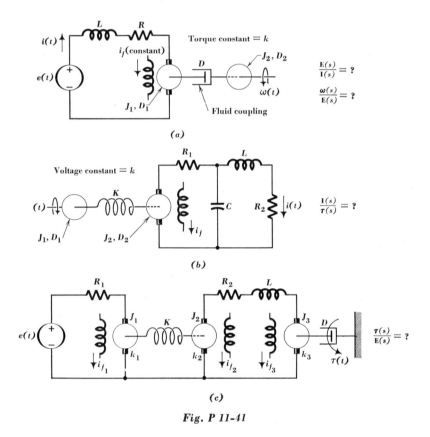

(a)

(b)

(c)

Fig. P 11-41

functions. The voltage and torque constants given in the sketches may be assumed to include the appropriate factors to obtain Φ from i_f. That is, for this problem you may assume that the torque and voltage equations are

$$\tau = (ki_f)i$$
$$e = (ki_f)\omega$$

11-6 ROTATING-FIELD MACHINES

To introduce the subject of rotating-field machines, let us recall the torque equation which we derived in Sec. 11-4 [Eq. (11-124)]:

$$\tau = k_r i_r \Phi_p \sin \delta \qquad (11\text{-}133)$$

The assumptions leading to this equation were sinusoidal rotor current distribution (hence sinusoidal rotor flux distribution) and sinusoidal stator flux distribution.† The direction of the torque was such that it tended to decrease δ, the angle between the maximum of the stator flux distribution and the maximum of the rotor flux distribution.

As was pointed out previously, if the rotor flux distribution remains stationary with respect to the rotor and if the stator flux remains stationary with respect to the stator, then rotation of the rotor due to the torque will decrease δ until the torque becomes zero. In order to have a useful machine, a torque angle must be maintained even though the rotor rotates. Commutation, one method of maintaining a torque angle, has already been discussed. In a commutating machine, both the rotor flux and the stator flux remain fixed in space even though the rotor itself rotates. It is not necessary to keep these two flux distributions stationary in order to maintain a torque angle. That is to say, a torque angle exists as long as there is a relative angle between the maxima of rotor flux and the stator flux—regardless of the fact that these flux distributions may not be stationary in space. In other words, rotation of the rotor, with an attendant rotation of the rotor flux, will not reduce the torque angle if the stator flux is made to rotate ahead of the rotor flux.

PRODUCTION OF A ROTATING FIELD The question that arises from the discussion above is whether the stator flux distribution can be made to rotate. To show how this can be accomplished, let us investigate a specific example in which a rotating field is produced. Figure 11-42 diagrammatically represents a machine which has three sets of stator coils. Let us assume that each set of coils produces an airgap flux which is sinusoidally distributed. For example, assume that the airgap flux due to coil set 1 is

$$\mathcal{B}_1 = k i_1 \cos \theta \qquad (11\text{-}134)$$

Let us further suppose that the other two sets of coils are distributed around the stator so that their flux distributions are displaced $\pm 120°$

---

† If the distribution for either stator or rotor is not sinusoidal, the general principles of torque production will be unaltered, but the exact form of Eq. (11-133) will no longer hold. The variation of torque with angle δ will no longer be the simple sine function of Eq. (11-133).

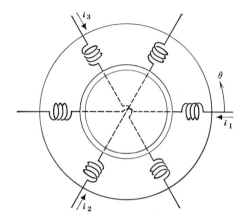

*Fig. 11-42. A diagrammatic repre-
sentation of a machine with three
separate stator windings. The windings are arranged so that the three
airgap flux distributions due to
these windings are sinusoidal and
are separated from each other by
120°.*

from the first. Thus

$$\mathcal{B}_2 = ki_2 \cos (\theta + 120°)$$
$$\mathcal{B}_3 = ki_3 \cos (\theta - 120°)$$
(11-135)

The net airgap flux distribution due to all three sets of stator
coils will be the sum of the three distributions above:

$$\mathcal{B}_s = \mathcal{B}_1 + \mathcal{B}_2 + \mathcal{B}_3 = k[i_1 \cos \theta + i_2 \cos (\theta + 120°)$$
$$+ i_3 \cos (\theta - 120°)] \quad (11\text{-}136)$$

It is not difficult to see that the net flux distribution will be sinusoidal,
with the magnitude and angle of its maximum depending upon the
magnitudes and directions of i_1, i_2, and i_3. Thus, we are led to the conclusion that variations in i_1, i_2, and i_3 will result in a motion of the flux
and that, perhaps, a properly adjusted variation of these currents will
produce a continually rotating field.

    To demonstrate that this proper adjustment actually exists, let
us specify the three currents i_1, i_2, and i_3 as equal-amplitude sinusoids
displaced relative to each other 120° in time phase. This condition can
be produced by connecting the coils to a balanced three-phase voltage
source. Thus

$$i_1 = I \cos \omega t$$
$$i_2 = I \cos (\omega t + 120°)$$
$$i_3 = I \cos (\omega t - 120°)$$
(11-137)

When these three currents are substituted into Eq. (11-136) and
trigonometric identities for cosines of sums of angles and products of
cosines are utilized, the resultant flux distribution is found to be

$$\mathcal{B}_s = 3kI \cos (\theta - \omega t)$$
(11-138)

    The flux distribution as given by Eq. (11-138) is seen to be a
simple 2-pole sinusoidal distribution which is rotating in the positive θ

direction at a velocity of ω radians/sec. We have thus achieved the goal we sought—a rotating stator flux.

We may now return to the interaction of rotor and stator flux distributions. If the rotor flux distribution is stationary with respect to the rotor (d-c rotor current with no commutation) and if the rotor is rotating at synchronous speed $\omega_r = \omega$, an equilibrium torque angle can be maintained. That is, if the stator flux is given by Eq. (11-138) and the rotor flux by

$$\mathcal{B}_r = A i_r \cos\left(\theta + \delta - \omega t\right) \qquad (11\text{-}139)$$

then the manipulations which led to Eq. (11-124) or (11-133) can be repeated with the same result: the variable ωt drops out, and the torque given by Eq. (11-133) is applicable to this synchronous machine.

CHARACTERISTICS OF SYNCHRONOUS MACHINES   The machine we have just described is called a 3-phase synchronous motor. This type of motor is of great importance, and further discussion of its characteristics is in order. A comparison with the commutating motors with which we have dealt previously should prove enlightening. In the commutating machines, $\sin\delta$ is constant, being fixed by the structure of the machine. Consequently, the torque is directly proportional to the product of the rotor current and the total stator flux. As was pointed out in the preceding section, holding the stator flux constant by separate excitation results in a linear relation between the torque and the rotor current. Hence, these machines can be analyzed by linear techniques.

Although a synchronous motor differs considerably from a commutating machine in structure and excitation, it nevertheless obeys the same general torque equation.† There are, of course, important differences. The synchronous motor runs at a fixed speed, whereas the commutator motor may have very large variations in speed. The torque angle is not fixed in a synchronous motor. It will vary with variations in load torque. As we shall see shortly, this produces nonlinearities which complicate the analysis of this type of machine.

STEADY-STATE CONDITIONS IN A THREE-PHASE SYNCHRONOUS MOTOR
Let us investigate the behavior of this machine under the following conditions: (1) the load torque is constant at a value τ_l; (2) the rotor current and flux are constant; (3) the voltage applied to the stator is balanced 3-phase; (4) the previous assumptions of linear iron, sinusoidal flux distributions, etc., continue to hold. Consequently, the

† This further demonstrates a fact which we hope all our readers will appreciate: all electromechanical energy-conversion devices are basically very similar, although the details of their structure and design may tend to obscure this attribute.

following torque equation applies:

$$\tau_l = k_1 I \sin \delta \qquad (11\text{-}140)$$

All the constant factors have been absorbed into the constant k_1, and I is the magnitude of the sinusoidal current in the stator windings.

In Eq. (11-140) it is the applied voltage, rather than the current magnitude I, which is known. Therefore, in order to apply the equation, we must be able to relate I to the applied voltage. To accomplish this, we must first discuss the voltages induced in the windings of this machine. Each stator coil sees a changing flux which is due to the rotating stator field. This particular flux variation will exist irrespective of the conditions that apply to the rotor. Since this changing flux is proportional to I, it will induce a voltage proportional to I. Hence, we may represent its effect by an inductance in an electrical model of this machine.

The rotating flux of the rotor will also induce a voltage in the stator coils. This voltage will be proportional to the rotor current, which we have considered constant. Since the rotor flux is sinusoidal and lags behind the stator flux by the torque angle δ, the rotor-flux-induced voltage will lag the stator-flux-induced voltage by δ deg. The sum of these two induced voltages must equal the applied voltage (assuming no resistive drops in the stator coils). This fact can be used to construct the electrical model of Fig. 11-43, which represents one phase of this 3-phase machine. The other two phases would be identical.

In addition to the electrical model of Fig. 11-43, we can also construct a phasor diagram which illustrates the various pertinent voltages, currents, and fluxes. This is done in Fig. 11-44. With the aid of this diagram we can relate torque to the electrical parameters of our model. Let us first rewrite the torque expression of Eq. (11-133) in a slightly modified form:

$$\tau_l = k_2 \Phi_r \Phi_s \sin \delta \qquad (11\text{-}141)$$

The two terms Φ_r and Φ_s are the total flux per pole of the rotor and of the stator. They are, of course, directly proportional to $\mathcal{B}_r$ and $\mathcal{B}_s$.

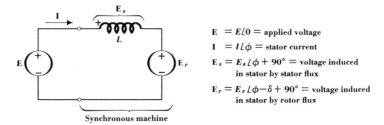

$$\mathbf{E} = E\angle 0 = \text{applied voltage}$$
$$\mathbf{I} = I\angle\phi = \text{stator current}$$
$$\mathbf{E}_s = E_s\angle\phi + 90° = \text{voltage induced in stator by stator flux}$$
$$\mathbf{E}_r = E_r\angle\phi - \delta + 90° = \text{voltage induced in stator by rotor flux}$$

Synchronous machine

Fig. 11-43. An electrical model of one phase of a 3-phase synchronous machine.

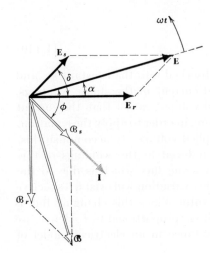

Fig. 11-44. Phasor diagram for one phase of a synchronous machine. Note that $\mathcal{B}_s$ and I lag E_s by 90°, while $\mathcal{B}$ lags E by 90° and $\mathcal{B}_r$ lags E_r by 90°.

The magnitudes of $\mathbf{E}_r$ and $\mathbf{E}_s$ are directly proportional to Φ_r and Φ_s. Consequently, Eq. (11-141) may be rewritten as

$$\tau_l = k_3 E_r E_s \sin \delta \qquad (11\text{-}142)$$

We note from Fig. 11-44 that $E_s \sin \delta$ is the same quantity as $E \sin \alpha$. Using this to modify Eq. (11-142) yields the following torque equation:

$$\tau_l = k_3 E_r E \sin \alpha \qquad (11\text{-}143)$$

Equation (11-143) is more useful than the preceding torque equations because E_r and E are constants and do not vary with the load torque. As a consequence, there is a simple and direct relation of proportionality between the torque and the sine of the angle α. For this reason we shall call α the synchronous torque angle.

Equation (11-143) may be used to find the synchronous torque angle α for different required torques. Knowing α enables us to use the phasor diagram of Fig. 11-44 to find the stator current. Alternatively,

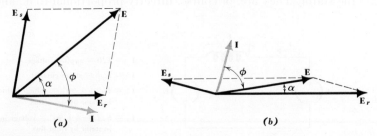

Fig. 11-45. Phasor diagrams for a synchronous motor operation under two sets of conditions. (a) Underexcited, large load, lagging power factor; (b) overexcited, small load, leading power factor.

we could use the model of Fig. 11-43 to compute the current. To illustrate this, Fig. 11-45 shows two phasor diagrams for a synchronous machine operating under two conditions. In part *a* the motor is operating with a heavy load, so that α is large; in addition, the rotor current is adjusted so that E_r is less than E. In this case the motor draws a large lagging current. In part *b*, the load and α are small; in addition, the rotor current is large, so that E_r is greater than E. Under these conditions the motor draws a large leading current. By adjusting the rotor current, a synchronous motor can be made to operate with a leading or lagging power factor. Unloaded synchronous motors with large rotor currents (overexcited) are used as synchronous capacitors to adjust power-factor angles in normally inductive loads.

Our discussion of the steady-state characteristics of the 3-phase synchronous motor has been quite brief. Although some further topics are introduced in the problems, the total coverage can hardly be classified as more than an abbreviated introduction to this topic. However, the basic principles have been placed in evidence.

TRANSIENT CONSIDERATIONS As has been pointed out, a synchronous motor operates at one speed only, the synchronous speed.† Consequently, we might be inclined to conclude that such a motor does not have a transient behavior or that, if it does, it is unimportant. Neither of these conclusions would be completely valid, as will be demonstrated shortly. It is true that the motor speed does not vary over a large range, as do commutator motors. Nevertheless, transient conditions of the load will cause transients within the motor itself. Let us investigate one example of such transient phenomena.

Suppose that a synchronous motor is running at synchronous speed with no mechanical load applied. If negligible friction is assumed, the synchronous torque angle α will be zero. If a mechanical load τ_l is suddenly applied at $l = 0$ (say by applying a brake), what will be the effect upon the rotor motion and the stator current? The applied load torque must be supplied by the electrical torque [Eq. (11-143)] plus the mechanical torque supplied by the motor owing to changes in momentum. Assuming no frictional or compliance forces, we have the mechanical equilibrium equation

$$\tau_l = k_3 E_r E \sin \alpha + J \frac{d^2\theta}{dl^2} \tag{11-144}$$

---

† Because of this, some means must be used to get the synchronous motor up to synchronous speed before it can become operable. In many cases the method used is not capable of supplying a large amount of torque. When this is the case, the mechanical load must be connected to the synchronous motor after it has reached synchronous speed.

The rotor angular position is†

$$\theta = \omega t + \alpha \tag{11-145}$$

Thus
$$\frac{d^2\theta}{dt^2} = \frac{d^2\alpha}{dt^2} \tag{11-146}$$

If we substitute Eq. (11-146) into Eq. (11-144) and make the further assumption that α is so small that sin α can be replaced by α (a linearizing assumption), then

$$J\frac{d^2\alpha}{dt^2} + k_3 E_r E\alpha = \tau_l \tag{11-147}$$

This form of equation is an old friend of ours—the equation of simple harmonic motion. The solution can be written immediately:

$$\alpha = A(1 - \cos \beta t) \tag{11-148}$$

where
$$\beta = \sqrt{\frac{k_3 E_r E}{J}}$$

$$A = \frac{\tau_l}{k_3 E_r E}$$

Note that the coefficient A is the ratio of the applied torque to the maximum torque developed by the motor. This solution is plotted in Fig. 11-46a.

The behavior we have found above is certainly not to be desired. It would be much more satisfactory to have α approach its final value without the large oscillations of Eq. (11-148). We have run into the same problem in different guises several times in previous investigations. If we add some damping, that is, a term $D\, d\alpha/dt$, to Eq. (11-147), the response can be made to look like that shown in Fig. 11-46b. Damping of this form can be achieved by adding damping windings to the rotor. The effect of damping windings (shorted coils) will become apparent in the following discussion of induction motors.

INDUCTION MOTORS We have seen how a rotating stator field can be utilized to develop torque in synchronous motors. A reasonable question to ask at this point is the following: Might it be possible for a rotating stator field to develop an average torque when the rotor is not moving at synchronous speed? The answer to this question must be yes if we are to have a noncommutating motor which has a starting torque. A little thought on this subject would probably lead to the following idea. Let the rotor coils be wound in a manner similar to the stator, so that the application of a balanced 3-phase voltage to the rotor would produce a rotating rotor field, and let the applied voltage to the rotor

† The resultant flux phasor $\mathfrak{B}$ (the phasor sum of $\mathfrak{B}_s$ and $\mathfrak{B}_r$) is rotating at a constant ω radians/sec, since it is directly proportional to **E**. The rotor flux phasor $\mathfrak{B}_r$, which coincides with the rotor in position, lags $\mathfrak{B}$ by α deg.

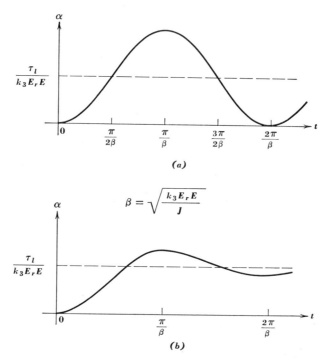

Fig. 11-46. *The response (synchronous torque angle α) of a synchronous motor to a small step increase in the load torque, (a) without damping and (b) with damping.*

have a frequency $(\omega - \eta)$ radians/sec, where ω is the frequency of the voltage applied to the stator. Under these conditions a rotor velocity of η radians/sec would produce conditions which are essentially equivalent to a synchronous motor running at synchronous speed.

The drawback to the system suggested above is that its success depends upon the user's having a second power source, in addition to the usual 60-cps 3-phase source. This second source must operate at a lower (preferably variable) frequency. For this reason we shall discard the idea as first suggested. But the principle of the idea is worth further elaboration. Is there a more practical way of producing a rotor field which rotates with respect to the rotor at such a velocity that the stator sees it traveling at synchronous speed? Here again the answer is yes, and the device which does this is called an induction motor.

To explain the operation of an induction motor, let us turn to Fig. 11-47. Part *a* of this figure illustrates a smooth iron rotor which we assume to be rotating with velocity η. The stator itself is not shown, but the sinusoidal stator flux distribution (rotating at velocity ω) is represented. Now let us assume that the rotor has a single turn of wire around it, as is shown. Since the stator flux is rotating with a velocity $\omega - \eta$ with respect to the rotor and its single coil, the flux linking the

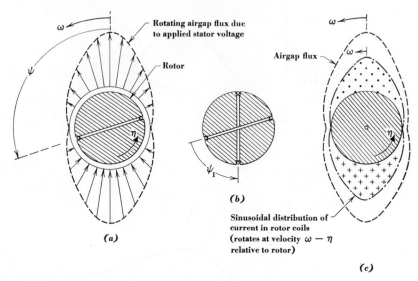

Fig. 11-47. Flux and current distributions pertinent to describing the operation of an induction motor.

coil will be varying with time. Consequently, there will be a voltage induced in this coil. A little calculation (see Prob. 11-55) will show that this induced voltage is

$$e_0 = A(\omega - \eta) \cos \psi \qquad (11\text{-}149)$$

where A is a constant depending upon maximum flux density, rotor radius, and length. The angle ψ is seen to be $\psi_0 - (\omega - \eta)t$. Consequently, Eq. (11-149) becomes

$$e_0 = A(\omega - \eta) \cos [\psi_0 - (\omega - \eta)t] \qquad (11\text{-}150)$$

If a second coil is added to the rotor, as is shown in Fig. 11-47b, its induced voltage will be

$$e_1 = A(\omega - \eta) \cos [\psi_0 + \psi_1 - (\omega - \eta)t] \qquad (11\text{-}151)$$

If three or more of these rotor coils are placed symmetrically around the rotor, the currents caused by the induced voltages will produce a flux distribution which is rotating with a velocity $\omega - \eta$ relative to the rotor. Figure 11-47c indicates the amplitudes of the currents that will flow if there are a large number of rotor coils. As would be expected from Eqs. (11-150) and (11-151), this distribution is sinusoidal. Moreover, if the currents are in phase with the induced voltages, the maximum of the current distribution will coincide with the maximum of the airgap flux. The last statement is equivalent to saying that the torque angle α is 90° for this machine. Furthermore, α will always be 90° as long as the current in the rotor coils is in phase with the induced voltages.

From the discussion above, we would deduce that the torque-speed curve for an induction motor should look like the dashed line in Fig. 11-48. The reason for presuming this straight-line characteristic is as follows. The magnitude of the airgap flux is constant, since the magnitude of the applied voltage to the stator is constant. The rotor coil currents increase linearly as η decreases, since the induced voltages are proportional to $\omega - \eta$. With a constant torque angle and airgap flux, the torque as given by Eq. (11-133) is directly proportional to the rotor current.

The solid line in Fig. 11-48 indicates the shape of an actual torque curve for an induction motor. The deviation from the straight dashed line can be explained as follows. As is shown by Eq. (11-150), the frequency of the voltages induced in the rotor coils is $\omega - \eta$. Consequently, as the slip† increases, the coil voltages will increase in frequency as well as in magnitude, and the coil inductance will begin to take effect. The impedance will increase, with the result that the increase in the magnitude of the rotor current will no longer be linear. In addition, the rotor currents will lag behind the induced voltages, so that α will become more than 90° and sin α will decrease. The net effect yields the illustrated curve.

The discussion above once again puts in evidence the inherent nonlinearity of electromechanical energy-conversion devices. An exact analysis of the dynamic behavior of an inductance motor over its complete range of operation cannot be carried out by using strictly linear methods. However, for small variations in the excitation or load parameters, appropriate small-signal linear models may be utilized. In addition, the electrical part alone, or the mechanical part alone, of an inductance motor may be represented by a linear model (Prob. 11-56).

† The slip is $(\omega - \eta)/\omega$.

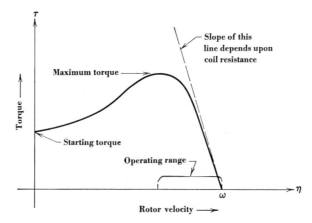

Fig. 11-48. The speed-torque curve for a typical induction motor.

In almost any dynamic application of induction motors, linear-model analysis, although not completely accurate, will yield helpful information concerning the machine's behavior.

The induction motor essentially completes our discussion of the variations in motor types. Almost every electric motor can be classified as one of four types: commutator (stationary stator and rotor fields), synchronous (rotating stator and d-c rotor fields), induction (rotating stator and a-c rotor fields), or a combination of the first three. Much more could be said about induction motors, but in view of the scope of this text, further investigation must be restricted to the problems.

11-7 SUMMARY

This chapter has introduced a considerable amount of new material. New quantities have been defined, new symbols used, new techniques employed, and new systems investigated. To clear up any possible confusion, let us reemphasize the basic ideas of this chapter.

Perhaps the most important point is the concept of energy conservation and equilibrium. This concept can be applied to any system, both to derive force or torque equations and to verify and check results when analysis is started from other than energy considerations. If, in the process of analysis, we keep in mind that Eqs. (11-1) and (11-2) must always be satisfied, we shall be well prepared to handle a large variety of problems.

The general technique of applying energy conservation to electromechanical energy conversion can be summarized as follows. The electrical stored energy will take one of two forms:

$$W_e = \tfrac{1}{2}Ce^2 \tag{11-152}$$

or
$$W_e = \tfrac{1}{2}\Sigma\Sigma L_{jk}i_ji_k \tag{11-153}$$

The capacity or the inductances will not be constant but will depend upon mechanical position. Consequently, there will be a change in the energies given above when there is mechanical motion. Since energy must be conserved, we can utilize Eq. (11-1) or (11-2) to calculate the mechanical forces which are produced. This method was applied in the derivation of Eqs. (11-9), (11-11), (11-29), and others.

Unfortunately, the differential equations which describe the characteristics of these energy-conversion devices are almost always inherently nonlinear. For small-signal conditions, the nonlinear equations can usually be reduced to linear approximations. When this is accomplished, further analysis proceeds along the lines developed in the earlier chapters. It is quite often convenient, although not necessary, to represent the energy-conversion device by a model which is completely mechanical or completely electrical. A good example of this technique is given in Fig. 11-5.

The nonlinearity problem was increased when we considered devices utilizing ferromagnetic material. Once again, under some conditions and with appropriate assumptions, linear approximations can be utilized. When this is not possible, graphical or numerical analysis (probably employing a digital computer) must be used.

The chapter as a whole serves as a good example of the process of analysis in engineering. Starting with certain physical laws and facts concerning the devices under investigation, we have attempted to derive a mathematical model which would adequately represent the device. For the most part, we have sought a linear model. The process has involved assumptions, approximations, and idealizations. The adequacy of the derived model can be judged only in terms of how well it predicts and explains the observed characteristics of the actual device.

PROBLEMS

11-42 Equation (11-136) is equivalent to the following expression:

$$\mathfrak{B}_s = kA \cos(\theta + \psi)$$

Find A and ψ if:

    (a) $i_1 = 1$ amp $i_2 = 3$ amp $i_3 = -2$ amp
    (b) $i_1 = -1$ amp $i_2 = 3$ amp $i_3 = 3$ amp

11-43 Carry out the derivation leading from Eqs. (11-136) and (11-137) to Eq. (11-138).

11-44 What should i_1, i_2, and i_3 be in Eq. (11-136) if the stator flux is to rotate in the negative θ direction, that is, if $\mathfrak{B}_s$ is to be $3kI \cos(\theta + \omega t)$, instead of $3kI \cos(\theta - \omega t)$, as in Eq. (11-138)?

11-45 Using Eq. (11-136), find the currents $i_1(t)$, $i_2(t)$, and $i_3(t)$ which will make $\mathfrak{B}_s$ have the form $3kI \cos[\theta - \xi(t)]$, where $\xi(t)$ is the function drawn in the figure.

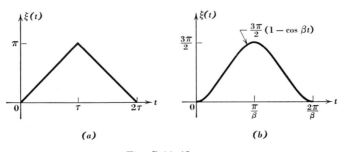

(a)   (b)

Fig. P 11-45

11-46 Suppose each of the three stator windings produces a $2n$-pole flux distribution; that is,

$$\mathcal{B}_1 = ki_1 \cos n\theta$$
$$\mathcal{B}_2 = ki_2 \cos (n\theta + 120°)$$
$$\mathcal{B}_3 = ki_3 \cos (n\theta - 120°)$$

What is the net flux distribution if i_1, i_2, and i_3 are given by Eqs. (11-137)?

11-47 Suppose that the amplitudes of the 3-phase currents of Eqs. (11-137) are not equal. In this case, the amplitudes are designated I_1, I_2, and I_3, rather than all being I. Show that the net flux distribution $\mathcal{B}_s$ can be separated into three sinusoidal components, each with a constant peak value. One component rotates in one direction, another in the opposite direction, and the third is stationary in space.

11-48 (a) Using the results of the previous problem or employing some other means, show that the flux distribution produced by a single-phase winding is equivalent to two equal-amplitude components rotating in opposite directions.

(b) Discuss the resultant flux distribution if the stator windings consist of two 2-phase windings, four 4-phase windings, six 6-phase windings, n n-phase windings.

11-49 Discuss how the appropriate value of L to insert in the model of Fig. 11-43 could be determined from tests (voltmeter, ammeter, watt-meter, torque measurements) run on an actual motor. Could the proper value of $\mathbf{E}_r$ be determined in this way? What other information could be obtained from such measurements that would make it possible to refine the simple model shown? Modify the model given to take into account various losses within the machine.

11-50 A 220-volt 3-phase synchronous motor is designed to yield a rated load output of 50 hp. The rated load is to be 75 per cent of the maximum possible load. At the rated load the motor is to operate at a leading power factor of 0.8. Assuming the complete validity of the model of Fig. 11-43, find the inductance L and the magnitude (rms) of $\mathbf{E}_r$. Plot the magnitude and phase of $\mathbf{I}$ versus the per cent of rated load. If this motor has a 4-pole stator winding, what is the load torque at rated load?

11-51 The typical curves shown are called synchronous-motor V curves. Discuss and explain their shape.

11-52 A synchronous motor becomes a generator when an applied mechanical torque maintains a negative synchronous torque angle α, that is, when the rotor flux distribution leads the net (resultant) airgap flux by an angle α. Discuss the characteristics that you would expect of such a generator. Draw phasor diagrams similar to those of Fig. 11-45 which would apply to such a generator under various electrical load conditions.

11-53 Figure 11-46 illustrates the mechanical behavior of a synchronous motor following application of a step of load torque. Plot the amplitude

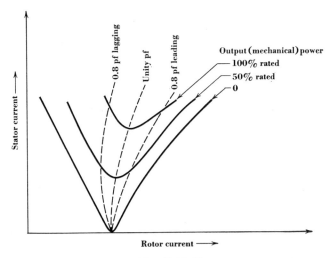

Fig. P 11-51

and phase of the stator current **I** (versus time) which would result from the illustrated mechanical behavior. What would β be for a 10-hp motor?

11-54 Discuss the solution of Eq. (11-144) when α is too large to allow the substitution of α for sin α. Compare this with the problem of solving for the motion of a pendulum.

11-55 (*a*) Derive Eq. (11-149). In particular, what is A in terms of the parameters of the motor?

(*b*) In the development of the principles of induction motors, the rotor coils were treated as a large number of separate single-turn coils. In a squirrel-cage induction motor, the single turn consists of copper bars, but all these coils are shorted together at each end of the rotor. Show that the analysis given here applies to a squirrel-cage motor.

11-56 The illustrated circuit may be used as an electrical model

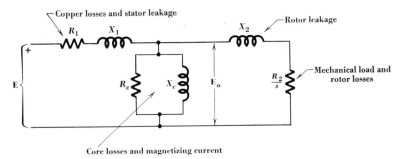

E_n is proportional to the net airgap flux, $s = \dfrac{\omega - \eta}{\omega}$, where $\omega =$ stator flux velocity and $\eta =$ rotor velocity

Fig. P 11-56

(1 phase) of an induction motor. Derive this model, explaining what each element in the model represents and how it can be measured. Show that the mechanical power developed is $3I_2{}^2R_2(1 - s)/s$. (To complete this problem, it may be necessary to refer to standard texts on a-c machinery.)

11-57 Referring to the discussion in the text and using the equivalent circuit of the previous problem, draw phasor diagrams for induction motors operating at various values of slip. Point out the similarities and differences between your diagrams and the synchronous-motor diagrams of Fig. 11-45.

11-58 According to Eq. (11-143) a synchronous motor which is required to produce a particular output torque τ_l may do so by operating at a torque angle α between 0 and 90° or at 180° − α, which is between 90 and 180°. Nevertheless, a synchronous motor will never operate with a synchronous torque angle larger than 90°. Explain this. Why does your argument not apply to induction motors which do operate with torque angles between 90 and 180°?

11-59 Discuss how a rotating-field machine could be constructed so that it would have the starting torque of an induction motor but would run as a synchronous motor.

11-60 A single-phase stator produces two equal counterrotating flux distributions (Prob. 11-48a). Discuss the operation of a single-phase induction motor, in particular its starting torque. Discuss the stator flux distributions that would be produced by the two stator arrangements illustrated. Could these be used to construct a single-phase induction motor with a nonzero starting torque?

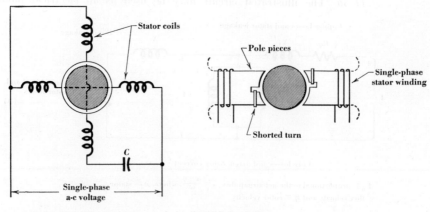

Fig. P 11-60

feedback and control systems

A field of engineering which is of major importance today and which is bound to become increasingly important in the future is the field of automatic control.† As industrial processes, transportation systems, communication systems, weapon systems, and other processes become increasingly complex, the techniques used in controlling them have and will become more and more sophisticated. Many automatic control systems use mechanical and electrical elements in combination with conversion devices between electrical and mechanical energy. Consequently, a short chapter on this topic is appropriate, both as an introduction to this important field and as a further example of the analysis techniques developed in the preceding chapters.

12-1 THE FEEDBACK CONTROL SYSTEM

We shall divide control systems into two classes and devote our attention to one of them. The first, which will be of no interest to us, is the *open-loop*, or *nonfeedback*, type of control system. The control systems which we shall investigate are the *closed-loop*, or *feedback*, type. In the latter class are the systems in which the process output affects the control of the process—hence the terms feedback and closed-loop. The process output does not directly affect the process control in open-loop systems.

SOME EXAMPLES We shall begin by discussing two simple and closely related control systems as examples of the two classes. Consider the timer on a fairly modern kitchen oven. The housewife can put a roast in the oven, set the timer, and then spend the afternoon at a bridge party. The timer will turn the oven on at the proper time and turn it off again after an interval preset by the housewife. In this simple

† Nearly synonymous terms are *servomechanisms, servo systems,* and *regulating systems.*

open-loop system the control of the oven has nothing to do with the actual state of the system output, the roast.

A feature which appears on some of the more expensive ovens is a meat thermometer which controls the oven. Once again, the housewife, off to her bridge party, puts the roast in the oven and sets the timer. Now, however, instead of the oven's being turned off after a preset time interval, it is turned off after the roast, as indicated by the meat thermometer, reaches the desired internal temperature. In this control system the state of the process output, the roast, influences the control. There is a feedback from the output to the input, the input being the electrical power or gas being fed to the oven.

Clearly, the second of the two control systems above has distinct advantages over the first. The first depends upon the housewife's being a good judge of just how long a particular roast should be cooked at a certain temperature. The second system is independent of the house-wife's judgment and will perform satisfactorily with all types and sizes of roasts, even if there is a discrepancy between the oven temperature setting and the actual oven temperature.

The two examples above, though unsophisticated, aptly point out the differences between open-loop and closed-loop (feedback) control systems. Where the process is subject to influences which are not entirely predictable, it is necessary, in order to ensure accurate control of the output, for the state of the output to influence the control.

AN ELECTROMECHANICAL EXAMPLE   Let us now consider a typical example of an electromechanical system employing feedback control. Suppose we have a large mass which we wish to rotate through some prescribed angle from a remote-control position. A gun turret on a military airplane, a crane in a factory, the rudder of an ocean liner—these are all possible examples of such a system. Associated with the mass to be moved will be friction and compliance. The torque to rotate the mass

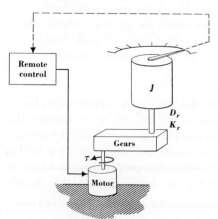

Fig. 12-1. An electromechanical control system.

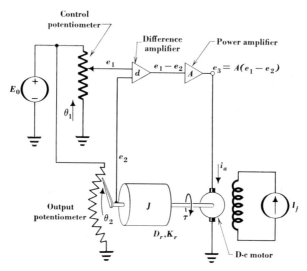

Fig. 12-2. *A closed-loop system for controlling the position of the mass with moment of inertia J.*

will be supplied by a motor, say a d-c motor, operating through a set of gears. Figure 12-1 diagrammatically illustrates the system.

In order to position the mass accurately by means of an open-loop system, it would be necessary to know all the system parameters with a greater degree of precision than is possible. Consequently, we turn to a feedback system in which the position of the mass is fed back to the control unit. The feedback path is shown by the dashed line in Fig. 12-1.

One way in which the output position information can be utilized to bring about the proper positioning of the mass is illustrated by Fig. 12-2. The control and output potentiometers are constructed so that the voltages e_1 and e_2 are proportional to angle:

$$e_1 = \alpha\theta_1$$
$$e_2 = \alpha\theta_2$$
(12-1)

As Fig. 12-2 shows, if the angle θ_2 of J does not equal θ_1, there will be a difference voltage† $e_1 - e_2$ which will actuate the motor, which, in turn, will rotate J until $\theta_2 = \theta_1$.

Before we begin a quantitative investigation of control systems such as the one shown in Fig. 12-2, let us see what we can say qualitatively on the basis of our investigation to this point. The first thing to note is that the system of Fig. 12-2 will position the rotating mass

† It is not difficult to design an electronic amplifier whose output is the difference of two input voltages. See Sec. 12-3 for a discussion of such amplifiers.

accurately even though many of the system parameters either are not known precisely or are variable over a relatively wide range. As long as the two potentiometers are precisely calibrated and matched to each other, the other parameters, such as E_0, A, I_f, J, D_r, and K_r, can all vary over reasonable ranges without affecting the final accuracy of positioning. Obviously, this system is superior to an open-loop system that attempts to accomplish the same end.

The second thing to note is that the control system of Fig. 12-2 is a transducer (two-port network). The input quantity is the voltage e_1. The output is the angular position θ_2. Or if we prefer, we can call the voltage e_2 the output. We may treat it as an all-electrical or an all-mechanical two-port by transforming the mechanical part to its electrical equivalent or vice versa. Consequently, if the system is linear, we may analyze and treat it in the same way that we have utilized other transducers in previous chapters. That is, from the linear differential equations describing the system, or by other methods which bypass the differential equations, we can obtain the appropriate transfer functions or two-port parameters in the s domain. With these functions, we can compute the various transient responses of interest, frequency-response curves, pole-zero plots, and other system characteristics.

One additional matter to be discussed is the question of stability. Whenever a system such as the one of Fig. 12-2 contains feedback, there is a distinct possibility of the system's being unstable. By this we mean that the system will have a response with no input, that is, a response which grows in magnitude until the system parameters change because of nonlinear effects or until the system fails because of the excessive amplitude of the variables, such as current and force. Quite naturally, an unstable system is completely inoperable as a control device. This is obviously an important factor to consider in the analysis and design of control systems. We shall investigate the stability of feedback systems at more length in Sec. 12-2.

BLOCK DIAGRAMS AND TRANSFER FUNCTIONS For the analytical work which follows, we shall hypothesize the linearity of the complete control system. From our experience in the previous chapter with electromechanical energy-conversion devices, we know that this hypothesis will not be justified for all systems. Once again, though, the analysis of linear models is a logical first step toward analysis of all control systems, both linear and nonlinear.

In Fig. 12-3 we have drawn block diagrams of various possible feedback arrangements. To clarify the notation we have used, let us discuss system d of Fig. 12-3. The input quantity is represented in the s domain by $\mathbf{E}_i$. This quantity could be voltage, torque, velocity, or any of the other electrical or mechanical variables we have dealt with.

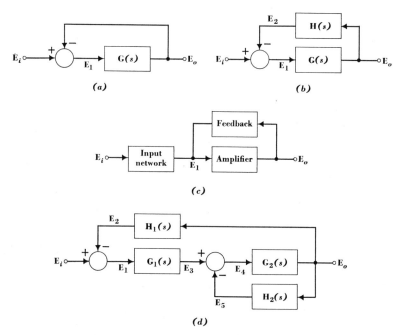

Fig. 12-3. Block diagrams of various feedback systems.

The system output is $\mathbf{E}_o$. The circles represent summing or differencing devices. Thus

$$\begin{aligned}\mathbf{E}_1(s) &= \mathbf{E}_i(s) - \mathbf{E}_2(s)\\ \mathbf{E}_4(s) &= \mathbf{E}_3(s) - \mathbf{E}_5(s)\end{aligned} \tag{12-2}$$

The rectangular boxes represent two-port devices, with the appropriate transfer function enclosed in each box. Thus

$$\begin{aligned}\mathbf{E}_3(s) &= \mathbf{E}_1(s)\mathbf{G}_1(s)\\ \mathbf{E}_o(s) &= \mathbf{E}_4(s)\mathbf{G}_2(s)\\ \mathbf{E}_2(s) &= \mathbf{E}_o(s)\mathbf{H}_1(s)\\ \mathbf{E}_5(s) &= \mathbf{E}_o(s)\mathbf{H}_2(s)\end{aligned} \tag{12-3}$$

The system illustrated in Fig. 12-3c differs from the other three mainly in the details of analysis. It represents an electronic feedback amplifier. We shall postpone the discussion of this type of system to Sec. 12-3.

THE OVER-ALL, OR CLOSED-LOOP, TRANSFER FUNCTION, which is the ratio of $\mathbf{E}_o$ to $\mathbf{E}_i$, is the function which is of most interest. From it we determine transient responses, frequency responses, and stability information. Let us find the over-all transfer function for one of the systems of Fig. 12-3. We shall find $\mathbf{E}_o/\mathbf{E}_i$ in terms of $\mathbf{G}(s)$ and $\mathbf{H}(s)$, which we may assume to be known.

For the system of Fig. 12-3b, the following relationships are given:

$$\mathbf{E}_1 = \mathbf{E}_i - \mathbf{E}_2$$
$$\mathbf{E}_o = \mathbf{E}_1\mathbf{G} \qquad\qquad (12\text{-}4)$$
$$\mathbf{E}_2 = \mathbf{E}_o\mathbf{H}$$

The equations given above are easily manipulated to form the closed-loop transfer function:

$$\frac{\mathbf{E}_o}{\mathbf{E}_i} = \frac{\mathbf{G}(s)}{1 + \mathbf{G}(s)\mathbf{H}(s)} \qquad\qquad (12\text{-}5)$$

This equation also applies to the unity feedback system of Fig. 12-3a, where $\mathbf{H}(s) = 1$. The system of Fig. 12-3d is seen to be a feedback system within a feedback system. The over-all transfer function for this double feedback system is given below in Eq. (12-6). This derivation, which is similar to that above, is left as a problem for the reader.

$$\frac{\mathbf{E}_o}{\mathbf{E}_i} = \frac{\mathbf{G}_1\mathbf{G}_2}{1 + \mathbf{G}_1\mathbf{G}_2\mathbf{H}_1 + \mathbf{G}_2\mathbf{H}_2} \qquad\qquad (12\text{-}6)$$

Usually, the transfer functions, $\mathbf{G}_1$, $\mathbf{G}_2$, . . . and $\mathbf{H}_1$, $\mathbf{H}_2$, . . . , will be ratios of polynomials in s. Consequently, the closed-loop transfer function will also be a ratio of polynomials in s. The roots of these latter polynomials will be the zeros and poles of the closed-loop transfer function and hence will determine the behavior of the system. In Sec. 12-2 and in the example to follow, we shall discuss how the positions of these poles and zeros are related to the original transfer functions.

FURTHER ANALYSIS OF THE ELECTROMECHANICAL SYSTEM OF FIG. 12-2 The block diagram which applies to our electromechanical example is the one shown in Fig. 12-3a. As mentioned above, Eq. (12-5) is applicable to the system represented in this figure. Therefore, with $\mathbf{H}(s) = 1$, we merely have to find $\mathbf{G}(s)$ and then substitute it into Eq. (12-5) in order to find the over-all transfer function.

For the system of Fig. 12-2, $\mathbf{G}(s)$ would be $\mathbf{E}_2/(\mathbf{E}_1 - \mathbf{E}_2)$ or, with the feedback loop open, $\mathbf{E}_2/\mathbf{E}_1$. In order to find these voltage ratios, let us turn to Fig. 11-41, which shows the model that is applicable to the analysis of the d-c motor used in our system. Let us assume the following conditions: the transfer function of the power amplifier is simply the constant A, the rotor inductance of the d-c motor is negligible, there is no compliance in the drive between motor and rotating mass, and the combined moment of inertia of motor and mass is J. With these assumptions, a model which represents the system without feedback can be derived from Fig. 11-41. This model is illustrated in Fig. 12-4.

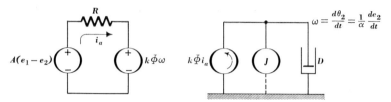

Fig. 12-4. *A combined electrical and mechanical model applicable to the control system of Fig. 12-2. The feedback path is not included in this drawing.*

The differential equations which apply to the model of Fig. 12-4 are as follows:

$$Ri_a + \frac{k\Phi}{\alpha}\frac{de_2}{dt} = A(e_1 - e_2)$$

$$\frac{J}{\alpha}\frac{d^2e_2}{dt^2} + \frac{D}{\alpha}\frac{de_2}{dt} = k\Phi i_a \tag{12-7}$$

In the s domain the equations above become

$$R\mathbf{I}_a(s) + \frac{k\Phi s}{\alpha}\mathbf{E}_2(s) = A[\mathbf{E}_1(s) - \mathbf{E}_2(s)]$$

$$\frac{J}{\alpha}s^2\mathbf{E}_2(s) + \frac{D}{\alpha}s\mathbf{E}_2(s) = k\Phi\mathbf{I}_a(s) \tag{12-8}$$

The ratio of $\mathbf{E}_2(s)$ to $[\mathbf{E}_1(s) - \mathbf{E}_2(s)]$ is found by first eliminating $\mathbf{I}_a(s)$ in the equations above and then computing the ratio:

$$\mathbf{G}(s) = \frac{\mathbf{E}_2(s)}{\mathbf{E}_1(s) - \mathbf{E}_2(s)} = \frac{B}{s(s + \beta)} \tag{12-9}$$

The two new symbols appearing in the equation above have the following values:

$$B = \frac{\alpha A k\Phi}{RJ} \qquad \beta = \frac{RD + k^2\Phi^2}{RJ} \tag{12-10}$$

Using the $\mathbf{G}(s)$ of Eq. (12-9), we find that the closed-loop transfer function as given by Eq. (12-5) becomes

$$\frac{\mathbf{E}_2(s)}{\mathbf{E}_1(s)} = \frac{B/s(s + \beta)}{1 + B/s(s + \beta)} = \frac{B}{s(s + \beta) + B} = \frac{B}{s^2 + \beta s + B} \tag{12-11}$$

At this juncture, some important points can be ascertained by a comparison of the open-loop transfer function, Eq. (12-9), and the closed-loop transfer function, Eq. (12-11). In particular, let us examine the effect which the gain A of the power amplifier has upon the two transfer functions. In contrast to the other parameters, which are likely to be difficult or impossible to change, A can generally be varied over a wide range of values with relative ease.

In Eq. (12-9), A is included only in the numerator, a constant. Consequently, A can affect only the level of the response, not

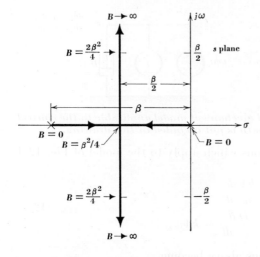

Fig. 12-5. The loci of the poles of the closed-loop transfer function given by Eq. (12-11). The variation in pole position is brought about by a change in B which is directly proportional to the power amplifier gain A.

the form, since for this transfer function the pole and zero locations are determined by the denominator. The role which A plays in the closed-loop system is considerably more important. Here A not only affects the level of the responses but also partially determines their shape, through its control of the pole positions of the closed-loop transfer function. This characteristic is graphically illustrated in Fig. 12-5, where the loci of the pole positions are plotted as B changes because of a variation in A.

Let us turn now to an investigation of the time response of our electromechanical control system. For this particular system, the input (and corresponding response) which is of most interest is a step, that is, a sudden change of the control setting from one position to another. Assuming a unit-step input,

$$e_1(t) = \begin{cases} 0 & t < 0 \\ 1 & t > 0 \end{cases} \tag{12-12}$$

$$\mathbf{E}_1(s) = \frac{1}{s} \tag{12-13}$$

we find that the system response is

$$\mathbf{E}_2(s) = \frac{B\mathbf{E}_1(s)}{s^2 + \beta s + B} = \frac{B}{s(s^2 + \beta s + B)} = \frac{1}{s} - \frac{s + \beta}{s^2 + \beta s + B} \tag{12-14}$$

The time-domain response corresponding to Eq. (12-14) can be computed through the use of the Appendix. It is, for $B < \beta^2/4$ and $t > 0$,

$$e_2(t) = 1 - \frac{1}{a - b}[(\beta - b)e^{-bt} - (\beta - a)e^{-at}] \tag{12-15}$$

with $\quad a = \frac{\beta}{2} + \sqrt{\frac{\beta^2}{4} - B} \qquad b = \frac{\beta}{2} - \sqrt{\frac{\beta^2}{4} - B} \tag{12-16}$

For $B = \beta^2/4$,

$$e_2(t) = 1 - \left(1 + \frac{\beta t}{2}\right) e^{-\beta t/2} \tag{12-17}$$

and for $B > \beta^2/4$,

$$e_2(t) = 1 - \frac{\sqrt{B}}{\omega_0} e^{-\beta t/2} \sin(\omega_0 t + \psi) \tag{12-18}$$

with $\qquad \omega_0 = \sqrt{B - \frac{\beta^2}{4}} \qquad \psi = \tan^{-1}\sqrt{\frac{4B}{\beta^2} - 1} \qquad$ (12-19)

     The response to a unit-step input is plotted in Fig. 12-6 for four values of B. Note that these curves could have been predicted quite accurately by the pole positions plotted in Fig. 12-5. The curves of Fig. 12-6 show clearly that the gain of the power amplifier can be an important factor in adjusting the characteristics of the system response. If the gain is low, so that $B \cong \frac{1}{2}\beta^2/4$, the step response is quite slow. With a gain increase such that $B = \beta^2/4$, the minimum rise time without overshoot is obtained. A further increase in gain will produce overshoot, but usually a small overshoot can be tolerated in exchange for the faster response so obtained. For example, the response with $B = 2\beta^2/4$ would probably be considered superior to the one with $B = \beta^2/4$. Additional increase in gain will produce large oscillations, which are undesirable.

     The preceding discussion of the step response can be summarized as follows. The time scale of the response is determined by the system elements, such as R, J, and D. (The time axis in Fig. 12-6 depends upon β, which in turn is determined by the system elements above.) The actual form of the response within this time scale is directly influenced by the amplifier gain A.

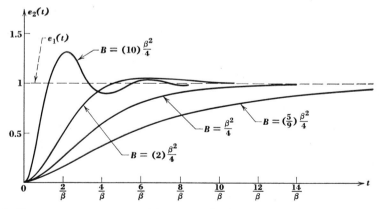

Fig. 12-6. The unit-step response (closed-loop) of the control system shown in Fig. 12-2. See also Figs. 12-4 and 12-5 and Eqs. (12-10) to (12-19).

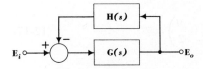

Fig. 12-7. Block diagram of a linear model of a feedback control system.

SUMMARY   The essential fact about feedback control systems is that the system output influences the input. This is absolutely necessary in any but the simplest control systems, since accurate control with no feedback would require knowledge of all the system parameters with a degree of precision that is not reasonably possible. Feedback systems may appear in a great variety of forms and may contain many types of elements. They may be linear, nearly linear, or very nonlinear. However, an important portion of them can be represented by the block diagram of Fig. 12-7. This diagram illustrates a linear two-port system with a transfer function

$$\frac{\mathbf{E}_o(s)}{\mathbf{E}_i(s)} = \frac{\mathbf{G}(s)}{1 + \mathbf{G}(s)\mathbf{H}(s)} \tag{12-20}$$

The open-loop transfer function is $\mathbf{G}(s)$, and the feedback transfer function is $\mathbf{H}(s)$. Both of these functions enter into the formation of the closed-loop transfer function given by Eq. (12-20). Usually the open-loop transfer function $\mathbf{G}(s)$ will contain a constant multiplier which is called the open-loop gain. Since $\mathbf{G}(s)$ is in the denominator of Eq. (12-20), the gain plays an important part in controlling the positions of the poles of the closed-loop transfer function. The effect of the gain was demonstrated in the preceding example. Equation (12-20) will be investigated further in the next section.

PROBLEMS

12-1   (a) Derive Eq. (12-6). (b) Find the over-all transfer functions for the systems shown.

12-2   Find and plot the open-loop and closed-loop amplitude and phase response of the system of Fig. 12-4, that is, $|\mathbf{E}_o(s)/\mathbf{E}_i(s)|$ and $\angle \mathbf{E}_o/\mathbf{E}_i$ for $s = j\omega$ versus ω. (Use the values of B given in Fig. 12-6.)

12-3   Draw the equivalent circuit for the system of Fig. 12-2 if the d-c motor rotor current is supplied by a constant-current source and the power amplifier drives the stator field coil. Include the resistance and inductance of the stator coil. Find the closed-loop transfer function for this system. Plot the loci of the closed-loop poles as A is varied.

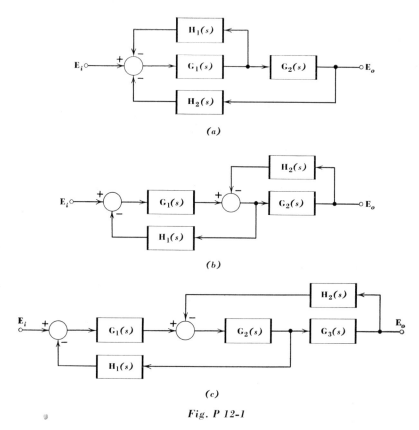

(a)

(b)

(c)

Fig. P 12-1

How will this system respond to a step function, as compared with the system discussed in the text, if $L/R \ll D/J$?

12-4 Find and plot the closed-loop response of the system of Fig. 12-4 to a "ramp" input, that is, $e_1(t) = ct$ for $t > 0$, with c a constant. Do this for several values of B. What is the error $e_1(t) - e_2(t)$ for large values of t?

12-5 The diagram illustrates a proposed design for varying the position of a large mass over a minute range with great accuracy. Draw an equivalent linear model of this system and find the open-loop and closed-loop transfer functions. You may assume that ω_0 and the natural frequencies of the electrical system from input through amplifier are quite high compared with the natural frequencies of the driving coil and mechanical system. Discuss any other assumptions you make in order to linearize the system. Locate the poles of the closed-loop transfer function and discuss their behavior as the gain A is varied. Discuss the response of the system to a step-function input. Discuss the system behavior if the control capacitor is made to vary sinusoidally about a constant value $C_1 = C_0(1 + a \sin \omega_c t)$, with $\omega_c \ll \omega_0$.

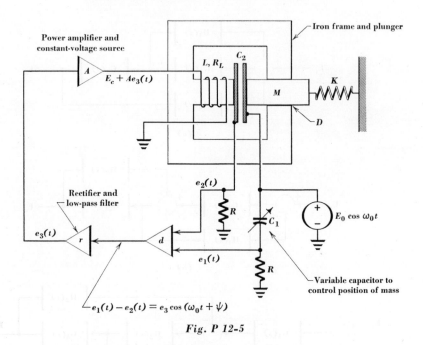

Power amplifier and
constant-voltage source

A

$E_c + Ae_3(t)$

L, R_L

C_2

Iron frame and plunger

M

K

D

$e_2(t)$

Rectifier and
low-pass filter

$e_3(t)$

r

d

R

C_1

$+ \atop -$

$E_0 \cos \omega_0 t$

$e_1(t)$

R

Variable capacitor to
control position of mass

$-e_1(t) - e_2(t) = e_3 \cos (\omega_0 t + \psi)$

Fig. P 12-5

12-2 STABILITY OF FEEDBACK SYSTEMS

As was mentioned earlier, feedback systems may become unstable in certain circumstances. A very brief reason for this possibility can be given before we begin a quantitative analysis. An energy source exists somewhere within each of the feedback systems we are investigating. The output from this energy source is controlled by the input variable. But since part of the output is fed back to the input, the energy source influences itself. Consequently, it is possible for the feedback to be such that the output causes the energy source to increase its output. This larger output is fed back and causes an even larger output. The result is an exponential growth of the output until failure of the system or some change in the system parameters occurs.

A REVIEW OF THE NATURAL RESPONSES OF LINEAR SYSTEMS It will be helpful to spend a little time reviewing some of the concepts introduced in the early chapters of this text. Consider a simple linear electrical or mechanical system, excited by a driving function $y(t)$, which has a response satisfying a linear differential equation of the following form:

$$a \frac{d^2x}{dt^2} + b \frac{dx}{dt} + cx = y(t) \qquad (12\text{-}21)$$

The solution of this equation will consist of two parts: the homogeneous, or natural, solution and the particular, or forced, solution. The natural solution is obtained by setting $y(t)$ equal to zero. This solution will be the complete solution if there is no driving function and will be part of the total solution when there is a driving function.

The natural solution of Eq. (12-21) can be found by assuming that $x(t)$ is of the form e^{st}. Thus the homogeneous form of Eq. (12-21) becomes

$$(as^2 + bs + c)e^{st} = 0 \tag{12-22}$$

The values of s which satisfy this equation are the roots of the polynomial $as^2 + bs + c$. Each root may take one of three forms—purely real, purely imaginary, or complex:

$$s_1 = \sigma_1 \quad \text{or} \quad j\omega_1 \quad \text{or} \quad \sigma_1 + j\omega_1 \tag{12-23}$$

Consequently, the natural response of the system will be composed of terms of the form $e^{(\sigma_1 + j\omega_1)t}$.

In all the passive systems which we investigated, the real part of each root, that is, $\sigma_1, \sigma_2, \sigma_3, \ldots$, was negative. This indicated, of course, that each of the natural-response terms was a decaying exponential and would eventually die out. That this must be true for all passive networks can be argued on a purely physical basis. Since the natural response occurs with no driving function, and hence is due to a finite amount of stored energy, it follows that it must decay because of the energy dissipation which is always present in physical systems.

There is nothing in the mathematics of the polynomial $as^2 + bs + c$ which restricts its roots to the left half of the s plane.† This restriction is purely physical, being based upon the passivity of the system. If the system contains a source of energy, then we may no longer assume that the natural responses must die out. It is possible that one of the response terms of the form $e^{(\sigma_1 + j\omega_1)t}$ will have a positive σ_1. This would mean that this particular response term is growing exponentially, rather than decaying. When one or more of the natural-response terms is a growing exponential, the system is said to be unstable.

TRANSFER FUNCTIONS AND INSTABILITY We found earlier that when linear systems become more complex, it is convenient to carry out the analysis in the s domain. Thus, sets of linear differential equations become sets of algebraic equations, and their solutions take on the following form in the s domain:

$$\mathbf{E}_o(s) = \mathbf{T}(s)\mathbf{E}_i(s) \tag{12-24a}$$

$$\mathbf{T}(s) = \frac{P(s)}{Q(s)} = \frac{b_m s^m + b_{m-1} s^{m-1} + \cdots + b_1 s + b_0}{a_n s^n + a_{n-1} s^{n-1} + \cdots + a_1 s + a_0} \tag{12-24b}$$

† If a, b, and c are not all of the same sign, at least one root will be in the right half plane. Higher-degree polynomials may have right-half-plane roots even if the coefficients are all of the same sign.

As was pointed out in Sec. 7-3, the roots of the denominator polynomial $Q(s)$ determine the natural-response terms. Thus, with an input $\mathbf{E}_i(s)$ which is an impulse† $[\mathbf{E}_i(s) = 1]$, the system response will be

$$e(t) = c_1 e^{s_1 t} + c_2 e^{s_2 t} + c_3 e^{s_3 t} + \cdots \qquad (12\text{-}25)$$

where $s_1, s_2, s_3, \ldots$ are the roots of $Q(s)$. If any of the roots of $Q(s)$ [the poles of $\mathbf{T}(s)$] have positive real parts, then the corresponding natural-response term will be a growing exponential, and the system will be unstable.

DETERMINATION OF TRANSFER-FUNCTION POLE POSITIONS   In the analysis and design of control systems (and other feedback systems), it is of vital importance to determine whether the system can be unstable and, if so, under what conditions. From the discussion above, we see that the investigation of stability corresponds to determining where the transfer-function poles are located and how their positions are affected by variation in the system parameters.

Let us concentrate our attention on the transfer function given in Eq. (12-20). The techniques applied to this transfer function may be extended readily to more complex transfer functions. For lumped-parameter systems, the transfer functions $\mathbf{G}(s)$ and $\mathbf{H}(s)$ will be ratios of polynomials in s. Consequently, the closed-loop transfer function may be written as follows:

$$\mathbf{T}(s) = \frac{\mathbf{E}_o(s)}{\mathbf{E}_i(s)} = \frac{\mathbf{G}(s)}{1 + \mathbf{G}(s)\mathbf{H}(s)} = B \frac{P_1/Q_1}{1 + A \dfrac{P_1 P_2}{Q_1 Q_2}} \qquad (12\text{-}26)$$

where P_1, Q_1, P_2, and Q_2 are polynomials in s. The constants A and B are extracted so that the coefficient of the highest power of s in each polynomial is unity. We shall call A the *gain*.

We wish to locate the poles of the transfer function given by Eq. (12-26). At first glance it appears that the poles of $\mathbf{T}(s)$ may arise in two ways: poles of P_1/Q_1 due to zeros of Q_1 and poles due to zeros of $1 + A \dfrac{P_1 P_2}{Q_1 Q_2}$. More careful inspection shows that the poles of P_1/Q_1 in the numerator are canceled by the poles of the P_1/Q_1 in the denominator.‡ Therefore, $\mathbf{T}(s)$ has poles where and only where

$$1 + A \frac{P_1 P_2}{Q_1 Q_2} = 0 \qquad (12\text{-}27)$$

---

† As will be recalled from Sec. 9-3, initial stored energy can be treated as an appropriate impulse applied at $t = 0$.

‡ This can be demonstrated by clearing $\mathbf{T}(s)$ of fractions to yield

$$\mathbf{T}(s) = \frac{P_1 Q_2}{Q_1 Q_2 + A P_1 P_2}$$

Note that if P_2 has a root at the same point as Q_1, this particular pole

In determining the stability of the system, the basic question to be answered is the following: Is Eq. (12-27) satisfied for some value of s in the right half plane? If so, the system is unstable. The answer to the preceding question may be determined in the following ways.

FINDING THE ROOTS OF THE DENOMINATOR POLYNOMIAL If we clear Eq. (12-27) of fractions, we see that it is equivalent to

$$Q_1Q_2 + AP_1P_2 = 0 \qquad (12\text{-}28)$$

Standard techniques may be used to find the roots of the polynomial $Q_1Q_2 + AP_1P_2$.† However, root finding is quite tedious for polynomials of high degree and must be repeated over and over again when we seek the transfer-function pole movements due to parameter variation.

THE ROUTH TEST‡ The Routh test, which is a straightforward algebraic method of determining whether a polynomial has roots in the right half plane, may be employed. Although this method gives the number of roots with positive real parts, it does not locate them other than in the right- or left-hand plane. Consequently, it fails to indicate the degree of stability or instability. The Routh test does not lend itself to determining the pole movements as parameters are varied.

THE NYQUIST STABILITY CRITERION§ The Nyquist method makes use of the amplitude and phase plots (vs. frequency) of the open-loop transfer function $\mathbf{G}(s)\mathbf{H}(s)$. It indicates graphically the number of right-half-plane poles and the effect of gain on stability, but it does not determine the exact locations of the poles.

THE ROOT-LOCUS METHOD The root-locus technique, which was introduced in Sec. 5-5, locates the transfer-function poles as system parameters are varied. It therefore gives considerably more information than the methods described above. The basic principles of the root-locus method, as applied to Eq. (12-26), can be explained as follows. Consider this rearrangement of Eq. (12-27):

$$\frac{1}{A}\,\mathbf{G}(s)\mathbf{H}(s) = \frac{P_1P_2}{Q_1Q_2} = -\frac{1}{A} = \frac{1}{A}\,\angle\,180° \qquad (12\text{-}29)$$

---

of P_1/Q_1 will not be canceled. This does not create a special problem, but one should be aware of the fact if this occurs. The uncanceled poles will not vary in position with changes in the gain.

† For a good discussion of root-finding methods, see David F. Tuttle, Jr., "Network Synthesis," vol. 1, appendix A, John Wiley & Sons, Inc., New York, 1958.

‡ J. J. D'Azzo and C. H. Houpis, "Feedback Control System Analysis and Synthesis," sec. 4-10, McGraw-Hill Book Company, Inc., New York, 1960.

§ *Ibid.*, chap. 9.

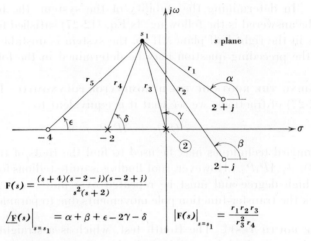

$$F(s) = \frac{(s+4)(s-2-j)(s-2+j)}{s^2(s+2)}$$

$$\left. \underline{/F(s)} \right|_{s=s_1} = \alpha + \beta + \epsilon - 2\gamma - \delta \qquad \left. |F(s)| \right|_{s=s_1} = \frac{r_1 r_2 r_3}{r_3^2 r_4}$$

Fig. 12-8. A graphical technique for finding the magnitude and phase of a function $F(s)$ *at a particular point* s_1 *in the* s *plane.*

The left-hand side of Eq. (12-29) is a function of s and has a magnitude and phase for every point in the s plane. In order to satisfy the equation, this phase must be 180° or an odd multiple of 180°. Without too much difficulty we can construct the curves in the s plane upon which $P_1 P_2 / Q_1 Q_2$ has a phase angle of 180°. Figure 12-8 illustrates the graphical method of finding the phase angle of a function at a particular point in the s plane. Once these curves are established, it is a simple matter to find what value of A corresponds to any point on the curve.

A PARTICULAR EXAMPLE   Let us find the locations of the poles for the two systems shown in Fig. 12-9 and their motion as A is varied. For both of these systems, Eq. (12-29) becomes

$$\frac{1}{A} G(s)H(s) = \frac{1}{s(s+1)(s+2)} = \frac{1}{A} \angle 180° \qquad (12\text{-}30)$$

The poles of the function above are plotted in Fig. 12-10, and from these the contours of 180° phase angles are plotted. The reciprocal of

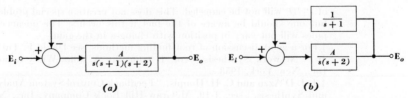

Fig. 12-9. Two feedback systems. The closed-loop transfer functions for these two examples have the same pole positions but different zeros.

the magnitude of the function along these lines is equal to A. Several values of A are indicated in the figure.

The root-locus plot of Fig. 12-10 indicates that the two control systems are stable for $A < 6$ and are unstable for $A > 6$. From this figure we can, without computation, make a reasonable estimate of the transient and frequency response of the system for any value of A in the stable region. To do this, we must take account of any zeros that are in the closed-loop transfer function. For the system of Fig. 12-9a there are no zeros in the finite s plane. The system of Fig. 12-9b has one zero at $s = -1$.

Before going on to other topics, a few comments are in order concerning the construction of the root-locus plot of Fig. 12-10. The 60° asymptotes occur because, for large s, the angle contributed by each pole will be the same. Since there are three poles and the total angle must be 180°, the angle of each must approach 60°. If there were two poles or three poles and a zero, the asymptotes would be at $\pm 90°$. Rules can be derived for finding the intersection of the asymptotes with the real axis, the position of the breakaway points (where the loci leave the axis), the intersection of the loci with the imaginary axis, the

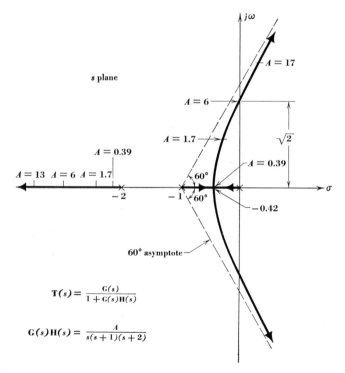

Fig. 12-10. *A root-locus plot showing the contours on which the poles of the closed-loop transfer function move as* A *is varied. The transfer function corresponds to the two systems shown in Fig. 12-9.*

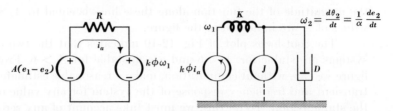

Fig. 12-11. A linear model for the open-loop condition of the control system shown in Fig. 12-2. The moment of inertia of the motor is neglected. The drive-shaft compliance is K.

angles at which the loci leave and arrive at the open-loop poles and zeros, and other properties helpful in root-locus construction.†

AN ELECTROMECHANICAL EXAMPLE To illustrate how we can obtain a system like the one shown in Fig. 12-9a, let us return to the electro-mechanical positioning device of Fig. 12-2. For this example, we shall assume that the shaft between motor and mass has considerable torsional compliance. With the further assumption that the moment of inertia of the motor rotor is negligible,‡ the electromechanical model for finding the open-loop transfer function is as shown in Fig. 12-11.

The differential equations for this system are

$$Ri_a + k\Phi\omega_1 = A(e_1 - e_2)$$

$$\frac{1}{K}\int (\omega_1 - \omega_2)\, dt = k\Phi i_a \qquad (12\text{-}31)$$

$$J\frac{d\omega_2}{dt} + D\omega_2 + \frac{1}{K}\int (\omega_2 - \omega_1)\, dt = 0$$

Since

$$\omega_2 = \frac{1}{\alpha}\frac{de_2}{dt}$$

then

$$\omega_2(s) = \frac{1}{\alpha} sE_2(s)$$

and the s-domain representations of Eqs. (12-31) are, in matrix form,

$$\begin{bmatrix} 0 & R & k\Phi \\ \dfrac{-1}{\alpha K} & -k\Phi & \dfrac{1}{sK} \\ \dfrac{s}{\alpha}\left(sJ + D + \dfrac{1}{sK}\right) & 0 & \dfrac{-1}{sK} \end{bmatrix} \times \begin{bmatrix} \mathbf{E}_2(s) \\ \mathbf{I}_a(s) \\ \omega_1(s) \end{bmatrix} = \begin{bmatrix} A[\mathbf{E}_1(s) - \mathbf{E}_2(s)] \\ 0 \\ 0 \end{bmatrix}$$

$$(12\text{-}32)$$

† Most texts on servomechanisms contain a detailed list of these rules. See, for example, *ibid.*, sec. 7-8.

‡ It must be admitted that this is an unrealistic assumption, for it is improbable that such a system would have significant torsional compliance and yet have a negligible rotor moment of inertia. We have assumed a negligible moment of inertia in order to simplify our analysis. Inclusion of the moment of inertia would not change the fact that such a system can become unstable.

It follows that

$$G(s) = \frac{E_2(s)}{E_1(s) - E_2(s)} = \frac{A\alpha/JKk\Phi}{s\left[s^2 + s\left(\dfrac{D}{J} + \dfrac{R}{Kk^2\Phi^2}\right) + \dfrac{DR + k^2\Phi^2}{JKk^2\Phi^2}\right]}$$

$$(12\text{-}33)$$

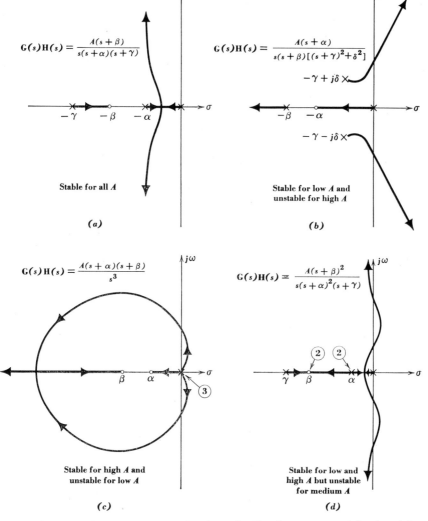

$$G(s)H(s) = \frac{A(s+\beta)}{s(s+\alpha)(s+\gamma)}$$

Stable for all A

(a)

$$G(s)H(s) = \frac{A(s+\alpha)}{s(s+\beta)[(s+\gamma)^2 + \delta^2]}$$

$-\gamma + j\delta$

$-\gamma - j\delta$

Stable for low A and
unstable for high A

(b)

$$G(s)H(s) = \frac{A(s+\alpha)(s+\beta)}{s^3}$$

Stable for high A and
unstable for low A

(c)

$$G(s)H(s) = \frac{A(s+\beta)^2}{s(s+\alpha)^2(s+\gamma)}$$

Stable for low and
high A but unstable
for medium A

(d)

Fig. 12-12. Root-locus diagrams for four feedback systems with closed-loop transfer functions $T(s) = G(s)/[1 + G(s)H(s)]$. The curves show the motion of the closed-loop poles as A increases from zero to infinity.

Thus we see that $\mathbf{G}(s)$ for this system is of the form

$$\mathbf{G}(s) = \frac{B}{s(s + \alpha)(s + \beta)} \tag{12-34}$$

Consequently, the pole behavior of the closed-loop transfer function will be similar to that shown in Fig. 12-10. (Note that three poles on the negative real axis will give the same general type of loci as Fig. 12-10, irrespective of their exact positions on that axis.)

CONCLUDING REMARKS   If the transfer function of a system has all its poles in the left half of the s plane, the system is stable. If one or more of the poles move into the right half plane, the system becomes unstable. Consequently, an analytic investigation of the stability of a system means a determination of the pole positions of the transfer function. There are several methods of finding the pole positions, each with its advantages and disadvantages. We have chosen to illustrate the root-locus method since it tends to yield more information than do the other techniques.

The root-locus method involves plotting the loci of the roots of the denominator polynomial of the closed-loop transfer function. This is accomplished by plotting the loci of the points which correspond to a 180° phase angle of the open-loop transfer function $\mathbf{G}(s)\mathbf{H}(s)$. A typical root-locus plot is shown in Fig. 12-10. Some additional root-locus diagrams are given in Fig. 12-12.

PROBLEMS

12-6   For each of the feedback systems illustrated in the diagram:

(*a*) Make a root-locus diagram and indicate whether the system can be stable or unstable.

(*b*) Find the frequency and gain for the intersection of the loci with the imaginary axis.

(*c*) Indicate the positions of the zeros of the closed-loop transfer function.

12-7   Try to derive a set of rules which will be helpful in constructing root-locus diagrams. In particular, derive rules for the behavior of the loci when $s \to \infty$, for the intersection of these asymptotes with the real axis, for the position of the breakaway points, and for the angle of departure and arrival of loci at poles and zeros.

12-8   It is often necessary in various kinds of analyses to find the roots of a polynomial $P(s)$. There are standard iterative ways of finding the roots with any desired degree of accuracy. These methods are most successful and rapid when one starts with a reasonably close approximation to the roots. The root-locus technique can be used to obtain these first approximations. We wish to solve $P(s) = 0$. We can separate $P(s)$

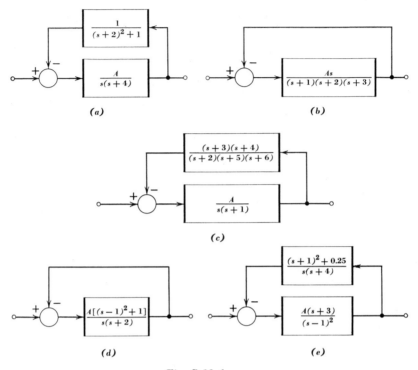

Fig. P 12-6

into two convenient parts (say the higher powers of s and the lower powers):

$$P(s) = p(s) + q(s) = 0$$

We then divide through by $q(s)$ to obtain $p(s)/q(s) + 1 = 0$. This can be solved graphically with a root-locus plot. Using this method, find the approximate roots of the following polynomials:

(a) $s^3 + 3s^2 + 7s + 5$
(b) $s^4 + 12s^3 + s^2 - 102s + 88$
(c) $s^5 + s^4 + 3s^3 + 3s^2 - 4s - 4$
(d) $s^5 - s^3 - 4s^2 - 2s - 4$

12-9   The system illustrated consists of a feedback system within a feedback system. Draw a root-locus diagram for the inner system. Indi-

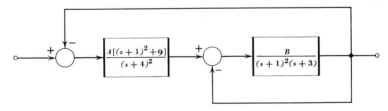

Fig. P 12-9

cate the pole positions for three or four values of B. For each of the values of B, draw the root-locus diagram for the complete system.

12-10 The following rule is often stated concerning the stability of a feedback system: If the open-loop steady-state gain [including the feedback path, that is, $|\mathbf{G}(j\omega)\mathbf{H}(j\omega)|$] is greater than unity when the feedback is in phase [that is, $\angle \mathbf{G}(j\omega)\mathbf{H}(j\omega) = 180°$], then the system will be unstable when the feedback path is closed. This rule is usually true, and it is frequently helpful, since the steady-state frequency response of the open-loop system can quite often be easily measured. Discuss the relationship of this rule to the root-locus method (use Fig. 12-10). Will the rule apply to the systems of Fig. 12-12c and d? Explain.

12-3 FEEDBACK AMPLIFIERS AND OSCILLATORS

Feedback is quite often incorporated into the design of electronic circuits.† In this section we shall discuss some of the reasons for doing this. The analysis technique for electronic devices with feedback is essentially identical to the technique for control systems. However, the idealized type of system—with perfect adding, differencing, and isolation between transfer-function blocks—cannot always be assumed, as has been done heretofore.

THE OPERATIONAL AMPLIFIER WITH FEEDBACK Analogue computers and similar devices require a set of basic electronic units which serve the functions illustrated in Fig. 12-13. With these units, each of which corresponds to a linear operation, it is possible to solve linear differential equations. (Units representing nonlinear operations would extend the applicability to nonlinear differential equations.) A block diagram of an analogue-computer arrangement for solving a differential equa-

† It is not unusual to have unwanted feedback in electronic circuits. This is usually due to stray inductive and capacitive coupling or coupling through a common source, such as a power supply.

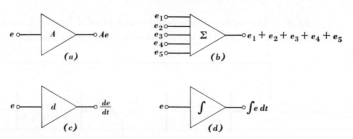

Fig. 12-13. Four basic units, or building blocks, for use in an analogue computer. (a) Amplifier, multiplication by a constant; (b) adder; (c) differentiator; (d) integrator.

Differential equation to be solved, $\dfrac{d^2x}{dt^2} + 4\dfrac{dx}{dt} - 3x = y(t)$

First step, $\dfrac{d^2x}{dt^2} = y(t) - 4\dfrac{dx}{dt} + 3x$

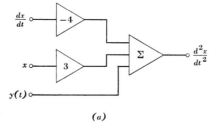

(a)

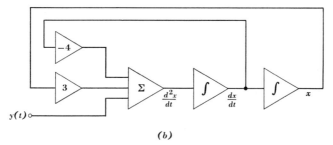

(b)

Fig. 12-14. Combination of the basic units of Fig. 12-13 for machine solution of a differential equation.

tion is shown in Fig. 12-14. By the proper utilization of feedback, the basic building blocks of Fig. 12-13 can be constructed.

Figure 12-15*a* illustrates a model which we can use to represent a large variety of vacuum-tube or transistor amplifier circuits. The parameter μ is usually very large—10^4 to 10^7. Using this model, we wish to design the basic units of Fig. 12-13. An input and a feedback resistor have been added to the amplifier model in Fig. 12-15*b*. With this arrangement of feedback, the voltage transfer function is found

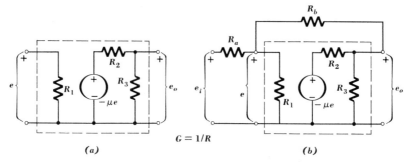

$G = 1/R$

(a)   (b)

Fig. 12-15. (a) The equivalent circuit for an electronic amplifier; (b) the same amplifier with input and feedback resistors added.

as follows. Writing node equations for the two unknown node voltages (we assume that a known voltage e_i is applied) produces the expressions

$$(G_1 + G_a + G_b)e - G_3 e_o = G_a e_i$$
$$(\mu G_2 - G_b)e + (G_2 + G_3 + G_b)e_o = 0 \qquad \text{(12-35)}$$

The conductance parameters G are the reciprocals of the resistances. Solution of the above equations yields

$$\frac{e_o}{e_i} = \frac{-(G_a/G_b)}{\dfrac{(G_1 + G_a + G_b)(G_2 + G_3 + G_b)}{G_b(\mu G_2 - G_b)} + 1} \qquad \text{(12-36)}$$

All the conductances in the expression above will be small and of approximately the same magnitude, 10^{-4} to 10^{-6}. Consequently, the fraction term in the denominator will be small compared with unity (because of the large μ). It is therefore permissible to replace Eq. (12-36) with the following simplified form:

$$\frac{e_o}{e_i} = \frac{-G_a}{G_b} = -\frac{R_b}{R_a} \qquad \text{(12-37)}$$

The results expressed in Eq. (12-37) are very important. The ratio of the input and output voltages is dependent only upon the ratio of the input to the feedback resistors. This is true as long as μ is very large. R_1, R_2, R_3, and μ can all vary over reasonably wide ranges without affecting the ratio of e_o to e_i.

From the derivation above, we see that the feedback arrangement of Fig. 12-15b produces a unit which satisfies the requirements of the basic amplifier unit of Fig. 12-13a. The amplification A is equal to $-(R_b/R_a)$. If a positive A is required, a cascade of two units will be necessary.

AN INTEGRATOR UNIT It is not difficult to see that in the preceding example, if we assume no appreciable loading of the output, the amplifier of Fig. 12-15a can be approximated by the simple amplifier block shown in Fig. 12-16a. (The value of μ in the two cases will be slightly different.) Assuming that this simplification continues to hold true, let us replace the feedback resistor of Fig. 12-15b with a capacitor. Writing the node equation for the node with voltage e and assuming

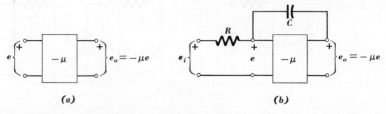

(a)   (b)

Fig. 12-16. (a) *A model of a basic amplifier with gain* $-\mu$; (b) *the amplifier with an input resistor and a feedback capacitor added.*

that the amplifier input resistance is still R_1, as per Fig. 12-15a, we obtain

$$\frac{e - e_i}{R} + \frac{e}{R_1} + C\frac{d}{dt}(e - e_o) = 0 \qquad (12\text{-}38)$$

Noting that $e_o = -\mu e$, we can modify Eq. (12-38) so that it yields

$$\frac{RC(1 + \mu)}{\mu}\frac{de_o}{dt} + \frac{R + R_1}{R_1\mu}e_o = -e_i \qquad (12\text{-}39)$$

With μ large and $t < RC\mu$ (see Prob. 12-13), Eq. (12-39) may be approximated by

$$RC\frac{de_o}{dt} = -e_i \qquad (12\text{-}40)$$

Hence

$$e_o = -\frac{1}{RC}\int e_i\,dt \qquad (12\text{-}41)$$

Thus, we see that the circuit of Fig. 12-16b acts as an integrator. With $RC = 1$, it may be used as the basic integrator unit of Fig. 12-13d. The other basic units of Fig. 12-13 are discussed in the problems.

FEEDBACK AMPLIFIERS In addition to the computer applications discussed above, feedback is often utilized in amplifiers whose purpose is simply to amplify. Some, but not all, of the reasons for employing feedback are discussed in the following paragraphs.

Feedback is used to *stabilize* unstable amplifiers. In Sec. 12-2 it was shown that feedback can cause instability. It is not difficult to extend the results of that section to show how feedback can make an unstable system stable. For example, suppose an electronic amplifier or a control system has the open-loop transfer-function pole-zero plot shown in Fig. 12-17a. This unstable state could be the result of some

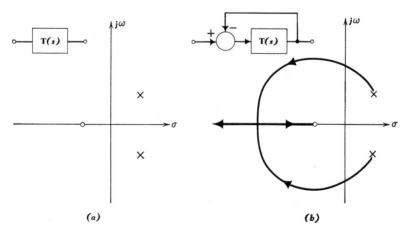

(a)   *(b)*

Fig. 12-17. *(a) The positions of the poles and zero of the open-loop transfer function of an unstable amplifier; (b) the root-locus diagram for the amplifier, showing that it can become stable upon the addition of the feedback loop.*

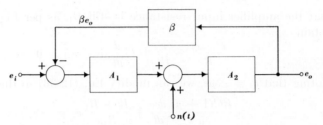

Fig. 12-18. A feedback amplifier with noise and distortion added after the first stages of amplification.

unavoidable internal feedback loop. Utilizing root-locus methods, we see from Fig. 12-17b that by closing the over-all feedback loop, the system can be made stable as the right-half-plane poles move into the stable region.

Feedback is used to *flatten and extend the frequency response* of amplifiers. It is clear from the root-locus plots of Figs. 12-10 and 12-12 that the addition of feedback shifts the transfer-function pole positions. In many cases this shift extends and flattens the frequency response of the amplifier (see Fig. 12-10 and Prob. 12-18).

Feedback is used to *decrease* the effects of *noise and distortion* in amplifiers. In many amplifiers—high-fidelity audio amplifiers, for example—noise and distortion are produced in the final, high-power stages. The addition of feedback will decrease these unwanted effects. Figure 12-18 illustrates a feedback amplifier in which the noise and distortion produced in the later stages are represented by the additive input† $n(t)$.

The output voltage is found in the following manner:

$$e_o = A_2[n(t) + A_1(e_i - \beta e_o)]$$
$$= \frac{A_1 A_2 e_i + A_2 n}{1 + A_1 A_2 \beta} \tag{12-42}$$

The output voltage may be separated into two parts: the desired signal component S_f and the undesired noise component N_f:

$$S_f = \frac{A_1 A_2 e_i}{1 + A_1 A_2 \beta} \qquad N_f = \frac{A_2 n}{1 + A_1 A_2 \beta} \tag{12-43}$$

The output signal-to-noise ratio is

$$\frac{S_f}{N_f} = \frac{A_1 e_i}{n} \tag{12-44}$$

† Distortion is a nonlinear, nonadditive process. However, as is demonstrated in Chap. 13, the distorted signal can be represented as a sum of signals. Thus, the model of Fig. 12-18 is a reasonable way of representing both additive noise and distortion. It should be emphasized that the distortion we are discussing here is not the distortion of signal shape due to the filtering action of a combination of linear elements.

Let us compare the result above with the signal-to-noise ratio that would be obtained from the same amplifier without the feedback loop. We see that, without feedback,

$$S_{wf} = A_1 A_2 e_i \qquad N_{wf} = A_2 n$$
$$\frac{S_{wf}}{N_{wf}} = \frac{A_1 e_i}{n} \tag{12-45}$$

At first glance, it would seem that feedback does not improve the situation at all. However, before making any rash judgments let us investigate further.

Suppose the amplifier must provide a certain amplification B. For example, B might equal the ratio of the voltage required to drive a loudspeaker to the signal voltage available from a record pickup. Furthermore, let A_2 be fixed by the requirements of the particular kind of final stage needed to drive the loudspeaker. Consequently, in the amplifier without feedback,

$$A_1 A_2 = B \qquad A_1 = \frac{B}{A_2}$$
$$\frac{S_{wf}}{N_{wf}} = \frac{B e_i}{A_2 n} \tag{12-46}$$

Thus, the signal-to-noise ratio without feedback depends upon B/A_2, which, according to our argument above, is fixed. In the feedback amplifier,

$$\frac{A_1 A_2}{1 + A_1 A_2 \beta} = B \tag{12-47}$$

Now we can let A_1 be very large, in which case β must, of course, be made equal to $1/B$. Now we see that the proper gain B is provided while A_1 is allowed to become very large, with the result that $S_f/N_f \rightarrow \infty$. This, of course, is the desired result.

There is one cautionary note which should be added at this point. We have seen in a number of examples in this chapter that an increase in open-loop gain will often result in instability of the closed-loop system. Since the open-loop gain A_1 is to be made very large in the amplifier above, the amplifier must be designed carefully to prevent instability. In the particular model above, we have treated the transfer functions as constants, with no poles or zeros. Consequently, this model will remain stable, regardless of the magnitude of A_1. An actual amplifier, however, will have some poles and zeros in its open-loop transfer function (though the model used above may be a good approximation to the actual amplifier over the frequency range of interest). Consequently, unless the poles and zeros are properly located, the actual amplifier may become unstable as A_1 is made large.

OSCILLATORS Several of the feedback systems discussed in Sec. 12-2 become unstable when the gain A is increased sufficiently. A typical example is shown in Fig. 12-10, where an open-loop gain greater than 6 produces instability. In each of these cases, if A is held at the proper value, a pair of poles will be positioned exactly on the $j\omega$ axis. When in this condition, the feedback system is neither strictly stable nor strictly unstable; it is an oscillator.

With a pair of poles on the imaginary axis at $\pm j\omega_0$, the system transfer function will have the following form:

$$\mathbf{T}(s) = \frac{P(s)}{(s^2 + \omega_0{}^2)Q(s)} \tag{12-48}$$

If all the other poles [roots of $Q(s)$] are in the left-hand plane, the impulse response of the system will be

$$e_0(t) = a \cos(\omega_0 t + \theta) + f(t) \tag{12-49}$$

The part of the response labeled $f(t)$ consists of functions which are all decaying exponentially. Thus, the output from the system, after sufficient time has elapsed for the transients to die out, will be a steady-state sinusoidal wave.

Oscillators are necessary parts of many electrical systems. Consequently, it behooves us to discuss some practicalities of producing a system for which Eqs. (12-48) and (12-49) apply. It is not at all difficult to design a feedback system which will become unstable and which hence could serve as an oscillator. Figure 12-19 illustrates an oscillator

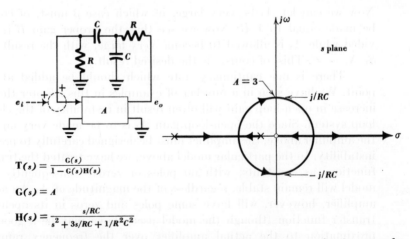

$$\mathbf{T}(s) = \frac{G(s)}{1 - G(s)H(s)}$$

$$G(s) = A$$

$$H(s) = \frac{s/RC}{s^2 + 3s/RC + 1/R^2C^2}$$

Fig. 12-19. An oscillator circuit and the root-locus diagram for its transfer-function poles. If the gain A is 3, the system will oscillate with a frequency of $1/2\pi RC$ cps.

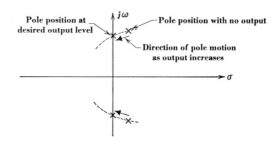

Fig. 12-20. Variation in pole positions as the output level changes. The pole movement is caused by a change in gain due to a nonlinear circuit element.

circuit with its root-locus diagram. Note that since a minus sign occurs between the 1 and the $\mathbf{G}(s)\mathbf{H}(s)$ term in the denominator of $\mathbf{T}(s)$, the root loci follow $0°$, $360°$, . . . phase contours.

The problem in oscillator design is to maintain the gain at the proper value. If it is too high, the oscillations will increase in amplitude, usually until a nonlinear operating region is reached. The output then is usually a highly distorted sine wave. If the gain is too low, the oscillations will decrease in magnitude and die out. A nonlinear element in the system can be employed to maintain the proper gain. If a nonlinear resistor is placed in the amplifier circuit, the amplifier gain will decrease as the output signal increases in magnitude. Thus, when the oscillator is first turned on, there will be no output, and the poles will be in the right half plane. Any small disturbance, such as noise, will start a growing transient. As the output increases to the desired magnitude, the gain will decrease to the point where the poles are on the $j\omega$ axis and the proper magnitude of oscillations is just maintained. Figure 12-20 illustrates this process.

SUMMARY   Feedback is often used in electrical circuits in order to achieve various objectives. The techniques of analysis are not altered by the addition of feedback. However, in certain circuits, simplifying approximations can often be made which will greatly decrease the complexity of analysis. This is true for the analogue-computer circuits, in which considerable simplification is possible because of the very high open-loop gain. As in the case of other two-port systems, an understanding of the characteristics of feedback systems is greatly aided by a knowledge of the positions of the poles and zeros of the transfer functions.

PROBLEMS

12-11   Using the four units of Fig. 12-13, draw block diagrams of analogue-computer arrangements which will yield solutions of the following differential equations:

(a) $\dfrac{d^3x}{dt^3} - 4\dfrac{d^2x}{dt} + 10x = 100$

(b) $\dfrac{dx}{dt} - 2x + \dfrac{dy}{dt} = 0$

$4x + \dfrac{dy}{dt} + 2y = f(t)$

(c) $\dfrac{d^2x}{dt^2} + 4\dfrac{dx}{dt} - x + 2\dfrac{d^2y}{dt^2} - 10y = 20$

$2\dfrac{d^3x}{dt^3} - \dfrac{dx}{dt} + \dfrac{d^3y}{dt^3} + \dfrac{d^2y}{dt} + y = 0$

12-12 Assume these values for the parameters of the circuit of Fig. 12-15b: $R_a = R_b = R_1 = 10^6$ ohms, $R_2 = R_3 = 10^4$ ohms, $\mu = 10^6$. Find the percentage error due to approximating Eq. (12-36) with Eq. (12-37). With a voltage source e_i applied at the input, what is the Thévenin equivalent circuit for Fig. 12-15b as seen at the output terminals? In computing the impedance looking in at the output terminals, the internal source must not be shorted, since it is not an independent source.

12-13 Show that, with the parameter values of Prob. 12-12 and C substituted for R_b, it is permissible to replace Fig. 12-15b by Fig. 12-16b. With $R = 10^6$ ohms, $C = 10^{-6}$ farad, and a step voltage applied to the input terminals of Fig. 12-16b, compute and plot the percentage error between e_o and $-\int e_i\,dt$ as a function of time.

12-14 Compute the output voltages of the illustrated circuits in terms of their input voltages. Assume that μ is very large, say 10^6.

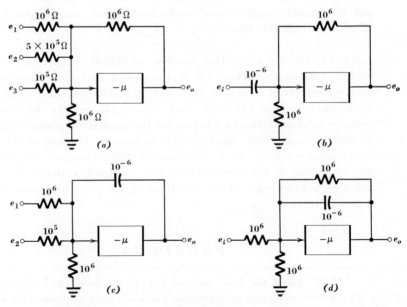

Fig. P 12-14

12-15 Find the closed-loop transfer function for the feedback amplifier shown. Find the pole locations of this transfer function for $A = -1, 0, 1,$ 2, 3, 4, and sketch the loci in the s plane. Sketch the expected unit-impulse responses for each of the values of A given above.

Fig. P 12-15

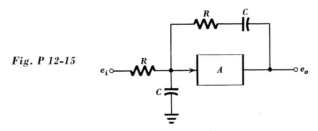

12-16 The network shown is claimed to be an adequate representation of the small-signal behavior of a simple transistor amplifier stage. The following parameter values may be assumed as typical: R (base lead resistance) = 40 ohms, R_b (base resistance) = 1,500 ohms, R (load resistance) = 1,000 ohms, C_c (collector capacitance) = 2×10^{-12} farad, C_e (emitter capacitance) = 2×10^{-10} farad, g_m (mutual conductance) = 4×10^{-2} mho. Find the transfer function and pole positions of this device. Estimate how long it will take for the natural-behavior terms in the unit-step response to die away to negligible amounts.

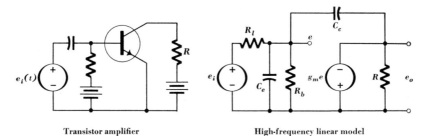

Transistor amplifier   High-frequency linear model

Fig. P 12-16

12-17 Suppose that the amplifier block labeled A in Fig. 12-19 can be

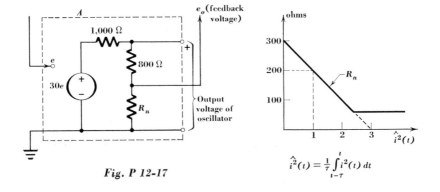

$$\hat{i^2}(t) = \frac{1}{\tau} \int_{t-\tau}^{t} i^2(t)\, dt$$

Fig. P 12-17

represented by the model shown in the diagram. The nonlinear resistor R_n has the characteristics shown. The value of its resistance depends upon the square of the current through it averaged over the previous τ sec. If R and C of Fig. 12-19 are such that $RC = 10^{-4}$ and the averaging time τ is 10^{-2} sec:

(a) Find the pole positions when the feedback loop is first closed.

(b) Find the signal output a long time after the feedback loop is closed.

(c) Assuming a 1-μv noise impulse applied at the instant the loop is closed, determine how long it will take for the oscillator output to reach its final value. Make any simplifying approximations that you find necessary.

12-18 In order to see how feedback can extend the frequency response of an amplifier, let us consider the resistance-capacitance-coupled amplifier which was discussed in Sec. 7-5. A single stage of such an amplifier has a transfer function with pole-zero locations as shown in the figure. A negative feedback path $(-\beta)$ is added so that the closed-loop transfer function is

$$T(s) = \frac{G(s)}{1 + \beta G(s)}$$

(a) Plot the root-locus diagram for this transfer function for the case $\alpha = 1,\ \gamma = 2$.

(b) Plot $|T(s)|_{s=j\omega}$ versus ω for the cases $\beta A = 0, 2, 10$ (fixed A, variable β, α and γ as in part a).

(c) Consider the cascade of two identical stages of amplification. In this case,

$$G(s) = \frac{As^2}{(s + \alpha)^2(s + \gamma)^2}$$

Repeat parts a and b for this situation.

(d) Repeat parts a and b for feedback around three identical stages. Discuss the stability of this system. At what frequencies and for what values of $A\beta$ might this system oscillate? For what value of $A\beta$ does this system give the flattest frequency response?

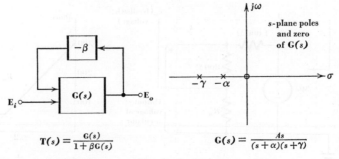

$$T(s) = \frac{G(s)}{1 + \beta G(s)} \qquad\qquad G(s) = \frac{As}{(s+\alpha)(s+\gamma)}$$

Fig. P 12-18

fourier analysis

In this text we are concerned with the analysis of linear mechanical and electrical systems—or, more accurately, with the analysis of linear models of such systems. A somewhat oversimplified and restricted definition of analysis, as used above, is as follows: Analysis is the determination of the response of a particular network when the excitation is given. In other words, it is the determination of a set of linear differential equations and their solution. Our introduction to the analysis we speak of is essentially complete. That is, we have introduced all the basic techniques which are necessary in order to find the response to any determinate† excitation.

The purpose of this chapter is not so much to introduce new or different techniques of analysis as to approach from a different direction the methods already developed. In particular, we wish to carry out a development which will lead us along a different path to the s-domain techniques introduced in Chap. 7. This path starts with the Fourier series, leads to the Fourier transform, and thence to the Laplace transform. We lump these three topics into a single term—Fourier analysis.

The path to be followed in this chapter differs in a number of aspects from that followed in the first seven chapters. It will be at a higher, more abstract level, which is natural, considering that it benefits from the foundation laid in all the preceding chapters. The approach we shall take will be more purely mathematical than that followed in the first seven chapters, in which considerable physical insight was applied. It is to be hoped that the material in this chapter will aid in developing a deeper understanding of the contents of the first seven

---

† A nondeterminate, or random, excitation is a function which cannot be expressed explicitly. That is, it is an excitation which can be expressed only in terms of probabilities and statistics. Network analysis with random excitations is beyond the scope of this text. It can be said, however, that the techniques applicable to random excitations are based to a large extent on the methods introduced in this text.

chapters—and of all the others, for that matter. Similarly, the investigation we begin here should be greatly enhanced by the knowledge gained from the rest of the book.

Fourier analysis is a very broad subject, and we can only hope to introduce some of its simpler aspects in this chapter. We shall begin with the study of Fourier series.

13-1 FOURIER SERIES

Let us introduce the subject of Fourier series through an example. Suppose that the voltage applied to the linear passive network in Fig. 13-1a has the periodic waveform with period T illustrated in Fig. 13-1b. The steady-state current response $i(t)$ is to be found. We shall assume that the network is fairly complex, that is, that the two-port-network parameters are ratios of polynomials in s which are not of low degree.

One approach to the solution of this problem is to use impulse-response–impedance methods. In this case the s-domain representation of $e(t)$ is found by means of the technique developed in Sec. 7-7, then the s-domain representation of $i(t)$ is immediately computed, and finally the time-domain response is found through a partial-fraction expansion of $\mathbf{I}(s)$. Although requiring rather complex algebraic manipulations, this method is quite valid; indeed it is much the most practical method when the transient response is desired. However, for steady-state calculations, Fourier series methods offer distinct advantages. Perhaps their greatest advantage is that they provide an insight into the characteristics of linear systems under periodic excitation which is not given by s-domain techniques. In addition, the Fourier series techniques which we shall now investigate serve as a first step in our alternative development of the s-domain techniques. When this chapter

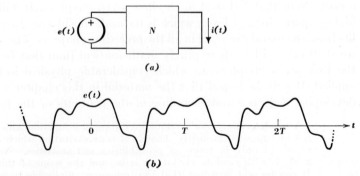

Fig. 13-1. (a) A linear network with a driving voltage which is periodic with period T; (b) the driving voltage e(t).

is completed, it will be clear that the Fourier series methods, although they may not appear so at first, are closely related to the *s*-domain techniques introduced in Chap. 7 (particularly those of Sec. 7-7 and Prob. 7-35).

Let us return to our example. We have decided to put aside temporarily the *s*-domain techniques of Sec. 7-7. We shall also discard the idea of writing differential equations and then solving them. (This method, though applicable, is quite involved, and it eventually reduces to the Fourier series method we are now developing.) What else might we try? If we knew no other methods and we were required to produce some sort of solution, a logical step would be to seek a solution by approximation. That is, we could try to obtain an approximation to the true solution of the circuit problem by using methods with which we were familiar.

Let us say, for example, that we choose an approximation for the excitation $e(t)$:

$$e_a(t) \cong e(t) \tag{13-1}$$

If $e_a(t)$ is a type of function which our techniques can handle, we shall be able to calculate the response $i_a(t)$ to the driving function $e_a(t)$. This response will be an approximation to the actual response:

$$i_a(t) \cong i(t) \tag{13-2}$$

Clearly, if $e_a(t)$ is a close approximation to the actual voltage $e(t)$, then the calculated response $i_a(t)$ will be a close approximation to the true response.

THE METHOD OF APPROXIMATION In choosing an approximation to the voltage $e(t)$, we must, of course, keep in mind that our choice of waveform is limited. We must choose an approximation for which we can readily calculate the circuit response. The obvious choices are constant d-c voltages or pure sine waves, since we can easily find the circuit responses to them. We have as yet no guarantee that one or a combination of these waveforms will give an adequate approximation to our original voltage. However, this is a plausible starting point.

Let us proceed by selecting first a very simple approximation, though possibly a poor one, and then repeatedly modifying it, with the eventual goal of arriving at a good approximation. The simplest possible approximation to $e(t)$ would be a constant, that is, a d-c voltage. Thus,

$$e_a(t) = c_0 \cong e(t) \tag{13-3}$$

The obvious choice for c_0 is the average value of our original waveform:

$$c_0 = \frac{1}{T} \int_0^T e(t) \, dt \tag{13-4}$$

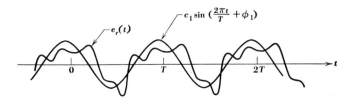

Fig. 13-2. *A sine wave of period T, with amplitude c_1 and phase angle $c\phi_1$, which approximates the remainder function $e_r(t)$.*

The response to the d-c voltage c_0 would be a d-c current i_0, which is the d-c component of the actual response $i(t)$:

$$i_0 = \frac{1}{T} \int_0^T i(t)\, dt \qquad (13\text{-}5)$$

Obviously, the constant term alone will not be a sufficiently close approximation to most periodic waveforms. That is to say, removal of the average component leaves a remainder term $e_r(t)$ which cannot be neglected.

$$e_r(t) = e(t) - c_0 \qquad (13\text{-}6)$$

The logical step at this point is to add a second function to c_0 to form a new approximation.† This second term will be an approximation to the remainder term $e_r(t)$:

$$e_a(t) = c_0 + e_1(t) \cong e(t) \qquad (13\text{-}7)$$
$$e_1(t) \cong e_r(t) \qquad (13\text{-}8)$$

We have used the simplest approximating function, a constant, in the first step. In this next step, let us employ another simple function, a pure sinusoid with the same period as the original waveform:

$$e_1(t) = c_1 \sin\left(\frac{2\pi t}{T} + \phi_1\right) \qquad (13\text{-}9)$$

We wish to adjust the amplitude and phase of this sinusoid so that it is as close an approximation to $e_r(t)$ as possible. Figure 13-2 illustrates a possible choice for c_1 and ϕ_1 which gives the appearance of a good fit. Although it is possible to obtain a reasonable approximation by adjusting the amplitude and phase "by eye," an analytic method of selecting c_1 and ϕ_1 is to be preferred.

MINIMUM-MEAN-SQUARED-ERROR APPROXIMATIONS There are a number of measures which could be used to judge the degree to which $e_1(t)$ approximates $e_r(t)$. We could adjust c_1 and ϕ_1 so that the maximum

† Adding new terms to improve the approximation is logical, since we are dealing with linear networks. Superposition applies, and the solution to a sum of excitations is the sum of the responses to each individual term of the excitation.

difference between $e_1(t)$ and $e_r(t)$ is minimized. That is,

$$\text{Minimize } [\max|e_r(t) - e_1(t)|] \tag{13-10}$$

or we could adjust c_1 and ϕ_1 to minimize the average of the magnitude of the difference:

$$\text{Minimize } \left[\frac{1}{T} \int_0^T |e_r(t) - e_1(t)| \, dt \right] \tag{13-11}$$

There are other measures as well, but the one which is most convenient mathematically is the average of the squared difference between $e_1(t)$ and $e_r(t)$. This measure, called the mean-squared error (mse), is expressed as follows:

$$\text{mse} = \frac{1}{T} \int_0^T [e_r(t) - e_1(t)]^2 \, dt \tag{13-12}$$

Let us now attempt to formulate a method of determining the values of the amplitude and phase of our approximation that will yield the minimum mean-squared error. The mathematical manipulations in the following development will be more tractable if we express $e_1(t)$ as a sum of sine and cosine terms:

$$e_1(t) = a_1 \cos \frac{2\pi t}{T} + b_1 \sin \frac{2\pi t}{T} \tag{13-13}$$

The amplitude and phase constants may be determined from the coefficients of the sine and cosine terms:

$$c_1 = \sqrt{a_1{}^2 + b_1{}^2} \qquad \phi_1 = \tan^{-1} \frac{a_1}{b_1}$$

$$a_1 = c_1 \sin \phi_1 \qquad b_1 = c_1 \cos \phi_1 \tag{13-14}$$

If the expression for $e_1(t)$ given by Eq. (13-13) is inserted into Eq. (13-12), we obtain

$$\text{mse} = \frac{1}{T} \int_0^T \left[e_r(t) - a_1 \cos \frac{2\pi t}{T} - b_1 \sin \frac{2\pi t}{T} \right]^2 dt \tag{13-15}$$

When the integrand is squared and the integration is carried out term by term, we obtain the following expression:

$$\text{mse} = \frac{1}{T} \left[\int_0^T e_r{}^2(t) \, dt - 2a_1 \int_0^T e_r(t) \cos \frac{2\pi t}{T} \, dt \right.$$

$$\left. - 2b_1 \int_0^T e_r(t) \sin \frac{2\pi t}{T} \, dt + \frac{a_1{}^2 T}{2} + \frac{b_1{}^2 T}{2} \right] \tag{13-16}$$

In order to simplify the expression above, let us utilize the following notation:

$$\alpha_1 = \int_0^T e_r(t) \cos \frac{2\pi t}{T} \, dt$$

$$\beta_1 = \int_0^T e_r(t) \sin \frac{2\pi t}{T} \, dt \tag{13-17}$$

Thus, Eq. (13-16) becomes

$$\text{mse} = \frac{1}{T}\left[\int_0^T e_r{}^2(t)\,dt - 2a_1\alpha_1 - 2b_1\beta_1 + \frac{a_1{}^2 T}{2} + \frac{b_1{}^2 T}{2}\right] \quad (13\text{-}18)$$

Now let us complete squares in the expression above by adding and subtracting $2\alpha_1{}^2/T$ and $2\beta_1{}^2/T$:

$$\text{mse} = \frac{1}{T}\left[\int_0^T e_r{}^2(t)\,dt - \frac{2\alpha_1{}^2}{T} - \frac{2\beta_1{}^2}{T} + \frac{2\alpha_1{}^2}{T} - 2\alpha_1 a_1 + \frac{a_1{}^2 T}{T} \right.$$
$$\left. + \frac{2\beta_1{}^2}{T} - 2b_1\beta_1 + \frac{b_1{}^2 T}{2}\right]$$
$$= \frac{1}{T}\left[\int_0^T e_r{}^2(t)\,dt - \frac{2\alpha_1{}^2}{T} - \frac{2\beta_1{}^2}{T} + \frac{T}{2}\left(\frac{2\alpha_1}{T} - a_1\right)^2 \right.$$
$$\left. + \frac{T}{2}\left(\frac{2\beta_1}{T} - b_1\right)^2\right] \quad (13\text{-}19)$$

We now wish to select a_1 and b_1 so that the mse is minimized. Noting first that the mse is never negative, we can see by inspection of Eq. (13-19) that the mse is minimized when

$$a_1 = \frac{2\alpha_1}{T} = \frac{2}{T}\int_0^T e_r(t)\cos\frac{2\pi t}{T}\,dt \quad (13\text{-}20)$$

$$b_1 = \frac{2\beta_1}{T} = \frac{2}{T}\int_0^T e_r(t)\sin\frac{2\pi t}{T}\,dt \quad (13\text{-}21)$$

Thus, we have arrived at a pair of analytic expressions which enable us to select the amplitude and phase of a sinusoid which is the best approximation, in the minimum-mse sense, to the waveform $e_r(t)$.

A reasonable question to ask at this point is the following: Although it has been shown that specifying a_1 and b_1 by Eqs. (13-20) and (13-21) yields the best approximation to $e_r(t)$, does this $e_1(t)$, when added to c_0, give the best approximation, in the minimum-mse sense, to $e(t)$? Rather than answer this question immediately, we shall proceed further in the approximation process, ultimately obtaining a result which will contain not only the answer but other useful information as well.

The next step in the approximation procedure is to add another term to our first two in order to get a closer fit to $e(t)$:

$$e_a(t) = c_0 + e_1(t) + e_2(t) \cong e(t) \quad (13\text{-}22)$$

The logical choice for $e_2(t)$ is another sine wave with the same periodicity as $e(t)$, that is, a wave having either the same frequency as $e(t)$ or a frequency which is an integer multiple of the basic frequency of $e(t)$. Having already used a sine wave with the same frequency, we now choose a sine wave with a frequency just twice the basic frequency. Thus,

$$e_2(t) = a_2\cos\left(2\,\frac{2\pi t}{T}\right) + b_2\sin\left(2\,\frac{2\pi t}{T}\right) \quad (13\text{-}23)$$

We could now repeat the process of minimizing the mse and obtaining expressions for a_2 and b_2. However, let us save a considerable amount of work by combining a number of steps in our approximation procedure. From the foregoing, we can see that the $(n + 1)$st approximation to our original waveform would have the following form:

$$e_a(t) = c_0 + e_1(t) + e_2(t) + e_3(t) + \cdots + e_n(t) \cong e(t) \quad (13\text{-}24)$$

$$e_k(t) = a_k \cos \frac{k2\pi t}{T} + b_k \sin \frac{k2\pi t}{T} \quad (13\text{-}25)$$

We can now minimize the mse and obtain expressions which will yield values for all the a_k and b_k:

$$\text{mse} = \frac{1}{T} \int_0^T [e(t) - e_a(t)]^2 \, dt = \frac{1}{T} \int_0^T \left[e(t) - c_0 - \sum_{k=1}^n e_k(t) \right]^2 dt$$

$$= \frac{1}{T} \int_0^T \left[e(t) - c_0 - \sum_{k=1}^n a_k \cos \frac{k2\pi t}{T} + b_k \sin \frac{k2\pi t}{T} \right]^2 dt \quad (13\text{-}26)$$

With the notation

$$\alpha_k = \int_0^T e(t) \cos \frac{k2\pi t}{T} \, dt \qquad k = 0, 1, 2, \ldots \quad (13\text{-}27)$$

$$\beta_k = \int_0^T e(t) \sin \frac{k2\pi t}{T} \, dt \qquad k = 1, 2, 3, \ldots \quad (13\text{-}28)$$

Eq. (13-26) becomes

$$\text{mse} = \frac{1}{T} \left[\int_0^T e^2(t) \, dt - 2c_0\alpha_0 - 2a_1\alpha_1 - 2b_1\beta_1 - 2a_2\alpha_2 - 2b_2\beta_2 \right.$$
$$- \cdots - 2a_n\alpha_n - 2b_n\beta_n + c_0{}^2 T + \frac{a_1{}^2 T}{2} + \frac{b_1{}^2 T}{2} + \frac{a_2{}^2 T}{2} + \frac{b_2{}^2 T}{2}$$
$$\left. + \cdots + \frac{a_n{}^2 T}{2} + \frac{b_n{}^2 T}{2} \right] \quad (13\text{-}29)$$

Now we add and subtract for each k, $2\alpha_k{}^2/T$, and $2\beta_k{}^2/T$ in order to complete squares. (For $k = 0$ we add and subtract $\alpha_0{}^2/T$.)

$$\text{mse} = \frac{1}{T} \left[\int_0^T e^2(t) \, dt - \frac{\alpha_0{}^2}{T} - \frac{2\alpha_1{}^2}{T} - \frac{2\beta_1{}^2}{T} - \frac{2\alpha_2{}^2}{T} - \frac{2\beta_2{}^2}{T} \right.$$
$$- \cdots - \frac{2\alpha_n{}^2}{T} - \frac{2\beta_n{}^2}{2} + T\left(\frac{\alpha_0}{T} - c_0\right)^2 + \frac{T}{2}\left(\frac{2\alpha_1}{T} - a_1\right)^2$$
$$+ \frac{T}{2}\left(\frac{2\beta_1}{T} - b_1\right)^2 + \frac{T}{2}\left(\frac{2\alpha_2}{T} - a_2\right)^2 + \frac{T}{2}\left(\frac{2\beta_2}{T} - b_2\right)^2$$
$$\left. + \cdots + \frac{T}{2}\left(\frac{2\alpha_n}{T} - a_n\right)^2 + \frac{T}{2}\left(\frac{2\beta_n}{T} - b_n\right)^2 \right] \quad (13\text{-}30)$$

The expression above will be minimized if we choose our constants as follows:

$$c_0 = \frac{\alpha_0}{T} = \frac{1}{T} \int_0^T e(t) \, dt \tag{13-31}$$

$$a_k = \frac{2\alpha_k}{T} = \frac{2}{T} \int_0^T e(t) \cos \frac{k2\pi t}{T} \, dt \tag{13-32}$$

$$b_k = \frac{2\beta_k}{T} = \frac{2}{T} \int_0^T e(t) \sin \frac{k2\pi t}{T} \, dt \tag{13-33}$$

To summarize the development above, we can make the following statement: When approximating a periodic waveform by a constant and a sum of sine waves,

$$e(t) \cong e_a(t) = c_0 + \sum_{k=1}^n a_k \cos \frac{k2\pi t}{T} + b_k \sin \frac{k2\pi t}{T} \tag{13-34}$$

the best approximation in the minimum-mse sense is obtained when the coefficients are specified by Eqs. (13-31) to (13-33).

The method for obtaining the best approximation of the form given by Eq. (13-34) has been developed. How good is this best approximation? When the expression of Eq. (13-30) is minimized by selecting coefficients as given in Eqs. (13-31) to (13-33), the mse becomes

$$\text{mse} = \frac{1}{T} \left[\int_0^T e^2(t) \, dt - \frac{\alpha_0^2}{T} - \frac{2}{T} \sum_{k=1}^n (\alpha_k^2 + \beta_k^2) \right]$$

$$= \frac{1}{T} \int_0^T e^2(t) \, dt - c_0^2 - \frac{1}{2} \sum_{k=1}^n (a_k^2 + b_k^2) \tag{13-35}$$

In interpreting the expression above, it is helpful to note that the values of a_k and b_k are independent of the number of terms in the approximation. In other words, in answer to the question following Eq. (13-34), adding more terms to our approximation will not alter the value of the coefficients selected earlier. This means that, in Eq. (13-35), as we increase n and subtract more and more positive quantities, the mse must become smaller and smaller. This last fact suggests that if n is increased indefinitely, the mse could possibly become zero.

It can be proved, and we shall discuss this later, that an infinite series of this form will in fact converge to the original periodic function. That is, as $n \to \infty$, mse $\to 0$, and

$$e(t) = c_0 + \sum_{k=1}^\infty a_k \cos \frac{k2\pi t}{T} + b_k \sin \frac{k2\pi t}{T} \tag{13-36}$$

$$c_0 = \frac{1}{T} \int_0^T e(t) \, dt \tag{13-37a}$$

$$a_k = \frac{2}{T} \int_0^T e(t) \cos \frac{k2\pi t}{T} \, dt \qquad (13\text{-}37b)$$

$$b_k = \frac{2}{T} \int_0^T e(t) \sin \frac{k2\pi t}{T} \, dt \qquad (13\text{-}37c)$$

Since $e(t)$ is a periodic function with period T, the limits of integration in the integrals above can be chosen in any manner, provided that they cover one period. That is, $-T/2$ and $T/2$ or τ and $(\tau + T)$ could replace 0 and T as the lower and upper limits in Eqs. (13-37) without affecting the results.

The series above is called a *Fourier series* in honor of the French mathematician Joseph Fourier, who introduced these series in 1822, in his book on the mathematical theory of conduction of heat in solids. The mathematical fact expressed by Eq. (13-36) is an extremely important factor in the analysis of linear systems. Through the use of Fourier series we can express any† periodic function as a sum of sine waves. The response of the system to each member of the series can be found, and since the system is linear, the response to the original waveform will be the sum of the responses to each sinusoid. This development, which at first thought appears to have limited application, actually opens up a large area of investigation and analysis—known as Fourier, harmonic, or frequency analysis—and furnishes tools of utmost value to the engineer.

EXAMPLE OF FOURIER SERIES CALCULATIONS Let us take as an example the problem of determining the Fourier series for the function illustrated in Fig. 13-3. We first note that this function, expressed analytically as

$$f(t) = \begin{cases} \sin \dfrac{\pi t}{\tau} & \text{for } 0 \le t \le \tau \\ 0 & \text{for } \tau \le t \le 2\tau \end{cases} \qquad (13\text{-}38)$$

$$f(t \pm n2\tau) = f(t) \qquad n = 1, 2, 3, \ldots$$

† One can describe certain pathological periodic functions for which no Fourier series exists—for example, functions which possess non-integrable infinities or which have an infinite number of maxima and minima in a finite interval. However, any periodic function that can arise in a physical system can be represented by a Fourier series.

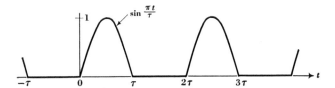

Fig. 13-3. A periodic waveform $f(t)$.

has a period 2τ. Thus

$$T = 2\tau$$

$$f_1 = \frac{1}{T} = \frac{1}{2\tau} \tag{13-39}$$

$$\omega_1 = 2\pi f_1 = \frac{2\pi}{T} = \frac{\pi}{\tau}$$

where f_1 and ω_1 are the fundamental cyclic and radian frequencies.

The coefficients for the Fourier series are computed as follows:

$$c_0 = \frac{1}{T}\int_0^T f(t)\, dt = \frac{1}{2\tau}\int_0^\tau \sin\frac{\pi t}{\tau}\, dt = \frac{1}{\pi} \tag{13-40}$$

$$a_k = \frac{2}{T}\int_0^T f(t)\cos\frac{k 2\pi t}{T}\, dt = \frac{1}{\tau}\int_0^\tau \sin\frac{\pi t}{\tau}\cos\frac{k\pi t}{\tau}\, dt \tag{13-41}$$

It is helpful to make the following change of variables:

$$x = \frac{\pi t}{\tau} \qquad dt = \frac{\tau}{\pi}\, dx \tag{13-42}$$

$$\text{When } t = 0,\ x = 0 \qquad \text{When } t = \tau,\ x = \pi$$

Thus,

$$a_k = \frac{1}{\pi}\int_0^\pi \sin x \cos kx\, dx = \frac{1}{\pi}\int_0^\pi \frac{1}{2}[\sin (x + kx) + \sin (x - kx)]\, dx$$

$$= \frac{1}{2\pi}\left[-\frac{\cos (1 + k)x}{1 + k} - \frac{\cos (1 - k)x}{1 - k} \right]_0^\pi$$

$$= \begin{cases} \dfrac{-2}{\pi(k^2 - 1)} & \text{for } k \text{ even} \\[2mm] 0 & \text{for } k \text{ odd} \end{cases} \tag{13-43}$$

In a similar manner,

$$b_k = \frac{1}{\pi}\int_0^\pi \sin x \sin kx\, dx = \frac{1}{\pi}\int_0^\pi \frac{1}{2}[\cos (x - kx) - \cos (x + kx)]\, dx$$

$$= \frac{1}{2\pi}\left[\frac{\sin (1 - k)x}{1 - k} - \frac{\sin (1 + k)x}{1 + k} \right]_0^\pi$$

$$= 0 \qquad \text{for all } k \text{ except } k = 1 \tag{13-44}$$

$$b_1 = \frac{1}{\pi}\int_0^\pi \sin^2 x\, dx = \frac{1}{2} \tag{13-45}$$

Consequently, the Fourier series for the function of Fig. 13-3 is

$$f(t) = \frac{1}{\pi} + \frac{1}{2}\sin\frac{\pi t}{\tau} - \frac{2}{\pi}\left(\frac{1}{3}\cos\frac{2\pi t}{\tau} + \frac{1}{15}\cos\frac{4\pi t}{\tau} + \frac{1}{35}\cos\frac{6\pi t}{\tau} + \cdots \right)$$

$$= \frac{1}{\pi} + \frac{1}{2}\sin\omega_1 t - \frac{2}{\pi}\sum_{k=1}^{\infty}\frac{\cos 2k\omega_1 t}{4k^2 - 1} \tag{13-46}$$

PROBLEMS

13-1   Find the Fourier series for the saw-tooth wave shown in the figure. What is the mse in representing $f(t)$ if only the first term in the series is used? If only the first two terms are used? If only the first three terms? If only the first n terms?

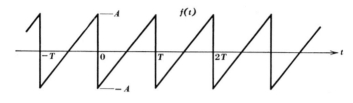

$$T = 1 \text{ sec}$$

Fig. P 13-1

13-2   Find the Fourier series for the illustrated waveforms.

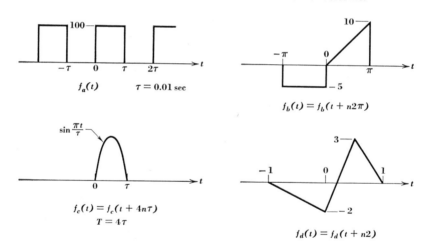

Fig. P 13-2

13-3   Show that Eq. (13-36) can be expressed in the following two forms:

$$e(t) = c_0 + \sum_{k=1}^{\infty} c_k \sin\left(\frac{k2\pi t}{T} + \phi_k\right)$$

$$= c_0 + \sum_{k=1}^{\infty} c_k \cos\left(\frac{k2\pi t}{T} + \theta_k\right)$$

13-4   Consider a periodic function $f(t)$ whose Fourier series coefficients a_k and b_k have been found by means of Eqs. (13-37). Show by integrating

Eqs. (13-37) by parts that the Fourier series coefficients for the derivative $f'(t)$ and the integral $f^{(-1)}(t)$ of $f(t)$ are as follows:

$$a'_k = \frac{k2\pi}{T} b_k \qquad b'_k = \frac{-k2\pi}{T} a_k$$

$$a_k^{(-1)} = \frac{-T}{k2\pi} b_k \qquad b_k^{(-1)} = \frac{T}{k2\pi} a_k$$

What restrictions must be placed on the original function in order for the above expressions to be valid? In other words, under certain restrictions, a Fourier series for a function may be differentiated term by term or integrated term by term to yield the derivative or integral of the function. To illustrate this development, find the Fourier series, if they exist, of the integral of $f(t)$, Prob. 13-1; the derivative of $f_a(t)$, Prob. 13-2; and the derivative of $f_d(t)$, Prob. 13-2.

13-2 FURTHER TOPICS IN THE STUDY OF FOURIER SERIES

EVEN AND ODD FUNCTIONS AND THEIR RELATIONSHIPS TO FOURIER SERIES
We shall now examine certain properties of functions and their effect on the determination of Fourier series. An even function may be defined as follows:

$$\mathcal{E}(t) = \mathcal{E}(-t) \tag{13-47}$$

Examples of even functions are $\cos \omega t$, t^2, t^4, $|t|$, and e^{-t^2}. Odd functions have the following property:

$$\mathcal{O}(t) = -\mathcal{O}(-t) \tag{13-48}$$

Examples of odd functions are $\sin \omega t$, t, t^3, and $\tan \omega t$.

There are a number of mathematical operations which can be carried out on even or odd functions and which yield even or odd functions. For example, let us consider the sum of two even functions,

$$\mathcal{E}_1(t) + \mathcal{E}_2(t) = f(t) \tag{13-49}$$

Now let us examine the properties of $f(-t)$:

$$f(-t) = \mathcal{E}_1(-t) + \mathcal{E}_2(-t) = \mathcal{E}_1(t) + \mathcal{E}_2(t) = f(t) \tag{13-50}$$

Hence, the sum of two even functions is an even function. A second example is the product of an even and an odd function:

$$\mathcal{E}(t)\mathcal{O}(t) = f(t) \tag{13-51}$$

$$f(-t) = \mathcal{E}(-t)\mathcal{O}(-t) = \mathcal{E}(t)[-\mathcal{O}(t)] = -f(t) \tag{13-52}$$

Thus, the product of an even and an odd function is an odd function.

The two examples above, in addition to several other similar relationships, are summarized below. The proofs of these relationships are left to the reader.

$$\mathcal{E}_1(t) + \mathcal{E}_2(t) = \text{even function} \qquad (13\text{-}53a)$$
$$\mathcal{O}_1(t) + \mathcal{O}_2(t) = \text{odd function} \qquad (13\text{-}53b)$$
$$\mathcal{E}_1(t)\mathcal{E}_2(t) = \text{even function} \qquad (13\text{-}53c)$$
$$\mathcal{O}_1(t)\mathcal{O}_2(t) = \text{even function} \qquad (13\text{-}53d)$$
$$\mathcal{E}(t)\mathcal{O}(t) = \text{odd function} \qquad (13\text{-}53e)$$
$$\frac{d\mathcal{E}(t)}{dt} = \text{odd function} \qquad (13\text{-}53f)$$
$$\frac{d\mathcal{O}(t)}{dt} = \text{even function} \qquad (13\text{-}53g)$$
$$\mathcal{E}_2[\mathcal{E}_1(t)], \; \mathcal{E}[\mathcal{O}(t)], \; \mathcal{O}[\mathcal{E}(t)] = \text{even functions} \qquad (13\text{-}53h)$$
$$\mathcal{O}_2[\mathcal{O}_1(t)] = \text{odd function} \qquad (13\text{-}53i)$$

Two other properties of even and odd functions which we shall find very important are

$$\int_{-\tau}^{\tau} \mathcal{E}(t) \, dt = 2 \int_0^{\tau} \mathcal{E}(t) \, dt \qquad (13\text{-}54)$$

$$\int_{-\tau}^{\tau} \mathcal{O}(t) \, dt = 0 \qquad (13\text{-}55)$$

We shall demonstrate now that any function can be decomposed into a sum of an even and an odd function. Let $f(t)$ be a function which is neither even nor odd. An even function can be constructed from $f(t)$ in the following way:

$$f_e(t) = \tfrac{1}{2}[f(t) + f(-t)] \qquad (13\text{-}56)$$

An odd function is synthesized in a similar manner:

$$f_o(t) = \tfrac{1}{2}[f(t) - f(-t)] \qquad (13\text{-}57)$$

It is easy to see that

$$f(t) = f_e(t) + f_o(t) \qquad (13\text{-}58)$$

Therefore, any function may be considered to consist of an even and an odd part, with these parts given by Eqs. (13-56) and (13-57).

Let us now discuss the importance of the relationships developed above in the theory and determination of Fourier series. First, we note that the constant plus the cosine terms in the series must equal the even part of the function and that the sine terms must equal the odd part. This fact can be verified when we calculate the coefficients. Thus,

$$a_k = \frac{2}{T} \int_{-T/2}^{T/2} f(t) \cos \frac{k2\pi t}{T} \, dt = \frac{2}{T} \int_{-T/2}^{T/2} [f_e(t) + f_o(t)] \cos \frac{k2\pi t}{T} \, dt \qquad (13\text{-}59)$$

Since $\cos \omega t$ is an even function, the product in the integrand above yields an even and an odd function. The odd function integrates to zero, and we are left with

$$a_k = \frac{2}{T} \int_{-T/2}^{T/2} f_e(t) \cos \frac{k2\pi t}{T} \, dt = \frac{4}{T} \int_0^{T/2} f_e(t) \cos \frac{k2\pi t}{T} \, dt \qquad (13\text{-}60)$$

Similarly,

$$b_k = \frac{2}{T} \int_{-T/2}^{T/2} f_o(t) \sin \frac{k2\pi t}{T} \, dt = \frac{4}{T} \int_0^{T/2} f_o(t) \sin \frac{k2\pi t}{T} \, dt \quad (13\text{-}61)$$

$$c_o = \frac{1}{T} \int_{-T/2}^{T/2} f_e(t) \, dt = \frac{2}{T} \int_0^{T/2} f_e(t) \, dt \quad (13\text{-}62)$$

Only the even part of the function is needed in calculating the constant term and the coefficients of the cosine terms, whereas only the odd part is needed in calculating the coefficients of the sine terms.

To illustrate the foregoing discussion, let us turn our attention again to the function shown in Fig. 13-3. The even and odd parts of this function can be found by applying Eqs. (13-56) and (13-57):

$$f_e(t) = \begin{cases} -\dfrac{1}{2} \sin \dfrac{\pi t}{\tau} & -\tau \le t \le 0 \\[2mm] \dfrac{1}{2} \sin \dfrac{\pi t}{\tau} & 0 \le t \le \tau \end{cases} \quad (13\text{-}63)$$

$$f_o(t) = \frac{1}{2} \sin \frac{\pi t}{\tau} \quad (13\text{-}64)$$

These two functions are illustrated in Fig. 13-4. Equation (13-64) tells us immediately that the sine terms in the series are limited to the single fundamental-frequency term with a coefficient $\frac{1}{2}$. This, of course, agrees with our previous results. Utilizing Eqs. (13-60) and (13-63) to calculate the a_k coefficients yields

$$a_k = \frac{4}{2\tau} \int_0^\tau \frac{1}{2} \sin \frac{\pi t}{\tau} \cos \frac{k2\pi t}{\tau} \, dt \quad (13\text{-}65)$$

This expression agrees with Eq. (13-41.) Cognizance and utilization of the properties of even and odd functions will, in many cases, decrease and simplify the operations necessary in working with Fourier series.

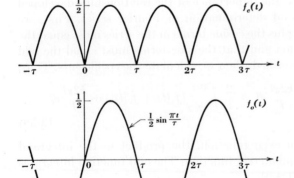

Fig. 13-4. The even and odd parts of the $f(t)$ shown in Fig. 13-3.

THE EFFECT ON A FOURIER SERIES OF A TRANSLATION OF THE ORIGIN OR A TRANSLATION OF THE PERIODIC FUNCTION In the analysis of systems with periodic driving functions, we have invariably been unconcerned with the placement of the time origin. In our previous work it was immaterial whether a sinusoidal driving function was called $\sin \omega t$ or $\cos \omega t$ or $\sin (\omega t + \theta)$. The system responses to such driving functions were always given relative to a common reference, such as the driving function, and the variable t was seldom expressed. We should expect that the placement of the time origin for any periodic driving function could be made arbitrarily, with no important effect on the analysis of the system. Let us investigate this question with some care.

Assume that the Fourier series for a periodic function $f(t)$ has been found and is expressed in the following form:

$$f(t) = c_0 + \sum_{k=1}^{\infty} c_k \sin \left(\frac{k2\pi t}{T} + \phi_k \right) \qquad (13\text{-}66)$$

Let us now redefine the function by shifting our time axis. The new time variable t' will be defined so that $t' = 0$ when $t = \tau$, that is, $t' = t - \tau$. With the new time variable, the same periodic function is

$$g(t') = f(t' + \tau) = c_0 + \sum_{k=1}^{\infty} c_k \sin \left[\frac{k2\pi (t' + \tau)}{T} + \phi_k \right]$$

$$= c_0 + \sum_{k=1}^{\infty} c_k \sin \left(\frac{k2\pi t'}{T} + \psi_k \right) \qquad (13\text{-}67)$$

where
$$\psi_k = \phi_k + \frac{k2\pi\tau}{T} \qquad (13\text{-}68)$$

A shift of the time origin—or, equivalently, a translation in time of a periodic function—causes an increase or decrease in the phase angle of each member of the Fourier series representing the function. The magnitude of the phase shift of the kth harmonic is $k2\pi\tau/T$ radians and is positive for a shift of the origin to the right, or an advance of the function, and is negative for a leftward shift, or a delay of the function. The amplitude coefficients c_k are unchanged by a time shift. When the Fourier series is expressed in the form involving both sines and cosines, the a_k's and b_k's are varied by a time shift. Since

$$a_k = c_k \sin \phi_k \qquad b_k = c_k \cos \phi_k \qquad (13\text{-}69)$$

the time translation assumed above results in new coefficients:

$$a_k' = c_k \sin \left(\phi_k + \frac{k2\pi\tau}{T} \right) \qquad b_k' = c_k \cos \left(\phi_k + \frac{k2\pi\tau}{T} \right) \qquad (13\text{-}70)$$

This form of the series may therefore have a considerably different appearance after a time shift, although the function being represented is unchanged in shape.

THE EXPONENTIAL FORM OF THE FOURIER SERIES We have discussed two forms in which a Fourier series may be written. One form consists of sums of sines and cosines without phase angles, and the other consists of a sum of sines or cosines with phase angles included. Thus a periodic function may be expressed in a number of ways, as is illustrated below:

$$
f(t) = c_0 + \sum_{k=1}^{\infty} a_k \cos k\omega_1 t + b_k \sin k\omega_1 t
$$

$$
= c_0 + \sum_{k=1}^{\infty} c_k \sin (k\omega_1 t + \phi_k)
$$

$$
= c_0 + \sum_{k=1}^{\infty} c_k \cos (k\omega_1 t + \theta_k) \tag{13-71}
$$

where

$$
c_k = \sqrt{a_k^2 + b_k^2} \qquad \phi_k = \tan^{-1} \frac{a_k}{b_k} \qquad \theta_k = \tan^{-1}\left(-\frac{b_k}{a_k}\right) \tag{13-72}
$$

Since sines and cosines can be expressed in terms of exponentials, another form for the series can be added to those above:

$$
f(t) = c_0 + \sum_{k=1}^{\infty} \frac{a_k}{2} (e^{jk\omega_1 t} + e^{-jk\omega_1 t}) - \frac{jb_k}{2} (e^{jk\omega_1 t} - e^{-jk\omega_1 t})
$$

$$
= c_0 + \sum_{k=1}^{\infty} \frac{a_k - jb_k}{2} e^{jk\omega_1 t} + \sum_{k=1}^{\infty} \frac{a_k + jb_k}{2} e^{-jk\omega_1 t}
$$

$$
= \sum_{k=-\infty}^{\infty} \gamma_k e^{jk\omega_1 t} \tag{13-73}
$$

In order for this last step to be valid, we must define γ_k as follows:

$$
\gamma_k = \begin{cases} c_0 & \text{for } k = 0 \\ \dfrac{a_k - jb_k}{2} & \text{for } k > 0 \\ \dfrac{a_{|k|} + jb_{|k|}}{2} & \text{for } k < 0 \end{cases} \tag{13-74}
$$

By expressing the sines and cosines in Eqs. (13-37) in exponential form and then substituting into Eq. (13-74), it can be shown that

$$\gamma_k = \frac{1}{T} \int_0^T f(t) e^{-jk\omega_1 t} \, dt \qquad (13\text{-}75)$$

where

$$\omega_1 = \frac{2\pi}{T}$$

for all values of k.

The coefficients γ_k of the exponential Fourier series are complex numbers. The magnitude and angle of these complex numbers can be found by a comparison of Eqs. (13-72) and (13-74).

$$|\gamma_k| = \frac{c_{|k|}}{2} \qquad (13\text{-}76)$$

$$\begin{aligned} \angle \gamma_k &= \theta_{|k|} & \text{for } k > 0 \\ \angle \gamma_k &= -\theta_{|k|} & \text{for } k < 0 \end{aligned} \qquad (13\text{-}77)$$

We shall discuss the exponential series at greater length in Sec. 13-4. For the present we may simply consider it another form for expressing the Fourier series for a periodic function.

GRAPHICAL OR NUMERICAL COMPUTATION OF FOURIER SERIES As we have stated, any periodic function can be represented by a Fourier series, and a technique for computing the Fourier coefficients for such a series has been developed. This technique, as given in Eqs. (13-37) and (13-75), involves the integration of the periodic function after it has been multiplied by sinusoids or exponentials. If the periodic function is given in analytic form, computation of these integrals usually reduces to thumbing through a table of integrals. It is not uncommon, however, for the periodic function to be given in graphical, rather than analytic, form. For example, a periodic function appearing on an oscilloscope could be photographed to yield a graphical representation. With such a function the integrations of Eqs. (13-37) and (13-75) must be computed in a different manner.

To illustrate the computation of the Fourier series coefficients for a periodic function given graphically, consider Fig. 13-5. One cycle of the periodic wave is shown in this figure. An approximation to the integral over one period of this function is obtained as follows. The period T is divided into N equal intervals of width Δt. The value of the function is obtained from the graph for each of the N division points. It is clear from the figure that the area under $f(t)$ is approximated by the sum of the areas under the rectangles of height $f(t_n)$ and width Δt:

$$\int_0^T f(t) \, dt \cong \sum_{n=1}^N f(t_n) \, \Delta t \qquad (13\text{-}78)$$

Since

$$\Delta t = \frac{T}{N} \qquad (13\text{-}79)$$

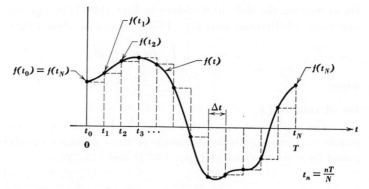

Fig. 13-5. The graph of one period of a periodic function. The period T is divided into N equal increments: $t_0 - t_1, t_1 - t_2, t_2 - t_3, \ldots, t_{N-1} - t_N$. The value of $f(t)$ is obtained from the graph for each division point: $t_1, t_2, t_3, \ldots, t_N$.

Eq. (13-78) may be modified to yield

$$\frac{1}{T} \int_0^T f(t) \, dt \cong \frac{1}{N} \sum_{n=1}^{N} f(t_n) \tag{13-80}$$

This expression is consequently an approximate formula for obtaining c_0.

The value of the function $f(t) \cos (k2\pi t/T)$ for $t = t_n$ can be easily computed for each n from 1 to N. The integral of this function can then be approximated in a similar manner:

$$a_k = \frac{2}{T} \int_0^T f(t) \cos \frac{k2\pi t}{T} \, dt \cong \frac{2}{N} \sum_{n=1}^{N} f(t_n) \cos \frac{k2\pi t_n}{T} = a'_k \tag{13-81}$$

The coefficients of the sine terms are

$$b_k = \frac{2}{T} \int_0^T f(t) \sin \frac{k2\pi t}{T} \, dt \cong \frac{2}{N} \sum_{n=1}^{N} f(t_n) \sin \frac{k2\pi t_n}{T} = b'_k \tag{13-82}$$

It should be clear that the degree to which the summations approximate the integrals will depend both upon the character of $f(t)$ and upon the size of N. If $f(t)$ is fairly smooth or if N is large, the approximation will be reasonably accurate. Since sampling the function at a finite number of places tends to mask the high-frequency variations in the signal, we should expect that the number of harmonics one could use accurately in a Fourier series obtained graphically would be definitely limited. This expectation is heightened when we consider that a Fourier series with M harmonics contains $(2M + 1)$ pieces of information about the periodic function (that is, the M a_k's, the M b_k's, and c_0). Consequently, we should surely have to sample the graphical function at $(2M + 1)$ or more places if we wished to carry the series to M harmonics.

Let us illustrate the above point further by investigating an approximate Fourier series containing M harmonics which is obtained by graphical methods using $(2M + 1)$ samples. Making use of Eqs. (13-80) to (13-82) with $N = 2M + 1$, we obtain the following results:

$$f(t) \cong f_a(t) = c_0' + \sum_{k=1}^{M} a_k' \cos \frac{k2\pi t}{T} + b_k' \sin \frac{k2\pi t}{T}$$

$$= \frac{1}{2M+1} \sum_{n=1}^{2M+1} f(t)_n + \sum_{k=1}^{M} \left\{ \left[\frac{2}{2M+1} \sum_{n=1}^{2M+1} f(t_n) \cos \frac{k2\pi t_n}{T} \right] \right.$$

$$\times \cos \frac{k2\pi t}{T} + \left[\frac{2}{2M+1} \sum_{n=1}^{2M+1} f(t_n) \sin \frac{k2\pi t_n}{T} \right] \sin \frac{k2\pi t}{T} \right\} \quad (13\text{-}83)$$

The expression above may be simplified by interchanging the order of summation and employing a trigonometric identity [Eqs. (3-4) to (3-6)]:

$$f(t) \cong f_a(t) = \frac{1}{2M+1} \sum_{n=1}^{2M+1} f(t_n) \left[1 + 2 \sum_{k=1}^{M} \left(\cos \frac{k2\pi t_n}{T} \cos \frac{k2\pi t}{T} \right. \right.$$

$$\left. \left. + \sin \frac{k2\pi t_n}{T} \sin \frac{k2\pi t}{T} \right) \right]$$

$$= \frac{1}{2M+1} \sum_{n=1}^{2M+1} f(t_n) \left[1 + 2 \sum_{k=1}^{M} \cos \frac{k2\pi}{T} (t_n - t) \right] \quad (13\text{-}84)$$

It can be shown (see Prob. 13-15) that

$$1 + 2 \sum_{k=1}^{M} \cos kx = \frac{\sin \left[(2M + 1)x/2 \right]}{\sin (x/2)} \quad (13\text{-}85)$$

Consequently, Eq. (13-84) may be written as follows:

$$f(t) \cong f_a(t) = \frac{1}{2M+1} \sum_{n=1}^{2M+1} f(t_n) \frac{\sin \left[(2M + 1)\pi(t - t_n)/T \right]}{\sin \left[\pi(t - t_n)/T \right]} \quad (13\text{-}86)$$

Before discussing the general characteristics of Eq. (13-86), let us determine to what degree the function $f_a(t)$ approaches $f(t)$ at the sampling points. That is, we wish to find $f_a(t)$ for $t = t_m = m \, \Delta t$. Making use of the fact that

$$\Delta t = \frac{T}{N} = \frac{T}{2M+1} \quad (13\text{-}87)$$

$$\frac{\pi(t_m - t_n)}{T} = \frac{\pi(m - n) \, \Delta t}{T} = \frac{\pi(m - n)}{2M + 1} \quad (13\text{-}88)$$

the evaluation of $f_a(t_m)$ yields

$$f(t_m) \cong f_a(t_m) = \frac{1}{2M+1} \sum_{n=1}^{2M+1} f(t_n) \frac{\sin \pi(m-n)}{\sin \dfrac{\pi(m-n)}{2M+1}} \quad (13\text{-}89)$$

Since

$$\frac{\sin \pi(m-n)}{\sin \dfrac{\pi(m-n)}{2M+1}} = \begin{cases} 2M+1 & \text{for } m=n \\ 0 & \text{for } m \neq n \end{cases} \quad \begin{array}{l} m = 1, 2, 3, \ldots, \\ 2M+1 \end{array}$$

$$(13\text{-}90)$$

we finally find that

$$f(t_m) \cong f_a(t_m) = f(t_m) \quad (13\text{-}91)$$

In words, the development leading from Eq. (13-83) to Eq. (13-91) tells us that our approximate Fourier series, containing M harmonics and obtained from $(2M+1)$ samples of the function $f(t)$, will actually equal that function at each value of t corresponding to the sampling points. In general, of course, $f_a(t)$ will not equal $f(t)$ between the sample points, but if the transition of $f(t)$ between these points is smooth, the deviation between the two functions will be small.

This property just discussed leads to another result of considerable interest. Suppose that $f(t)$ contains no frequencies above the Mth harmonic—in other words, that $f(t)$ can be expressed exactly by a Fourier series limited to the first M harmonics:

$$f(t) = c_0 + \sum_{k=1}^{M} a_k \cos \frac{k2\pi t}{T} + b_k \sin \frac{k2\pi t}{T} \quad (13\text{-}92)$$

The function $f_a(t)$ of Eqs. (13-83) to (13-89) was shown to equal $f(t)$ at $(2M+1)$ points of the period. Thus, the right-hand side of Eq. (13-92) equals the right-hand side of Eq. (13-83) at $(2M+1)$ distinct points of a period. This can be true only if

$$c_0 = c_0' \qquad a_k = a_k' \qquad b_k = b_k' \quad (13\text{-}93)$$

which means that the functions are equal everywhere. Consequently, when a periodic function contains no harmonics above the Mth, it can be represented exactly by the following expression:

$$f(t) = \frac{1}{2M+1} \sum_{n=1}^{2M+1} f(t_n) \frac{\sin [(2M+1)\pi(t-t_n)/T]}{\sin [\pi(t-t_n)/T]} \quad (13\text{-}94)$$

Equation (13-94) is called the sampling theorem for periodic functions and is closely related to the sampling theorem for nonperiodic band-limited functions. These two sampling theorems are extremely important in the study of communication systems. We shall delay further discussion of Eq. (13-94) until Sec. 13-4, where a closely related expression occurs.

We leave the topic of the graphical computation of Fourier series with the comment that if it is necessary to obtain the series by this method for more than a few waveforms, it will be advisable to investigate some systematic techniques which minimize the number of computations.†

SUMMARY   Although we shall have more to say concerning Fourier series, this is a good point to pause for a moment to review our results and to consider the directions in which we should like to continue our investigation. The Fourier series representation of a periodic function has been developed in a practical way for a very practical reason. The practical reason was that we needed to represent the periodic function in a form which would permit us, with reasonable ease, to find the response of a linear system when the periodic function was the driving function. The practical way used to carry this out was to represent the periodic function as a sum of sinusoids, since by superposition we can easily find the response of a linear system to a sum of sinusoids. (We shall discuss system responses to periodic driving functions in the next section.) After taking the logical step of attempting to approximate the periodic function by a sum of sinusoids with the same periodicity, we faced the remaining problem of assigning optimum values to the amplitude and phase of these sinusoids.

The amplitude and phase were chosen in such a way as to minimize the mean-squared error between function and approximation. With the coefficients selected in this manner, we arrived at the Fourier series. It should be emphasized at this time that minimization of the mean-squared error is a logical and convenient way of obtaining a series which approximates the periodic function, but it is not the only way of obtaining a reasonable approximation. When the periodic function is to be approximated by a series with only a finite number of terms, other methods of selecting the coefficients can lead to approximations which could be considered better. This matter will be discussed in Sec. 13-4.

Equation (13-35) indicated that each additional term in the Fourier series decreases the mean-squared error between function and approximation. Consequently, it is logical to expect the infinite Fourier series not only to approximate but actually to equal the periodic function it represents. We postponed the proof of this to Sec. 13-4 and proceeded to work under the assumption that the infinite Fourier series equals the function it represents.

† See, for example, M. G. Salvadori and K. S. Miller, "The Mathematical Solution of Engineering Problems," McGraw-Hill Book Company, Inc., New York, 1948.

electrical and mechanical networks

We investigated a number of forms in which a Fourier series can be expressed, together with certain properties of functions important in the determination of Fourier series. The results of these investigations are summarized in Table 13-1.

TABLE 13-1 *Fourier Series Relationships*

A function $f(t)$ is periodic with period T if

$$f(t + nT) = f(t) \qquad n = \pm 1, \pm 2, \pm 3, \pm 4, \ldots$$

The fundamental cyclic and radian frequencies of the function are defined as

$$f_1 = \frac{1}{T} \qquad \omega_1 = \frac{2\pi}{T}$$

The function is represented by a Fourier series as follows:

$$f(t) = c_0 + \sum_{k=1}^{\infty} a_k \cos k\omega_1 t + b_k \sin k\omega_1 t$$

$$= c_0 + \sum_{k=1}^{\infty} c_k \sin (k\omega_1 t + \phi_k)$$

$$= c_0 + \sum_{k=1}^{\infty} c_k \cos (k\omega_1 t + \theta_k)$$

$$= \sum_{k=-\infty}^{\infty} \gamma_k e^{jk\omega_1 t}$$

where

$$c_0 = \frac{1}{T} \int_0^T f(t)\, dt \qquad \gamma_k = \frac{1}{T} \int_0^T f(t) e^{-jk\omega_1 t}\, dt$$

$$a_k = \frac{2}{T} \int_0^T f(t) \cos k\omega_1 t\, dt = \frac{4}{T} \int_0^{T/2} f_e(t) \cos k\omega_1 t\, dt$$

$$b_k = \frac{2}{T} \int_0^T f(t) \sin k\omega_1 t\, dt = \frac{4}{T} \int_0^{T/2} f_o(t) \sin k\omega_1 t\, dt$$

$$c_k = \sqrt{a_k^2 + b_k^2} \qquad \phi_k = \tan^{-1} \frac{a_k}{b_k} \qquad \theta_k = -\tan^{-1} \frac{b_k}{a_k}$$

$$|\gamma_k| = \frac{c_{|k|}}{2} \qquad \angle \gamma_k = \begin{cases} \theta_{|k|} & \text{for } k > 0 \\ -\theta_{|k|} & \text{for } k < 0 \end{cases}$$

A function and its even and odd parts are related as follows:

$$f(t) = f_e(t) + f_o(t)$$
$$f_e(t) = \tfrac{1}{2}[f(t) + f(-t)] \qquad f_o(t) = \tfrac{1}{2}[f(t) - f(-t)]$$

PROBLEMS

13-5 Prove the relationships of Eqs. (13-53).

13-6 Prove Eqs. (13-54) and (13-55).

13-7   Find the even and odd parts of the periodic functions of Prob. 13-2 and thus determine the Fourier series for additional functions.

13-8   Prove that the Fourier series for a periodic function which has the property

$$f\left(t + \frac{T}{2}\right) = -f(t)$$

will contain only odd harmonics. That is, prove that a_k and b_k will be zero if k is an even number. If $f(t)$ has the property above, what symmetry properties (about $t = T/4$) will $f_e(t)$ and $f_o(t)$ have?

13-9   Draw periodic functions each of which has one of the following properties in its Fourier expansion:
      (*a*) Cosine terms only with all harmonics present.
      (*b*) Sine terms only with all harmonics present.
      (*c*) Both cosine and sine terms with only odd harmonics.
      (*d*) Cosine terms only with odd harmonics only.
      (*e*) Sine terms only with odd harmonics only.
      (*f*) Cosine terms in odd harmonics only and sine terms in even harmonics only.

13-10   Consider the function of x shown in the figure. We can assume that $f(x)$ is either zero for $x < 0$ and $x > a$ or that it is nonzero. Discuss how one could write a Fourier series which converged to $f(x)$ for $0 < x < a$ but not necessarily elsewhere. Draw the periodic function defined by this Fourier series if the series contains cosine terms only, sine terms only, both sines and cosines.

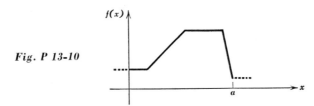

Fig. P 13-10

13-11   If the function $f_a(t)$ of Prob. 13-2 is shifted right or left by an amount $\tau/2$, the resulting function is even and consequently will have only cosine terms in its Fourier series. Using the results expressed by Eqs. (13-67) and (13-68), find this cosine series by transforming the series for $f_a(t)$.

13-12   Derive Eqs. (13-75) to (13-77).

13-13 Find the exponential Fourier series for the periodic functions, one period of which is shown in the illustration.

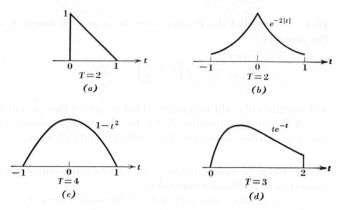

Fig. P 13-13

13-14 Compute the approximate Fourier series containing four harmonics for a function $f(t)$ which has the following values at $t = t_n = nT/9$: $t_0 = t_9 = 0$, $t_1 = 1$, $t_2 = 2$, $t_3 = 0$, $t_4 = -1$, $t_5 = 1$, $t_6 = -1$, $t_7 = -1$, $t_8 = -1$.

13-15 Prove Eq. (13-85). [HINT: By long division, $1/(1 - y) = 1 + y + y^2 + y^3 + \cdots$ and $(1 - y^{n+1})/(1 - y) = 1 + y + y^2 + \cdots + y^n$. The relations above hold when $y = e^{jx}$ or e^{-jx}. Furthermore, trigonometric functions can be expressed in terms of exponential functions.]

13-3 THE RESPONSE OF LINEAR SYSTEMS TO PERIODIC DRIVING FUNCTIONS

The application of superposition in finding linear system responses to nonsinusoidal periodic driving functions was discussed briefly in the last section. We shall devote the present section to a more detailed investigation of this topic. According to the superposition theorem, the response of a linear system to a sum of driving functions is the sum of responses to each driving function taken individually. Consequently, the response of a linear system to a periodic driving function is the sum of the responses to each term of the Fourier series which represents the driving function.

A MECHANICAL-SYSTEM EXAMPLE The force illustrated in Fig. 13-6c is applied to the mechanical system of Fig. 13-6a. The velocity of the mass M_2 is to be found. The ratio of the velocity $v(t)$ to the applied

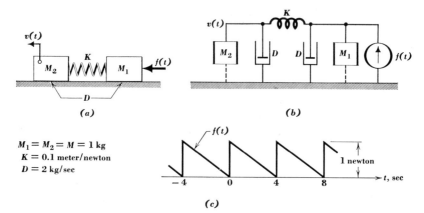

Fig. 13-6. (a) *A mechanical system,* (b) *the network diagram, and* (c) *the force applied to it.*

force $f(t)$ if both are varying exponentially—that is, the transfer function—is

$$\mathbf{T}(s) = \frac{\mathbf{V}}{\mathbf{F}} = \frac{1}{s^3 KM^2 + s^2 2KMD + s(2M + KD^2) + 2D}$$

$$= \frac{10}{s^3 + 4s^2 + 24s + 40} \tag{13-95}$$

The Fourier series for the applied force is

$$f(t) = \frac{1}{2} + \frac{1}{\pi}\left[\frac{\sin{(\pi t/2)}}{1} + \frac{\sin{\pi t}}{2} + \frac{\sin{(3\pi t/2)}}{3} + \cdots\right]$$

$$= \frac{1}{2} + \sum_{k=1}^{\infty}\frac{1}{\pi k}\sin{k\omega_1 t} \qquad \text{newtons} \tag{13-96}$$

where

$$\omega_1 = \frac{\pi}{2} \qquad \text{radians/sec} \tag{13-97}$$

We can now find the response to each term of the series above by utilizing Eq. (13-95). For the response to the constant term, we let $s = 0$ and find that

$$\mathbf{T}(s)\Big|_{s=0} = \frac{1}{4} \tag{13-98}$$

Thus, the constant term of the response is

$$v_0 = f_0\mathbf{T}(0) = \frac{1}{8} \tag{13-99}$$

For the first sinusoidal term with radian frequency $\pi/2$, we find the magnitude and angle of the transfer function with $s = j\pi/2$:

$$\mathbf{T}(s)\Big|_{s=j\pi/2} = \frac{10}{-j\pi^3/8 - \pi^2 + j12\pi + 40} = \frac{10}{30.13 + j33.82}$$

$$= 0.221\underline{/-48.4°} \tag{13-100}$$

Consequently, the first-harmonic term of the response is

$$v_1(t) = \frac{0.221}{\pi} \sin\left(\frac{\pi t}{2} - 48.4°\right) \tag{13-101}$$

In a similar manner, the responses to the higher harmonics are found to be

$$\mathbf{T}(s)\,|_{s=j\pi} = 0.226\underline{/-90°} \tag{13-102}$$

$$v_2(t) = \frac{0.226}{2\pi} \sin\,(\pi t - 90°) \tag{13-103}$$

$$\mathbf{T}(s)\,|_{s=j3\pi/2} = 0.204\underline{/-173.9°} \tag{13-104}$$

$$v_3(t) = \frac{0.204}{3\pi} \sin\left(\frac{3\pi t}{2} - 173.9°\right) \tag{13-105}$$

$$\mathbf{T}(s)\,|_{s=j2\pi} = 0.064\underline{/140.5°} \tag{13-106}$$

$$v_4(t) = \frac{0.064}{4\pi} \sin\,(2\pi t + 140.5°) \tag{13-107}$$

$$v_5(t) = \frac{0.0276}{5\pi} \sin\left(\frac{5\pi t}{2} + 125°\right) \tag{13-108}$$

$$v_6(t) = \frac{0.0146}{6\pi} \sin\,(3\pi t + 117.4°) \tag{13-109}$$

In general terms, the velocity response is given by the Fourier series expressed below:

$$v(t) = \tfrac{1}{8} + \sum_{k=1}^{\infty} \frac{|\mathbf{T}(jk\omega_1)|}{\pi k} \sin\,[k\omega_1 t + \angle \mathbf{T}(jk\omega_1)] \qquad \text{m/sec} \tag{13-110}$$

If a plot of the velocity was desired, the constant and first six harmonics as given above would be more than sufficient to compute an accurate curve.

AN ELECTRICAL-CIRCUIT EXAMPLE The exponential Fourier series for the voltage shown in Fig. 13-7a is

$$e(t) = \sum_{k=-\infty}^{\infty} \gamma_k e^{jk\omega_1 t}$$

where

$$\omega_1 = 200\pi \qquad \text{radians/sec} \tag{13-111}$$

$$\gamma_k = \frac{100}{k\pi} \sin\,0.2k\pi$$

When a voltage of the form Ee^{st} is applied to the circuit of Fig. 13-7b, the current response is Ie^{st}, where

$$\frac{\mathbf{I}}{\mathbf{E}} = \mathbf{Y}(s) = C\left(s + \frac{1}{RC}\right) \tag{13-112}$$

Since the voltage applied to the circuit is a sum of exponentials, it immediately follows that the current response is given by the following

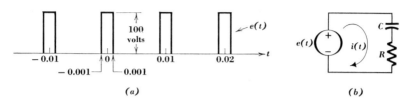

Fig. 13-7. (a) *A periodic voltage* $e(t)$; (b) *a circuit to which* $e(t)$ *is applied.*

exponential Fourier series:

$$i(t) = \sum_{k=-\infty}^{\infty} \lambda_k e^{jk\omega_1 t} \tag{13-113}$$

The coefficients λ_k are found by combining Eqs. (13-111) and (13-112):

$$\lambda_k = \frac{C(jk\omega_1 + 1/RC)\, 100 \sin 0.2k\pi}{k\pi} \tag{13-114}$$

POWER AND ENERGY The power dissipated in an element is often one of the quantities we wish to find in analyzing a system under periodic excitation. For example, we may desire to know the heat produced in the frictional contact between the mass M_2 and the ground plane of Fig. 13-6 or the power dissipated in the resistor of Fig. 13-7. Since power and energy are not linear functions of applied voltage, current, force, or velocity, superposition cannot generally be applied directly in computing the power in an element (see Probs. 9-1 and 9-2). When the driving function is the sum of terms of a Fourier series, however, the total average power does equal the sum of the average powers due to each term in the series. The reason for this is the orthogonality of the sine and cosine functions (see Prob. 13-18).

To develop the fact just stated, we may note that the average power developed, respectively, in mechanical and electrical resistances is

$$P_D = \frac{1}{T} \int_0^T Dv^2(t)\, dt = \frac{1}{T} \int_0^T \frac{f^2(t)}{D}\, dt \tag{13-115}$$

$$P_R = \frac{1}{T} \int_0^T Ri^2(t)\, dt = \frac{1}{T} \int_0^T \frac{e^2(t)}{R}\, dt \tag{13-116}$$

With periodic excitation, the velocity, force, current, or voltage appropriate to the equations above can be determined in the form of a Fourier series. Then, the mean-squared value of this function, multiplied by the proper constant, must be computed in accordance with these equations. It follows from Eq. (13-35), however, that the mean-squared value of the function can be expressed in terms of the Fourier series coefficients. With an infinite Fourier series, the mean-squared error between function and series is zero, so that Eq. (13-35) becomes

$$\frac{1}{T} \int_0^T e^2(t)\, dt = c_0{}^2 + \frac{1}{2} \sum_{k=1}^{\infty} (a_k{}^2 + b_k{}^2) \qquad (13\text{-}117)$$

A similar relationship holds for the exponential Fourier series:

$$\frac{1}{T} \int_0^T e^2(t)\, dt = \sum_{k=-\infty}^{\infty} |\gamma_k|^2 = \gamma_0{}^2 + 2 \sum_{k=1}^{\infty} |\gamma_k|^2$$

$$= c_0{}^2 + \frac{1}{2} \sum_{k=1}^{\infty} c_k{}^2 \qquad (13\text{-}118)$$

Utilizing the two equations above, we may rewrite Eqs. (13-115) and (13-116) as

$$P_D = D \left[\sum{}^2 \right]_v = \frac{1}{D} \left[\sum{}^2 \right]_f \qquad \text{watts} \qquad (13\text{-}119)$$

$$P_R = R \left[\sum{}^2 \right]_i = \frac{1}{R} \left[\sum{}^2 \right]_e \qquad \text{watts} \qquad (13\text{-}120)$$

where the notation used above is defined as follows:

$$\left[\sum{}^2 \right]_x = \left[c_0{}^2 + \frac{1}{2} \sum_{k=1}^{\infty} a_k{}^2 + b_k{}^2 \right] = \left[c_0{}^2 + \frac{1}{2} \sum_{k=1}^{\infty} c_k{}^2 \right]$$

$$= \sum_{k=-\infty}^{\infty} |\gamma_k|^2 \qquad (13\text{-}121)$$

The subscript x indicates that the terms in the summations are the coefficients of the Fourier series for $x(t)$.

In accordance with the definition of the rms value of a function, the rms value of a periodic function $f(t)$ is

$$[f(t)]_{\text{rms}} = \sqrt{\left[\sum{}^2 \right]_f} \qquad (13\text{-}122)$$

SUMMARY   The ratio of the response of a linear system to a driving function which is exponential (e^{st}) is the transfer function $\mathbf{T}(s)$. For a driving function which is periodic with a Fourier series

$$d(t) = \sum_{k=-\infty}^{\infty} \gamma_k e^{jk\omega_1 t} = c_0 + \sum_{k=1}^{\infty} c_k \sin(k\omega_1 t + \phi_k) \qquad (13\text{-}123)$$

the response function will be

$$r(t) = \sum_{k=-\infty}^{\infty} \gamma_k \mathbf{T}(jk\omega_1) e^{jk\omega_1 t}$$

$$= c_0 \mathbf{T}(0) + \sum_{k=1}^{\infty} c_k |\mathbf{T}(jk\omega_1)| \sin[k\omega_1 t + \phi_k + \angle\mathbf{T}(jk\omega_1)] \qquad (13\text{-}124)$$

PROBLEMS

13-16 Use the constant and the first four harmonics of the series computed for the velocity of M_2 (Fig. 13-6) to illustrate this velocity graphically.

13-17 A velocity source

$$v(t) = 2 + \sin 0.1t + \sum_{k=1}^{\infty} \frac{2}{k^2} \cos 0.1kt \qquad \text{m/sec}$$

is applied to the mechanical system shown in the figure. What is the velocity of the mass? What is the power being dissipated in the frictional resistance?

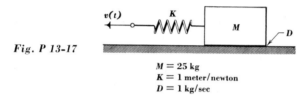

Fig. P 13-17

$$M = 25 \text{ kg}$$
$$K = 1 \text{ meter/newton}$$
$$D = 1 \text{ kg/sec}$$

13-18 Prove that

$$\frac{1}{T} \int_0^T \left(c_0 + \sum_{k=1}^{\infty} a_k \cos \frac{k2\pi t}{T} + b_k \sin \frac{k2\pi t}{T} \right)^2 dt = c_0^2 + \frac{1}{2} \sum_{k=1}^{\infty} a_k^2 + b_k^2$$

by actually squaring the summation and then carrying out the integration. This proof is essential in the derivation of Eq. (13-29) from Eq. (13-26).

13-19 The periodic voltage applied to a load is

$$e(t) = \sum_{k=-\infty}^{\infty} \gamma_k e^{jk\omega_1 t} = c_0 + \sum_{k=1}^{\infty} a_k \cos k\omega_1 t + b_k \sin k\omega_1 t$$

The resultant current flow is

$$i(t) = \sum_{k=-\infty}^{\infty} \lambda_k e^{jk\omega_1 t} = c_0' + \sum_{k=1}^{\infty} a_k' \cos k\omega_1 t + b_k' \sin k\omega_1 t$$

Prove that the average power delivered by the voltage source is

$$P = \sum_{k=-\infty}^{\infty} \gamma_k \lambda_{-k} = c_0 c_0' + \frac{1}{2} \sum_{k=1}^{\infty} a_k a_k' + b_k b_k'$$

13-20 The **z** parameters of a two-port network are

$$\mathbf{z}_{11} = \mathbf{z}_{22} = \frac{s^2 + 2s + 2}{s + 1} \qquad \mathbf{z}_{12} = \mathbf{z}_{21} = \frac{1}{s + 1}$$

A voltage

$$e(t) = \sum_{k=-\infty}^{\infty} \frac{100}{4 - jk} e^{jkt}$$

is applied at port 1. What is the open-circuit voltage at port 2? What is the current flowing in at port 1? What is the average power delivered by the source?

13-4 THE CONVERGENCE OF FOURIER SERIES AND THE GIBBS PHENOMENON

In Sec. 13-1 we derived the Fourier series for a periodic function by selecting the coefficients of the sine and cosine terms so that the mean-squared error between the series and the function would be minimized. The fact that the mean-squared error decreased with each additional term in the series suggested that the infinite series would converge to the function it represented. We accepted this as a fact and proceeded to examine the Fourier series and some of its properties. Now we return to the question of proving the convergence of the Fourier series. We note first that a steady decrease of the mse as the number of terms in the series is increased does not constitute a sufficient proof, since the mse could asymptotically approach some minimum value without vanishing. Clearly, further proof is necessary.

No rigorous proof of the convergence of Fourier series will be attempted here.† However, a development will be advanced which should convince the reader that the Fourier series actually does converge to the function it represents. More important than the proof in this development are some of the auxiliary facts and techniques which will be discovered.

THE PARTIAL SUM OF A FOURIER SERIES In mathematical analysis we are often interested, as we are in studying Fourier series, in the behavior of a function as some parameter of the function becomes infinite. In many cases, simply letting the parameter become infinite produces an indeterminate result. The solution to this impasse is to determine the function's behavior for large but finite values of the parameter and then deduce the limiting case as the parameter increases without limit. Directing our approach as suggested above, let us consider the sum of a large but finite number of terms of the Fourier series which represents the periodic function $f(t)$:

---

† The interested reader is referred to R. V. Churchill, "Fourier Series and Boundary Value Problems," McGraw-Hill Book Company, Inc., New York, 1941.

$$f(t) \cong f_n(t) = \sum_{k=-n}^{n} \gamma_k e^{jkt} \tag{13-125}$$

$$\gamma_k = \frac{1}{2\pi} \int_0^{2\pi} f(\xi)e^{-jk\xi}\, d\xi \tag{13-126}$$

We have assumed that the period of $f(t)$ *is* 2π. This will not decrease the generality of our development, but it does simplify the notation somewhat, as $2\pi/T = \omega_1 = 1$. Since the integration yielding the coefficients γ_k involves a definite integral, we are free, in Eq. (13-126), to change the variable of integration from t to ξ.

Substituting the value for γ_k given in Eq. (13-126) into Eq. (13-125) and then interchanging the order of summation and integration yield

$$f_n(t) = \sum_{k=-n}^{n} \frac{1}{2\pi} \int_0^{2\pi} f(\xi)e^{-jk\xi}\, d\xi\, e^{jkt}$$

$$= \frac{1}{2\pi} \int_0^{2\pi} f(\xi) \sum_{k=-n}^{n} e^{jk(t-\xi)}\, d\xi \tag{13-127}$$

Now, by combining the positive and negative exponentials to obtain cosine terms, we may rewrite Eq. (13-127) as

$$f_n(t) = \frac{1}{2\pi} \int_0^{2\pi} f(\xi)[1 + 2\cos(t-\xi) + 2\cos 2(t-\xi)$$

$$+ \cdots + 2\cos n(t-\xi)]\, d\xi$$

$$= \frac{1}{2\pi} \int_0^{2\pi} f(\xi)\, \frac{\sin[(2n+1)(t-\xi)/2]}{\sin[(t-\xi)/2]}\, d\xi$$

$$= \frac{1}{2\pi} \int_0^{2\pi} f(\xi)g(\xi - t)\, d\xi \tag{13-128}$$

where

$$g(\xi - t) = \frac{\sin[(2n+1)(\xi-t)/2]}{\sin[(\xi-t)/2]} = \frac{\sin[(2n+1)(t-\xi)/2]}{\sin[(t-\xi)/2]} \tag{13-129}$$

The step from a sum of cosines to the function $g(\xi - t)$ was made once before, in Eq. (13-85), and was to be derived in Prob. 13-15.

THE SCANNING INTEGRAL   Our manipulations on the partial Fourier series representing $f(t)$ have led to the interesting result shown in Eq. (13-128). We started with a sum of terms involving coefficients given by an auxiliary equation and ended with a simple integral involving our original function f and a second function g, which we shall call the *scanning function*. The type of integral obtained in Eq. (13-128) is quite important, since it reoccurs often in other types of analyses, as well as in our development here. Because of the importance of this

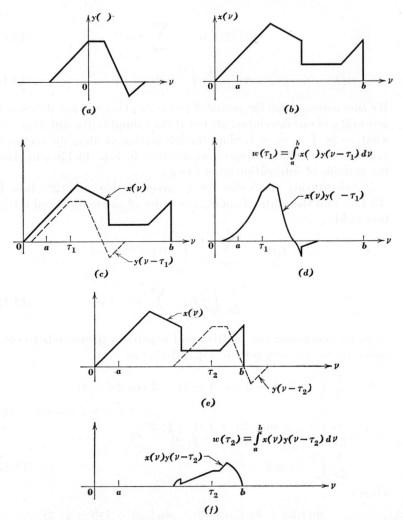

Fig. 13-8. (a) *Scanning function* $y(\nu)$ *and* (b) *the function* $x(\nu)$ *to be scanned.* (d) *The product* $x(\nu)y(\nu - \tau)$ *for* $\tau = \tau_1$. *This product is obtained from* (c) *and is integrated to obtain* $w(\tau_1)$. (e) *and* (f) *yield* $w(\tau)$ *for* $\tau = \tau_2$.

integral, which we shall call the *scanning integral*,† it is appropriate to take this opportunity to investigate it in some detail.

Let us consider the scanning integral below, which produces the function $w(\tau)$:

$$w(\tau) = \int_a^b x(\nu)y(\nu - \tau)\,d\nu \qquad (13\text{-}130)$$

The scanning function is $y(\nu - \tau)$, and the function being scanned is $x(\nu)$. The scanning interval is from a to b. Let us assume for the moment

---

† The same integral or very similar ones are also called *correlation*, *cross-correlation*, and *convolution* integrals.

that the scanning and scanned functions are as illustrated in Fig. 13-8a and b. We do not require that all scanning functions have the form given by Eq. (13-129). Remembering that $y(\nu - \tau)$ is the function $y(\nu)$ translated to the right by an amount τ, we see that $w(\tau)$ is found by translating the scanning function to the right by τ, multiplying it by the scanned function, and then integrating the result from a to b. These steps are illustrated in Fig. 13-8c to f.

The reason for the term scanning function should now be clear. The scanning function acts a little like a window which slides past the function being observed. The "light" coming through this window of varying opacity is integrated by the observer, who gives a level for the observed function for that particular position of the window.

SCANNING FUNCTIONS THAT REPRODUCE THE SCANNED FUNCTION Figure 13-9a and b illustrate another set of scanning and scanned functions. The particular scanning function shown has the property of being a reasonably good window. Let us discuss what we mean by this. We note first that the area under this scanning function is unity; that is,

$$\int_{-\infty}^{\infty} y(\nu) \, d\nu = 1 \qquad (13\text{-}131)$$

Second, since this scanning function has a constant value $1/\alpha$ over its range and is zero otherwise, the scanning integral of Eq. (13-130) reduces to

$$w(\tau) = \frac{1}{\alpha} \int_{\tau-\alpha/2}^{\tau+\alpha/2} x(\nu) \, d\nu \qquad (13\text{-}132)$$

Thus, to obtain $w(\tau)$, we simply average $x(\nu)$ between $\nu = \tau - \alpha/2$ and $\nu = \tau + \alpha/2$. Consequently, with this narrow scanning function of unit area, $w(\tau)$ is a close approximation to $x(\nu)$.

In Fig. 13-9c, where $w(\tau)$ has been drawn, we can see the degree to which $w(\tau)$ approximates $x(\nu)$. The approximation is very good in regions where $x(\nu)$ varies slowly. In regions in which $x(\nu)$ varies considerably over an interval of width α, the approximation degenerates. It should be clear that by making α smaller, this scanning function will reproduce $x(\nu)$ more accurately. In the limit, as $\alpha \to 0$, the width of this scanning function becomes zero, and the height becomes infinite; but the area remains unity, and $x(\nu)$ is reproduced exactly:

$$\int_a^b x(\nu)[\lim_{\alpha \to 0} y\,(\nu - \tau)] \, d\nu = \int_a^b x(\nu)\delta(\nu - \tau) \, d\nu = x(\tau) \quad (13\text{-}133)$$

The limit of this scanning function (as $\alpha \to 0$) is called a δ function. It is essentially identical to the unit impulse which was introduced in Sec. 7-3. We have chosen, in this circumstance, to use the term δ function rather than unit impulse for a number of reasons. The term δ function has a more mathematical connotation than unit impulse, which is

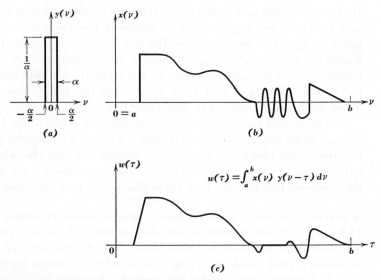

Fig. 13-9. (a) *A rectangular scanning function with unit area;* (b) *the function to be scanned;* (c) *the function produced by the integral reproduces* $x(\nu)$ *in regions of slow variation and fails in regions of rapid variation.*

almost invariably used in a physical sense. Since the context here is mathematical and since Eq. (13-133) is the basic defining equation for the δ function, we shall use this term throughout the remainder of this chapter.

Now, the particular scanning function illustrated in Fig. 13-9a is not unique in its property of very nearly reproducing the function it scans. It is not difficult to see that any function $y(\nu)$ which has a tall narrow pulse at $\nu = 0$ and which, when integrated, yields unit area will have this reproduction property. Furthermore, many of these functions can be made to approach a δ function as some parameter of the function is made to approach zero or infinity. That is to say, a number of different y functions can be found which depend upon a parameter α and which satisfy Eq. (13-133).

A PERIODIC SCANNING FUNCTION Before returning to our original partial Fourier series, let us reconsider the functions of Fig. 13-9 with a modification of the scanning function. Consider a scanning function which is exactly the same as the original one except that the rectangular pulse is repeated with period T. If $T \geq b - a$, then the function produced by this new scanning function will be exactly the same as the $w(\tau)$ of Fig. 13-9c except that it will be periodic with period T. Another example of periodic scanning is illustrated in Fig. 13-10.

THE FOURIER SERIES SCANNING FUNCTION AND INTEGRAL We now have sufficient background to carry on the investigation of the convergence

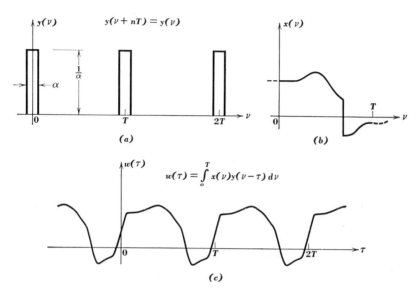

Fig. 13-10. (*a*) *A periodic scanning function.* (*b*) *The function being scanned. This function may have values for $\nu < 0$ and $\nu > T$, but they do not enter into the evaluation of $w(\tau)$ owing to the limits of integration.* (*c*) *The periodic function produced by this scanning integral.*

of Fourier series. First, let us examine the partial Fourier series. Figure 13-11 illustrates the scanning function of Eq. (13-129) for $n = 4$ and $n = 13$. Since this scanning function is similar to the one shown in Fig. 13-10, it will have the property of producing a periodic function which is nearly a replica of the function it scans. Furthermore, this periodic Fourier scanning function becomes, in the limit as $n \to \infty$, a series of periodic δ functions which reproduce the scanned function exactly.

This last statement is essentially equivalent to saying that the infinite Fourier series converges to the function it represents. We could prove that the Fourier scanning function does become a series of periodic δ functions, that is, that

$$\lim_{n \to \infty} \frac{1}{2\pi} \int_0^{2\pi} f(\xi)g(\xi - t)\,d\xi = f(t) \tag{13-134}$$

where $g(\xi - t)$ is given by Eq. (13-129). However, the proof is too involved to justify devoting space to it here. A careful study of Fig. 13-11, combined with the results of Probs. 13-23 and 13-24, should convince the skeptical reader.

The major difference between the Fourier scanning function of Fig. 13-11 and the periodic scanning function of Fig. 13-10 is the additional ripples, or overshoots, possessed by the Fourier scanning function. When the Fourier scanning function scans a function with a

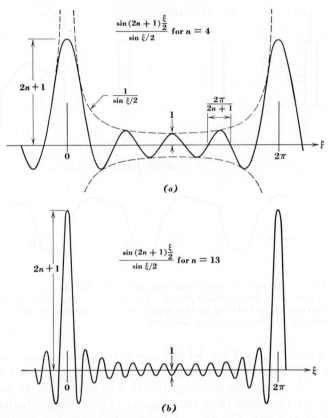

Fig. 13-11. *The periodic sampling function of Eq. (13-129). Note that the vertical scales in (a) and (b) differ by a factor of 2.*

discontinuity or a rapid variation, these ripples produce ripples, or over-shoot, in the approximating function. This effect, known as the *Gibbs phenomenon*, is illustrated in Fig. 13-12b.

The percentage of overshoot† at a discontinuity can be shown to be independent of the number of terms in the partial Fourier series. That is to say, as n is made larger and the scanning function becomes more like a series of δ functions, the scanned function is reproduced more accurately, but the overshoot at a discontinuity is not reduced. The width of the ripples following a discontinuity decreases as n increases, so that in the limit as $n \to \infty$ the Fourier series converges to the function it represents, no matter how closely the discontinuity is approached.

At a discontinuity the Fourier series converges to the center point of the discontinuity. This too is illustrated in Fig. 13-12b. The

---

† The first overshoot is approximately 9 per cent of the total discontinuity of the scanned function.

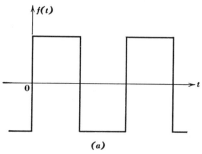

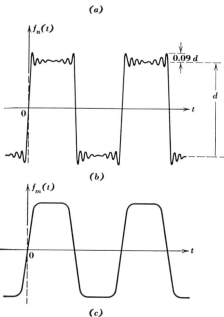

Fig. 13-12. (a) A square wave; (b) the approximation to the square wave formed by N terms of the Fourier series, n = 10; (c) another approximation using the same number of terms in a trigonometric series but with the high frequencies weighted less heavily.

way in which a Fourier series converges to the function it represents should now be fairly clear. The scanning function becomes narrower and higher as the number of terms in the series is increased, and this results in a better and better reproduction of the scanned function. Where the scanned function is continuous, the convergence is uniform; that is, we can find a large but finite number N such that, for $n > N$,

$$|f(t) - f_n(t)| < \epsilon \qquad \epsilon > 0 \qquad (13\text{-}135)$$

no matter how small we choose ϵ. Equation (13-135) will not hold at discontinuities, although we can make it hold as close to the discontinuity as we choose by making n sufficiently large.†

> † When Fourier first introduced his series, there was considerable opposition to his ideas on the grounds that a sum of continuous functions (the sines and cosines) could never converge to a discontinuous function. The principal factor contributing to this opposition was a lack of understanding at that time of the concept of the convergence of infinite series.

In dealing with the infinite Fourier series, the Gibbs phenomenon poses no problems, but when a function is represented by a finite series, it may be necessary to consider this effect. For example, we may have to construct a trigonometric series of n harmonics which will closely approximate the square wave of Fig. 13-12a and yet will not have the overshoots of the n harmonic Fourier series. Such a series can be formed† and will yield an approximation similar to the one illustrated in Fig. 13-12c (see Prob. 13-25). Such an approximation, although better in some respects, will have a greater mean-squared error than the Fourier approximation with the same number of harmonics.

PROBLEMS

13-21 Find $w(\tau)$ as given by Eq. (13-130) for the scanning and scanned functions shown in the figure.

13-22 If we take the time inverse of a function to form a scanning function, the resulting scanning integral is called a convolution integral:

$$w(\tau) = \int_{-\infty}^{\infty} x(\nu)y(\tau - \nu)\, d\nu = x(\tau)*y(\tau)$$

Show that $x(\tau)*y(\tau) = y(\tau)*x(\tau)$. Find $x(\tau)*y(\tau)$ if

$$x(\tau) = \begin{cases} 1 & \text{for } 0 < \tau < 1 \\ 0 & \text{otherwise} \end{cases}$$

$$y(\tau) = \begin{cases} e^{-\tau} & \text{for } \tau > 0 \\ 0 & \text{for } \tau < 0 \end{cases}$$

13-23 For $g(\xi - t)$ as given by Eq. (13-129), prove that

$$\frac{1}{2\pi} \int_0^{2\pi} g(\xi - t)\, d\xi = 1$$

for any value of t and n. [HINT: Use Eq. (13-85).]

13-24 If $f(x)$ is continuous for $a \leq x \leq b$, then

$$\lim_{n \to \infty} \int_a^b f(x) \sin nx\, dx = 0$$

Starting from this fact and assuming that the derivative of $f(x)$ exists, that is, that

$$f'(x)\Big|_{x=x_0} = \lim_{x \to x_0} \frac{f(x) - f(x_0)}{x - x_0} < \infty$$

† See E. A. Guillemin, "The Mathematics of Circuit Analysis," pp. 496–501, John Wiley & Sons, Inc., New York, 1949.

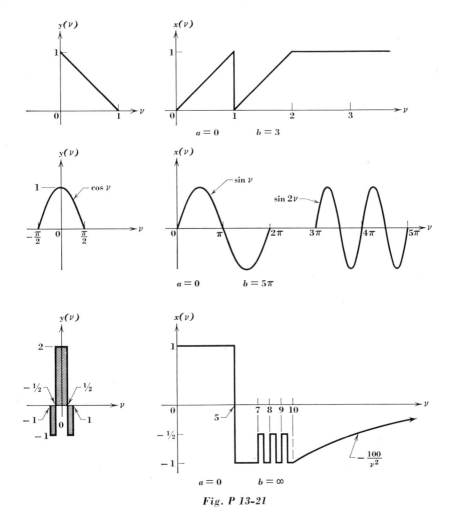

Fig. P 13-21

for each x_0 between a and b, prove that

$$\lim_{n \to \infty} \int_a^b \frac{f(x) \sin n(x - x_0)}{(x - x_0)} \, dx = \pi f(x_0)$$

[HINT: Rearrange the integral above so that $f'(x_0)$ appears, and make use of the fact that

$$\int_{-\infty}^{\infty} \frac{\sin u}{u} \, du = \pi$$

Now prove Eq. (13-134) for the case in which $f(t)$ is continuous with a finite derivative at all points. (The restrictions on $f(t)$ assumed here are stronger than necessary.)]

13-25   The partial Fourier series for $f(t)$,

$$f_n(t) = \sum_{k=-n}^{n} \gamma_k e^{jkt}$$

led to Eq. (13-128) and a scanning function which produced the Gibbs phenomenon. Define a new approximation to $f(t)$ as follows:

$$f'_n(t) = \sum_{k=-n}^{n} \lambda_k e^{jkt}$$

$$\lambda_k = \frac{n + 1 - |k|}{n + 1} \gamma_k$$

Show that this approximation produces the following scanning integral:

$$f'_n(t) = \frac{1}{2\pi} \int_0^{2\pi} f(\xi) h(\xi - t) \, d\xi$$

$$h(\xi - t) = \frac{1}{n+1} \left\{ \frac{\sin \left[(n+1)(\xi - t)/2 \right]}{\sin \left[(\xi - t)/2 \right]} \right\}^2$$

Draw a rough graph of $h(\xi)$ and compare with $g(\xi)$. Explain why this scanning function will produce no overshoot.

13-5   THE FOURIER TRANSFORM

We opened this chapter by posing a problem: How does one find the response of a linear system when the driving function is periodic but not sinusoidal? The technique used to solve this problem may be summarized as follows: The periodic function is expressed in terms of a sum of functions, namely, exponentials or sinusoids, each one of which yields an easily determined response; then, because of the linearity of the system, superposition is applicable, and the total response is found as a sum of the individual responses.

This general technique is employed in analyzing both linear and nonlinear systems under the influence of a variety of driving functions. That is, the driving function is expressed as a combination of appropriate functions, and the response is then a combination of the responses to these functions. The method just outlined is particularly applicable to linear systems, because of the superposition theorem.

In the remainder of this chapter the concepts developed in the preceding sections will be extended to nonperiodic functions. This extension will be made by calling upon a mathematical tool of considerable power, the *transform*.

TRANSFORMS AND TRANSFORMATIONS   Figure 13-13 is a graphical illustration of the Fourier series technique of finding the response of a linear system to a periodic driving function. This figure is general

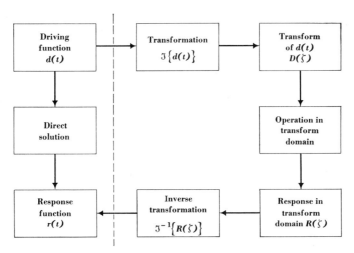

Fig. 13-13. *Two operations which lead from* $d(t)$ *to* $r(t)$. *To the left of the dashed line is the operation which yields* $r(t)$ *directly. To the right a corresponding operation is performed on the transform of* $d(t)$. *The inverse transform of the result of this right-hand operation yields* $r(t)$.

enough to serve also as a model of all transform methods. Let us discuss the meaning of Fig. 13-13 and then illustrate our discussion with two quite dissimilar examples.

Figure 13-13 may be interpreted as follows. We start with a function $d(t)$, or with a combination of such functions. Some prescribed operation is to be performed upon $d(t)$ in order to yield the response function, or the solution, $r(t)$. The direct operation is indicated by the portion of the figure to the left of the dashed line. Because the direct operation may be difficult, or tedious, or not well defined, it is often advantageous to take another path to the final solution. Rather than operate directly upon $d(t)$, we first express $d(t)$ in another form; that is, we transform $d(t)$ to a new function $D(\zeta)$. Corresponding to the original direct operation, there will be an easier operation to perform on $D(\zeta)$, yielding $R(\zeta)$. A transformation of $R(\zeta)$ produces the final solution $r(t)$. The transformation converting $d(t)$ to $D(\zeta)$ is called the direct transformation and is denoted by

$$\mathfrak{I}\{d(t)\} = D(\zeta) \tag{13-136}$$

The transformation from $R(\zeta)$ back to $r(t)$ is called the inverse transformation and is denoted by

$$\mathfrak{I}^{-1}\{R(\zeta)\} = r(t) \tag{13-137}$$

For an elemental example of transform methods, consider the following problem: *Given three numbers* x, y, *and* z, *find the product* xyz. The solution is very easy to find directly, but under some conditions, the following transform method is preferred. Each number is transformed by obtaining its logarithm:

$$X = \mathfrak{I}\{x\} = \log x \qquad Y = \mathfrak{I}\{y\} = \log y$$
$$Z = \mathfrak{I}\{z\} = \log z \qquad\qquad (13\text{-}138)$$

The operation in the transform domain which corresponds to multiplication of the original functions is addition. Thus,

$$W = X + Y + Z$$
$$xyz = \mathfrak{I}^{-1}\{W\} = \mathfrak{I}^{-1}\{X + Y + Z\} = \text{antilog } (X + Y + Z) \quad (13\text{-}139)$$

This is, of course, a familiar transform method; although the reader may never have considered it in this light before, he makes use of this technique every time he operates his slide rule.

For a further example of the transform method above, consider the problem of finding x^α when x and α are given and α is not an integer. Doing this directly is considerably more of a challenge than obtaining the product in the previous problem. This is a case in which the transform method would invariably be used, since raising to a power in the direct operation corresponds to simple multiplication in the transform domain. That is,

$$x^\alpha = \mathfrak{I}^{-1}\{W\} = \text{antilog } W \qquad\qquad (13\text{-}140)$$
where $$\qquad W = \alpha X = \alpha\mathfrak{I}\{x\} = \alpha \log x \qquad\qquad (13\text{-}141)$$

THE FOURIER SERIES TRANSFORM Obtaining the response of linear systems to periodic driving functions by the Fourier series method can also be considered a transform method. Instead of solving the set of simultaneous linear differential equations directly, we transformed the periodic driving function $f(t)$ into a new function γ_k:

$$\gamma_k = \mathfrak{I}\{f(t)\} = \frac{1}{T}\int_0^T f(t)e^{-jk\omega_1 t}\, dt \qquad \omega_1 = \frac{2\pi}{T} \qquad (13\text{-}142)$$

The direct solution of the system differential equations in the time domain corresponds, in the transform domain, to multiplication by an easily obtained transfer function:

$$\lambda_k = \gamma_k \mathbf{T}(jk\omega_1) \qquad\qquad (13\text{-}143)$$

The inverse transform which yields the final time-domain response function consists of a summation:

$$r(t) = \mathfrak{I}^{-1}\{\lambda_k\} = \sum_{k=-\infty}^{\infty} \lambda_k e^{jk\omega_1 t} \qquad\qquad (13\text{-}144)$$

The whole process above is diagramed in Fig. 13-14.

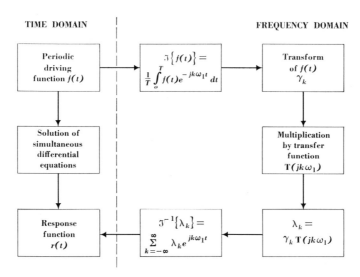

Fig. 13-14. A diagram illustrating the Fourier series transform method of finding the response of a linear system when the excitation is a periodic function.

THE FREQUENCY SPECTRUM We called γ_k as given by Eq. (13-142) a function. On the other hand, we know that the γ_k's are just a set of complex numbers, the coefficients of the complex Fourier series corresponding to $f(t)$. Is the idea of a function compatible with a set of numbers? If we adopt a fairly broad definition of function, there will be no problem.

We usually think of a function of a variable as a relationship which yields a continuous or semicontinuous curve as the variable takes on different values. This concept can be enlarged by defining a function as a relationship which assigns or yields a number (possibly complex) for each value of the variable. This definition obviously encompasses our usual concept of function and allows us to treat γ_k as a function in the following manner:

$$\gamma_k = \gamma_k(\omega) = \begin{cases} \gamma(\omega) & \text{for } \omega = k\omega_1 \\ 0 & \text{otherwise} \end{cases}$$

$$\gamma(\omega) = \frac{1}{T}\int_0^T f(t)e^{-j\omega t}\,dt \tag{13-145}$$

With γ_k defined in this manner, the complex Fourier series can be written as

$$f(t) = \sum_{k=-\infty}^{\infty} \gamma_k e^{jk\omega_1 t} = \sum_{k=-\infty}^{\infty} \gamma(\omega)\Big|_{\omega=k\omega_1} e^{jk\omega_1 t} = \sum_{k=-\infty}^{\infty} \gamma(k\omega_1)e^{jk\omega_1 t} \tag{13-146}$$

Soon we shall have reason to utilize this form of writing the complex Fourier series, but before doing so, let us discuss the function $\gamma_k(\omega)$.

The function $\gamma_k(\omega)$ is called the *frequency spectrum* of the function $f(t)$. Furthermore, since $\gamma_k(\omega)$ is nonzero only for discrete values of ω, it is called a discrete or a line spectrum. The frequency spectrum is complex; that is, $\gamma_k(\omega)$ has both a real and an imaginary part. It is often convenient, therefore, to separate the frequency spectrum into two parts, the amplitude spectrum $\alpha_k(\omega)$ and the phase spectrum $\Phi_k(\omega)$:

$$\alpha_k(\omega) = |\gamma_k(\omega)|$$

$$\Phi_k(\omega) = \angle\gamma_k(\omega) = \tan^{-1}\frac{\text{Im}\,[\gamma_k(\omega)]}{\text{Re}\,[\gamma_k(\omega)]} \tag{13-147}$$

$$\gamma_k(\omega) = \alpha_k(\omega)e^{j\Phi_k(\omega)} \tag{13-148}$$

To take an example, let us compute and plot the frequency spectrum of the periodic function illustrated in Fig. 13-15a.

$$\gamma_k(\omega) = \frac{1}{T}\int_0^T e^{-\alpha t}e^{-j\omega t}\,dt = \frac{1}{T}\frac{1 - e^{-(\alpha+j\omega)T}}{\alpha + j\omega} \tag{13-149}$$

$$\alpha_k(\omega) = \frac{(1 - 2e^{-\alpha T}\cos\omega T + e^{-2\alpha T})^{1/2}}{T(\alpha^2 + \omega^2)^{1/2}} \tag{13-150}$$

$$\Phi_k(\omega) = -\tan^{-1}\frac{(1 - e^{-\alpha T}\cos\omega T) - \alpha e^{-\alpha T}\sin\omega T}{\omega e^{-\alpha T}\sin\omega T + \alpha(1 - e^{-\alpha T}\cos\omega T)} \tag{13-151}$$

The expressions above are valid for $\omega = k\omega_1 = k2\pi/T$. The amplitude and phase spectra are plotted in Fig. 13-15b and c.

Let us pause for a moment to consider the significance of the concept of the frequency spectrum. We have nothing which is actually new; that is, we have computed the Fourier series coefficients in earlier sections and have noted that they have magnitude and phase. What is different is our viewpoint. We now treat the coefficients as a function of ω, a function in the frequency domain. Furthermore, since this frequency-domain function uniquely determines the time-domain function [through Eq. (13-146)], we are justified in adopting the following position: Every periodic function has two representations, one in the time domain and one in the frequency domain, which are transforms of each other and are therefore called a *Fourier series transform pair*:

$$\gamma_k(\omega) = \Im\{f(t)\} = \begin{cases} \dfrac{1}{T}\displaystyle\int_0^T f(t)e^{-j\omega t}\,dt & \text{for } \omega = k\omega_1 \\ 0 & \text{otherwise} \end{cases}$$

$$\tag{13-152}$$

$$f(t) = \Im^{-1}\{\gamma_k(\omega)\} = \sum_{k=-\infty}^{\infty} \gamma_k(k\omega_1)e^{jk\omega_1 t}$$

A vital point in relation to this development is the fact that finding the system response to a periodic driving function is very much easier in the frequency domain than in the time domain. This fact leads quite naturally to a question: Can nonperiodic time functions

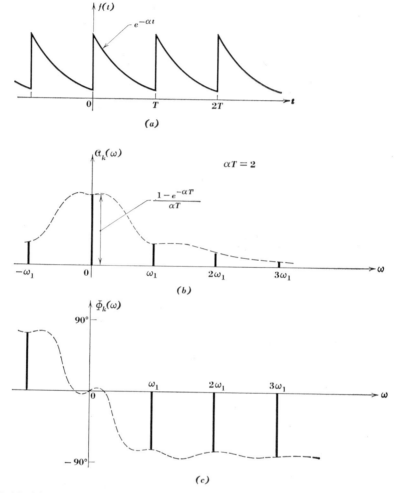

Fig. 13-15. *(a) A periodic waveform; (b) its amplitude spectrum; (c) its phase spectrum.*

be represented in the frequency domain, and if so, is the analysis of linear systems facilitated by operating in this domain?

THE FOURIER TRANSFORM The answer to both parts of the question above is yes. We can derive the transformations which transform a time-domain function to a frequency-domain function and back again by starting with a periodic time function. Then, by letting the period become infinite, we can cause the function to become nonperiodic and the Fourier series transformations to become the Fourier integral transformations, or, in short, the Fourier transform.

In order to facilitate this development, let us modify the transformations of Eqs. (13-152). The limits of integration in the direct transform will be translated to make the integration symmetrical about the origin, and the $1/T$ factor will be shifted from the direct to the inverse transform. Thus,

$$F_k = T\gamma_k = T\gamma_k(\omega) = \begin{cases} F(\omega) & \text{for } \omega = k\omega_1 \\ 0 & \text{otherwise} \end{cases}$$

$$F(\omega) = \int_{-T/2}^{T/2} f(t)e^{-jk\omega_1 t}\, dt \qquad (13\text{-}153)$$

$$f(t) = \sum_{k=-\infty}^{\infty} \frac{1}{T} F_k e^{jk\omega_1 t} = \sum_{k=-\infty}^{\infty} \frac{1}{T} F(k\omega_1) e^{jk\omega_1 t} \qquad (13\text{-}154)$$

Finally, let us change notation slightly and call the fundamental radian frequency $\Delta\omega$:

$$\omega_1 = \frac{2\pi}{T} = \Delta\omega \qquad (13\text{-}155)$$

With this change, Eq. (13-154) becomes

$$f(t) = \frac{1}{2\pi} \sum_{k=-\infty}^{\infty} F(k\,\Delta\omega)e^{jk\,\Delta\omega\, t}\,\Delta\omega \qquad (13\text{-}156)$$

At this point a diagram should prove helpful. Figure 13-16 illustrates a periodic function and its frequency spectrum. Note that as the period is made larger, or, equivalently, as $\Delta\omega$ is made smaller, the spectral lines move closer together. In the limit as $T \to \infty$, $\Delta\omega \to 0$, the spectral lines become packed so closely together that $F_k(\omega)$ changes from a discrete function to the continuous function $F(\omega)$. In this limiting process, the function $F(\omega)$ becomes

$$F(\omega) = \lim_{T \to \infty} \int_{-T/2}^{T/2} f(t)e^{-j\omega t}\, dt = \int_{-\infty}^{\infty} f(t)e^{-j\omega t}\, dt \qquad (13\text{-}157)$$

What happens to the inverse transform, Eq. (13-156), in this limiting process? If we recall that an integral was first defined as a limit of a summation, we see that

$$f(t) = \lim_{\Delta\omega \to 0} \frac{1}{2\pi} \sum_{k=-\infty}^{\infty} F(k\,\Delta\omega)e^{jk\,\Delta\omega\, t}\,\Delta\omega$$

$$= \frac{1}{2\pi} \int_{-\infty}^{\infty} F(\omega)e^{j\omega t}\, d\omega \qquad (13\text{-}158)$$

The two equations above define the Fourier transform by which a nonperiodic time function can be expressed as a function in the fre-

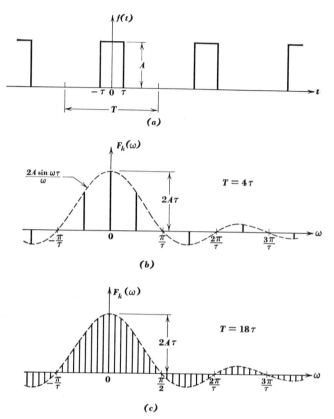

Fig. 13-16. (a) *A periodic time function* $f(t)$ *with period* T; (b) *the discrete frequency spectrum when* $T = 4\tau$; (c) *the discrete frequency spectrum when* $T = 18\tau$. *Since* $f(t)$ *is even,* $F_k(\omega)$ *is purely real.*

quency domain, and vice versa. We shall denote the Fourier transform by a script $\mathfrak{F}$ in the following manner:†

$$\mathfrak{F}\{f(t)\} = F(\omega) = \int_{-\infty}^{\infty} f(t)e^{-j\omega t}\,dt$$

$$\mathfrak{F}^{-1}\{F(\omega)\} = f(t) = \frac{1}{2\pi} \int_{-\infty}^{\infty} F(\omega)e^{j\omega t}\,d\omega \tag{13-159}$$

The derivation of Eqs. (13-159) has been heuristic rather than rigorous. The reader who is a little dubious about the development above is well within his rights. It is always wise to view derivations

† The definitions of the Fourier transform given by various authors show a number of minor differences in notation. Some authors place the $1/2\pi$ in the direct transform or place $1/\sqrt{2\pi}$ in both the direct and the inverse transforms. Others interchange the minus sign in the exponent, and still others substitute $2\pi f$ for ω and integrate with respect to cyclic frequency rather than radian frequency. We have chosen this form because it agrees most closely with the Laplace transform, which is considerably more standardized in notation.

which involve limiting processes, as these do, with a certain degree of skepticism. Problem 13-26 is designed to convince the skeptic.

PROPERTIES OF THE FOURIER TRANSFORM   The first property that must be considered is that of existence. That is, under what conditions does a time-domain function have a transform, and vice versa? Basically this reduces to the question of the existence of the integrals in Eqs. (13-159). These integrals will converge if

$$\int_{-\infty}^{\infty} |f(t)|\, dt < \infty \tag{13-160}$$

$$\int_{-\infty}^{\infty} |F(\omega)|\, d\omega < \infty \tag{13-161}$$

If a time function satisfies Eq. (13-160), it will have a Fourier transform, and if a frequency function satisfies Eq. (13-161), it will have an inverse transform. In a few cases, Eqs. (13-160) and (13-161) are too restrictive; that is, transforms do exist for a few functions which do not satisfy Eqs. (13-160) and (13-161). We shall discuss these later.

A number of important and interesting properties of Fourier transforms are listed in Table 13-2. Proofs and comments for some of the pairs in the table are given below.

It should be understood that the relationships stated in Table 13-2 apply only if the transforms actually exist. For example, the transform of the integral of Fig. 13-17a does not exist, because $h(t)$ does not satisfy Eq. (13-160). Consequently, relationship 8 of Table 13-2 is not applicable, even though the transform of $f(t)$ itself does exist.

We shall prove a few of the relationships of Table 13-2, leaving the rest as problems. Relationship 7 can be shown by integrating the integral transformation by parts:

$$\mathfrak{F}\left\{\frac{df(t)}{dt}\right\} = \int_{-\infty}^{\infty} \frac{df(t)}{dt}\, e^{-j\omega t}\, dt$$

$$= f(t)e^{-j\omega t}\Big|_{-\infty}^{\infty} + j\omega \int_{-\infty}^{\infty} f(t)e^{-j\omega t}\, dt$$

$$= j\omega F(\omega) \tag{13-162}$$

The final equality in the above expression depends upon $f(t)$ equaling zero for $t = \pm\infty$. This will necessarily be true if $f(t)$ satisfies Eq. (13-160).

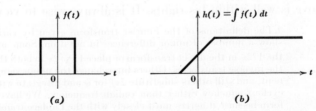

Fig. 13-17. *A function $f(t)$ and its integral $h(t)$. $\mathfrak{F}\{f(t)\}$ exists, but $\mathfrak{F}\{h(t)\}$ does not.*

TABLE 13-2   *Fourier Transform Properties*

Time Domain	Frequency Domain	
1. $f(t)$	$F(\omega)$	
2. $af(t) + bg(t)$	$aF(\omega) + bG(\omega)$	
3. $f(-t)$	$F(-\omega) = F^*(\omega)$	[i.e., the complex conjugate of $F(\omega)$]
4. $f(t + a)$	$F(\omega)e^{j\omega a}$	
5. $f(t)e^{j\omega_0 t}$	$F(\omega - \omega_0)$	
6. $f(at)$	$\dfrac{1}{a} F\left(\dfrac{\omega}{a}\right)$ $a > 0$	
7. $\dfrac{df(t)}{dt}$	$j\omega F(\omega)$	
8. $\int f(t)\,dt$	$\dfrac{F(\omega)}{j\omega}$	
9. $tf(t)$	$j\dfrac{dF(\omega)}{d\omega}$	
10. $\dfrac{f(t)}{t}$	$\dfrac{1}{j} \int F(\omega)\,d\omega$	
11. $\int_{-\infty}^{\infty} f(\tau)g(t - \tau)\,d\tau$	$F(\omega)G(\omega)$	
12. $\int_{-\infty}^{\infty} f(\tau)g(\tau + t)\,d$	$F^*(\omega)G(\omega)$	
13. $f(t)g(t)$	$\dfrac{1}{2\pi} \int_{-\infty}^{\infty} F(\xi)G(\omega - \xi)\,d\xi$	

Relationship 10 is also derived by an integration by parts. First we adopt the following notation:

$$F^{(-1)}(\omega) \triangleq \int F(\omega)\,d\omega \triangleq \int_{-\infty}^{\omega} F(\omega)\,d\omega \qquad (13\text{-}163)$$

If $F^{(-1)}(\omega)$ has an inverse transform, it must satisfy Eq. (13-161). Hence,

$$F^{(-1)}(\omega) = 0 \qquad \text{for } \omega = \pm\infty \qquad (13\text{-}164)$$

The last expression is utilized as follows:

$$\mathfrak{F}^{-1}\{F(\omega)\} = f(t) = \frac{1}{2\pi} \int_{-\infty}^{\infty} F(\omega)e^{j\omega t}\,d\omega$$

$$= \frac{1}{2\pi} \left[F^{(-1)}(\omega)e^{j\omega t} \Big|_{-\infty}^{\infty} -jt \int_{-\infty}^{\infty} F^{(-1)}(\omega)e^{j\omega t}\,d\omega \right]$$

$$= \frac{t}{j2\pi} \int_{-\infty}^{\infty} F^{(-1)}(\omega)e^{j\omega t}\,d\omega \qquad (13\text{-}165)$$

Dividing both sides by t yields relationship 10:

$$\frac{f(t)}{t} = \frac{1}{j} \left[\frac{1}{2\pi} \int_{-\infty}^{\infty} F^{(-1)}(\omega)e^{j\omega t}\,d\omega \right] = \mathfrak{F}^{-1}\left\{ \frac{1}{j} F^{(-1)}(\omega) \right\} \qquad (13\text{-}166)$$

Relationships 11 to 13 indicate that convolution and scanning in the time domain correspond to simple multiplication in the frequency domain. Likewise, convolution and scanning in the frequency domain are equivalent to multiplication in the time domain. Let us prove relationship 12:

$$\mathfrak{F}\left\{\int_{-\infty}^{\infty} f(\tau)g(\tau + t) \, d\tau\right\} = \int_{-\infty}^{\infty}\left[\int_{-\infty}^{\infty} f(\tau)g(\tau + t) \, d\tau\right]e^{-j\omega t} \, dt$$

$$= \int_{-\infty}^{\infty} f(\tau)\int_{-\infty}^{\infty} g(\tau + t)e^{-j\omega t} \, dt \, d\tau$$

$$= \int_{-\infty}^{\infty} f(\tau)G(\omega)e^{+j\omega\tau} \, d\tau$$

$$= F^*(\omega)G(\omega) \qquad (13\text{-}167)$$

In this last derivation, we interchanged the order of integration and then utilized relationship 4.

Equation (13-167) may be rewritten in the following form:

$$\int_{-\infty}^{\infty} f(\tau)g(\tau + t) \, d\tau = \frac{1}{2\pi}\int_{-\infty}^{\infty} F^*(\omega)G(\omega)e^{j\omega t} \, d\omega \qquad (13\text{-}168)$$

Now, if we take the special case where $g(t) = f(t)$, Eq. (13-168) becomes

$$\int_{-\infty}^{\infty} f(\tau)f(\tau + t) \, d\tau = \frac{1}{2\pi}\int_{-\infty}^{\infty} |F(\omega)|^2 e^{j\omega t} \, d\omega \qquad (13\text{-}169)$$

and

$$\int_{-\infty}^{\infty} f^2(t) \, dt = \frac{1}{2\pi}\int_{-\infty}^{\infty} |F(\omega)|^2 \, d\omega \qquad (13\text{-}170)$$

These last two equations are quite important. The left-hand side of Eq. (13-169) is called the autocorrelation function of $f(t)$, and the right-hand side is seen to be the inverse transform of the squared amplitude spectrum of $f(t)$. The left-hand side of Eq. (13-170) is called the energy of the function $f(t)$. That is, if $f(t)$ was a current through a 1-ohm resistor, the left-hand side would be the total energy dissipated in the resistor. Equation (13-170) indicates that the total energy can be found by integrating the square of the time function or the square of the amplitude spectrum.

SOME SPECIAL FOURIER TRANSFORM PAIRS As was mentioned earlier, we can define Fourier transforms for some functions which do not satisfy Eqs. (13-160) and (13-161). In order to facilitate this, let us amplify our remarks of Sec. 13-4 concerning δ functions. A δ function is defined, not as a normal function is, but in terms of its effect upon other functions:

$$\int_{-\infty}^{\infty} \delta(t)f(t) \, dt = \int_{-\epsilon}^{\epsilon} \delta(t)f(t) \, dt = f(0) \qquad \epsilon > 0$$

$$\int_{-\infty}^{\infty} \delta(t - \tau)f(t) \, dt = \int_{\tau-\epsilon}^{\tau+\epsilon} \delta(t - \tau)f(t) \, dt = f(\tau) \qquad (13\text{-}171)$$

There are numerous functions which become δ functions in the limit as one of their parameters approaches zero or infinity. The following example is of particular interest here:

$$\lim_{\lambda \to \infty} \frac{\sin \lambda t}{\pi t} = \delta(t) \qquad (13\text{-}172)$$

Now let us find the Fourier transform for the function

$$f(t) = \begin{cases} \cos \omega_0 t & |t| < T \\ 0 & |t| > T \end{cases} \qquad (13\text{-}173)$$

$$F(\omega) = \int_{-T}^{T} \cos \omega_0 t \, e^{-j\omega t} \, dt = \frac{\sin (\omega + \omega_0) T}{\omega + \omega_0} + \frac{\sin (\omega - \omega_0) T}{\omega - \omega_0}$$

$$(13\text{-}174)$$

If we let T become infinite, we obtain the following transform pair:

$$\mathcal{F}\{\cos \omega_0 t\} = \pi[\delta(\omega + \omega_0) + \delta(\omega - \omega_0)] \qquad (13\text{-}175)$$

All the transform pairs of Table 13-3 can be obtained in a similar manner.†

TABLE 13-3   *Some Special Fourier Transform Pairs*

$f(t)$	$F(\omega)$
1. $\cos \omega_0 t$	$\pi[\delta(\omega + \omega_0) + \delta(\omega - \omega_0)]$
2. $\sin \omega_0 t$	$j\pi[\delta(\omega + \omega_0) - \delta(\omega - \omega_0)]$
3. 1	$2\pi \delta(\omega)$
4. $e^{j\omega_0 t}$	$2\pi \delta(\omega - \omega_0)$
5. $\delta(t + t_0)$	$e^{j\omega t_0}$
6. $\frac{1}{2}[\delta(t + t_0) + \delta(t - t_0)]$	$\cos \omega t_0$
7. $\frac{1}{2}[\delta(t + t_0) - \delta(t - t_0)]$	$j \sin \omega t_0$

LINEAR SYSTEM SOLUTIONS   Unless we can employ the Fourier transform in system analysis, its development up to this point has been a mere academic exercise. If we refer to Fig. 13-14 and to the derivation leading to the Fourier transform, particularly Eqs. (13-157) and (13-158), we see that Eq. (13-158) can be replaced by

$$r(t) = \lim_{\Delta\omega \to 0} \frac{1}{2\pi} \sum_{k=-\infty}^{\infty} F_k(k \, \Delta\omega) \mathbf{T}(jk \, \Delta\omega) e^{jk \, \Delta\omega \, t} \, \Delta\omega$$

$$= \frac{1}{2\pi} \int_{-\infty}^{\infty} F(\omega) \mathbf{T}(j\omega) e^{j\omega t} \, d\omega \qquad (13\text{-}176)$$

† It should be noted that

$$f(t) = \begin{cases} \cos \omega_0 t & \text{for } t > 0 \\ 0 & \text{otherwise} \end{cases}$$

does not have a Fourier transform, although $f(t) = \cos \omega_0 t$ for all t does.

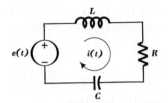

Fig. 13-18. An electrical circuit.

In words, Eq. (13-176) states that *if a driving function $f(t)$ with Fourier transform $F(\omega)$ is applied to a linear system with transfer function $\mathbf{T}(s)$, then the response $r(t)$ has a Fourier transform which is $F(\omega)\mathbf{T}(j\omega)$.*

Equation (13-176) was obtained by a limiting process upon the response to a periodic function. Let us verify this result by an example in which we use a different approach. Let us find the current which flows in the circuit of Fig. 13-18 when the applied voltage $e(t)$ has a Fourier transform $E(\omega)$. The appropriate differential equation for this system is

$$e(t) = L\frac{di(t)}{dt} + Ri(t) + \frac{1}{C}\int i(t)\,dt \qquad (13\text{-}177)$$

Since both sides of this equation are equal, the Fourier transforms of both sides must be equal:

$$\mathfrak{F}\{e(t)\} = \mathfrak{F}\left\{L\frac{di}{dt} + Ri + \frac{1}{C}\int i\,dt\right\} \qquad (13\text{-}178)$$

Let us assume that the response function $i(t)$, whatever it is, has a Fourier transform $I(\omega)$. Consequently, we can utilize relationships 2, 7, and 8 of Table 13-2 to obtain the expression

$$E(\omega) = \left(j\omega L + R + \frac{1}{j\omega C}\right) I(\omega) \qquad (13\text{-}179)$$

Thus, $$I(\omega) = \frac{E(\omega)}{j\omega L + R + 1/j\omega C} = \frac{E(\omega)}{\mathbf{Z}(s)}\bigg|_{s=j\omega} \qquad (13\text{-}180)$$

Finally, employing the inversion transformation, we obtain

$$i(t) = \frac{1}{2\pi}\int_{-\infty}^{\infty}\frac{E(\omega)}{\mathbf{Z}(j\omega)}e^{j\omega t}\,d\omega \qquad (13\text{-}181)$$

Equation (13-181) is exactly what we would obtain if the statement following Eq. (13-176) were applied directly.

RESTRICTIONS AND LIMITATIONS   There are two very important limitations in connection with the analysis of systems by Fourier transform methods. The first has already been introduced. Whenever the system driving function or response function does not satisfy Eq. (13-160), the system solution cannot be found by Fourier transform methods.†

† An exception to this statement is provided by the transform pairs of Table 13-3.

For example, if the resistance in the circuit of Fig. 13-18 were zero, the current response would not decay to zero and hence would not have a Fourier transform. Hence, the step from Eq. (13-178) to Eq. (13-179) would not be valid.

The second limitation is in the handling of initial conditions. Equation (13-176) is applicable, as is the technique leading to Eq. (13-181), if no energy is stored in the system before the application of the driving function. If there is initial stored energy, two paths are open. One is to add to the Fourier transform solution the natural solution (complete with arbitrary constants) and then to satisfy the initial boundary conditions. The other is to use impulse and constant sources, as is discussed in Sec. 9-3 and illustrated in Table 9-1. This method requires the utilization of the transform pairs of Table 13-3.

Of these two limitations, the first is obviously the more serious. The Laplace transform method of system analysis overcomes the first limitation and handles the second in a somewhat more satisfying manner. The Laplace transform method, which we have, in fact, been employing since Chap. 7, will be discussed in the next section.

ADVANTAGES OF THE FOURIER TRANSFORM METHOD At this point the skeptical reader probably is bothered by a question something like this: Since the s-domain (Laplace transform) techniques that we have been using appear to accomplish everything that the Fourier transform does and more, why bother with the Fourier transform? There are two reasons. The first is that the Fourier transform leads naturally into the Laplace transform and therefore serves as a convenient precedent for any discussion of the Laplace transform. Second, there are a number of situations in which the Fourier transform is more convenient or in which the Laplace transform cannot be applied at all.

A good example of an area where the Fourier transform can be employed to advantage and where the use of the Laplace transform would present serious difficulties is the analysis of idealized systems. For example, we may wish to discuss a system which contains an ideal bandpass filter. That is, the transfer function is†

$$T(\omega) = \begin{cases} 1 & \text{for } \omega_1 < |\omega| < \omega_2 \\ 0 & \text{otherwise} \end{cases} \qquad (13\text{-}182)$$

In the s domain we can only handle functions which approximate $T(\omega)$, and these are quite complex. The Fourier transform analysis of a system with this transfer function can be quite simple. It so happens

---

† Lightface capital letters, as in the term $T(\omega)$, indicate Fourier transforms and transfer functions. Boldface notation, as in $\mathbf{T}(j\omega)$, indicates an s-domain function in which we have substituted $j\omega$ for s. Since the transfer function of Eq. (13-182) could not be obtained from an s-domain transfer function, lightface notation is employed.

that the transfer function defined above is not physically realizable. However, the mathematical analysis of such systems by Fourier transform methods is still valid, and such analyses are often helpful in the analysis and understanding of realizable systems.

A second area where Fourier transforms are of great use is in the analysis of random signals and noise. A discussion of this subject is beyond the scope of this text. We can say, though, that the analysis of these functions and of the linear systems in which they occur differs little from that above.

PROBLEMS

13-26 Define

$$f_a(t) = \int_{-\Omega}^{\Omega} F(\omega) e^{j\omega t} \, d\omega$$

$$F(\omega) = \int_{-\infty}^{\infty} f(\xi) e^{-j\omega \xi} \, d\xi$$

Express $f_a(t)$ in the form of a scanning integral. Then investigate its behavior as $\Omega \to \infty$. Make use of Prob. 13-24.

13-27 Prove that if $f(t)$ is a real function (not imaginary or complex), then $\mathcal{C}(\omega) = |F(\omega)|$ is an even function of ω and $\Phi(\omega) = \angle F(\omega)$ is an odd function.

13-28 Prove relationships 2 to 6, 9 to 11, and 13 of Table 13-2.

13-29 Find the solution of Prob. 13-22 by utilizing relationship 11 of Table 13-2.

13-30 Derive the following Fourier transform pairs:

	$f(t)$		$F(\omega)$
(a)	$\begin{cases} 1 & \text{for } |t| < \tau \\ 0 & \text{otherwise} \end{cases}$		$\dfrac{2 \sin \omega\tau}{\omega}$
(b)	$e^{-t^2/2}$		$e^{-\omega^2/2}$
(c)	$\dfrac{1}{t^2 + a^2}$		$\pi e^{-|\omega|}$

13-31 Prove that

$$\int_0^\infty \frac{\sin^2 x}{x^2} \, dx = \frac{\pi}{2}$$

[HINT: Utilize Eq. (13-170).]

13-32 Show that if $f(t)$ is even, then

$$F(\omega) = 2 \int_0^\infty f(t) \cos \omega t \, dt$$

and that if $f(t)$ is odd, then

$$F(\omega) = 2j \int_0^\infty f(t) \sin \omega t \, dt$$

13-33   Find the Fourier transforms of the following functions:

(a) $f(t) = \begin{cases} 0 & \text{for } t < -\tau \\ 1 & \text{for } -\tau < t < 0 \\ -1 & \text{for } 0 < t < \tau \\ 0 & \text{for } t > \tau \end{cases}$

(b) $f(t) = e^{-|t|} \cos \omega_0 t$

(c) $f(t) = \dfrac{t}{[(t-a)^2 + b^2]^2}$

(d) $f(t) = \begin{cases} \cos \omega_0 t & \text{for } |t| < \dfrac{\pi}{2\omega_0} \\ 0 & \text{otherwise} \end{cases}$

(e) $f(t) = \begin{cases} te^{-10t} & \text{for } t > 0 \\ 0 & \text{otherwise} \end{cases}$

(f) $f(t) = (1 + \cos \omega_1 t) \cos \omega_2 t$

13-34   The Fourier transform of the impulse response of a linear system is the transfer function $T(\omega)$. Demonstrate and discuss this fact, using simple systems as an aid in the demonstration.

13-35   An ideal lowpass filter with bandwidth ω_0 radians/sec has a transfer function as shown in the figure. What is the impulse response of this filter if the impulse (δ function) is applied at $t = 0$? What does this indicate about the realizability of this filter?

Fig. P 13-35

13-36   In the diagram, each block has the following transfer function:

$$T(\omega) = \frac{F_2(\omega)}{F_1(\omega)} = e^{-\omega^2/2}$$

Assume that, when the blocks are connected as shown, the over-all transfer function is the product of the individual transfer functions. $T_n(\omega) = [T(\omega)]^n$. Find the impulse response (time domain) of n stages. Plot for $n = 1, 2, 4, 10$.

Fig. P 13-36

13-37 Find and plot the current flowing in the circuit if the applied voltage is (*a*) the pulse of Prob. 13-30*a*, (*b*) the pulse of Prob. 13-33*a*. Assume $\tau = 1$. Show that the response to both of these pulses is the same up to $t = 0$. Find the total energy dissipated in the resistor for both (*a*) and (*b*). Calculate this in both the time domain and the frequency domain.

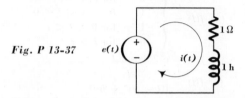

Fig. P 13-37 $e(t)$ $i(t)$ $1\,\Omega$ $1\,\text{h}$

13-38 If the force applied to the system illustrated is that of Prob. 13-33*e*, find the resultant velocity. What is the total energy dissipated in the frictional resistance?

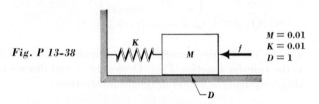

Fig. P 13-38 K M f $M = 0.01$ $K = 0.01$ $D = 1$ D

13-39 The system response $r(t)$ to a driving function is (in the frequency domain) $R(\omega) = F(\omega)H(\omega)$, where $H(\omega)$ is the transform of the impulse response $h(t)$. But, according to relationship 11 in Table 13-2, the time function corresponding to $F(\omega)H(\omega)$ is

$$r(t) = \int_{-\infty}^{\infty} f(\tau)h(t - \tau)\, d\tau = f(t) * h(t)$$

In other words, the response function is the convolution of the driving function and the impulse response. Discuss the significance of this fact. Derive this fact by expressing the driving function as a summation of narrow square pulses. The response to each pulse approaches an impulse response (times a Δt term) as the width of the pulse approaches zero. The limit of the summation of responses becomes the convolution integral above.

13-6   THE LAPLACE TRANSFORM

As has been pointed out, the *s*-domain techniques in use since Chap. 7 are essentially Laplace transform methods of system analysis. Judging from the title of this section, we have put the cart before the horse—six chapters before the horse. It is about time for us to start examining the horse.

The previous chapters have shown that it is not necessary to study the Laplace transform as such in order to make use of the tools provided by this transform. However, some discussion of the principal attributes of this transform should increase the appreciation of the tools it provides.

FROM FOURIER TRANSFORM TO LAPLACE TRANSFORM   The Fourier transform provides a method for transforming time functions to another domain (the frequency domain) and back again. This process is of great value, since it is usually considerably easier to obtain linear system solutions in the frequency domain than in the time domain. This transform method fails whenever the time functions fail to satisfy Eq. (13-160). This is a serious shortcoming, since we often wish to analyze systems when the driving or response functions are of this type.

In order to overcome this limitation, let us try to alter the Fourier transform to a point where it can handle such functions. When we have done this, we shall have to check to make sure that linear system solutions can be carried out in the new transform domain. We start with the standard Fourier transform:

$$F_1(\omega) = \int_{-\infty}^{\infty} f(t)e^{-j\omega t} \, dt \,\bigg|\, f(t) = \frac{1}{2\pi} \int_{-\infty}^{\infty} F_1(\omega)e^{j\omega t} \, d\omega \quad (13\text{-}183)$$

We then change the lower limit of the direct-transform integral from $-\infty$ to 0, which is equivalent to taking the direct Fourier transform of $f(t)u(t)$, where

$$u(t) = \begin{cases} 1 & \text{for } t > 0 \\ 0 & \text{for } t < 0 \end{cases} \quad (13\text{-}184)$$

Thus, a new pair of transformations, one step removed from those of Eq. (13-183), are generated:

$$F_2(\omega) = \int_{0}^{\infty} f(t)e^{-j\omega t} \, dt \,\bigg|\, f(t)u(t) = \frac{1}{2\pi} \int_{-\infty}^{\infty} F_2(\omega)e^{j\omega t} \, d\omega \quad (13\text{-}185)$$

The left-hand equation above will not exist if $f(t)$ does not approach zero fast enough as $t \to \infty$. However, if we multiply $f(t)$ by a function which does approach zero, the integral can be made to converge. A good multiplying function is $e^{-\sigma_0 t}$ with σ_0 a positive constant.

$$F_3(\omega) = \int_{0}^{\infty} f(t)e^{-\sigma_0 t}e^{-j\omega t} \, dt \,\bigg|\, f(t)u(t)e^{-\sigma_0 t} = \frac{1}{2\pi} \int_{-\infty}^{\infty} F_3(\omega)e^{j\omega t} \, d\omega \quad (13\text{-}186)$$

The right-hand equation above can be modified by multiplying both sides by $e^{\sigma_0 t}$. Since $e^{\sigma_0 t}$ does not depend upon ω, it can be placed inside the integral:

$$F_3(\omega) = \int_0^\infty f(t)e^{-\sigma_0 t}e^{-j\omega t}\, dt \,\Big|\, f(t)u(t) = \frac{1}{2\pi}\int_{-\infty}^\infty F_3(\omega)e^{\sigma_0 t}e^{j\omega t}\, d\omega$$

(13-187)

Let us replace $\sigma_0 + j\omega$, wherever it appears, with s.

$$\mathbf{F}(s) = \int_0^\infty f(t)e^{-st}\, dt \,\Big|\, f(t)u(t) = \frac{1}{2\pi}\int_{-\infty}^\infty F(s)e^{st}\, d\omega \quad (13\text{-}188)$$

Since $s = \sigma_0 + j\omega$, with σ_0 a constant, the $d\omega$ above can be replaced by $(1/j)\, ds$, with the appropriate change in the limits of integration:

$$\mathbf{F}(s) = \int_0^\infty f(t)e^{-st}\, dt \,\Big|\, f(t)u(t) = \frac{1}{2\pi j}\int_{\sigma_0 - j\infty}^{\sigma_0 + j\infty} F(s)e^{st}\, ds \quad (13\text{-}189)$$

The last two expressions, which are the Laplace transformations, are what we set out to find: a direct and an inverse transformation, not too different from the Fourier transform, which can handle functions which do not satisfy Eq. (13-160). The condition, equivalent to Eq. (13-160), which must now be satisfied in order for the transformations above to be valid is

$$\int_0^\infty |f(t)e^{-\sigma_0 t}|\, dt < \infty$$

(13-190)

There will usually be a minimum value which σ_0 must exceed to make Eq. (13-190) hold. This minimum value is called the *abscissa of absolute convergence* (aac). Table 13-4 shows the aac for various $f(t)$'s.

TABLE 13-4   *The Abscissa of Absolute Convergence for Various Time Functions*

$f(t)$		$\sigma_0 > aac$
K	any constant	$\sigma_0 > 0$
at^n	$n \geq 0$	$\sigma_0 > 0$
$e^{\alpha t}$	$\alpha > 0$	$\sigma_0 > \alpha$
$e^{-\alpha t}$	$\alpha > 0$	$\sigma_0 > -\alpha$
A pulse such that $f(t) = 0$ for $t > \tau$		$\sigma_0 > -\infty$
$\cos \omega_0 t$		$\sigma_0 > 0$
e^{t^n}	$n > 1$	No satisfactory σ_0; the transform does not exist

Since the transformations above are valid for all σ_0's greater than some minimum value, let us treat σ_0 as a variable and call it σ. Thus,

$$s = \sigma + j\omega$$

(13-191)

Let us try to clarify the foregoing with the help of Fig. 13-19. The direct transform of Eq. (13-189) is valid for any σ greater than the

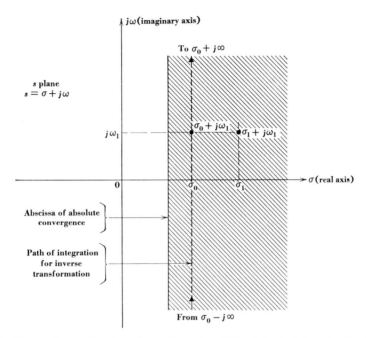

Fig. 13-19. The s plane, showing the region of validity (shaded) for the Laplace transformations of Eq. (13-189).

abscissa of absolute convergence. Hence, that expression can be used to obtain $\mathbf{F}(s)$ for s anywhere in the shaded portion of the diagram. For example, $\mathbf{F}(s)$ at the points $s = \sigma_0 + j\omega_1$ and $s = \sigma_1 + j\omega_1$ could be obtained by substituting these expressions for s into the function of s given by the direct transform. In particular, $\mathbf{F}(s)$ could be evaluated for each point along the path of integration shown in the figure. Consequently, the integration of the inverse transformation could be accomplished on this path. The choice of σ_0 is arbitrary as long as it is larger than the aac. Therefore, any path of integration in the shaded portion parallel to the one shown is satisfactory.

Thet ransformations of Eq. (13-189) are valid in the shaded region of Fig. 13-19. $\mathbf{F}(s)$, a function of the complex variable s, is very well behaved in this region. It is what is called an analytic function. A theorem from the theory of functions of a complex variable states (in simplified form): *An analytic function which is defined in some region of the s plane may be uniquely extended into the rest of the plane.* A simple example will explain this.

Suppose $f(t) = e^{\alpha t}$. If we utilize the direct transformation of Eq. (13-189), which will be valid for $\sigma > \alpha$, we find that $\mathbf{F}(s) = 1/(s - \alpha)$. The theorem above means simply that this last expression can be used to define an $\mathbf{F}(s)$ which extends over the whole s plane. The inverse transformation must still be carried out along a path to the right of the aac.

PROPERTIES OF THE LAPLACE TRANSFORM Let us rewrite Eq. (13-189) in slightly modified form:

$$\mathcal{L}\{f(t)\} = \mathbf{F}(s) = \int_0^\infty f(t)e^{-st}\,dt \tag{13-192}$$

$$\mathcal{L}^{-1}\{\mathbf{F}(s)\} = f(t) = \frac{1}{2\pi j}\int_{\sigma_0-j\infty}^{\sigma_0+j\infty} \mathbf{F}(s)e^{st}\,ds \tag{13-193}$$

In Eq. (13-193), we have dropped the $u(t)$ that appeared in Eq. (13-189). Strictly speaking, it still should be included. However, it is standard practice to dispense with this term, with the understanding that *the inverse Laplace transformation always produces a time function which is zero for $t < 0$*. Assuming that this fact will be remembered, we shall drop the reminder $u(t)$. Accordingly, if we write

$$\mathcal{L}^{-1}\left\{\frac{1}{s+\alpha}\right\} = e^{-\alpha t} \tag{13-194}$$

it should be understood that we mean

$$\mathcal{L}^{-1}\left\{\frac{1}{s+\alpha}\right\} = e^{-\alpha t}u(t) \tag{13-195}$$

Since the inverse transformation of Eq. (13-193) is somewhat difficult to carry out, it is convenient to construct a table of transform pairs by using the direct transformation. Then, when it is necessary to find the inverse transform of some $\mathbf{F}(s)$, the table may be consulted. Such a table is given in the Appendix. Other more extensive tables are available.†

To the transform pairs given in the Appendix, those of Table 13-5, which characterize the important properties of the Laplace transform, should be added.

Relationships 1 to 4 in Table 13-5 can be demonstrated quite readily. These are left to the reader. To derive the Laplace transform of the derivative 5, we proceed as follows, using integration by parts:

$$\mathcal{L}\{f'(t)\} = \int_0^\infty f'(t)e^{-st}\,dt = f(t)e^{-st}\Big|_0^\infty + s\int_0^\infty f(t)e^{-st}\,dt$$

$$= s\mathbf{F}(s) - f(0) \tag{13-196}$$

The term $f(t)e^{-st}$ must be zero at $t = \infty$, or else Eq. (13-190) will not be satisfied. At $t = 0$, $f(t)e^{-st}$ poses no problem if $f(t)$ is continuous. The value is just $f(0)$, since $e^{-st} = 1$ for $t = 0$. If $f(t)$ is discontinuous at

---

† See, for example, M. F. Gardner and J. L. Barnes, "Transients in Linear Systems," John Wiley & Sons, Inc., New York, 1942.

TABLE 13-5   *Properties of the Laplace Transform*

$f(t)$	$F(s)$
1. $af(t) + bg(t)$	$aF(s) + bG(s)$
2. $f(t - a)u(t - a)$	$e^{-as}F(s)$
3. $f(t)e^{-at}$	$F(s + a)$
4. $f(at)$	$\dfrac{1}{a}F\left(\dfrac{s}{a}\right)$
5. $\dfrac{df(t)}{dt} \triangleq f'(t)$	$sF(s) - f(0_+)$
6. $\displaystyle\int f(t)\,dt \triangleq f^{(-1)}(t)$	$\dfrac{F(s)}{s} + \dfrac{f^{(-1)}(0_+)}{s}$
7. $\displaystyle\int_0^t f(\tau)g(t - \tau)\,d\tau$	$F(s)G(s)$

$t = 0$, $f(0)$ is not defined. In order to overcome this problem, we must interpret Eq. (13-192) as meaning

$$F(s) = \lim_{\epsilon \to 0} \int_\epsilon^\infty f(t)e^{-st}\,dt \qquad \epsilon > 0 \qquad (13\text{-}197)$$

Thus, Eq. (13-196) becomes

$$\mathcal{L}\{f'(t)\} = \lim_{\substack{\epsilon \to 0 \\ \epsilon > 0}} [sF(s) - f(\epsilon)] = sF(s) - f(0_+) \qquad (13\text{-}198)$$

For example, if

$$f(t) = \begin{cases} 0 & \text{for } t < 0 \\ 2e^{-t} & \text{for } t > 0 \end{cases} \qquad (13\text{-}199)$$

then $f(0_+) = 2$.

The derivation of relationship 6 in Table 13-5 is similar to that above. To prove relationship 7, we note first that

$$\int_0^t f(\tau)g(t - \tau)\,d\tau = \int_0^\infty u(t - \tau)f(\tau)g(t - \tau)\,d\tau \qquad (13\text{-}200)$$

The reason for this is that

$$u(t - \tau) = \begin{cases} 1 & \text{for } \tau < t \\ 0 & \text{for } \tau > t \end{cases} \qquad (13\text{-}201)$$

We take the Laplace transform of both sides of Eq. (13-200) and then change the order of integration:

$$\mathcal{L}\left\{\int_0^t f(\tau)g(t - \tau)\,d\tau\right\} = \int_0^\infty e^{-st} \int_0^\infty u(t - \tau)f(\tau)g(t - \tau)\,d\tau\,dt$$
$$= \int_0^\infty f(\tau) \int_0^\infty u(t - \tau)g(t - \tau)e^{-st}\,dt\,d\tau \qquad (13\text{-}202)$$

Using relationship 2 from Table 13-5, we find that the inner integral becomes $e^{-\tau s}G(s)$. Therefore,

$$\mathcal{L}\left\{\int_0^t f(\tau)g(t - \tau)\,d\tau\right\} = \int_0^\infty G(s)f(\tau)e^{-s\tau}\,d\tau$$
$$= F(s)G(s) \qquad (13\text{-}203)$$

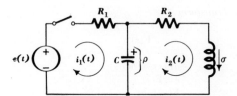

Fig. 13-20. A circuit with initial stored energy. The switch is closed at $t = 0$.

SYSTEM SOLUTIONS BY LAPLACE TRANSFORM METHODS We shall take a simple system and show that the Laplace transform method of finding the system response is identical to the techniques introduced in Chap. 7. In Fig. 13-20 the switch is closed at $t = 0$. At $t = 0_-$, energy is stored in the circuit in the form of the voltage ρ across the capacitor and the current σ in the inductor.†

Using the loop currents shown in the diagram, we can write the loop equations for $t > 0$ as

$$R_1 i_1(t) + \frac{1}{C} \int i_1(t)\, dt - \frac{1}{C} \int i_2(t)\, dt = e(t)$$

$$-\frac{1}{C} \int i_1(t)\, dt + \frac{1}{C} \int i_2(t)\, dt + R_2 i_2(t)\, dt + L\frac{di_2}{dt}(t) = 0 \quad (13\text{-}204)$$

When we take the Laplace transform of both sides of both equations, we obtain

$$R_1 \mathbf{I}_1(s) + \frac{1}{C}\left[\frac{\mathbf{I}_1(s)}{s} + \frac{i_1{}^{(-1)}(0_+)}{s}\right] - \frac{1}{C}\left[\frac{\mathbf{I}_2(s)}{s} + \frac{i_2{}^{(-1)}(0_+)}{s}\right] = \mathbf{E}(s)$$

$$-\frac{1}{C}\left[\frac{\mathbf{I}_1(s)}{s} + \frac{i_1{}^{(-1)}(0_+)}{s}\right] + \frac{1}{C}\left[\frac{\mathbf{I}_2(s)}{s} + \frac{i_2{}^{(-1)}(0_+)}{s}\right] + R_2 \mathbf{I}_2(s)$$
$$+ L[s\mathbf{I}_2(s) - i_2(0_+)] = 0 \quad (13\text{-}205)$$

Now we note that

$$\frac{1}{C}\int_{-\infty}^{0} [i_1(t) - i_2(t)]\, dt = \frac{1}{C}[i_1{}^{(-1)}(0_+) - i_2{}^{(-1)}(0_+)] = \rho \quad (13\text{-}206)$$

and
$$i_2(0_+) = \sigma \quad (13\text{-}207)$$

Therefore, Eqs. (13-205) may be written in the following form:

$$\left(R_1 + \frac{1}{sC}\right)\mathbf{I}_1(s) - \frac{1}{sC}\mathbf{I}_2(s) = \mathbf{E}(s) - \frac{\rho}{s}$$
$$-\frac{1}{sC}\mathbf{I}_1(s) + \left(sL + R_2 + \frac{1}{sC}\right)\mathbf{I}_2(s) = L\sigma \quad (13\text{-}208)$$

We need go no further. Equations (13-208) are exactly the equations we would obtain by using the methods introduced in Chap. 7 and the technique of handling initial stored energy exemplified by Table 9-1.

---

† Since energy cannot be transferred instantaneously, we may assume that the same ρ and σ exist at $t = 0_+$.

13-7 SUMMARY

This has been a long chapter. The essence of the chapter, however, is revealed in three pairs of equations:

$$f(t) = \sum_{k=-\infty}^{\infty} \gamma_k e^{jk\omega_1 t} \qquad\qquad \gamma_k = \frac{1}{T}\int_0^T f(t)e^{-jk\omega_1 t}\,dt \quad (13\text{-}209)$$

$$f(t) = \frac{1}{2\pi}\int_{-\infty}^{\infty} F(\omega)e^{j\omega t}\,d\omega \qquad F(\omega) = \int_{-\infty}^{\infty} f(t)e^{-j\omega t}\,dt \quad (13\text{-}210)$$

$$f(t) = \frac{1}{2\pi j}\int_{\sigma_0-j\infty}^{\sigma_0+j\omega} \mathbf{F}(s)e^{st}\,ds \qquad \mathbf{F}(s) = \int_0^{\infty} f(t)e^{-st}\,dt \quad (13\text{-}211)$$

There are two ways of viewing or interpreting these equations. One is to say that they show that every time function is just a sum of exponentials multiplied by appropriate constants. (The integrals can be considered the limiting cases of summations.) When the equations are viewed in this way, finding the linear system response to any driving function reduces to finding the system response to exponential driving functions. This, of course, is quite easy, because of the nature of the systems we have chosen to study.

The second interpretation is in terms of transform theory. Any time function encountered in a physical system can be transformed by at least one of the transformations into a new domain. In this new domain the system solution can be obtained by simpler operations than would be required in the time domain. Once the solution is found in the transform domain, an inverse transformation can be used to return to the time domain.

Both of these interpretations are valid. Either or both may be utilized. The second seems more natural during the actual process of obtaining the system response. The first seems more appropriate in striving for an intuitive appreciation of the physical behavior of a system.

Much more could be said about Fourier analysis and transform methods, but further discussion must be left to other texts.

PROBLEMS

13-40 Derive relationships 1, 2, 3, 4, and 6 of Table 13-5.

13-41 Find the Laplace transforms of the following functions (see the Appendix): (a) t, (b) t^n, (c) $\cos \beta t$, (d) $\sin \beta t$, (e) $t \cos \beta t$, (f) $e^{-\alpha t} \sin \beta t$, (g) $(e^{-\alpha t} - e^{-\beta t})/t$.

13-42 The pulse represented in the figure is the sum of the functions shown. Each of these functions has a simple transform. Consequently, the Laplace transform of the pulse is easily found by adding these elementary transforms. Use this technique to find the Laplace transform of the other illustrated pulses.

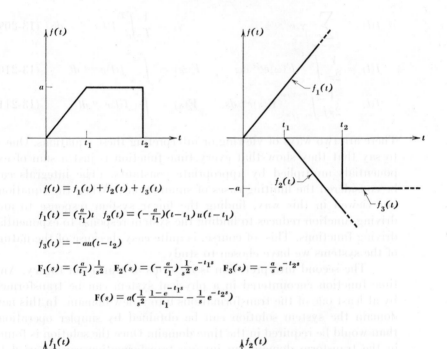

$$f(t) = f_1(t) + f_2(t) + f_3(t)$$

$$f_1(t) = (\tfrac{a}{t_1})t \quad f_2(t) = (-\tfrac{a}{t_1})(t-t_1)\,u(t-t_1)$$

$$f_3(t) = -au(t-t_2)$$

$$F_1(s) = (\tfrac{a}{t_1})\tfrac{1}{s^2} \quad F_2(s) = (-\tfrac{a}{t_1})\tfrac{1}{s^2}e^{-t_1 s} \quad F_3(s) = -\tfrac{a}{s}e^{-t_2 s}$$

$$F(s) = a\left(\tfrac{1}{s^2}\frac{1-e^{-t_1 s}}{t_1} - \tfrac{1}{s}e^{-t_2 s}\right)$$

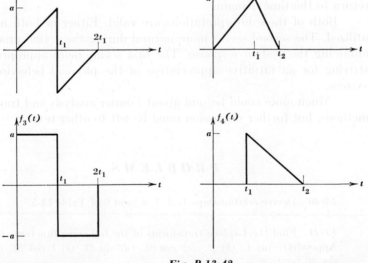

Fig. P 13-42

13-43   The Laplace transform of $f(t)$ in the figure is $\mathbf{F}(s)$. Prove that the Laplace transform of the periodic extension of $f(t)$ is

$$\mathcal{L}\{f_p(t)\} = \frac{\mathbf{F}(s)}{1 - e^{-\tau s}} = \mathbf{F}_p(s)$$

What are the positions of the poles of $\mathbf{F}_p(s)$, that is, the zeros of $(1 - e^{-\tau s})$? $\mathbf{F}_p(s)$ can be expanded in a partial-fraction expansion [see Eqs. (7-35) and (7-36)]

$$\mathbf{F}_p(s) = \sum_{k=-\infty}^{\infty} \frac{a_k}{s - s_k}$$

where s_k are the zeros of $1 - e^{-\tau s}$. For simple poles of $\mathbf{F}_p(s)$, and in this example they are all simple,

$$a_k = (s - s_k)\mathbf{F}_p(s)\Big|_{s=s_k} = \frac{(s - s_k)\mathbf{F}(s)}{1 - e^{-\tau s}}\Big|_{s=s_k} = \frac{\mathbf{F}(s_k)}{\tau}$$

Hence, show that the a_k's are the Fourier exponential series coefficients and that $\mathcal{L}^{-1}\{\mathbf{F}_p(s)\}$ yields this series. Discuss the significance of the developments above.

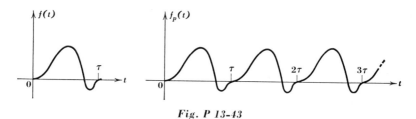

Fig. P 13-43

13-44   If $\mathbf{F}(s) = \mathcal{L}\{f(t)\}$, then in some cases $\mathbf{F}(s)\Big|_{s=j\omega} = \mathcal{F}\{f(t)\}$. State the conditions under which this relationship may be employed.

13-45   Discuss the relationship between the pole positions of an $\mathbf{F}(s)$ and the abscissa of absolute convergence.

13.41 The Laplace transform of $\Delta(t)$ is the limit $t \to \infty$. Prove that the Laplace transform of the periodic extension of $F(t)$ is

$$\mathcal{L}\{F_p(t)\} = \frac{F(s)}{1 - e^{-sT}}$$

What are the positions of the poles of F_p? that is, the zeros of $1 - e^{-sT}$? $F_p(s)$ can be expanded in a partial fraction expansion [see Eqs. (7.35) and (7.36)],

$$F_p(s) = \sum \frac{J}{s - s_n}$$

where s_n are the zeros of $1 - e^{-sT}$. For simple poles of $F_p(s)$ and in this example they are all simple.

$$J_n = \alpha_n F_p(s_n) \qquad (s_n = \alpha_n/F(s_n)) \qquad \text{Res} F$$

Hence show that the α_n are the Fourier exponential series coefficients and that $F^{-1}[F_p(s)]$ yields this series. Discuss the significance of the development above.

Fig. P 13-43

13-43 If $F(s) = \mathcal{L}\{f(t)\}$, then in some cases $f(t) = \lim_{s \to \infty} sF(s)$. State the conditions under which this relationship may be employed.

13-44 Discuss the relationship between the pole positions of the $F(s)$ and the absence of absolute convergence.

points of departure

This chapter has two objectives. The first is to recapitulate and unify the basic points of the previous chapters. The second is to discuss a few of the concepts of analysis which we have not investigated in the preceding sections. These unexamined concepts will constitute future topics of study for most of the readers of this text.

14-1 A REVIEW

There is one basic pervasive concept which not only underlies the techniques and methods introduced in this text but also forms a foundation of study in all the physical sciences. This is the concept of the mathematical model. The mathematical model is the link between the pristine world of pure mathematics and the real world around us. It is the real world which we observe and measure. However, when we attempt to predict and explain our observations, we do so by hypothesizing an appropriate mathematical model which can be analyzed by mathematical means.

The mathematical analysis of a physical system involves, first, the observation of the system or the various parts which combine to form the system. From these observations, we construct models, with their associated mathematical relationships. Usually we combine a number of simpler models to form the final model of the system. In the process of combining the simpler models, we find it necessary to assert further mathematical relationships which apply to the combination of models.

Having constructed a model and its mathematical relationships, we proceed to analyze the model by any mathematical technique which is appropriate. The suitability of a particular model will depend upon how well the model behavior, or response, as found by mathematical analysis, agrees with the observed behavior of the physical system. In summary, the mathematical study of physical systems consists of these steps:

1. Observation and measurement of the physical system and components
2. Construction of the model
3. Mathematical analysis of the model
4. Comparison of the model response to the system response

The purpose of this text has been primarily to study step 3 for a special class of models, the linear models of electrical and mechanical systems. We have discussed to some extent the other steps, but these discussions have been subordinate to the main stream of effort, the mathematical analysis of linear models.

We have emphasized in the preceding chapters and reemphasized in the discussion above the fact that our study concerns the analysis of models. The ease with which one loses sight of the fact that the model is but a representation of the actual system motivates this stress. The model may be an entirely adequate representation or, at times, a totally or partially inadequate representation. Any discussion pertaining to the adequacy of models almost automatically brings in the term approximation. Approximations are made in choosing a model to represent a system. Subsequently, further approximations may be useful in carrying out the mathematical analysis. In all cases the engineer who is studying the system must decide upon the adequacy of the model and the degree of approximation that can be tolerated. This decision, for the most part, must be based upon the requirements of the particular study and upon the judgment of the engineer. A thorough understanding of the mathematical analysis of various models is an important prerequisite in making such decisions.

THE LINEAR LUMPED MODELS OF ELECTRICAL AND MECHANICAL SYSTEMS
We have confined our attention almost exclusively to models which are linear and lumped. What is meant by "lumped"? The meaning of this term will be clarified by the counterexample of distributed systems, which will be discussed in Sec. 14-3. At this point, however, we may define lumped systems in the following way. In a lumped model the energy in the system is considered to be stored or dissipated in distinct, isolated elements (masses, springs, dashpots, inductors, capacitors, resistors). Furthermore, it is assumed that any disturbance initiated at any point of the system is immediately felt at all other points. In other words, the effect of distance between elements and of the finite amount of time necessary to transmit energy over these distances is neglected. Systems in which these assumptions do not hold are called distributed systems.

The models we have studied have been composed of combinations of lumped elements. The lumped elements have been assumed linear. That is, the mathematical relationships between the system variables (force, velocity, voltage, current) have been linear for each of the elements. These relationships are summarized in Table 1-2. The mathematical relationships which govern the combination of these elements (D'Alembert's and Kirchhoff's laws) are additive. Hence, the mathematical equations of the complete model are also linear.

Linear, as used above, may be defined succinctly in the following manner. An operation (equation, transformation) $\Im$ operating on a function f and yielding a function g,

$$\Im\{f_1\} = g_1 \qquad \Im\{f_2\} = g_2 \tag{14-1}$$

is a linear operation if

$$\Im\{af_1 + bf_2\} = ag_1 + bg_2 \tag{14-2}$$

for all values of the constants a and b.

The statement of Eq. (14-2) is essentially synonymous with a statement of the superposition theorem. The fact that the integro-differential equations describing our electrical and mechanical systems† were linear, and hence that superposition could be applied, was of extreme importance in the development of our analysis techniques. The impedance methods, operation in the s domain, loop and node analysis, matrix methods, Fourier analysis, Laplace transform techniques—all these are dependent upon the linearity of the system. In Sec. 14-2 we shall briefly discuss some of the problems of dealing with nonlinear systems.

CONCLUDING REMARKS In studying the analysis of linear electrical and mechanical networks, one is quite likely to let the trees obscure one's view of the forest. Powerful concepts and techniques are introduced and mastered—impedances, poles and zeros, phasors, transformations, matrices, and many others. It is not surprising that students sometimes forget that they are simply attempting to solve one or more linear differential equations with constant coefficients. The various techniques provide valuable tools for solving these equations, but the student should not lose sight of the underlying significance of these differential equations in his effort to master the tools.

With this final word of advice, we shall pass from those topics discussed in the preceding chapters to a number of topics which were not investigated.

---

† It should be understood that when we speak of the equations pertaining to a physical system, we mean the equations of the mathematical models of the physical systems.

14-2 NONLINEAR SYSTEMS

In the discussion above, we have emphasized the importance of linearity in our studies of systems analysis. It is appropriate at this time to devote a little space to a preview of the problems of nonlinear system analysis.† This investigation will undoubtedly illuminate our motives for restricting this text to linear systems.

Quite general procedures have been developed for the solution of linear integrodifferential equations with constant coefficients. No such general procedures are possible in working with nonlinear differential equations, for whereas there is only one way in which an equation can be linear, there are an infinity of ways in which an equation can be nonlinear. Consequently, a technique which yields the solution of one nonlinear equation may be fruitless when applied to another.

A simple example of a nonlinear electrical circuit is provided by Fig. 14-1. The inductor and capacitor are normal linear elements, but the dissipative element is nonlinear. The graphs give four possible voltage-current curves for this element. If the voltage applied to the circuit were known and the current were to be found, the optimum method for accomplishing this would depend upon which of the curves applied and upon the magnitude and form of the applied voltage.

METHODS OF NONLINEAR SYSTEMS SOLUTIONS As was mentioned above, there is no one general method which can be applied for the solution of all nonlinear systems. However, we can list some general techniques, one of which is likely to yield a satisfactory solution.

EXACT MATHEMATICAL SOLUTIONS If the mathematical relationships between variables for each nonlinear element are known, nonlinear differential equations can be written for the system. For example, suppose that the voltage-current relationship for the nonlinear element of Fig. 14-1 has the form

$$e = Ai^3 = A\left(\frac{dq}{dt}\right)^3 \tag{14-3}$$

Consequently, the differential equation describing the circuit response to the applied voltage would be

$$L\frac{d^2q}{dt^2} + A\left(\frac{dq}{dt}\right)^3 + \frac{q}{C} = e_a(t) \tag{14-4}$$

Although Eq. (14-4) looks reasonably simple, finding a solution in terms of tabulated mathematical functions may be impossible.

---

† The Selected Bibliography lists several texts which are devoted to the analysis of nonlinear electrical and mechanical networks.

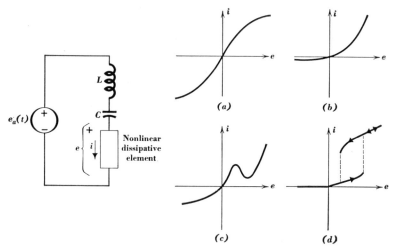

Fig. 14-1. An electrical circuit containing a nonlinear dissipative element. The graphs indicate four possible voltage-current curves which could apply to this nonlinear element.

Whether such a solution exists will depend upon the form of $e_a(t)$. If such a solution does not exist, Eq. (14-4) and other nonlinear differential equations may be solved approximately by numerical methods.† These methods usually involve prodigious amounts of calculation and are best left to the high-speed computers. A single nonlinear differential equation such as Eq. (14-4) is difficult to solve, and if the system under analysis is complex enough to produce a set of nonlinear differential equations, the solution is extremely difficult indeed.

Graphical relationships such as those in Fig. 14-1 can usually be approximated by analytic expressions. Thus, it is almost always possible to derive an approximate differential equation which is applicable to a particular system. This will be necessary if the system solution is to be found by numerical methods.

GRAPHICAL TECHNIQUES The relationships between variables for nonlinear elements can usually be put in graphical form. The four graphs of Fig. 14-1 are typical examples. These graphs can often be utilized in graphical procedures for finding system responses. An example of one graphical technique has already been demonstrated in Sec. 11-3, where the motion of the plunger magnet was investigated.

A second example of a graphical technique is given in the following discussion. Figure 14-2 represents a vacuum-tube circuit, the

† For example, see W. J. Cunningham, "Introduction to Nonlinear Analysis," chap. 2, McGraw-Hill Book Company, Inc., New York, 1958.

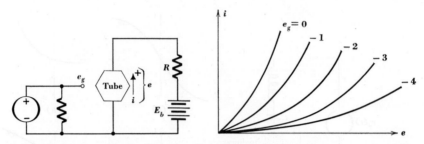

Fig. 14-2. A vacuum-tube circuit and the nonlinear characteristics of the tube.

hexagon representing the tube itself. The curves specify the behavior of the tube for different values of the control-grid voltage e_g. The constant voltage E_b minus the voltage across the resistor R must be the voltage e across the tube. A little thought will convince one that E_b and R determine a straight line on the tube characteristic graph and that the e-i operating point for the tube must fall somewhere upon this line. This line, called the load line, is drawn in Fig. 14-3a. Once the load line has been established, it is a simple matter to plot points on this line to arrive at the curve of Fig. 14-3b. Note that this new curve of e versus e_g is nearly linear. Hence, when the constant term is subtracted, e is just a multiple of e_g. This is the basis of the linear models of vacuum-tube circuits which we have used previously.

There is no standard graphical technique of nonlinear system analysis. The example above and the plunger-magnet example of Sec. 11-3 are just two of many possible methods.

LINEARIZATION The general difficulty of solving nonlinear differential equations, as opposed to the relative ease of solving linear equations,

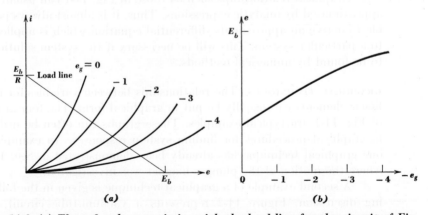

Fig. 14-3. (a) The tube characteristics with the load line for the circuit of Fig. 14-2. The circuit (R and E_b) restricts the operation of the tube to the load line. (b) A plot of the tube voltage e versus the control voltage e_g. This curve is derived graphically from the graph of part a.

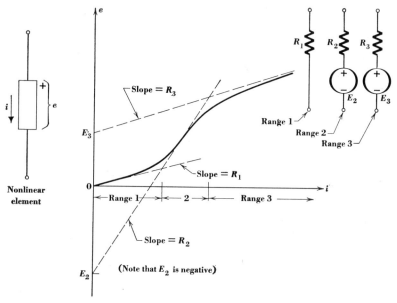

Fig. 14-4. *A nonlinear resistor, its e-i graph, and three linear models which may be used to represent it over three ranges of the voltage and current.*

motivates the methods which we shall discuss now. Systems which are nonlinear can usually be represented by a linear model which is a reasonable approximation over at least some range of the variables involved. The small-signal analyses of Chap. 11 are examples of such an approximation.

For another example of linearization, consider the dissipative element of Fig. 14-4 and its *e-i* graph. If we separate the curve into three ranges, we see that it can be fairly well represented in each of these ranges by a linear resistor in series with a constant-voltage source. The value of the voltage source is given by the intersection of the straight line with the *e* axis, and the resistance is the slope of the straight line.

If the rest of the circuit and its excitation were such that the voltage and current varied over a small range, the appropriate linear model could be selected and a small-signal analysis carried out. If the voltage and current varied over a wide range, a step-by-step (or piecewise) linear analysis would be necessary. Such an analysis may be accomplished in the following manner. Suppose that the transient response of the circuit is required and that the initial conditions are such that no current flows in the nonlinear resistor at $t = 0$. Therefore, the model for range 1 is selected, and the transient solution is found in the usual manner. The solution is then examined in order to find the time (say t_1) at which the variables leave range 1. The energy stored in the various energy-storage elements are computed for $t = t_1$, the model for range 2 is substituted for the previous model, and a new transient solution starting at t_1 is computed. This solution is inspected to find the time when the variables leave range 2. The whole process is repeated as often as necessary to yield a final solution.

It should be clear that the technique above can be made as accurate as desired by choosing smaller ranges, so that the straight-line approximation to the *e-i* curve will be very good.

In general, linearization is the most satisfactory way of analyzing nonlinear systems. Care must be exercised, however, to ensure that the errors inherent in the approximations do not become unreasonably large.

LINEAR EQUATIONS WITH TIME-VARYING COEFFICIENTS   We have chosen to mention linear varying-coefficient equations in this section because they, like nonlinear equations, are much more difficult to solve than linear constant-coefficient equations. Consider the following equation, which could be the equilibrium equation for a mass-spring system in which the spring compliance varies with time. (Compare Probs. 11-9 to 11-11.)

$$M \frac{d^2x}{dt^2} + D \frac{dx}{dt} + f(t)x = g(t) \qquad (14\text{-}5)$$

Equation (14-5) is linear, satisfying Eq. (14-2). However, the coefficients are not constant, and no general solution of it exists. Like nonlinear differential equations, linear differential equations with time-varying coefficients can be solved by numerical and approximate methods. Since these equations are linear, superposition can be applied and may be of considerable aid in finding the solution.

EXAMPLES OF SYSTEMS WHICH DEPEND UPON NONLINEAR NETWORK ELE-MENTS   It would not be surprising if the preceding discussion has had the effect of convincing the reader that all nonlinearities are undesirable. Admittedly, they certainly do not simplify the analysis problem. Nevertheless, many important and valuable devices depend upon the nonlinearity of certain network elements in order to operate. A number of these devices are introduced below.

A digital computer provides a prime example of a system which depends upon the nonlinearities of vacuum tubes or solid-state diodes and transistors. The important attribute of these devices, as far as digital-computer use is concerned, is their ability to assume, when operating in properly designed circuits, either of two stable states. This ability is produced by the nonlinearities of the devices. (A vacuum tube or solid-state diode possesses an *e-i* curve like curve *b* of Fig. 14-1.)

In the preceding chapter we saw that a nonsinusoidal periodic function possesses a number of higher harmonics of the fundamental frequency. By applying such a periodic function to a properly tuned

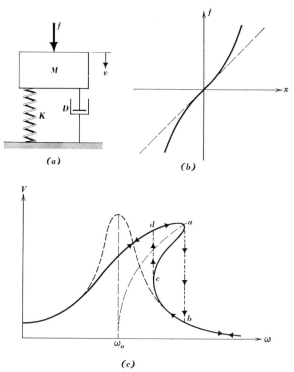

Fig. 14-5. Nonlinear resonance and the jump phenomenon. (a) A resonant mechanical network; (b) the nonlinear characteristics of the spring (solid curve); (c) the resonant curve for the network (for one particular amplitude of sinusoidal driving force). The jumps are from a to b for increasing frequency and from c to d for decreasing frequency.

filter, one of the higher harmonics may be extracted. The *harmonic generator* uses this principle to multiply the frequency of a sine wave. For example, a sinusoid of frequency f_1 may be produced by a crystal-controlled oscillator. This sinusoid is then amplified by a nonlinear amplifier, with the resultant production of higher harmonics. This distorted signal is passed through a tuned circuit, yielding a higher harmonic, say nf_1. This process can be repeated a number of times to yield large multiples of the original frequency f_1. Obviously such a harmonic generator depends upon the nonlinearities of the amplifier.

For the final example of a nonlinear network, observe the simple resonant mechanical system of Fig. 14-5a. If all three elements were linear and there were small damping, the velocity vs. frequency curve (constant-amplitude sinusoidal applied force) would look like the dashed curve of Fig. 14-5c. Let us assume that the spring is not completely linear—a very reasonable assumption. Suppose that the force is related to displacement as follows (Fig. 14-5b):

$$f = K(x + \alpha x^3) \tag{14-6}$$

With the spring force as given above, the resonance curve takes on the shape shown by the solid line in Fig. 14-5c. This type of resonant characteristic produces a *jump phenomenon*. With a constant-amplitude sinusoid applied, the magnitude of the velocity increases as the frequency is increased. At point *a* the amplitude jumps suddenly to point *b*. If we start at a frequency above resonance and then decrease the frequency, the amplitude follows the curve to point *c*, where it jumps to point *d*. Nothing like the characteristic described here occurs in linear systems.

14-3 LOOKING AHEAD

In this section we shall introduce and discuss briefly a few topics which either have not been investigated or have been only partially examined in this text. This discussion will serve as a preview of studies which logically follow and which are based upon the material in this book.

ADVANCED TOPICS IN THE ANALYSIS OF LUMPED LINEAR SYSTEMS Our introduction to the analysis of lumped linear electrical and mechanical systems has been fairly thorough. But as is usually the case, there is much that can be explored further and in more detail. For example, all the mechanical models which we have analyzed have been restricted to the purely translational (in one direction) or purely rotational (about one axis).

A simple example of a mechanical device which does not fit into either of the two classifications above is shown in Fig. 14-6. It consists of a mass mounted on two springs. The translational motion is limited by guides to one direction, but the mass can, in addition, rotate about its center as shown. A bit of pondering should convince us that for small displacements the equations of motion for this system will not differ from those we have dealt with before.

In order to solve a completely general case of mechanical motion, we should have to consider translational motion in three directions and rotational motion about three axes for each mass in the system. Obviously the differential equations describing such systems would

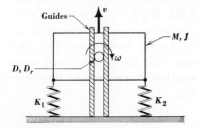

Fig. 14-6. A mass supported by two springs. The mass can move up and down in the vertical direction and can rotate about its center.

be numerous and complex. However, if the system is linear, the principles employed in setting up and solving these equations would be essentially the same as those developed for unidirectional systems.

The discussion above emphasizes the importance of mathematical methods which can cope with large numbers of complex equations. Hence, the further study of matrix methods, coupled with Laplace and Fourier transform techniques, is a logical sequel to the investigations of this text.†

SYNTHESIS Given an arrangement of lumped linear system elements (the network) and the excitation, we can find the response by analysis. The process of synthesis solves a different problem concerning the same three entities—the network, the excitation, and the response. If we are given the excitation and the desired response and asked what network will yield this response, the problem is one of synthesis.

It should be obvious, after a few moments' reflection, that the process of synthesis is several magnitudes more difficult than analysis. Whereas a solution always exists for the analysis problem, though it may be difficult to find, the synthesis problem may have no solution; and if it has a solution, it will have many solutions. That is to say, it is quite possible that no network exists which will give a specified response to a specified excitation. On the other hand, if a network does exist which satisfies the requirements, it will always be possible to find another which also satisfies the requirements.

Although fraught with difficulties, elegant and sophisticated techniques of network synthesis have been developed in the last four decades.‡ While no longer in its infancy, the field of network synthesis continues to grow vigorously. Needless to say, success in network synthesis is dependent upon a thorough knowledge of analysis.

DISTRIBUTED SYSTEMS To introduce the subject of distributed systems, let us pose the following problem. The long transmission line of Fig. 14-7a carries electrical energy from the source to the load. How can we determine the voltage in the line and load after the switch is closed? Considering our background to this point, we should probably hypothesize, as a first approximation to the system, the lumped linear

† A systematic method of determining the differential equations which describe a complex mechanical or electromechanical system becomes increasingly important as the system becomes more complex. Such a method can be developed through the use of *Lagrange's equations.* For a discussion of the utilization of Lagrange's equations, see J. A. Aseltine, "Transform Method in Linear System Analysis," chap. 6, McGraw-Hill Book Company, Inc., New York, 1958; or D. C. White and H. H. Woodson, "Electromechanical Energy Conversion," chap. 1, John Wiley & Sons, Inc., New York, 1959.

‡ Texts dealing with network synthesis are listed in the Selected Bibliography.

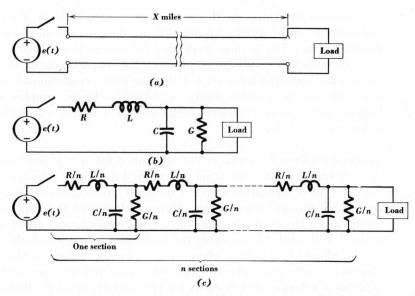

Fig. 14-7. (a) *A transmission line;* (b) *a crude lumped model;* (c) *a lumped model which yields a better approximation to the transmission line.*

model of Fig. 14-7b. The line would have a certain total resistance R, an inductance L, a capacitance C between the lines, and a leakage conductance G between the lines. These would be the parameter values of the first model.

Disappointment would be our due, for we should find that the response predicted by our model would not agree with the observed response of the actual transmission line. We should be too hasty, however, if we discarded completely this avenue of approach. A logical modification would be to have the resistance, inductance, capacitance, and conductance distributed along the length of the line. Consequently, the lumped model of Fig. 14-7c might reasonably be expected to yield an approximation which would be closer to the observed response. This expectation would be fulfilled, and as n was made larger, the approximation would improve.

The rather obvious next step would be to let n approach infinity. Our model now could hardly be called lumped, but we could still use methods of analysis developed for lumped circuits. Consider Fig. 14-8, which shows an infinitesimal section of the transmission line. The equilibrium equations for this section are†

$$\Delta e = R \, \Delta x \, i + L \, \Delta x \, \frac{di}{dt}$$

$$\Delta i = G \, \Delta x \, e + C \, \Delta x \, \frac{de}{dt}$$

(14-7)

† The higher-order terms such as $\Delta x \, \Delta i$ may be neglected.

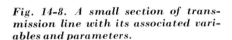

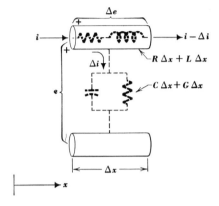

Fig. 14-8. A small section of trans-mission line with its associated vari-ables and parameters.

where R is the resistance per unit length, L the inductance per unit length, C the capacitance per unit length, and G the conductance per unit length. Dividing through by Δx and letting $\Delta x \to 0$, we should obtain (the minus signs arise through our choice of current direction and x direction):

$$-\frac{\partial e}{\partial x} = Ri + L\frac{\partial i}{\partial t}$$
$$-\frac{\partial i}{\partial x} = Ge + C\frac{\partial e}{\partial t}$$

(14-8)

The two simultaneous partial differential equations above describe the behavior of this distributed-system model just as the ordinary differential equations describe the lumped models. They are linear, and the methods of solving them are closely related to the methods we have studied in this text. Note that in the preceding example, the variables voltage and current are functions not only of time but also of distance x.

The bending and vibration of beams and other similar mechanical examples illustrate the same problems as the transmission line above. That is, a purely lumped model cannot adequately represent these distributed systems. Once again a parallel or analogous type of development could be carried out in the investigation of distributed mechanical and electrical systems.†

CONCLUDING REMARKS We have mentioned just a few of the many areas of investigation which are opening for the readers of this book. We conclude this volume with the hope that our readers are looking forward to these further investigations with eager anticipation and that this text will serve as a sturdy foundation for their future endeavors.

† For a text in which this method of parallel development is followed, see R. K. Moore, "Traveling-wave Engineering," McGraw-Hill Book Company, Inc., New York, 1960.

APPENDIX   Table of Unit-impulse Responses (Laplace Transform Pairs)†

$\mathbf{F}(s)$	$f(t)$ **after** $t = 0_+$
1. 1	Unit impulse at $t = 0$ $[\delta(t)]$
2. $\dfrac{1}{s}$	1 [unit step $= u(t)$]
3. $\dfrac{1}{s^2}$	t
4. $\dfrac{2}{s^3}$	t^2
5. $\dfrac{n!}{s^{n+1}}$	t^n
6. $\dfrac{1}{s + \alpha}$	$e^{-\alpha t}$
7. $\dfrac{\alpha}{s(s + \alpha)}$	$1 - e^{-\alpha t}$
8. $\dfrac{1}{(s + \alpha)^2}$	$te^{-\alpha t}$
9. $\dfrac{1}{(s + \alpha)(s + \beta)}$	$\dfrac{e^{-\alpha t} - e^{-\beta t}}{\beta - \alpha}$
10. $\dfrac{s}{(s + \alpha)(s + \beta)}$	$\dfrac{\beta e^{-\beta t} - \alpha e^{-\alpha t}}{\beta - \alpha}$
11. $\dfrac{1}{s(s + \alpha)(s + \beta)}$	$\dfrac{1}{\alpha\beta} + \dfrac{\beta e^{-\alpha t} - \alpha e^{-\beta t}}{\alpha\beta(\alpha - \beta)}$
12. $\dfrac{s}{s^2 + \beta^2}$	$\cos \beta t$
13. $\dfrac{\beta}{s^2 + \beta^2}$	$\sin \beta t$
14. $\dfrac{1}{s(s^2 + \beta^2)}$	$\dfrac{1}{\beta^2}(1 - \cos \beta t)$
15. $\dfrac{\beta}{(s + \alpha)^2 + \beta^2}$	$e^{-\alpha t} \sin \beta t$
16. $\dfrac{s + \alpha}{(s + \alpha)^2 + \beta^2}$	$e^{-\alpha t} \cos \beta t$
17. $\dfrac{1}{s[(s + \alpha)^2 + \beta^2]}$	$\dfrac{1}{\alpha^2 + \beta^2}\left(1 - e^{-\alpha t} \cos \beta t - \dfrac{\alpha}{\beta} e^{-\alpha t} \sin \beta t\right)$
18. $e^{-s\tau}$	Unit impulse at $t = \tau$ $[\delta(t - \tau)]$
19. $\mathbf{F}(s)e^{-s\tau}$	$f(t - \tau)u(t - \tau)$ [that is, $f(t)$ delayed by τ]

† For additional basic relationships, see Table 13-5.

selected bibliography

The following bibliography is neither complete nor necessarily inclusive of the best possible references in any particular area. Rather, it is a small selection of texts—for the most part, modern, readable, and readily available—which the authors feel should be interesting and useful to the readers of this book.

The first two references are historical in nature. They are the first papers to introduce what we call here the response-function method of circuit analysis.

1. A. E. Kennelly, The Impedances, Angular Velocities and Frequencies of Oscillating-current Circuits, *Proc. IRE*, **4**:47–78 (1916).
2. V. Bush, Oscillating-current Circuits by the Method of Generalized Angular Velocities, *Trans. AIEE*, **36**:207–221 (1917).

The next two references can provide fundamental background material to reinforce the material introduced in this text.

3. P. R. Clement and W. C. Johnson, "Electrical Engineering Science," McGraw-Hill Book Company, Inc., New York, 1960. (Develops lumped-parameter models from field-theory approach.)
4. H. M. Hansen and P. F. Chenea, "Mechanical Vibrations," John Wiley & Sons, Inc., New York, 1952.

Network topology and determination of loop and node equations are treated quite thoroughly by:

5. E. A. Guillemin, "Introductory Circuit Theory," John Wiley & Sons, Inc., New York, 1953.

The mathematics of network analysis, including matrices, determinants, and transform methods, are presented in:

6. E. A. Guillemin, "The Mathematics of Circuit Analysis," John Wiley & Sons, Inc., New York, 1949.
7. J. A. Aseltine, "Transform Method in Linear System Analysis," McGraw-Hill Book Company, Inc., New York, 1958.
8. M. F. Gardner and J. L. Barnes, "Transients in Linear Systems," John Wiley & Sons, Inc., New York, 1942.
9. D. K. Cheng, "Analysis of Linear Systems," Addison-Wesley Publishing Company, Reading, Mass., 1959.

The following two texts will provide much additional information in the areas of energy conversion and electrical machinery:

10. A. E. Fitzgerald and C. Kingsley, Jr., "Electric Machinery," McGraw-Hill Book Company, Inc., New York, 1952.
11. D. C. White and H. H. Woodson, "Electromechanical Energy Conversion," John Wiley & Sons, Inc., New York, 1959.

There are a very large number of books dealing with automatic control systems. Two that should be of interest to the reader are:

12. J. J. D'Azzo and C. H. Houpis, "Control System Analysis and Synthesis," McGraw-Hill Book Company, Inc., New York, 1960.
13. H. Chestnut and R. W. Mayer, "Servomechanisms and Regulating System Design," 2d ed., vol. 1, John Wiley & Sons, Inc., New York, 1959.

The following references will provide additional information on the analysis of nonlinear networks:

14. W. J. Cunningham, "Introduction to Nonlinear Analysis," McGraw-Hill Book Company, Inc., New York, 1958.
15. J. J. Stoker, "Nonlinear Vibrations," Interscience Publishers, Inc., New York, 1950.
16. W. L. Hughes, "Nonlinear Electrical Networks," The Ronald Press Company, New York, 1960.

Network synthesis is covered in each of the following two books:

17. E. S. Kuh and D. O. Pederson, "Principles of Circuit Synthesis," McGraw-Hill Book Company, Inc., New York, 1959.
18. D. F. Tuttle, "Network Synthesis," vol. 1, John Wiley & Sons, Inc., New York, 1958.

The analysis of distributed systems, both mechanical and electrical, is discussed in:

19. R. K. Moore, "Traveling-wave Engineering," McGraw-Hill Book Company, Inc., New York, 1960.

Dimensional analysis and various aspects of units and dimensions are covered in the following two references:

20. D. C. Ipsen, "Units, Dimensions, and Dimensionless Numbers," McGraw-Hill Book Company, Inc., New York, 1960.

21. C. M. Focken, "Dimensional Methods and Their Applications," Edward Arnold & Co., London, 1953.

index